S0-CBG-427

Agricultural Policy Under Economic Development

EARL O. HEADY

Professor of Economics and
C. F. Curtiss Distinguished
Professor of Agriculture

Iowa State University

Agricultural Policy Under Economic Development

Iowa State University Press, *Ames*, Iowa, USA

About the author . . .

Earl O. Heady, an internationally recognized authority in agricultural economics, is Professor of Economics and C. F. Curtiss Distinguished Professor of Agriculture at Iowa State University, and Executive Director, Center for Agricultural and Economic Adjustment, Iowa State University. A native Nebraskan, he completed his undergraduate training and M.S. degree at the University of Nebraska and earned the Ph.D. degree from Iowa State. He has been awarded an honorary D.Sc. degree from the University of Nebraska. Dr. Heady is the author of six books, now translated into four languages and used throughout the world. He has served as editor of seven books, has contributed chapters to 12 and has written over 300 scientific articles and monographs. His graduate program at Iowa State is widely recognized and his former students are located at nearly every major university in the United States and in many other countries.

Dr. Heady has been visiting professor at the University of Illinois, North Carolina State College and Harvard University. He has served as consultant for a number of groups, including the USDA Agricultural Marketing Service, the Tennessee Valley Authority, the Government of India and the Organization for European Economic Cooperation and Development. In 1960–61 he served as a Fellow of the Center for Advanced Studies in the Behavioral Sciences, Stanford, Calif. He is a member of the agricultural committee of the National Planning Association, has traveled and lectured extensively and has served as adviser to the Rockefeller Foundation on establishing a graduate training program in agricultural economics in India. Dr. Heady is a member of the American Economics Association, the American Farm Economics Association, the American Western Economics Association, the Econometrica Society, the International Agricultural Economics Association and the Canadian Agricultural Economics Society.

Manufactured in the U.S.A.

Library of Congress catalog card number: 62-9124

To Marian, Marilyn, Stephen and Barbara

Preface

THIS BOOK IS INTENDED mainly for students, professional economists and policy administrators. It was written to fill a void; namely, the lack of a book in policy which combines a fair amount of theory and analytical treatment with the more descriptive and literary analysis of agricultural structure and policy. We have attempted to "strike a balance" in these two approaches so that the volume might be useful to a broader group. Hence, while it does include some equations and graphs and a frequent focus on technical terminology, it also has a major content in purely literary manner. Those who are unacquainted with the more technical paraphernalia of economics, or those who dislike it, need not let the technical parts deter them. There are very large "stretches" which do not include technical terminology and can be read independently. Accordingly, we hope that the book can even serve usefully for farm leaders, educators, administrators and others who have a fundamental interest in agriculture and its economic structure and in the research, education and policy activities which relate to it.

Some will claim that we have used too much algebra; some that we have not used enough. If this proves true, we will likely have attained the proper "balance," given the current "state of the arts" in economics and communication. We frequently resort to some elementary algebra where outcomes relating to a "chain of relationships" need to be discussed and thus can be treated best. In these cases, we have used algebraic forms which are (1) as simple as possible in manipulation and arithmetic and (2) are appropriate for the purposes at hand. While particular and different forms are used at various places in the book, the conclusions flowing from the discussion are general and the form is not implied exactly for agriculture. This procedure differs not at all from the text which includes illustrative graphs. A graph itself represents a specific algebraic form of relationship, even if it is used as a "general model or illustration." We could have turned to pure abstraction in our selected mathematical example. However, to have done so, rather than to use illustrative forms and quantities, would have defeated our purpose of retaining a larger audience and would have put us to "great labors."

Our emphasis is on economic structure and policy of agriculture under economic development. The major problems of agriculture over the past five decades have been those stemming from economic growth and the particular organization of the industry. This will continue to be true in the decade ahead.

We believe that complete economic analysis of agriculture points to policy needs in: an equitable sharing of national economic growth to which agriculture contributes; a better distribution of developmental gains to the various strata of the industry in order that positive-sum outcomes in utility and welfare can be guaranteed; the specification of legislation which recognizes the political process in a democratic society and the constitutional guarantee of equality in opportunity for people regardless of the strata of agriculture and society which they represent; the continuation of economic progress in agriculture with a distribution of positive gains from it to both consumers and producers; the incorporation of conditions for agriculture which are elements of general social policy and industry environment; and the attainment of greater stability in an industry which is subject to wide fluctuations due to decisions of many independent competitive firms operating under the stochastic conditions of nature.

The contents of the book are in this framework. Analyzed in this framework, some facets of previous agricultural policy are more logical than formerly believed; some facets are less consistent with positive-sum welfare or utility gains for various population strata. Our analysis leads us to believe that previous policy interpretations have tended to be too extreme in their suppositions. At one extreme, agricultural policy has been analyzed as if: the environment is one of pure competition throughout the economy; positive-sum utility gains for the aggregate community automatically are guaranteed by all transfers of labor from farming; and that short-run costs of economic progress can be ignored, with focus alone on long-run equilibrium conditions. At the other extreme, policy has been analyzed as if: the economic environment outside of agriculture is nearly pure monopoly; farm people are unique and apart from the nonfarm population with an entirely different set of values; the short-run alone is relevant and positive-sum utility outcomes are not possible with transformation of agriculture under economic growth.

If we drop these extreme assumptions and examine policy within its more realistic setting, we can more easily specify economic reorganization which is consistent with economic growth and which is acceptable to more strata of people in the sense that positive-sum utility outcomes are assured.

We have devoted very little space to the description of past and present policies and legislation. Excellent treatments in this vein have been included in the books by Harold Halcrow (*Agricultural Policy of the United States*, Prentice-Hall, 1953) and M. R. Benedict (*Farm Policies of the United States, 1790–1950*, Twentieth Century, 1953). We have tried to cover the structure of agriculture which develops under economic growth and gives rise to direction in needed policy. We have also examined the growth process as it has been related to different types of public policy and as it poses policy needs in the future for an agriculture which is highly integrated with national society and which has preferences in this direction. Finally, an attempt has been made to analyze agricultural structure within a realistic setting of industry organization, competitive structure, welfare economics and political processes. The main focus of the analysis is on agriculture in the highly developed economy of the United States. However, the analysis of the basic interrlationships of agriculture and the total economy under economic growth is relevant regardless of the stage of development. Our analysis of the role of public and private sectors in economic development, of the contribution of agriculture to national growth and of basic conditions of growth, apply to any economy. We have emphasized fundamental relationships in structure of agriculture as national economic growth progresses from low to high stages of maturity. Finally, we have examined certain problems of agricultural structure and policy as they arise in nations at various stages of economic development.

I am indebted to numerous persons who either checked part of this manuscript or made calculations leading up to it. Included in this list are Luther Tweeten, Roger Mauldon, Lou Auer, Lon Cesal, Mel Skold, Norman Whittlesey and Glenn Helmers. This book was written during part of the period in which I was a Fellow of the Center for Advanced Studies in the Behavioral Sciences at Stanford, California.

EARL O. HEADY

Ames, Iowa, 1962

Contents

1

Policy Under Economic Development

HISTORY WILL PROVE that problems of agriculture follow a definite pattern over time and under economic development. This statement will apply to all countries, regardless of current income levels and resource productivity and the social systems which provide the decision environment for state planners or individual farmers. Quantities needed to prove this proposition are time and economic growth in sufficient magnitude.

The current problem settings of agriculture appear to be highly dissimilar over the globe. Hunger and food shortages prevail in some regions. The immediate problem is to find methods for increasing the supply of farm products. The problem is the obverse in other regions. Consumers are well fed. Surpluses exist and the problem is to restrain supply against other national needs. A common element exists among these extreme settings, however. Value productivity of human effort in agriculture is low, either absolutely or relative to earnings in nonfarm sectors. Still, the opportunities are different because nonfarm employment opportunties exist for absorbing agricultural labor in highly developed economies, but not in those where food is still scarce.

Differences in food supply exist not because of physical differentials in climate and natural resources, the causes or variables often cited, but because of uneven rates of economic development. Given economic growth and per capita incomes of current magnitudes in the United States, economic pressures on agriculture of India, Russia, or the Congo will be largely those experienced by North American farmers over the past several decades. Unfortunately, economic development previously has progressed slowly in such countries. Many decades will be necessary before they will experience the pleasure of farm problems in nature and magnitude of those prevailing in America. The term "pleasure" is used in long-run context.

Basic U.S. farm problems arise because per capita income and resource productivity have been pushed to high levels. Consumers are well off and food is abundant and of relatively small cost. Those who suffer hunger or malnutrition do so largely because of personal choice and motivation. Illness and misfortune cause a few to desire more food and improved nutrition, but high per capita income and low food costs together cause food to be among the lesser of consumer urgencies. In long-run context, America thus can proclaim the last half century largely as the period in which it transgressed from one with the masses concerned first with food and second with consumer goods extending beyond the basic elements of existence to one where the direct concern is with goods of affluence. Food for subsistence is taken for granted and is no longer the primary motivational force behind family economic activity.

This state of well being began emergence at the turn of the century, but only in the last several decades has it sharply focused on the mass of consumers. If it is not submerged in the flow of consumer goods or the ravages of atomic war at the end of another half century, American society may look back to this period of transition with pleasure and self-satisfaction. The pains of the transition then will be largely forgotten. The period can be remembered as the stage of growth in which primary concern turned from quest to overcome hunger, cold and sickness and major devotion of resources to it. Old-timers may even long for this period—accompanied as it was by farm surpluses, depressed farm incomes and large public outlays to ease the farm problem—against an affluent society searching for goods and services to entertain itself during time freed, by economic progress, from acquiring a living. Newer generations, however, will take it lightly as a stage relegated to history and worthy of less thought than a previous generation's decision to initiate and repeal prohibition, grant women suffrage, modify the income tax structure, invest in space exploration or reapportion legislatures. In an initial period of development, man's problems are of biological orientation: to have enough food and to dispel discomfort of hunger, cold and illness. In another period, it is to have enough food to allow expansion of his society. But in a later period, his problems have psychological orientation: in deciding, among the greater welter of goods and services within his means, the combination which leads to enjoyment rather than frustration.

In another half century, United States society will be better experienced in affluence. It will have learned how to cope with the economic and social problems which attend its first-stage attainment. It is then that problems of agriculture will have been of short-run context. In this sense, the current monograph is of short-run context. It deals with the problems of agricutlure and in wealthy society where economic growth is rapid but the stage of growth still causes problems to fall on agriculture and to be of public concern. This environment is one which likely will exist in the American economy through the 1970's. It is one which will gradually emerge in other countries as economic development progresses and societies are able to bend their concentration from pursuits to lessen basic human discomforts, to those allowing exploration of want patterns which have possibility of fulfillment under economic development.

Given the uneven progress of economic development over the world, however, much of the structure explained in this text will have application mainly over the next half century. But with the transpiration of time, American society will be more aware of the developmental process and will have provided environment which both facilitate and accommodate it. In the early 1960's the main problems of agriculture are inability of the industry to absorb the shocks and disturbances in equilibrium which stem from national economic progress stimulated from both private and public sectors.

AGRICULTURE IN A MORE STABLE ECONOMY

Problems of agriculture are noteworthy not only because they stem from high attainment in the cherished goal of economic opulence, but also because certain facets of economic security and industrial self determination attained by other sectors, as an outcome of social and political constructs of a free society, prevail less widely in agriculture. The major problems of the industry no longer can be framed as those of agriculture in an unstable economy. Great fluctuations and insecurity, such as that illustrating the 1930's, no longer characterizes national economic endeavor. True, small recessions have prevailed since World War II and will continue to do so. But mass unemployment will never be allowed to return. Even under national instability of magnitudes experienced in postwar years, farm income has suffered little, and sometimes not at all.

Agriculture has more typically faced relative income depression when the national economy and employment were at highest levels. Aside from that created by generally desired economic expansion, instability and insecurity have been much lessened at the national level. Instability of magnitude over the past century, or the human misery accompanying it, will not be repeated in the future. Growth will be promoted and attained not only as an end in itself but as a method of minimizing insecurity and instability. The American business community does not desire public legislation and research which concentrates on solutions to a depression of the magnitudes of the 1930's. It does not prefer monetary policy which turns money supply loose in a free market so that after major depression has come about it can be proven that a higher real price for money will eventually cause greater supply of it. Neither is it likely to prefer that efforts of scientists be devoted mainly to pure econometric explanation of the self-generating and distributed lag characteristics of the business cycle, under the assumption that these are natural or transcendental phenomena to be described and then left alone. It does not want governmental appropriations to provide public works and small purchases from a firm during extended recession. It does want positive monetary and fiscal policy to maintain growth and prevent major depressions.

American industry does not use unstable competition of "pure model" type, with price largely an unknown quantity. Instead, through self-administered and necessarily informal arrangements, price is given an important degree of short-run stability and competition is typically on other basis in the short run. Production and employment of plant are adjusted in the short run to prices which do not fluctuate in the manner of the pure competition model. To be certain, there is competition in sufficient magnitude to promote growth and progress, but not in the manner leading to great instability as under pure competition. Lessening of instability which arises under laissez faire approach to the business cycle, or from structure of prices under pure competition, likely allows business firms and industries to use investment strategies which give greater stimulus to economic growth. Faced with instability of pure price competition and deep business fluctuations, assets must be used more sparingly and in strategy to meet sudden setbacks. Provided with some stability in these areas, but with competition for "share of the market," in resource acquisition and in technology relating to production costs and consumer demand, business firms are able to invest more in research and development leading to progress.

The stability mechanisms preferred and used by industry lessen competition at the level of product price in the short run, but they allow intensification of competition in other directions. Over the long run, price competition does prevail because substitution possibilities are great across industries, commodities and resources. Optimally, progress is best promoted through policy which allows degree of security leading to investment in product and resource improvement or substitution, rather than in uncertainty precaution *per se.* It also is best promoted if those who invest are allowed some distribution of the gains. Herein lies a central issue of the farm policy problem.

In a similar vein, American labor does not desire policies which provide unemployment compensation during extended depressions, or even in mild recessions or "rolling adjustment." It, too, prefers positive policy which promotes economic growth and job opportunities. And like American business, it prefers some stability in price of its service, rather than to have each laborer serve in atomistic competition with all others under great fluctuation in rewards. It has been provided with legislation to bargain accordingly and has attained great short-run stability in expectation of prices of its services.

But labor, too, is competitive within its ranks; enough so that growth and progress results from this quantitatively largest input of the industrial complex. Labor also is competitive with capital, and prices of the two resources cannot deviate greatly from substitution rates without causing replacement of the former. Even that common element of all economic sectors, the consuming household, prefers similar positive orientation. Policies which provide the family with food stamps to prevent hunger during unemployment are not among its urgent desires. Neither is unemployment compensation which replaces a fraction of its normal income and maintains a portion of its usual expenditures during recession. Its preference is for public policy which promotes growth and extends its income and budget over the consumption plane.

Aside from war, the major threat to economic security is widescale unemployment and unused plant capacity—the return to the major depression. But this is a state incompatible with the wishes of any major domestic sector or with the nation's world responsibilities—including an image to be maintained in international political competition. The United States cannot afford a major depression, even in terms of sacrifice in world status. It will not have one and this point need not be labored. Economic growth is an important means for attaining a desired degree of security. It is pursued as a means of meeting world political competition and of contributing to that noble purpose of growth in underdeveloped world regions. But economic growth is more than this. It is the most effective means available in Western-type societies for preventing the violent business cycle and widescale unemployment of plant and labor. It will be pursued vigorously for these reasons.

Growth will characterize the American economy in future decades. Recessions or rolling adjustments, identified under newly coined descriptions, will prevail. But the nation will not allow a major portion of its resources to become unemployed. Growth itself does not solve the peculiar short-run problems of agriculture. Major farm problems arise mainly from economic progress. Others would exist in either the presence or absence of growth. During the 1960's, economic growth alone, in the absence of specific policy, will not erase either the surplus or poverty problems unique to agriculture. Growth will never solve the problems of price and income instability which grow out of farm commodity cycles.

PROBLEM OF COMMERCIAL AGRICULTURE IN ADVANCED SOCIETY

As part of the nation's total growth complex, technology has been advanced rapidly in agriculture. Developed land area once served as an important restraint on output and supply of food products. Relative to its productivity and to domestic food demand, the supply of land is now effectively greater than at any time in the past century. Space or building site has never served as restraint on supply of industrial firms.

Agriculture is now similar in the sense that land area or supply has been much reduced as restraint on the industry's commodity supply function. New technologies, represented by capital items such as chemicals and improved biological strains, have developed rapidly as substitutes for land. The marginal substitution rates of these capital items for land have been increasing since 1930. Capital items in the form of fertilizer, insecticides, improved varieties and machines also serve as substitutes for labor. Consequently labor input has declined greatly in response to (1) price of labor which is high relative to that of capital and (2) substitution rates which have grown to favor capital. High labor returns in industrial sectors also have served to increase the flow of labor from agriculture, a phenomenon partly reflected in the price complex favoring substitution of capital for labor in farming. If labor were an inanimate resource, transfer enforced by technological change and economic progress would give rise to concern by few people. But since labor does, in fact, have a household attached to it, the transfer can impose family sacrifices and costs, and many persons must accept it unwillingly.

National economic growth has differential impact on agriculture and industrial sectors because of magnitudes of income elasticities of demand. For aggregate food in physical form at the U.S. level of per capita incomes, the income elasticity effectively is zero; meaning that as income increases further, food poundage intake remains practically constant. Even the elasticity of aggregate food expenditures in respect to income is low—around .15. This indicates that consumers, wealthy in world standards, increase expenditures on food by less than 2 percent for each 10 percent increase in income. Most of this increase is allocated to packaging, freezing, improved quality and similar services incorporated with a given quantity of food.

Domestic growth in demand for food in physical form is restrained to the rate of population growth. This is in contrast to industries which produce goods of affluence where demand grows not only with population, but also as a function of per capita income. Income elasticities of demand exceed unity, indicating expenditure increase more than proportional to per capita income increase, for commodity aggregates such as kitchen mechanisms, recreation, education, communication, automobiles and others. These are the industries favored in investment return under economic growth, not only because of their high income elasticities but because growth-inspired technology also reduces their real costs of production. In contrast, technological change which reduces the real cost of production for agricultural commodities tends to be offset by price depression where shift in supply exceeds the rate of population growth. This indeed has been the situation of American agriculture in the two decades since 1940. The condition continues to prevail because of low labor mobility (relative to the magnitude of labor surplus created through new technology), a competitive structure favoring rapid technological advance, and the rapid injection of new technology as a result of its favorable pricing.

Economic growth and technological change also cause disruptions in selected nonfarm industries. Changes in consumer preferences, obsolescence of old techniques and new products cause plants and workers to become surplus relative to a particular activity. However, these resources often have much greater short-run flexibility and adaptability than those specialized to agriculture. Machines, manpower and buildings can be quite readily shifted, at a given location, from radios to television, from handwashing machines to automatic washers or from sausage grinders to boats. Barns, tractors and husbandry men are not so readily shifted from wheat to electronics or from hogs to automatic transmissions.

Industry and labor do not have complete security of income and employment, in respect to either aggregate economic fluctuations or "within rank" competition. But they have more effective short-run mechanisms and institutions for these purposes than does agriculture. Their competitive mold is obviously different from that of agriculture. Even on Main Street of the farm village, competition among merchants typically is not in terms of price, but in share of the market and in similar resources or restraint. Most aggregates of industry are more homogeneous than the agricultural industry, both in respect to commodity and other characteristics. The trade association, the professional organization or the labor union thus more often can speak with a single voice, as a lobby or economic pressure group. Not only does protective legislation exist, reflecting or providing the bargaining power of these groups, but also these groups more often possess means which can be initiated by member organizations.

Agriculture has protective legislation but generally lacks the power of self initiation. In aggregate it must depend mainly on public legislation to obtain means of increasing price and managing output. In contrast, oligopolistic industries can raise prices, through leader followship or tacit understanding. Similarly, labor can call a strike without prior persuasion of congressmen for the need. Neither of these two groups must wait through long legislative process for writing bills, obtaining committee clearance and in attaining legislative majority and presidential signature.

Mechanisms and Problems in Distribution of Progress Gains

Other firms and industries are competitors. Competition is difficult to stifle in a large and complex economy such as that of the United States. Substitution possibilities extend over broad ranges of industries and resources. If steel becomes too costly, substitution will be made through aluminum and other materials. If labor becomes too costly, capital and machines are substituted for it. Within an industry, firms develop new products and resource mixes in order to compete more effectively with each other. Over the long run, the price for product or resource of one set of firms cannot be separated from that of competing firm aggregates or industries. In the short run, however, industrial firms have much greater price stability than has agriculture. Competition exists, but more nearly over share of market for a given demand quantity at a given price. Through this structure of short-run price stability, major nonfarm resource and industry groups are able to hold onto a larger share of the gains of economic progress, before benefit of progress becomes spread predominantly to consumers.

Distribution of gains and losses of technical and economic progress provide the main basis for policy problems of commercial agriculture. Because of the demand and competitive structures characterizing agriculture, individuals within the industry must bear the major portion of costs associated with progress. As a competitive industry, the farm sector does not have effective means for retaining any large portion of the rewards from the technical advance which it initiates. These gains are quickly and widely dispersed to consumers and the processing sectors which connect farm firms with households. Because food demand in aggregate is inelastic, greater output brings smaller revenue to the aggregate of food producers. Accordingly, returns to resources are low because resources involve people who are not readily yanked from the industry. Older persons bear capital losses and often are unable to move to other industries to realize positive awards of progress.

Certainly this is the main policy issue for commercial agriculture in the decades ahead: How can it remain competitive in the sense of promoting progress and still realize an equitable share of the gains stemming from this progress? This condition has been attained much more in industry than in agriculture. One of our main concerns in this book is with policy to better guarantee positive-sum utility outcomes from progress. This is the essential concern of commerical farm policy in the decades ahead. Starting from the 1950's, the need is to bring a mix of conditions to agriculture which currently have wider application in nonfarm industry. This needed mix includes: better use of the pricing mechanism than during the 1950's; methods for retaining a more equitable share of the progress payoff in agricuture; and elimination of some extreme sacrifices from short-run price competiton. Industrial sectors have attained a workable degree of these conditions, but still compete on a long-run price basis, as well as on bases other than price in the short run. Under their mix of conditions they have made tremendous contributions to progress.

American society has set up precedent and mechanism, indicating that persons providing a basis for progress should be able to receive a positive share of the social payoff so generated. This sharing is guaranteed in patent laws. The first few farmers who adopt innovations do realize positive payoff. The masses who follow in adopting innovations and augmenting the supply function, however, are the ones who make the greatest absolute contribution to lessening the real price of food and to freeing resources from agriculture. Yet these producers are promised negative payoffs or costs for the contribution, because their incomes are reduced from the process under inelastic demand.

Other Income Problems

Policy problems arise mainly out of concern with income level. We have mentioned one broad problem of income giving rise to need for public farm policy; namely, policy to guarantee an equitable distribution of the gains and costs associated with progress in agriculture. This is the major policy problem of commercial agriculture. We treat it in detail in subsequent chapters. In addition, there are three other income problems which give rise to need for policy and which are discussed in subsequent chapters. A major one is that of low income and poverty in agriculture. Poverty is widerspread, in proportion of people, in agriculture than in the national economy. The two income problems mentioned thus far, equity in the distribution of real income gains from progress and poverty, have quite different settings. The first is more a problem of relative level of income; the second, more a problem of absolute level. The poverty problem stems but little from recent rapid progress of agriculture. It has cause of deeper and longer standing. But it poses an important problem in giving low-income people stranded in agriculture a larger opportunity to take advantage and participate in national economic progress. In this sense, it also can be termed a problem in economic progress.

The two remaining income problems of major or mass concern have much less relationship to economic growth. Both of these are almost purely problems in instability. One stems from the distributed lag or cobweb nature of producer response. It is represented by the commodity cycle, with rather violent inter-year fluctuation in price, production and farm income. Its reflection is notable for such commodities as hogs, potatoes, beef and others where the production period and the expectation models used by farmers leads to distinct commodity cycles. A second stems from the stochastic or random nature of weather. It is more particularly the problem, aside from irrigated areas, of agriculture west of the 100th meridian. But it does have reflection in other producing areas. Drouth and other calamities of weather wipe out income for a year or series of years, while farm costs continue. Both of the income problems stemming from instability variables touch upon large groups of producers but cannot be solved by farmers independently. They also call for group action, if their effects on income are to be lessened, of the nature discussed in later chapters.

ATTAINMENT OF BASIC GOALS AND PUBLIC POLICY

The centuries-sought primary goal or commodity of man is already attained in large degree by American society. He no longer need devote a major portion of his time and resources for acquiring food, shelter and medical aid to keep him alive. Aside from certain exotic characteristics of food, he takes it largely for granted as basic to life, but of little greater concern. Although its price is still higher, he views food per se in a category only slightly beyond water and air for human consumption.

The first visitor from Mars or other planet, brought to earth in space vehicles which are necessary commodities of rich societies, might ask perplexing questions to "man on the street" representation of American mores and values. He might ask: Why, in a society as rich as that in the United States, need anyone pay for food? Why is education largely provided free and allocated apart from prices while food is not, particularly since food for subsistence is necessary before one can enjoy and absorb education? Why are commodities of secondary and tertiary nature, such as waters for fishermen and duck hunters or national parks for general consumption, provided outside of the market when commodities of primary nature such as food are not? Why does a rich society encourage production of electricity to most consumers at reasonable price, with simultaneous guarantee to producers of market rates of resource returns, without doing so comparably for food? Why should communication through the postal system be completely socialized, with prices to consumers representing only a fraction of the per unit cost and with labor used for the enterprise rewarded at market rates, when food is essential for life and for existence to enjoy the services of communication? Why in general have so many goods of the secondary or tertiary nature been placed in the category of public utilities when a primary good has not?

There are reasons why America used this order and method for the supplying and pricing of different categories of goods. (The explanation might be hard to impress on the Martian, if he too came from a rich society with a particular set of values where the opposite ordering had been followed and had he not read the American Constitution. If he had read the Constitution, he might wonder why so many people of agriculture do not have access to equality of economic opportunity as against the general populace.) Perhaps our society did not consider this regime of food supply, factor return and consumer pricing because it could not foresee the level to which economic progress in general, and that of agriculture in particular, could be pushed. A century or more back, it may have supposed that the main preoccupation of man would continue to be that of food. Obviously, this is no longer true, with net income of agriculture being less than 5 percent of consumer disposable income and the agricultural labor force being less than 10 percent of the national labor force. Hence rather than make agriculture a public utility and provide a minimum quantity of food at zero price to all consumers, an alternative but quite similar route has been followed. Food itself has not been socialized or made into a public utility, but resources causing its supply to increase and its real cost to decline were so treated. Through public investment in research and development, society has augmented the agricultural supply function and diminished the resource demand function. Consequently food is produced abundantly and, because it fills biological preferences and has low demand elasticities, comes at low real cost to consumers.

To be certain, the market basket is not filled at low price. The cost of the market basket is at current levels more because of the amount of packages, tin foil, prizes, frozen condition, barbecue preparation and self-mix commodities incorporated with food, than because of high price for food per se. But even then, research and development has made food abundant and cheap, with less than 8 percent of the nation's non-land resources required to produce it. This proportion of resources for food will drop below 5 percent, or even lower if the international opportunities and responsibilities mentioned later are not exploited.

Effectively, this route to food and subsistence was more efficient than one which might have caused 25 percent of the nation's resources to be devoted to agriculture; with food per se available to consumers at zero price. The United States long has had definite and conscious public policy leading to the development of agriculture and the lessening of the real price of food. This developmental policy has had reflection over the past century largely in the public investment in, and conduct of, research and education leading to farm technical advance. (Previous to this period, it took the form explained later.)

This public investment, in agricultural colleges and the USDA, was highly successful in aggregate benefit to consumers and in greatly aiding the nation to attain affluent consumption level. But, to the public which provided the funds, to the staff and administrators of agricultural colleges and even to farmers themselves, this was largely an unwitting process and outcome. Research and development as a social or public activity was undertaken with focus on greater income or benefit to farmers. The fact that the consuming society would be a major beneficiary, a notable attainment and group, was not foreseen because early legislators, administrators and farmers had little knowledge of price and income elasticities of demand. In recent decades, wartime demand excluded, the rapid and continuous progress in technology and food supply has caused larger farm outputs to fetch smaller revenue; a debit in the agricultural economy but a credit in the consumer economy.

The Martian might ask: What could be better than abundant food at low price, if some economic sector is not caused to sacrifice for this noble attainment? From a consumer's standpoint, little could be better than abundant food at low price; unless the Martian took pity on "poor World persons" who must devote any part of their income and resources for acquiring food, and daily dropped a free bundle of food on each doorstep. The "food drop" would not, of course, be optimum for farmers; just as benevolence on the part of Switzerland, in providing each American family annually with a new car, would not cause U.S. auto producers to be made "better off." Public policy in economic development in food supply is a noble and worthy policy. It has been efficiently pursued in the United States and the returns to American society have been great.

Development of U.S. agriculture was not left to the forces of the free market, nor was there ever an attempt to completely replace the private sector in these activities. Gauged in its own progress rate and against agriculture of other nations, U.S. agriculture evidently has had a near-optimum mix of investment and assistance by the private and public sectors. The nature and extent of public assistance has changed with the passage of time, economic growth and alteration of demand elasticities. At earlier stages of growth, the public sector made a relatively greater contribution to progress of agriculture. Gradually, the private sector is coming to make the largest contribution. As indicated in a later chapter even research expenditures of private firms have come to equal or exceed those of land-grant colleges and the USDA.

In the broad perspective of time, shift in agricultural policy from that of early America to that of the present has been consistent with changes in economic structure and market possibilities. But in isolated decades, policy has not always been abreast of the change about agriculture. In the first century of the nation, most consumers were farmers and income gains to the latter meant utility gains to the former. Nearing the end of the second century, however, most consumers are not farmers and what is best for the next generation of consumers is not necessarily best for this generation of farmers. (This is a difference which disappears only if we look far enough into the future.) Historically, and unwittingly, American farm policy has been oriented appropriately towards consumers, if we consider the change in social structure mentioned above. In the long-run context of democratic society, consumer focus of policy is correct since this is the ultimate end of economic and political activity. Over several generations, in societies which do not maintain permanent and inflexible caste systems, consumers with origin in one producing sector are not unique from those with origin in another. In the short run, however, this is much less true and policy to benefit the present or future consuming society is not always consistent with benefit to a producing sector such as agriculture.

Fortunately for American society, early policy aimed at gain for agriculture, and with emphasis on economic development, particularly benefited subsequent generations of consumers; a type of "wind-fall profit" which did not serve in the payoff calculus with policy initiation. In recent decades, however, it has become necessary to distinguish between the gains to consumers of future generations and gains and losses of farmers in this generation. Agricultural policy has been formulated accordingly, with elements for gains to both existing side by side. Too frequently, and more than in past generations, these elements are in conflict within the current generation or decade—much more so than for developmental policies of a century ago. This point is illustrated in the brief historic review of policy which follows.

POLICY MEANING

Governments initiate and implement agricultural policy for one or both of two purposes: to benefit consumers or to provide gain to producers. Policies fall mainly under two categories: (1) developmental policy and (2) compensation policy.

We term *developmental policies* those which have focus on the supply functions of commodities and resources. Developmental policies generally have the purpose or effect of increasing commodity supply. Generally, too, they reduce the real price of food to consumers. In other words, the commodity supply function is shifted to the right, in price-quantity space, through reduction in the price of resources, through alteration of productivity coefficients entering the production function or through increase in supply and supply elasticities of resources used in agriculture.

We term *compensation policies* those which attempt to compensate farmers in various manners in order that positive-sum utility outcomes, or the Pareto-better conditions outlined later, can be better guaranteed. Thus while developmental policy has the effect of moving the supply schedule to the right, compensation policy tries to restrain the rate of supply increase, or to decrease supply, in order that farm income can be increased. Compensation policy also may operate on the variables of the food demand function, in order that commodity price and farm income might be increased. Or, it might be directed towards direct payments to compensate farm producers for sacrifices which fall on them as they contribute to advancing technology of agriculture. In developmental policy, the main effect is in causing supply to increase at a faster pace; in compensation policy, the main effect is to restrain supply, increase demand or make direct transfer payments.

The two general policies outlined above are those of major economic concern and political importance for commercial agriculture. Other policies have somewhat different purposes, but often can be classified under the above headings. The regulation of markets and protection of food quality under the Pure Food and Drug Act is an attempt to affect the supply function of farm commodity with particular characteristics. Soil Conservation policy is of specific nature, but it also is an attempt to alter the supply function of agricultural commodities in present and future time periods. Farm credit policy is one altering the price of a resource (capital) and is expected to have an effect in changing commodity supply functions of individual farm firms. Alteration of supply and demand functions is not the end or goal of farm policy, but only a means. The end of relevance is increased farm income or consumer welfare. In some societies, policy focuses on the food supply function with the major end of safeguarding consumer subsistence and utility. In others, policy focuses on the food supply function as a means of increasing farmer income. Developmental policy with effect of supply increase can provide gains to both producers and consumers under certain conditions of price elasticity of demand for food. Under other elasticity regimes, policy which shifts the supply function to the right provides positive payoff to consumers and some producers, but negative payoff to other producers.

Policies aimed at instability variables of agriculture have focus on the commodity supply function. For example, an ever-normal granary plan which causes the market supply of grain to be lessened in bumper years but increased in drought years operates on the supply function, but is hardly a developmental policy. Monetary policy and low interest rates—to increase the demand for money and the supply of employment opportunities—is a similar policy with effect on structural relationships underlying the market, but is not directly a national developmental policy. Laissez faire also is public policy, since the structure of the economy in respect to supply and demand of particular resources and commodities and the pattern of resource and income allocation has a particular configuration under it. It is a policy approach as much as is public ownership of resources to produce education through schools and communication through the postal system. In cases such as education, postal services and police protection, the public has made the decision that the services can be supplied more efficiently and equitably by public production than through private supply. In sectors where production and supply functions have been left to private firms and industries, society has made a similar decision. Our concern here, however, is with policy where the public has directly undertaken alteration of demand and supply functions of commodities or otherwise has altered the flow of income and the gains of progress among consumers and farm producers.

HISTORIC AND ECONOMIC PATTERN OF POLICY

The policy matrix of American agriculture has contained elements both for development of the industry and for income support or compensation. Developmental policy began with initiation of public decision-making by the United States as an independent nation. It has continued vigorously up to the present. Policy to support incomes and provide compensation is of much more recent origin, dating mainly back to the 1920's.

But even before initiation of the United States as an autonomous political entity, farm policy was already showing some of the characteristics of that followed today. Gray reports that production quotas were used in Virginia tobacco production as early as 1621.[1] "Stinting of production" was used to bolster prices. Each grower was allowed 1,000 plants with nine leaves harvested per plant. In 1630, quotas were raised to 2,000 plants per man, woman and child and tobacco was not to be sold at less than 6 pence per pound. Outright sale of tobacco, except through merchants, was prohibited. In the latter year, not more than 14 leaves per plant could be tended and only nine could be harvested. Over the period 1639–41, an aggregate annual quota of only 1,200,000 pounds of "good quality, stripped and smoothed tobacco" could be sold.

That the public should actively provide policy for agriculture was decided early in the nation's history. There was, of course, debate over

[1] L. C. Gray, *History of Agriculture in the Southern States to 1860*, Carnegie Institute, Washington, 1933, pp. 224–70.

whether the structure of agriculture should develop under the forces of the free market as they prevailed at that time, or under a mold provided through public policy. The latter became the basis under which agricultural development took place. In the debate between Hamilton and Jefferson, the former wanted to commercialize land distribution.[2] Evidently the supply would have been distributed to the private sector, with distribution to farmers then made accordingly. Jefferson, whose philosophy came to prevail, wanted greater access in total supply and a nation of farmers who worked their own land. Hamilton would have allowed large sales to individuals and speculators, with land sold to greatest financial advantage. Rather than Hamilton's plan of private sales and distribution, the pattern of the family farm was established in public distribution directly to farmers.

Initial Policy for Development of Agriculture

The American public has long played a direct and major role in the development of agriculture.[3] Its policy has not been laissez faire, but direct assistance and intervention in the market for factors; particularly if we consider technical knowledge as a particular resource. Developmental policy has had the effect of getting resources effectively utilized and of increasing the supply of agricultural commodities. Aside from ownership of productive units and resources, no other country has had a more direct and effective participation of the public sector in technical development and supply increase. Even initial development of agriculture was not left completely to the free market. The private sector contributed greatly to the growth and development of the industry, but so did the public sector.

Early policy for agriculture concentrated on the public acquisition and public distribution of land resources for farmers. The emphasis was accordingly because labor was abundant and prospective farmers possessed their own supply. Capital, while extremly short, was a lesser component of production in the techniques of the time. The public created agencies to disburse the supply and land was allocated at very specific prices. These prices for resources were just as purposeful as commodity price supports of recent decades. Land was provided to farmers at prices ranging from zero upward, depending on the time and the method used. The *immediate* purpose was to provide farmers and potential farmers with resources at favorable prices, as a means of increasing their income. The method was accepted as the "American way,"

---

[2] See M. R. Benedict, *Farm Policies of the United States, 1790–1950*, Twentieth Century Fund, New York, 1953, pp. 5–13.

[3] H. W. Broude (in G. J. Aitken (ed.) *The State and Economic Growth*, Social Science Research Council, New York, 1959) shows that for the U.S. economy, the government was decisive in westward development and while the public outlay was small, the public role in stimulating growth for the whole economy was large. He states that the government was never negligible, even in the most autonomous sectors. For a somewhat similar discussion, see Cyril E. Black, "The Politics of Economic Growth," *World Politics*, July 1961.

although it entailed public rationing rather than private sale and market distribution of land resources. Farmers of the time not only would have protested but would have taken musket in hand had it been otherwise, even though the next set of transactions in land were turned largely over to the market. The *secondary* (but perhaps the more important) purpose of this public policy was development of the nation and the consequent securing of its territories. Given the setting in respect to market development, population increase and demand elasticities, the immediate purpose was mainly compatible and complementary with the second purpose. Would-be farmers and settlers not only wished more income, but most even wanted a greater amount and variety of food and clothing. Public policy gave them land, or sold it at low price, and allowed them to have this increment in real income. It also caused the land to be settled and national income to grow.

But connecting the settler who benefited from government distribution and pricing of land and the consuming society was a market environment which allowed farmers to develop their land and increase commodity supply to the direct benefit of both groups. Under development and commercialization of agriculture, with production exceeding subsistence needs of families and a portion of output flowing to the market, the market was highly elastic and accommodated an expansion of supply. First, the population was increasing rapidly, and slow but steady industrialization led more of them to the city where they produced much less of their own food. Second, people were poor in today's standard and increase in supply leading to a decline in real price of food could cause per capita consumption to increase. Price elasticity of demand for food in aggregate probably was such that greater output selling at a lower price, with percentage increase in output being greater than percentage decline in price, fetched a larger farm revenue. Too, starting from a low level, increase in national and per capita income allowed a large parallel increase in per capita expenditures on food, except for the few commodities of the time which could be classed as inferior goods. Hence, the public policy of settling the lands and increasing the supply of farm commodities could qualify as effort to benefit both consumers and farm producers.

But since the majority of households were those of farms, only the one facet needed to be made explicit. To provide farmers with more resources was to provide them in the aggregate, with opportunity for even more income. Farmers who accepted this opportunity, by settling public land which was free or priced lowly, could remain on it accepting the capital gain forthcoming from a growing population and consumer market. Or, they could exercise right to the capital gain; selling the land and moving to new locations where public policy again provided them with resources at low prices. Much of the early ability of agriculture to develop and increase commodity supply stemmed from this capital gain; a source of developmental funds which grew not from the efforts of agriculture but from development of the economy around agriculture. As population, the national economy and market demand for farm commodities grew rapidly relative to agricultural supply, prices of developed land also grew. Farm assets and equity increased similarly and farmers could borrow greater quantities of funds, on the basis of capital gain in land values.

The capital gains, representing the difference between the publicly determined price at which land was distributed to settlers and that which came to prevail because of population and national economic growth, provided inheritances for the next generation of farmers. These inheritances provided capital which could serve for further development of agriculture (in either settled or new regions). This source of capital is often forgotten in comparisons which contrast the historic development of American agriculture with that currently found in India. Indian cultivators lack, because new land is not available, this opportunity for capital gain and its reinvestment in agricultural development.

As long as American public policy could provide farmers with favorably priced land and eventual capital gains, they sought little else. They were not pleased with the high cost of borrowed capital or with short-lived depressions. But since subsistence and a large family labor supply were in their possession, they could "wait out" the opportunity to realize the expected capital gain forthcoming from land development and growth of society. Given the conventional or customary goals and motivations in consumption, this opportunity stemming from public policy was highly acceptable and satisfactory. Farmers asked little more from the public. Relative to the standards of income and consumption, this policy of resource pricing policy had much more permanence in economic effect than commodity price policy of recent decades. Its longer-run effect was more akin to current policy which might provide farmers with several shares of IBM stock. These latter assets would augment real income by a small amount, but farmers could hold them for capital gain and purchase other assets from their sale. Or, they could hold the stock for retirement purposes. Both consumers and farmers would now be better off, had we reconstituted this historic capital gain policy and used funds devoted to price supports and storage of recent decades to purchase IBM or other growth stocks for farmers.

Complementarity in Early Developmental Policy

Agricultural development policy allowed complementarity among such goals as farm income attainment, consumer welfare and general economic growth during the first century of the United States as an independent nation. Farmers of average efficiency expected little more of public policy than that it provide them with resources to acquire current income at the standard subsistence level and the prospect of a capital gain for asset accumulation. Bravery, hard labor and insulation to hardship were required for utilization of this opportunity to overcome nature's niggardliness and the disadvantage of little capital. But simultaneous development of agriculture, increase in population and consumer sector and national economic growth fed one on the other. Policy concentrating on larger supply and low price of resources allows complementarity among the three goals of (1) increased farm income, (2) greater consumer welfare and (3) enhanced national economic growth, only under conditions where markets are expanding and demand is of sufficient elasticity in respect to price. This is true because policy leading to decrease in price or increase in quantity of resources has the strong effect of increasing product supply. We have no empirical quantities indicating magnitudes of price elasticities in the first century of American society. Apparently, however, the rate of population increase and restricted diets of consumers plus the elasticity of the international market, provided an elasticity regime which allowed greater output to be accompanied by greater revenue of agriculture. Population and demand for food increased at a pace equal to that of agricultural supply. A large portion of the increase in supply was consumed directly by a growing number of farm families. However, demand for food also grew rapidly in nonfarm consumer sectors. Without increase in food supply, the real price of food would have increased and/or population growth would have been restrained.

Second Stage in Agricultural Development Policy

This first and widely implemented public agricultural policy was highly successful. It was consistent both with income interest of farmers and national economic development. Nationally, gluts of farm products did not arise and the public was not forced to provide commodity storage and price supports to offset success in increasing supply of farm products. This policy had lasting effect for particular generations of farmers, as the feed back of economic development caused land values to increase and gave rise to capital gains largely apart from the efforts of those who broke out the soil. But opportunity for this early developmental policy ceased to exist with complete settlement of the public domain.

As a next step in policy for agriculture, society again looked in the direction of resource pricing and supply—variables related to supply of farm products. They turned to public support of research for agriculture. Although additional land for settlement at publicly determined prices was lacking, the equivalent existed in the possibility of new technology to increase the productivity of settled land. And the second major element of policy for agriculture turned in this direction. Research to increase the productivity of land and other resources could have been left entirely to the private sector. But American society did not choose to do so. It socialized research and set up the U.S. Department of Agriculture and the agricultural colleges to uncover new technology and communicate knowledge to farmers. This policy element was not forced on farmers. It came largely at their request, just as had been true of the previous policy in respect to land distribution and pricing.

Rudimentary knowledge of economic relationships and agricultural production processes would throw this element of policy in the same developmental category as previous land distribution and pricing. Both represent manipulation of variables by the public which tend to augment output and the supply function. This point is illustrated by the simple relationships below where particular algebraic forms are used for simplicity purposes. (Our analysis following involves only a shift in the supply function and not a change in structure as represented by a change in elasticity or slope of the supply function.) The production function for the industry (see footnote discussion) is (1.1) where Q_p is the quantity produced, X is resource input and π and b are coefficients of production.[4] The resource requirements equation is (1.2) and the

$$Q_p = \pi X^b \tag{1.1}$$

$$X = \pi^{-1/b} Q_p^{1/b} \tag{1.2}$$

$$Q_d = cP^{-e} \tag{1.3}$$

demand equation is (1.3) where Q_d is consumer purchase at specific price, P is price per unit, e is elasticity of demand and c reflects the effect of population, per capita income and other relevant demand variables. The industry supply equation becomes that in (1.4) where quantity produced in expressed as a function of the quantities already defined (see footnote 4).

$$Q_s = (b\pi^{1/b} P P_x^{-1})^{b/(1-b)} \tag{1.4}$$

$$R = c^{1/e} Q^{1-1/e} \tag{1.5}$$

[4] More exactly, $\pi = aX_1^{b_1}, X_2^{b_2}, \cdots, X_n^{b_n}$ and represents the production effect of fixed resources not under consideration at the moment while for the particular algebraic form, b is the elasticity of production. Selection of one algebraic form does not affect the conclusions since those presented are general.

In the relations discussed for equations (1.1) through (1.5) we simply skip several steps in aggregation, for purposes of simplified presentation of certain illustrations. For example, rather than present production and supply functions for individual firms and aggregate these to obtain a set of industry relations, we simply start with a production function for the industry, and move immediately to an industry supply function in a static context. We do so because our intent is the "simplest possible" presentation or illustration of certain conditions and outcome. To start in the more detailed manner of firms and aggregation would cause the presentation to be more complex and clumsy. (Some will charge that we have already made it too complex.) Other problems to be analyzed would have their focus of interest in the variances among strata of farms and in the nonstatic factors affecting decisions and supply response.

However, since our focus of interest here is in aggregate relations in production, especially in respect to *ex poste* outcomes in production, resource use and incomes, we feel justified in "abbreviating" our analysis in the manner outlined. We look upon it as the counterpart of graphical presentation in other books where concern is not exercised over simple presentation of aggregate relationship. While we recognize the limitations of the static, aggregate approach for selected purposes and predictions, we believe that they serve well for the goals of illustration at hand. If nothing else, the reader might satisfy himself by supposing that there are n firms in the industry which we portray here, and that the firms' production and supply functions are simply n^{-1} portion of those for the industry.

It is obvious that a reduction in P_x in (1.4), the per unit price of resource, is expected to cause production to increase. This is the expectation of developmental policy which lowers the price of a resource such as land. If we look upon technical knowledge as a resource, as it generally is, and the public lowers its price, output would be expected to increase similarly. If, however, we view the effect of technical change to be that of increasing the production coefficients π and b in (1.1), the effect will be similar, since larger magnitudes for these in (1.4) will also cause Q_s, supply quantity, to be greater. The total revenue of the industry, R, is derived from the demand equation as price times quantity and is expressed in (1.5).[5]

From this it is apparent that whether R, total revenue, increases with Q, quantity, will depend on the magnitude of e, the price elasticity coefficient in (1.3). If e, the price elasticity of demand, is 1.0, the value of $1-1/e$ is zero and greater output will not increase or decrease revenue with Q. If e is less than 1.0, $1-1/e$ is negative, causing revenue to decline as Q increases in (1.5). In the opposite case, where e is greater than 1.0, $1-1/e$ is positive causing R to become greater as Q increases. Evidently, the turn to research as the second major policy element for agriculture was under the unwitting belief of price elasticities of demand greater than unity. Only so could total revenue of agriculture be increased generally from an increase in supply, the expected result from technological improvement. The public thus adopted socialized research services as a means for increasing farm income. This was certainly the primary reason for policy which had the public, rather than the private, sector invest in and undertake the major portion of research and education in agriculture. Other secondary reasons may have existed and are mentioned in legislative documents. However, it is clear that the dominating reason for establishing socialized or public research for agriculture was to aid farmers and increase farm income. Major research for other economic sectors was left to private firms. But in agriculture, the public invested in its own research plants, hired the personnel and went about the production of new techniques, just as it had in producing postal and educational services.

The second stage of policy was initiated before the first, public distribution and pricing of land, was completed for two reasons: (1) The supply of unsettled public land, the basis of the first policy element, was nearing exhaustion and (2) farmers in older settled regions wished developmental gain similar to that which had accrued to their fathers and grandfathers—who needed move only a few hundred, rather than a few thousand, miles west to realize it. While refined elasticity estimates are lacking, the demand situation at time of establishing the agricultural colleges and USDA was one which allowed developmental

[5] This revenue relationship exists because $R=PQ$ and from (1.3) $P=c^{1/e}Q^{-1/e}$, with the latter value of P substituted into the revenue equation.

policy leading to an increase in supply, to be consistent with greater farm income. America's rate of population growth in the nineteenth century was one of the greatest on record for a major country. Foreign demand was expanding and a growing portion of the population was in cities and produced less of their food. The level of urban per capita income was not high and reduction in the real price of food, as well as national economic growth and per capita income improvement, provided demand elasticities favoring greater consumer outlays on food.

Establishment of the USDA and the land-grant colleges around 1860 did not result in an immediate burst in new technology and farm product supply. The main momentum in development of agriculture in the half century following the Civil War was probably the capital gains still flowing from early land policy and the effects of public education. Not until a quarter century later was federal aid for experiments made to states, although a fair number of states had already appropriated funds for this purpose. The Department of Agriculture was consolidated and raised to Cabinet status in the decades of the 1880's. The state experiment stations were created by the Hatch Act in 1887, the state extension services through the Smith-Lever Act of 1914 and vocational agricultural training by the Smith-Hughes Act in 1916. Hence, this general complex of agricultural development policy did not gain great momentum until after the turn of the century, although its basis had been created earlier. The major outpouring of results has been in the last four decades when federal and state appropriations have increased greatly and during a period when demand elasticities have been much less consistent with (1) greater income from increased supply and (2) certainty of positive-sum utility outcomes in the distribution of progress gains among producers and consumers. (See Chapter 16 for portions of outcome from technical improvement and greater resource use.)

However, the lack of a more vigorous research and education program as a means of augmenting agricultural revenue was not looked upon as a major restraint to opportunity for farming and farm income. Some public lands remained to be settled after 1860. Too, rapid growth in population and consumer demand, and the national economic development accompanying it, continued its feedback to agriculture. Further capital gains accrued to farmers in settled regions as land values grew and as more resources were used on given land. Improvement in agriculture did occur as farmers became acquainted with climatic and other characteristics of new regions and as their own practical experimentation bore fruits. Still, farmers sometimes experienced market gluts and were beginning to learn about depressions. This development was inevitable as farming moved more from subsistence to commercial, with a greater proportion of the product marketed. Initial public policy relating to demand increase arose accordingly. Land grants were made to railroads to catalyze development of marketing facilities, as well as to bring further settlement of the frontier and national development.

Agricultural developmental policy, expressed through public investment in research and educational facilities, picked up momentum as land area became fully settled. Creation of public facilities for production of new technology by society soon spread to every state. Many states now have several experiment stations. Appropriations for agricultural research and education has increased rapidly in recent decades. Public appropriations for these purposes have increased greatly since World War II, with the need sold to the public largely as a means of increasing farm income.

Acceptance of Developmental Policy

Agricultural developmental policies were readily accepted in the century and a half after formation of American society because (1) the stage of national economic development caused them to be successful in increasing farm income and (2) they were consistent with the particular value orientation of pioneer farmers. This value orientation revolved around individualism and freedom of decision. Agricultural developmental policies placed resources and techniques in farmers' possession, allowing them no less expression of individualism. The two goals, increased farm income and independence, were not competitive in the early stages of national economic development. Policies which gave farmers land at restrained prices or technical knowledge at zero prices simply provided the substance for more families to exercise individualism, or for given families to have more "decision subject matter." But at later stages of economic development and higher per capita incomes, with consumer stomachs filled to the limit of physical desires, demand elasticity settings need not cause agricultural developmental policies to produce positively of both farm income and greater opportunity in individualism.

Policy which calls for augmentation of resources in an industry is more universally popular and gives rise to discord less than policy which assumes an outflow or restrained quantity of resources in an industry. The reasons are evident. Under conditions causing the former to be appropriate, firms already in the industry are relatively profitable and new opportunities exist for resources, particularly human, which wish to enter the industry. But policy which assumes a restraint or outflow of resources, particularly labor, provides the opposite. Early agricultural development policies best corresponded with the former. Recent compensation and related policies more nearly have to assume the latter condition.

Other Agricultural Developmental Policies

Given the early setting in stage of national economic development, demand growth and elasticity regime, agricultural policy continued to reach towards the "favored developmental direction." With full settlement of public lands and continued population growth, the initial policy (land supply and price) for agriculture was "closed out." The second one (public supply and pricing of knowledge) was not yet moving ahead rapidly. Too, with full settlement of land supply attainment of the spatial restraint for agriculture, price of land increased greatly. And while this provided continued capital gain for established operators, it gave rise to large capital requirements for those who wished to purchase land and begin operations. It was only natural then, that a "next step" in policy was also developmental in character and was aimed at the supply and price of capital.

By 1912, the price and terms of agricultural credit were the concern of all three major political parties. This concern led to the Federal Farm Loan Act of 1916, giving rise to the Federal Land Bank system with the principal purposes of lower interest rates, longer terms for repayment and greater opportunity of farm purchase by tenants. It was supplemented with the creation of the Federal Intermediate Credit Banks in 1923. Agricultural development policy was extended further through credit supply and pricing by the Farm Credit Administration and Production Credit Administration in 1933, the Resettlement Administration in 1935, the Farm Security Administration in 1937, the Farmers Home Administration in 1946 and others directed at public impact in factor markets.

The major goal of all these policy elements was lower prices or greater supply of credit. The purpose was to increase the farmer's income through lowering credit costs and extending his capital by lessening the restraints on its supply. Effectively, public credit mechanisms also qualify as developmental policies. They are equivalent to reducing P_x or increasing X in equations (1.1) through (1.5). Hence, expectation is that they will increase supply, Q_s in (1.4), for the firm and for the industry. In respect to the firm, the immediate end is increase of income through greater output or lower factor cost. For the industry, aggregate increase in supply can cause revenue to increase only if demand elasticity is greater than unity.

Many other agricultural developmental policies have been tried by American society. Their results have sometimes been less general, with application to particular localities. Included in this category are the professional services of the Soil Conservation Service (SCS) and the monetary assistance of the Production and Marketing Administration (PMA, but subsequently ACS and ASC), both established in the early 1930's; and the Bureau of Reclamation established in 1902 with major purpose of large-scale water storage and irrigation development for arid lands. These policies also have led to lower costs and greater supply of particular resources for the agricultural production process.

Minor programs of the same general category, but recognized more directly as supply increasing policies, have included labor procurement and housing, subsidization of fertilizer production and pricing through tax allowances, and others of less importance. Also falling in the general category of agricultural developmental policy, in partial extent, have been public aid for farm-to-market roads, rural electrification and telephones. While these policy elements provide important communication and consumer services, they also provide services for the production process.

THE SHIFT TO AGRICULTURAL COMPENSATION POLICIES

The United States was never without a major policy for agriculture. It did not remain aloof from functions performed by the market in other economic sectors. In early history, it emphasized agricultural development policies. It acquired and distributed land resources under administered prices. It built plants to produce and distribute new technology, allowing new technical knowledge to become a "near" free good to farmers. It created institutions to obtain credit and supply it to farmers at administered price levels. The primary purpose of these developmental policies was to increase income by allowing the individual farmer to acquire resources at lower prices and augment their productivity.

In aggregative effect, these policies are consistent with greater income to the agricultural industry in the proper setting of economic development; namely, a rapidly growing population and national income, high price and income elasticities for food. Supplementing this favorable domestic demand situation over the first century and half of the nation was a receptive world market which readily absorbed farm product supply exceeding U.S. requirements. A favorable exchange situation existed over part of the period because of the nation's debtor position. With interest payments, immigrant remittances abroad, etc., exports could exceed imports. Rates of industrial development and population growth in Europe, in conjunction with this exchange situation, provided a fairly stable market outlet, absorbing large quantities of U.S. farm products and placing a lower restraint on price levels.

But this setting cannot continue forever under growth of national economies which is rapid and continuous. A stage finally is attained where level of consumer income allows approach of satiation of physical desire for food. Forward press on the resource development and supply side of agriculture then can become inconsistent with greater aggregate farm income.[6] This stage of national economic development was clearly being approached by the early 1920's, and to an extent even in previous decades. Too, only then was the second major agricultural development policy, public production of improved technology, beginning its large social payoff in greater farm productivity and lower supply price of food. The rate of population increase, with greater restraints on

---

[6] This condition can also arise in the opposite case where national economic development is extremely tardy, unemployment is great, per capita income is low, and export markets are lacking. Rapid increase in agricultural output then also promises to depress income.

immigration, was much lower than over the previous century. Demand growth no longer paced agricultural supply growth. Conditions during World War I and the few years preceding it had been a "golden period" for American agriculture (being exceeded only by the similar period, 1940–50). After World War I, the high elasticity of the foreign market also was dampened. The United States became a creditor nation and European countries were less able to purchase farm products from interest payments and dividends on foreign investment. Growth of U.S. industry also lessened demand for European manufactured goods from abroad. Exchange for purchase of U.S. farm products was diminished accordingly.

Turn to Agricultural Compensation Policies

In addition to a slackening in demand, farmers were caught in the 1920's with high priced land and large debts. The latter, high land values and large debts, typically was proposed as the basis for the depressed situation of agriculture. While high land values and large debts gave rise to difficulty, they did not represent the basic problem facing agriculture. The industry had come to the end of an era in national economic development. The variables underlying demand growth were not of previous magnitudes. Consumers now had relatively favorable incomes and were well fed. Food demand elasticities fell to smaller magnitudes and continued development of agriculture caused supply to increase faster than demand.

Farmers did identify this change in economic environment. They turned towards policies based on concepts of compensation and self help. Large national cooperatives for major commodities were created, in hopes that demand could be expanded through promotion and quality control of farm products. Also it was hoped that price could be improved through more orderly marketing and market management or supply control. The emphasis in these efforts was now opposite the agricultural developmental policies of the previous century. In effect, emphasis over the previous century had been in enlarging the magnitude of π, X and b and in decreasing the magnitude of P_x in (1.1) through (1.4); all with predicted effect of greater output. The new turn was in lessening Q_s in (1.4); equivalent to decreasing π, X and b (but not effectively attempted at the time) and in expanding c and e in the demand equation of (1.3).

In previous decades, farmers had organized their own cooperatives as a means of breaking grain and other market monopolies. Now, however, interest arose in using cooperatives—allowing orderly marketing—to obtain possible price and income gains under monopoly supply procedures. These self-help attempts based on large-scale commodity cooperatives were generally unsuccessful. Farmers were too great in number, too widely dispersed and produced commodities serving too greatly as substitutes for each other. Also, farmers were not easily organized into a voluntary group which could control marketings. Most planned commodity marketing organizations never really got under way and others proved of short life.

Inability of self-administered agricultural programs to increase demand and restrict supply caused farmers to look to the public for mechanisms and institutions which would overcome the inherent difficulties of voluntary organization. Not all farmers, then as now, favored turning to government for organizational aid and power, or in use of monopoly approaches. Yet major sentiment evidently favored this direction and the general approach was incorporated in major policy elements initiated in the late 1920's and after. With an extreme shrinkage in the terms of trade between agriculture and the rest of the economy in the 1920's, Congress passed, and President Coolidge vetoed, the McNary-Haugen two-price plan in both 1927 and 1928. Under it, domestic sales of major crops would have been restricted to amounts bringing the world price plus domestic tariff. The remainder of supply was to be sold in world market.

While it did not pass, the plan and the philosophy underlying it provided foundation and precedent for legislation and policy which followed. The Agricultural Marketing Act of 1929 was then passed, creating the Federal Farm Board; a first and formal step towards public compensation policy for agriculture. This act provided for lessening speculation, preventing inefficient and wasteful methods of distribution, aiding organizations of producers for unity of effort in marketing, creating producer-owned cooperatives and aiding in the control of surpluses. Some public action in price support loans and acquisition of commodities was initiated. But with the economic crash which followed in 1929, this legislation was small and ineffective. Even had the depression not followed immediately, the Agricultural Marketing Act alone probably could not have contained the coming explosion in agricultural productivity and supply.

The activities of the Federal Farm Board were a break from the past in the sense that focus was now shifted from developmental to compensation policies. It served as precedent to policies which followed. Legislation which followed in this same mold included the Agricultural Adjustment Act of 1933. It provided a more formal mold from which subsequent policy departed but little. The AAA, as it became known, provided directly for supply reduction and control, for direct monetary compensation or income transfers to farmers and for nonrecourse loans serving as price supports. These were major policy elements, serving even into the decade of the 1960's. Not only were methods provided for restraining inputs, reducing X in (1.5), but also for lessening output, reducing Q_s in (1.4). Farmers were paid a cash price to "deliver up" supply of idle land, to reduce hog farrowings and to plow up cotton and other crops. They also were paid cash for hogs and cattle which were killed.

While these steps were oriented to compensation policy, they were not without secondary effects as developmental policy. For example, price supports above market levels act on supply in the manner of increasing P in (1.4) and themselves serve as motivation for greater output. Adding to the complexity, an increase in commodity price has the effect of causing reduction in foreign sales, a market with greater price elasticity than the domestic market.

Largely, at the time, the AAA was looked upon as relief or emergency legislation, just as were PWA, NRA and other efforts to divert income and purchasing power into households and to raise the economy from the trough of depression and unemployment. The competitive nature, inelastic factor supply and proportionately large fixed costs of agriculture kept it producing at full speed during the depression. It did not need "pump priming" to bring about full employment of its resources. In contrast, unemployment of the nation's labor force ran as high as 15 million and industrial firms and sectors idled major portions of their plants to meet demand shrinkage and aid in price maintenance. The AAA, in major part and like other agencies, was looked upon as temporary measure to combat a short-run adversary.

An economic wisdom began to prevail, prior to World War II, that national economies attain maturity and may prevail in a state of equilibrium with a large degree of unemployment. An agricultural economic wisdom also prevailed; namely, that depression of price and income in agriculture were largely a function of national depression; that restoration of full employment and consumer incomes would return a favorable demand situation to agriculture. With intensive monetary and fiscal policy, as well as more direct emergency measures, the nation lifted itself from pure economic prostration during the late 1930's, although full employment was still far away. Then World War II broke out, providing full employment and a new demand situation for agriculture. Employment and growth in the national economy were maintained at high levels in the post-war period. Farming was highly profitable.

Starting in the early 1950's, however, the paths of national economic development and prosperity and agriculture parted ways in respect to relative magnitude of incomes. National and per capita income grew, but farm returns sagged. Temporary foreign demand for food ended. Agricultural supply had increased greatly during the war and post-war years, due to previous and ongoing public investments in developmental policies through the agricultural colleges and the USDA, growing developmental contributions of the private industry, the stimuli of war and favorable price relations, and the favorable capital position of agriculture. But it was obvious that solution to the basic commercial farm problem was no longer through the national economy, in full employment and further growth. The demand environment which had been consistent with public developmental policy for agriculture and farm income growth in the century and a half prior to 1920 had ended, at least temporarily.

Agricultural policy returned emphasis to the molds of the 1930's; to mechanisms which assumed temporary conditions to be overcome. Much legislation still existed, allowing activation of compensation-type policies used mainly in the decade prior to the war. The Commodity Credit Corporation, created in 1933, provided for price-support loans and for purchase and sale of commodities to stabilize and support prices. The 1934 Sugar Act, amendments to the AAA and its successor and the Soil Conservation Act of 1936 served for similar purpose. The Federal Surplus Commodities Corporation established in 1936 and providing for food subsidies and surplus purchase and disposal, the National School Lunch Act, and the Food Stamp Plan, all enacted with precedent in the 1930's and with emphasis on demand expansion were continued or amended during the 1940's and 1950's. This entire set of policy means, generally created in the 1930's, were again focused on agriculture as the 1950's gave rise to farm prices and incomes which not only shrank from their post-war highs, but continued to do so as national and per capita incomes grew to new highs.

The means employed into the 1960's also were those for which precedent was supplied in legislative action of the 1930's. Some of the measures, such as price supports, had been used during the war years as a method of increasing supply. They were used in the post-war surplus period as a method of supporting income; a use highly inconsistent with the supply conditions of the period. Other direct actions to lessen supply or increase demand and price also were initiated in post-war years. The 1954 Act allowed the Secretary of Agriculture to use compensatory payments for wool, augmenting the effective price and income of wool growers but allowing the commodity to compete freely in world markets. The original AAA allowed federal subsidy of export of farm products. This outlet, on market scale, was extended in the 1930's under the Jones-Connally Cattle Act, the Jones-Costigan Sugar Act and the Soil Conservation and Domestic Allotment Act of 1936.

But the truly large efforts in this direction came after the war, under particular provisions of the United Nations Relief and Rehabilitation Program, the Economic Security Administration and the Mutual Security Agency. While not all of these efforts correctly fall under farm policy, the latter became more the emphasis under later foreign-aid programs, especially Public Law 480. Policy began placing great emphasis on improving domestic producer price by shipping supplies to foreign countries where they might restrain prices. Potatoes were purchased and destroyed under the Steagell Amendment in 1946 and 1948. Other commodities were purchased similarly to lessen market supply and bolster prices. The Research and Marketing Act of 1949 was directed towards market and demand improvement. Acreage control and marketing quotas were reenacted. The 1956 Conservation Reserve Act serving for land withdrawal and a modification of earlier supply control methods, rested on direct cash payments for holding resources out of production.

In the swing from focus on developmental policies to compensation policies, power to manipulate variables which might lessen supply or increase demand were not left alone in the hands of public agencies. Bargaining or price setting power also was placed in farm producers' hands through enabling legislation. Precedents for federal marketing orders were provided in the original AAA of 1933 and several states followed with legislation providing for market orders. Federal legislation allowed quantity and quality control of product, with consequent price affects, for selected commodities. An extension, under the 1937 Agricultural Marketing Act, provides for minimum prices to producers of fluid milk. Hence, precedent in federal and state legislation was provided to place market or bargaining power, of the nature possessed by firms and labor unions in other industries, in the hands of farm producers.

POLICY TRANSITION

Post-war policy elements have fallen largely in the compensation vector. Initially, these elements were established to "live out" the emergency of the 1930's. They have not solved the basic problem of a commercial agriculture in a wealthy and expanding economy—at least for most major commodities. Supply has continued to grow, aided by public developmental policy and improved resources and resource prices by the private sector, at rates faster than domestic demand increase. Consumers have continued to gain in lower real price of food and in resources freed to produce nonfarm commodities. In general, the policies of the 1940's and 1950's have not yet solved the problem of progress in agriculture; namely, a distribution of positive gains over the consumer sector and costs or sacrifices over the farm sector which guarantees positive-sum welfare gains for the entire community. While they have provided compensation and put income into the hands of commercial farm families, they have done little in solving the poverty problem of agriculture. The most that can be said of policy since 1930 is that farmers and the public have partially come to recognize that a new problem setting exists in national economic development. Change in philosophy and emphasis is illustrated in shift between policy focusing mainly on agricultural development and that directed to agricultural compensation.

The policy transition has been one of variables manipulated, rather than one of direct government participation or intervention in market mechanisms in one period but not in the other. The magnitude of government compensation policy, whether measured in number of legislative acts, public agencies, expenditures or manpower employed in implementation, has been much larger in recent decades than developmental policy in early decades.[7] Yet it has been no more purposeful, or successful in terms of farmer economic interest, than early agricultural develop-

[7] This is not true in the relative sense of national income and wealth if we compare the value of public land distributed to farmers at particular prices in the first century and a half against the direct monetary costs of policies in the last three decades.

mental policy. In both cases, private firms and actions within and surrounding agriculture have dominated the decisions and resource use of the industry. Policies in both periods altered the decision-making environment, but no more so in the recent than in earlier decades.

SUMMARY

We have summarized the economic setting in which modern policy for agriculture must be formulated. The nation has always had a definite policy for agriculture. It has relied on market forces as the major variables in allocating resources and affecting decisions in both early and recent times. Yet, over its entire history, the American public has had policy which manipulated variables affecting the pricing of resources and products and the supply of and demand for both.

In early periods, American society was almost synonymous with agricultural society and what was best for one was clearly best for the other, in both the short run and the long run. National and per capita income were low and consumers in general were most intent on greater fulfillment of biologically based desires—food, shelter and escape from epidemic. This environment placed great premium on agricultural products relative to other commodities.

As industrialization developed, as income grew and as population doubled and trebled in short spans of time, the market had great absorptive power for agricultural products. In this situation, agricultural development policies for agriculture were ideal as means of attaining greater income. Society acted accordingly. It acquired, distributed and priced land; not through the market, but through its own institutions and at administered and purposeful prices. Resources could be drawn into agriculture and supply could be increased, with farm families with recipient of economic gain through (1) opportunity to produce their own food, (2) commercialization and sale in an expanding market and (3) capital gains, from title to land, through the feedback from national economic growth. Favorable export markets and exchange balances, with some continued public distribution and pricing of land to farmers, continued this favorable situation for agricultural developmental policy beyond the Civil War. As a second stage in agricultural developmental policy, the American public set up further socialized facilities; to produce new technology, to increase capital supply and to affect the pricing and supply of these resources.

But at another stage in economic growth, with the transition point coming around 1920, the nation had progressed to a point where agricultural developmental policy was no longer sufficient for gain to aggregate agriculture simultaneously with benefit to consuming society. The marginal urgency of commodities to fill primary or biological needs and their marginal rate of substitution for commodities filling secondary or psychological needs, had declined greatly. Demand elasticities fell low and demand growth no longer paced supply. It was then that American society turned to agricultural compensation policies to lessen supply, increase demand and to support commodity prices and income.

The compensation policies initiated in the 1930's and extended to the 1960's were those with origin in deep depression. Their reemployment had the same implicit assumption as at the outset: emergency to get by a temporary situation. But the farm problem which has existed for more than three decades, with war period excepted, is not one of short-run nature. It will not be solved with patch-work compensation policy held over from the last major depression, or by developmental policy which projects the economic structure of the past century into the next two decades. While they have eased the income recession for agriculture, recent compensation policies have added little to solution of the more basic problems which are long run in character. The basic problem of recent decades, a period of affluence in a wealthy society, has been accompanied by large-scale secondary ones: mammoth surpluses and high treasury costs of policy. The total agricultural policy mix, including developmental policy to increase supply and compensation policy to restrict supply and effect compensation payments, hardly recognizes that the era has changed. Yet the more general environment of economic and social policy has itself changed. While much of agricultural policy has been oriented to short-run relief and emergency, American society evidently does not view this structure as that of positive policy. Industry, labor and professional sectors view positive policy as that of long-run nature which encourages economic growth and the avoidance of major depression; rather than that which might overcome major short-run fluctuation once they have occurred. Business and labor prefer growing investment and employment opportunity, not relief in the form of small government orders and unemployment compensation during recession. A wealthy society such as the United States should be able to afford this positive long-run policy, though it is of even greater importance in less wealthy countries.

Agricultural policy needs to be converted to this longer-run horizon in an economic development framework. It should be consistent with the economic horizon ahead, rather than with the developmental environment of 1910 and the depression environment of 1930. Perhaps the difficulty with farm policy is that it has concentrated too much upon agriculture as a society or economic sector apart from general society. Agriculture is held in fixational image as an isolated sector of the hinterlands with a peculiar set of goals and values. Accordingly, action programs have not brought it abreast of the stability, price and bargaining institutions which are now traditional for other economic sectors. Research and education have too much supposed that its resources must be headed uniquely back into the industry. They have not quite realized that farm children as members of general society may prefer to be treated accordingly, with training which allows them to take advantage of the major growth sectors in an economy of affluence.

The Fundamental Policy Question

Agriculture has, through development, contributed greatly to the national economy. For a short period, agricultural development meant absorption of resources and expansion of output to feed a growing population and to keep the real price of food reasonable. Later, agricultural development meant release of labor resources to the industrial economy. The major contribution of agriculture in recent decades has been production of food in abundance at low real price to consumers. Demand elasticities have been driven low and greater output has shrunk revenue to agriculture.

This nonsymmetrical distribution of gains from farm progress poses the basic policy problem of agriculture: How can agriculture continue to contribute to national economic growth and consumer welfare without being penalized in income for doing so? This is the basic policy question which must be answered for agriculture during the '60's and '70's. Society prefers growth and economic stability, with the former desired as an end in its own right but also as a means to the latter. In growth so inspired, and also spurred through international challenges and humanitarian appeal, how can agriculture continue to contribute, yet retain some reward for its contribution to national economic progress? How can human resources in agriculture, in both commercial and low-income sectors, be given greater opportunity in the further national economic growth in prospect? These are questions which we wish to examine in later chapters.

2

Status and Problems Under Growth

OUR PURPOSE in this chapter is to further summarize the developing and prospective status of American agriculture. We delve into detail only far enough to bring the various facets of the current commerical farm problem into quantitative perspective. The broad economic and social framework in which the industry must now perform was indicated in the previous chapter. We now go back far enough into the data to show how certain variables in the total economic development complex help give shape to current changes in the structure of agriculture, and how these, along with developmental and compensation policies for the industry, have modified or expanded the industry in respect to resource use, factor demand, commodity supply, resource return, family incomes and relative magnitude in the national economy. Also, we wish to point out how the industry has changed, both internally and in respect to other parts of the economy, in response to stimuli from within agriculture and from the outside, as reflected in markets which connect it with industries furnishing resources to it and buying commodities from it. In the latter respect, labor is an important commodity which has been produced in agriculture and marketed elsewhere in the nation's economy.

Historically and world-wide, agriculture has certain outstanding uniformity. A first major uniformity has been the persistent tendency for low per capita income and underemployment or low value productivity of labor to prevail in agriculture. While low value productivities arise from somewhat different specific reasons, we find this relative underemployment of agriculture to exist in the United States, Canada and similar highly developed countries just as it does in Japan, India, Brazil, Germany, Poland, Russia and other countries at various stages in the economic development ladder. A second major uniformity revolves around the supply of food. It ordinarily is at one extreme or the other; either scarce, causing societies to allocate a large portion of their income to it, or abundant, causing prices and resource returns in agriculture to be depressed. The problem is supply in both instances, with a desire to accelerate the supply function in the one case and to restrain it in the other. The first is largely a problem of consumers, the second largely of producers. The U.S. farm problem is more one of producers.

THE TWO PROBLEMS OF SUPPLY

The uniformity which revolves around commodity supply, in the sense that it is small and a consumer problem in one case and is large and a producer problem in the other, prevails again because of the origin of man's desires and its reflection through price and income elasticities of demand. He has one set of desires which have biological origin. Food is one of these, and until it is reasonably attained, he places high priority on filling it. Income elasticities of demand are relatively great and a large portion of income and human effort must be allocated to food. In this extreme is India. Wants of psychological origin have small marginal urgency and the drive to alleviate hunger pangs outweighs the drive to see one's psychiatrist, to overcome the misery of choosing between the many alternatives in goods and use of nonworking time.

But after hunger is met and the fear of obesity arises, the marginal urgency of food and the price and income elasticities of demand drop low. The psychiatrist, to aid the consumer in his frustration, takes on greater marginal value than labor used to produce food, and farm producers find output straining against a market of little resiliency. In this extreme is the United States.

Never is it likely that a nation of two-car families will allow itself to be chronically undernourished. Investment will be made to keep food supply pressing against fairly inelastic requirements. This investment will be largely in improved technology. But should the "unlikely and worst" happen, and all secrets and potential of nature be exhausted, great opportunity in keeping well-fed still exist. First, wealthy societies are educated and have the knowledge, communication and means for birth control. If the "worst" happened, population and supply of consumers would and could be restrcted, to draw food demand back to food supply, and lessen food prices and still allow affluence in consumption. But also the degree of opulence in other directions could be lessened. For example, a portion of the resources allocated to producing second cars, home freezers, zippers for cigarette packages, and artichokes could be reallocated to potatoes and beef steak. Life would remain reasonably comfortable under consumption patterns and commodity supplies which only allowed variety and abundance in food, plain rather than colored television, one car per family, automatic washers and ordinary refrigerators, with metal for second cars and backyard broilers shifted to tractors and irrigation equipment.

For these reasons, food scarcity and hunger are not in sight for the United States even with a much larger population in the second half of the twentieth century. But most important, the secrets of nature are not fully exploited and agricultural supply can be moved further to the right by introduction of new technology (and the resources it represents), rather than by injecting large additional amounts of conventional resources representing existing technology, the two being equivalent means of moving the supply function to the right. The status of economic development will keep consumer real incomes high and the elasticities of food demand low.

This supply problem is the opposite of that in India where national economic development has been tardy and diets cannot be improved readily in the short run by restraints on population. Knowledge and communication are too small and incomes are too low to allow wide exercise or purchase of the means of birth control. Neither can resources be reallocated in significant amounts from other major consumption industries because a very small fraction of families consume autos, telephones, newspapers, electricity, stoves, door knobs, windows, floors, shoes and other run-of-the-mill consumer commodities of Western World. Societies such as India will invest in new technology to move the supply function to the right. The direct problem is supply, just as it is in the United States; the more basic problem is state of economic development, just as it is in the United States.

The two states of consumption patterns are less than 100 years apart in the United States, or in the United States as compared to India. In the 1860's important segments of American society also lived in earthen or sod houses without floors, although most enjoyed the luxury of hinged doors, windows, sets of dishes and chimneys. They, too, in economic isolation from other sectors of society, depended on the year's somewhat unpredictable supply of crops for grain to grind or sorghum to press. They did not worry about obesity. But economic progress has been rapid and this state of development has been completely wiped from the scene. The problem of U.S. agriculture and farm families will continue to be on the opposite side; namely, largeness of supply.

This problem will persist because American society will continue to invest heavily in resources and resource supply conditions which lead to increase in commodity supply. Perhaps it also will do so because it is wealthy enough to allow continuation of relative surpluses. The problem will persist in India as long as it cannot invest sufficiently in increasing food supply. One important economic and political problem of the world is: Can the food supply functions of different regions be added, with similar aggregation of demand functions, allowing equation of these aggregate functions in a manner to allow real prices of food to be lowered in less advanced countries and increased in advanced countries? Optimally this economic alternative in food supply aggregation needs to be examined against the alternative of aggregation in resource supply, particularly capital. Flexibility does not exist for wide aggregation in either manner at present. Hence, we return to a more inward examination of American agriculture within its predominant national setting, returning later to pose analysis of international aggregation needs and possibilities in food supply and demand.

RELATIVE MAGNITUDE OF AGRICULTURE

Agriculture is the dominating industry in primitive societies and less developed nations. This is true in the marginal importance which consumers attach to food, the proportion of national resources devoted to agriculture and portion of national income generated by farming. With economic progress and rise in per capita incomes, all of these magnitudes decline. A path in economic development is traced, with a smaller proportion of population on farms, with capital and labor of agriculture declining as a portion of the total and with income from farming being reduced as a fraction of national income. In short, economies "grow away" from agriculture as they progress—a structural change not always understood by those who try to maintain the historic ratio of agricultural to national economy.

Indifference Maps Underlying Proportionate Resource Allocation

The shift in relative importance of agriculture is a "natural law," since consumers first are biological phenomena with wants expressed accordingly. It is this rather than abandonment of agriculture by society which causes a decline in the relative importance of the industry with economic growth. The indifference map which relates food, particularly in quantity aspect, and other goods and services generally is of the nature in Figure 2.1. At extremely low level of income and small consumption, the indifference curve approaches u_1, food having great urgency in the sense that the marginal rate of substitution of other commodities for it is low or even zero. At a higher level of income, as illustrated by contour u_2, food begins to lose some urgency, the indifference curve departing more greatly from zero slope. But moving between income (budget lines) or utility levels paralleling u_1 and u_2, income elasticity of demand is high. The expansion of food consumption with greater income moves up the vertical axis until it approaches u_2, and little or no added income is allocated to nonfood commodities. With satisfaction of hunger, at least in food quantity and low-cost calories, the expansion paths relating proportionate expenditure on food and other commodities take the nature of *mn*, curving rightward and becoming horizontal (or perhaps sloping slightly negatively) at high income levels.

The first great stride in civilizations, the foundation stone of economic development, occurs at the point where the isocline breaks away from

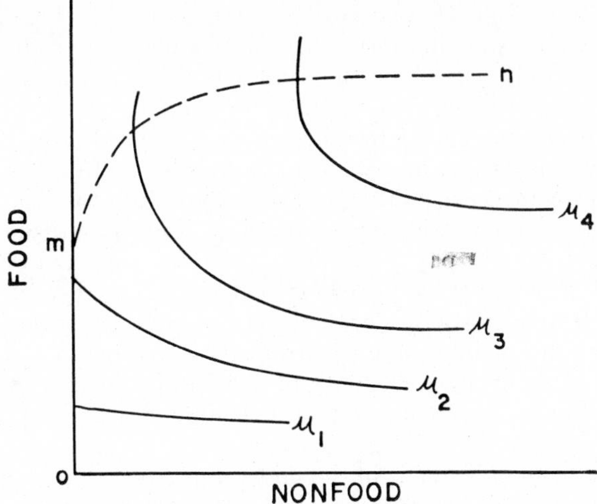

Fig. 2.1. Indifference Map With Food.

the vertical axis. Up to this point, the *om* section of the isocline, resources are still absorbed by agriculture as income increases. But at *m*, the trek from the farm has begun. With the expansion path eventually curving away from the food axis, or even if it is linear with positive slope intersecting the food axis at *m*, a declining proportion of consumers' expenditures on food is indicated.

If man's income is sufficiently high, as for indifference curves u_3 and u_4, a further increase in income will not cause him to consume more food, all of the income increment being allocated to other goods and the income elasticity being zero. Or, for indifference curves corresponding to high incomes or budget lines, the indifference curve effectively approaches a 90 degree angle, or a corner around which the budget line can swing without changing the relative mix of food and nonfood goods represented by a given indifference curve or level of welfare. The swing of the budget line, of course, is a reflection of the price of food relative to nonfood goods. Food price can decrease greatly, causing a corresponding increase in the slope of the budget line, without causing more than a slight swing of the consumer budget in the direction of a larger absolute intake of food. The price elasticity of demand is extremely low at this level of income. Or, stated conversely, food price must drop greatly, and slope of the budget line must increase extremely to cause even a small increase in food intake.

The slope of the indifference curve, corresponding to budget or income lines of higher location in the plane, is the quantitative indication of consumer's preference in respect to allocation and reward of resources for agriculture as he grows richer. When the mix of goods approaches portions of indifference curves with little or zero slope, priority is high for allocation of more resources to agriculture. In market economies, farm resources will be rewarded favorably under these conditions, particularly if they are in short supply. But when the mix approaches the vertical or "highly sloped" portions of the indifference curves, low marginal priority is placed on resources used for food. Those so engaged will be penalized in income if they are in surplus supply. Man may eventually reach a level of income and wealth where price and income elasticities of demand for food expenditures in aggregate drop to zero, as they are for air. Although man will scream and fight if his quantity of air is suddenly denied, he will pay no positive price for more than he now possesses. This has not yet happened for food, even in the United States, and price and income elasticities are not yet constants even though agriculture economists mainly have constrained them thus in measurements. Engel placed the income elasticity of demand for food around .7 in the 1880's. It now is much lower in the United States, and will decline further.

The U.S. farm industry is in the midst of a growth problem stemming from rapid economic and technological development and the phenomena illustrated in Figure 2.1. Pressure on income has been severe since 1950. However, the basic problem is of earlier origin. It began as early as the 1920's when farm income was low relative to nonfarm income. Then depression and war came along to obscure the basic problem and its consequences. But it returned in a magnitude which would have occurred more than two decades earlier, had there not been these two major disruptions, and had national economic growth continued unabated after World War I. It is a reflection of the simple growth model which we have begun to outline; of supply which is increasing rapidly and demand which grows in more retarded fashion.

FARM INCOME SQUEEZE

Agriculture in a wealthy, growing economy will generally be faced with a cost-price squeeze and a "dampening down" of income. The reason is: As incomes of consumers increase, food no longer becomes their major concern. They want more home appliances, better housing, television sets, recreation, travel and education. As the American consumer's income increases, it doesn't buy any more pounds of food, but simply changes the composition from fats, starchy foods and low-cost carbohydrates to more fresh vegetables, better cuts of meat, and fresh and canned fruit. Food consumed per person, measured in pounds, hasn't increased since 1920. For each 10 percent increase in incomes of consumers in recent decades, expenditures on food have increased by 1.5 percent or less, with most of this representing demand for improved quality and more processing and retailing services incorporated with food. The consumer doesn't consume a greater physical quantity of food. He consumes it in a different form and in a more convenient package. There is a limit to the size of his stomach; it does not stretch with his income, but he can stretch greatly the quantity of services he uses with food.

But in contrast, his expenditures increase rapidly on many nonfarm products as his income grows. With each 10 percent increase in income, his expenditures on items such as automobilies, clothing, recreation, home appliances, education and travel increase by 10 percent or more. In other words, as national income progresses and we become a wealthier nation, the consumer wants little if any more food, but much more of other goods and services. This situation will continue, aside from temporary setbacks, as national and per family income continues to increase. "Good living" no longer is characterized simply by getting enough food, clothing and shelter for subsistence.

Consumers express their wishes through prices paid in the market. As incomes increase, they are unwilling to place premium prices on farm products, but hold them down, indicating need for food mainly as there are more persons to feed. In contrast they pay prices as high or higher than previously for other products which they "prize" as incomes grow. In bidding higher prices for nonfarm goods and services, the consumer also bids up the cost of steel, labor, petroleum and other materials which produce the "more luxury" goods, although other market variables and forces aid this process. Consequently, the cost of tractors, lumber, fuel, fertilizer and other cost items of the farm is kept up. Since he wants materials used elsewhere, he causes the farmer to compete at a higher level of prices for materials which can either go into nonfarm products, or can be used as implements for farming.

This, then, is a cause of the farm price squeeze. The consumer says that he has a higher income and wishes relatively more of the nation's resources used for nonfarm goods, and fewer for farm goods. He wishes, as reflected in the market, labor transferred from farm accordingly. This cost-price squeeze, with the American consumer saying that too many people and resources are in agriculture, had already started in the 1920's. It is possible because of rapid economic progress and shift in food supply which outpaces demand growth.

The Longer Basis

This is the picture at the beginning of the 1960's. But to understand the deeper foundation upon which it rests, and the inherent difficulty in bringing economic balance to agriculture, it is useful to obtain longer-run perspective in quantities. Table 2.1 indicates the change which has taken place in relation of agriculture to the national economy over several decades. The pattern of change largely reflects that postulated in Figure 2.1. While the farm labor force increased with national economic growth up to 1910, it still declined in portion of the national total. The rapid decline in relative part of labor force in agriculture came, of course, after 1920 as technology favored the substitution of capital for labor and increased labor productivity, and as national growth caused income elasticities of demand for nonfarm goods to submerge those of the farm sector.

While capital in agriculture increased continuously, except for depression pause, it also declined almost continuously as a portion of the na-

TABLE 2.1

U.S. FARM RESOURCES AND INCOME AS PROPORTION OF NATION

	Labor Force*		Capital*		Net Product* or Income		Agriculture as Percent of Nation		
Year	Nation	Farm	Nation	Farm	Nation	Farm	Labor	Capital	Income
1820	2.9	2.1	—	—	.9	.3	71.8	—	34.4
1840	5.4	3.7	—	—	1.6	.5	68.6	—	34.6
1860	10.5	6.2	16.1	8.0	4.1	1.3	58.9	55.6	30.8
1880	17.4	8.6	43.6	12.2	6.6	1.4	49.4	27.9	20.7
1890	23.3	9.9	65.0	16.1	9.6	1.5	42.7	24.7	15.8
1900	29.1	10.9	87.7	20.4	14.6	3.0	37.5	23.3	20.9
1910	37.4	11.6	152.0	43.3	25.6	5.6	31.0	28.5	21.7
1920	42.4	11.4	374.4	83.8	79.1	10.6	27.0	22.4	13.4
1930	48.8	10.5	410.1	60.5	75.7	4.3	21.5	14.8	5.6
1940	55.6	9.5	424.2	43.9	81.9	4.6	17.2	10.4	5.6
1950	63.1	7.5	1,054.7	107.4	241.9	14.0	11.9	10.2	5.6
1960	68.4	4.5	—	—	416.9	12.0	6.7	9.1	2.9

* Million for labor and billion for capital and income. Income figures are disposable consumer's income and net income from farming. Farm capital includes land.

Source: Historical Statistics of the United States. Colonial Times to 1957, Series F 22–33 and USDA Statistics.

tional capital. But most striking is the decline in net income of farming as a proportion of disposable consumer income, a trend more or less paralleled in gross product of the two aggregate sectors. With the farm labor force now considerably less than 10 percent of the national total and net income less than 5 percent, income depression in agriculture even stands to have minor impact on national employment and income. This proposition was verified in the 1950's as farm income declined and national income grew. Demeter, goddess of agriculture, viewing her empirical importance in 1850 or before, could not have guessed her proportionate role in society could drop so low. But neither did her court show her the picture in Figure 2.1. By 1980 her share of labor force is likely to be less than 5 percent of total and her share of net income less than 2 percent. Agriculture is becoming so small in the total economy that aside from scientific sophistication, the estimator of demand relations scarcely needs to include an equation with directional effect from farm income to national income, and certainly not from farm commodity price to national income. By 1995, he may be at intersection of expansion path *omn* and curve u_4 in Figure 2.1, and thus able to predict commodity price, at a given point in time, as a function of output alone and demand quantity as a function of population, leaving out directional effect of national income on commodity price and being highly accurate with a single, simple equation.

But Figure 2.1 not only projects changes in economic shape as economic development progresses, it also projects changes in the shape of society itself and the relative political strength of different occupational sectors. Time provides an interesting chain with links in the sequence: biology→economic→political. The shift in the proportion of resources and income of agriculture follows a path linked to the extent to which biological preferences are filled and consumer outlays shift in large proportion to other commodities.

Linked to this shift in proportion of economy represented by agriculture is a shift in occupational distribution of population and the political strength of agriculture. While rural congressmen may fight vigorously to preserve their district, the expansion path in Figure 2.1 cannot be bent the other way, man having greater psychological than biological capacity for goods. Even in Russia, with sufficient progress and to the extent that collective farms prevail more for political purposes and to keep a large peasantry under control than to attain scale economies, economic development might likewise call for lifting a particular structure attached to rural life. Far up the isocline, the majority of resources will be in city and industry; the individualistic peasant can be given a larger plot of soil, or the collective for social control can be abandoned, because he will be outmanned and cannot win a revolution, even if he could start one.

At the summit of the consumption function, paths cross algebraically and ideologically. Attainment of high levels of economic development, and if the consumption function has an apex, the expansion paths, from whatever origin and direction, must cross or intersect. Hence, a common set of desires or good and service mix is indicated. Man can never attain this level but different societies will have greater uniformity in values and motives as they move towards it. Consumption at high levels thus is a logical, both in politics and mathematics, means of eliminating international ideological conflict.

The empirical shaping of this third link in economic and social development is indicated in Table 2.2. Populations and households of the nation were roundly 50 percent farm in 1850. By 1960 they were less than 10 percent and are headed towards 5 percent by 1975. Farm policy legislation will not reflect any overpowering political strength of agriculture in 1980. Instead, it will be an expression of society's economic sympathy for the industry, or its desire for togetherness to provide agriculture with the economic and social mechanisms for guaranteeing level and lessening instability of income which prevails elsewhere in the economy.

In one manner, the data on national shares of resources and income in agriculture overstate the decline in relative magnitude and importance; in another way they do not. In respect to the first, technological change in agriculture has caused the substitution of inputs fabricated off the farm for those which formerly were produced on the farm. The resources for power are now found in cities and tractor plants rather than in oat fields and on farms. Chemicals, fertilizers and many other inputs represent similar shifts in origin. Too, some processing of outputs has now shifted to marketing firms. Few farms have churns, producing prints of

TABLE 2.2

SHARE OF FARM POPULATION AND HOUSEHOLDS IN THE NATION

	Population (million)			Households (million)		
Year	Nation	Farm	Farm as Percent of Nation	Nation	Farm	Farm as Percent of Nation
1840	17.1	9.0	52.6	—	—	—
1850	23.3	11.7	50.2	—	—	—
1860	31.5	15.1	48.1	—	—	—
1870	39.9	18.4	46.0	—	—	—
1880	50.3	23.0	45.7	—	—	—
1890	63.1	26.4	41.8	12.7	4.8	37.6
1900	76.1	29.4	38.7	16.0	5.7	35.6
1910	91.9	32.1	34.9	20.2	6.1	30.2
1920	105.7	31.6	29.9	24.5	6.8	27.7
1930	122.4	30.2	24.7	30.0	6.6	22.1
1940	131.8	30.5	23.2	35.2	7.1	20.4
1950	151.1	25.1	16.6	43.6	5.7	13.4
1960	179.3	21.2	11.3	52.2	4.1	7.8
1975*	244.9	15.0	6.2	—	—	—

Source: Historical Statistics of the United States Colonial Times to 1957. Series A 1–3, Statistical Abstract of the United States, 1960 and Agricultural Statistics, 1955 and 1960.

butter to be exchanged for groceries. But even if the nonfarm inputs are added, agriculture is still a declining portion of national economy, in the manner of the "consumer cross-section" in Figure 2.1.

In respect to the second point, the political strength of agriculture is not similarly represented by aggregation of laborers in tractor plants and farm operators. Workers in tractor plants are more likely to vote with automobile workers than with farmers. The management and lobbying representatives of industries producing farm inputs more nearly see a connection with agriculture. They may vote or pressure with agriculture for policies which will increase their sales of inputs; for example, in payments to subsidize lime and fertilizer. But some may press in opposite directions of farm groups; for example, in high price supports and large storages. But politically, at the polls, their number is much fewer than the number of horses and mules which they replaced—the owners of the latter doing the voting, of course.

Share of Expenditures on Food

Consumers have little understanding of the extent to which development of agriculture has reduced the real cost of food and the proportion of the budget going to it. This is true because food is no longer the major input of the goods and services carried away from the supermarket. Increasingly, purchases at the grocery are for packaging, freezing and similar services; or the substitution of frozen vegetables and fruits for canned ones, or canned form for dried form and exotic foods for plain foods. Services in foods are substitutes for maids in the household and the general trend will continue.

Today's housewife does not wish, in the manner of her great grandmother, to develop muscles, by pushing buttons on electric stoves and automatic washers and dryers. She wants to develop intellect in the manner of graduate students, and to do her part in leadership to solve community and international problems. The Indian housewife would like a little more millet or rice, or even a scythe to replace her sickle. A Russian housewife would like more than two rooms for six people. But economic development in the United States allows a different pattern of choice for most consumers.

While the income elasticity of demand for food is low, that for the services which go with food is much higher. Income elasticity of demand for expenditures on food at retail has been in the level of .15 in the recent decade, including both the food and service components. However, the services with food have an income elasticity ranging from .6 to 1.2, depending on whether they refer simply to services incorporated with food consumed in homes or to food eaten away from home. With higher income elasticities for services than for food, even the total of the food processing and marketing complex gradually declines in proportion that is purely agriculture as indicated in Table 2.3. Farmers and agricultural administrators sometimes pose the problem of agriculture as that of "the declining share of the consumer's dollar to the farmer." As the last column of the table suggests, this proportion declines as the housewife attaches greater marginal urgency to the package containing food, the dishes which serve it or the mechanization which cooks it, than to the food itself. The Research and Marketing Act of 1949 was passed largely to head the farmer's share of the consumer's dollar back towards the levels of earlier decades. Marketing research was initiated to accomplish as much, but the fight is an uphill one against the income expansion path illustrated in Figure 2.1. The most certain, and perhaps the only, way of attaining this rollback would be to return per capita incomes to the 1900 level. Not many people would favor this means.

GROWTH IN OUTPUT

In the absence of a large breakthrough in foreign markets and as consumers become wealthy, the extent of the opportunity for expansion by U.S. agriculture is tied largely to growth in population. Farm price and

TABLE 2.3

ALLOCATION OF CONSUMER EXPENDITURE FOR SPECIFIED COMMODITIES

Year	Percent of Total Consumer Expenditures				Percent of Consumer's Food Dollar to the Farmer
	Food	Housing	Medicine	Recreation	
1910	34.0	19.3	2.7	3.0	44.0
1920	33.3	15.2	3.0	3.6	43.0
1930	27.4	15.2	4.8	5.6	39.0
1940	30.9	12.6	4.9	5.2	40.0
1950	30.6	10.5	5.0	5.8	39.1
1960	24.7	12.9	5.5	6.0	38.6

income problems arise in about the extent to which growth in supply exceeds growth in demand; or, domestically, in extent that growth in farm output exceeds growth in population. Because of low demand elasticities for farm products, a slight excess in growth of output causes severe depression of farm prices, incomes and factor returns. The supply curve has indeed shifted to the right more rapidly than the demand function, over recent decades, as illustrated in Figure 2.2.

In the 1950's, output grew at a rate of 2.5 percent per annum. Over the 20 years, 1941–60, it grew at the rate of 2.3 percent per year. Population grew at a rate of 2.3 percent during the 1950's and at the rate of 1.7 percent over the two decades. While the rate of population increase slightly exceeded output growth between 1920 and 1930, demand still pressed on supply because export markets had receded and demand elasticities turned low at this time. The excess rate of production increase has been small, with annual output exceeding total uses (domestic market and surplus disposal) by only about 6 percent for grains and 2 percent in total during the late 1950's and early 1960's. This excess depressed prices greatly, however, to the extent that price supports allowed downward flexibility.

Over a longer period of time, a rate of increase in output which exceeds population increase causes chronic depression of income and pressure towards relaxation of resources used in the industry. Transfer of resources from agriculture would lessen or remove the depression of inincomes and resource returns, even with somewhat lower equilibrium prices for farm commodities. However, mobility of many resources in agriculture is low in the short run. This is true of labor with community attachments and skills oriented to agriculture, to buildings and machinery with low reservation prices or salvage values, and particularly to land which has little alternative in nonfarm use and has large time and transfer costs in shift from wheat to grass or from cotton to forestry.

While the threat of larger populations is suggested as a reason for rapid increase in the productivity of agriculture, it appears unlikely that population can outpace agriculture's ability to extend output through the 1970's, and certainly not in the 1960's. Should population ever begin to press on supply, farm income and resource returns will benefit, because of the low price elasticity of demand for food, should the supply elasticity be low for resources which might be drawn into agriculture. It is unlikely, however, that population will press on food supply in the United States during the sixties or seventies. The nation has too many natural resources which still are ineffectively utilized. It is rich and has many more of other resources that could be transferred into agriculture should the real price of food begin to rise. As mentioned previously, labor and steel could be transferred from autos and refrigerators to build more fertilizer plants or dams and irrigation equipment. Also, there is much slack in the distribution of resources to foods themselves. More chicken and less beef consumed would allow more meat from a given grain supply. If we ate wheat and oats as fancy breakfast foods and

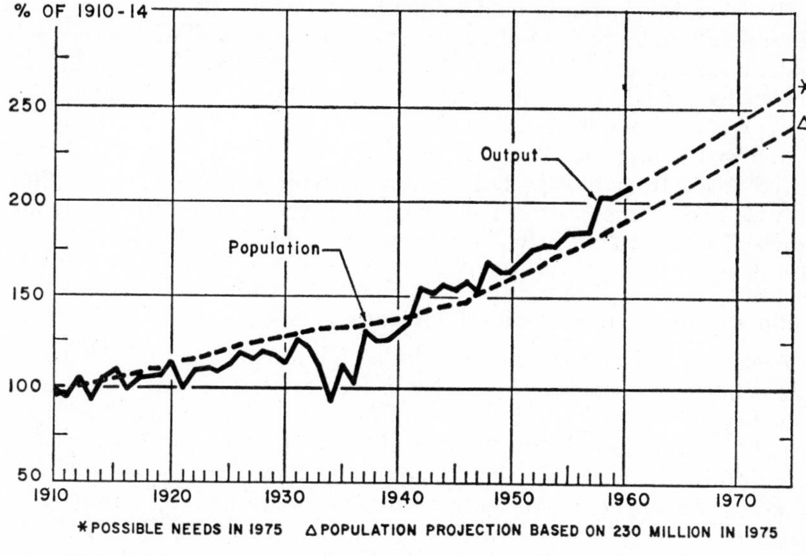

Fig. 2.2. U.S. Agricultural Production and Population, 1910–60, and Projections, 1960–75.

cocktail snacks we could get more calories and energies than when they are used as inputs for animals. The pricing system would draw resource allocation rapidly in these directions, should demand grow sufficiently to cause food prices to rise sharply against prices of nonfood commodities.

Even with a continuing "grading up" of the human diet, we can continue to produce abundantly for the next decade by upgrading the diets of animals and by using more fertilizer, improved varieties and general technical advance already known and in sight. Also, soil scientists indicate that a large acreage can, with heavier fertilization, be shifted from rotations to continuous cropping with greater output resulting from land resources. Recent projections, proven to be accurate in recent years, provide empirical footing for this statement.[1] Barton and Roger's early projections (see Figure 2.2) show estimated growth in total use of U.S. farm products of around 50 percent from 1956–57 to 1975 and estimated production which can match this increase, given the current excess rate of growth in output beyond domestic consumption. (Also see the "upsurge" in rate of growth shown in Figure 16.1.) Their more recent projections suggest that a population of 230 million persons and some increase in exports by 1975 would require somewhat more than a 35 percent increase in food output.[2]

[1] G. T. Barton and R. O. Rogers, *Farm Output; Past Changes and Projected Needs,* Agr. Info. Bul. No. 162, USDA.

[2] R. O. Rogers and G. T. Barton, *Our Farm Production Potential, 1975,* Agr. Info. Bul. No. 233, USDA.

However, this increase could be met by an increase of 20 million acres of cropland under one set of conditions and with a decline in cropland under a second set of conditions. Both conditions assume only technical knowledge already existing. Certainly new technology will be added to the current stock during this period. (See the investment figure for research in Chapter 16.) Analysis by Black and Bonnen indicates similarly.[3] Aside from unexpected war or extreme change in population growth, and on the basis of technology now known, the current rate of growth in output evidently can stay well ahead of growth in population and demand through the 1970's.

Ratio of Supply and Demand Increase

American society, affluent and with a high level of per capita income, is not likely to let absolute scarcity of food arise. The important question for the next decade is not: Can output be increased faster than population, at declining real price of food? Instead the basic policy question is: At what rate should supply be allowed to increase if consumers are to benefit sufficiently and farmers are not to sacrifice as a result of progress in agriculture? Different levels of prices, incomes and resource returns in agriculture will prevail, depending on the rate at which "supply shifters" are injected into the industry. The major supply shifters are new technology and lower real prices for factors, the latter reflecting the nature of shifts in supply functions for resources used in agriculture. Whether greater output, from lower factor prices or increased resource productivity, increases or decreases net income of agriculture in the short run will depend on the rate of increase in supply relative to demand.

With an income elasticity of demand which is effectively zero at the farm level, price and income for an agriculture can be maintained only if the rate of increase in supply is equal to that of demand. Turning to a simple algebraic form, to simplify the analysis and to refrain from leadening the analysis, we illustrate this point below. (Again, to keep the example more "manageable," we concern ourselves only with shift in the supply function and not with changes in its slope.)

In equation (2.1) we suppose a short-run demand function of the nature explained for equation (1.3) where $e = .4$.[4] Equation (2.2) is the industry production function, with X and Z magnitudes of two categories

[3] See J. T. Bonnen, *American Agriculture in 1965. Policy for American Agriculture and the Relation to Economic Growth and Stability,* Joint Economic Report, 85th Congress. Also see R. P. Christensen, S. E. Johnson, and R. Baumann, *Production Prospects for Wheat Feed and Livestock,* ARS 43-115, USDA, 1959.

[4] c may be considered to include the aggregate effect of other variables at given level; or $c = (I, P_n, N, T)$ where I is per capita income, P_n is the price of other commodities, N is population and T is other variables causing demand to change, etc. In later chapters we examine changes which relate to alteration in the slope and elasticity of production and supply functions. Our analysis of the production function to simply cause it to shift rightward and take supply in the same direction has its counterpart effect in factor price changes which shift output in the same manner.

of resource inputs. (See the footnote discussion of equations 1.1–1.5 for discussion of the methodology and illustrations; as well as indication of relationship of firm and industry functions.) However, we suppose that one, Z, is fixed in the short run with the production function in (2.3) resulting.

(2.1) $$Q_d = cP^{-.4}$$

(2.2) $$Q_p = aX^{.8}Z^{.2}$$

(2.3) $$Q_p = \pi X^{.8}$$

(2.4) $$Q_s = .4\pi^5 P_x^{-4} P^4$$

(2.5) $$cP^{-.4} = .4\pi^5 P_x^{-4} P^4$$

(2.6) $$P_1 = 1.23c^{.23}\pi^{-1.14} P_x^{.91}$$

(2.7) $$Q_1 = .92c^{.91}\pi^{.45} P_x^{-.36}$$

(2.8) $$R_1 = (P_1Q_1) - (\pi^{-1.25} P_x Q_1^{1.25})$$

Leaving aside temporarily the effects of uncertainty and institutions, static supply function in (2.4) is derived by setting $P_x(dQ_p/dX)^{-1}$ from (2.3) equal to P, product price, and solving for supply quantity, Q_s. Equating demand and supply in (2.5) and solving for short-run equilibrium quantities, we express price and output respectively in (2.6) and (2.7). Short-run industry profit above fixed costs is (2.8). Now if demand shifts "horizontally" by multiplication of (2.1) by λ and supply by multiplication of the production function is (2.3) by Γ, the new equilibrium price, P_2, is (2.9) and the new equilibrium output is (2.10).

(2.9) $$P_2 = \frac{\lambda^{.23}}{\Gamma^{1.14}} P_1$$

(2.10) $$Q_2 = \lambda^{.91}\Gamma^{.45} Q_1$$

(2.11) $$\lambda = \Gamma^5$$

Price will decline if λ, the demand shifter, is smaller than the magnitude indicated in (2.11). Quite obviously, this general condition held true for farm products in aggregate over the decade of the 1950's, and on into the 1960's. The new short-run industry profit (net above fixed costs) is that in (2.12). With shift of the demand function by λ and shift of the

(2.12) $$R_2 = \frac{\lambda^{1.15}}{\Gamma^{.68}} R_1$$

(2.13) $$\lambda = \Gamma^{.59}$$

production function by Γ, revenue in the second period, R_2, will not be greater than that in the first period unless the demand shifter has a value larger than that indicated in (2.13). It does not have to be so large as to maintain price because technical change lowers per unit costs.

Observation of American agriculture of the last decade would indicate that the shift coefficient for supply has been so large relative to the coefficient for demand that price and net revenue have both declined. Of course, other coefficients have changed so that the shifts have not been alone in a "horizontal" direction. We illustrate some of these types of changes (e.g., in the coefficients attaching to prices in the demand function and to the production function) at a later point. Gross revenue has been maintained for commodities such as corn, wheat and cotton only through government price support programs. Net revenue has declined because of the upward movement of factor prices, total costs increasing for this reason and because a larger proportion of purchased inputs are used.

Income Trends

The rates of change indicated in Figure 2.2 and the relationships illustrated in equations (2.1) through (2.10) have been operative in U.S. agriculture for the last decade. Net income of agriculture has declined in face of greater output, growing national income, increased population and decline in value of the dollar. Increased physical efficiency and greater output, a solution frequently posed by agriculturists, is not the answer to this aggregate income problem. It alone never will be a short-run answer in a market where price elasticities are extremely less than unity. This point is emphasized in Table 2.4. Net income of agriculture declined greatly after 1951 and per capita income of persons in agriculture also declined, even though farm population declined by 16 percent between 1950 and 1960. Income of farm persons did not fall lower, on average, only because of increased off-farm work of farm people, with the total income from the two sources in 1959 being just about equal to the 1951 level.

TABLE 2.4

INDICES AND VALUES OF SPECIFIED INCOMES AND OUTPUT SERIES

Year	Index of Agricultural Output (1940=100)	National Income (billion)	Net Income From Agriculture (billion)	Per Capita Income		
				Nonfarm	Farm from agriculture	Farm from all sources
1940	100	$ 82	$ 4.6	$ 685	$174	$ 262
1945	116	181	12.4	1,312	554	720
1950	123	242	14.0	1,585	626	838
1951	127	279	16.3	1,763	751	983
1952	132	292	15.3	1,849	711	962
1953	133	306	13.3	1,902	666	931
1954	133	302	12.7	1,849	660	916
1955	138	330	11.8	1,975	610	883
1956	139	351	11.6	2,073	600	897
1957	139	367	11.8	2,102	665	933
1958	150	368	14.0	2,066	768	1,043
1959	153	400	11.8	2,216	609	960
1960	158	418	12.0	2,290	622	986

Source: Economic Report of the President, 1960 and USDA Outlook Charts, 1960.

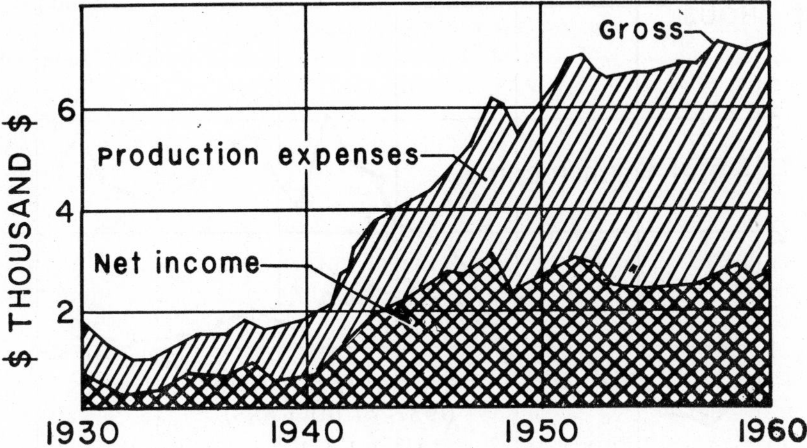

Fig. 2.3. Trends in Gross and Net Income and Production Expenses of Agriculture (Source: USDA Outlook Charts).

The income problem is a relative one. Money and real income of agriculture is high compared to other countries and with that of two decades back. (See Figures 3.5 and 3.6.) But U.S. farmers have not, in aggregate, been realizing the gain in money and real income continuing for the rest of the economy. Some sectors of agriculture have realized a large reduction in both. Net farm income has lagged behind the national economy more than has gross income of agriculture. All economic quantities have moved up with inflation, but decline in value of money has not offset the effect of greater output and inelastic demand in gross farm income. As mentioned previously, costs have risen due to inflation of all factor prices and a growing proportion of purchased inputs used in the industry. As Figure 2.3 illustrates, net income has extended over a plateau as production expenses take a larger bite out of gross income. Under growth and rising per capita real incomes, a problem exists when a major group does not realize significant gain from this general forward press. As Figure 2.4 shows, the purchasing power of farmers' net income has actually declined over the last decade. The monetary impact has fallen harder on commercial or high production farms than on small and low production farms. This point is illustrated in Figure 2.5, in comparison of farms with more and less than $2,500 in gross value of sales. Income from farm sources has decreased much more for the former than for the latter. Total family income of low production farms has actually increased with greater income from off-farm sources, the dominating element of income for the group. It is true, of course, that $2,500 is a low gross sales and a true commercial farm could have only small income at this volume.

The contrast of Figure 2.5 would be even greater if we separated the two groups at gross income of $7,500; a larger proportion of farmers with sales between $2,500 and $7,500 having off-farm work than those with

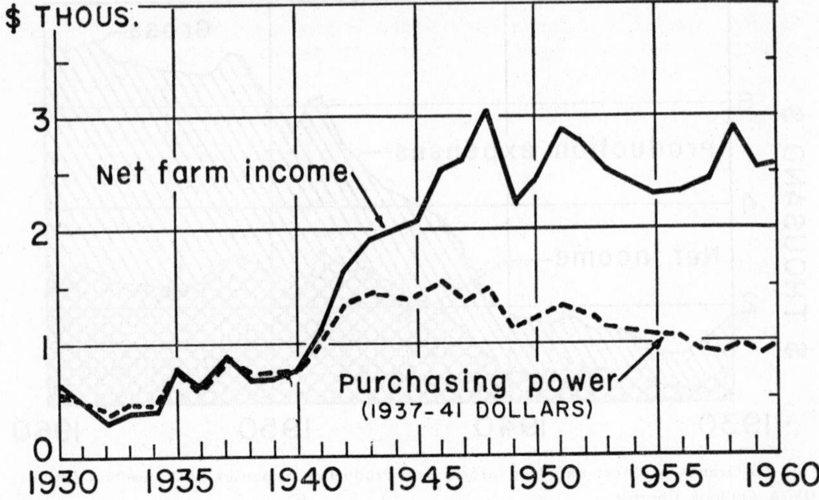

Fig. 2.4. Farm Operators' Net Income Per Farm and Its Purchasing Power (Source: USDA).

greater volume. But historically, persons of the lowest income strata of agriculture have gained only meagerly from national economic progress.

RESOURCE ADJUSTMENTS

The answer to the income problem would seem simple. A recent Secretary of Agriculture suggested some elementary arithmetic: divide the declining numerator, total farm income, by a declining denominator,

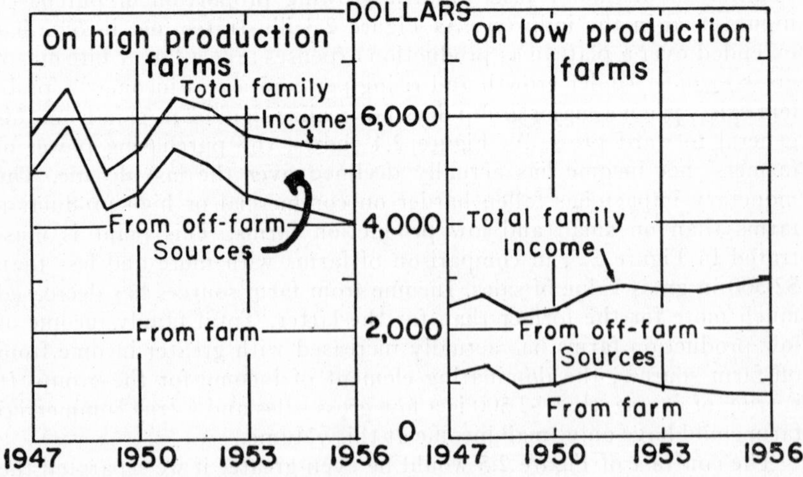

Fig. 2.5. Average Income of High Production (Gross Sales of $2,500 or More) and Low Production (Less Than $2,500 Sales) Farm Operator Families (Source: USDA).

TABLE 2.5

NUMBER OF FARMS BY SIZE OF ACREAGE GROUP, UNITED STATES, SPECIFIED YEARS, 1930–59

Item	1930	1940	1945	1950	1954	1959
Number of farms (thousands):						
Under 10 acres	359	506	595	485	484	240
10 to 49 acres	2,000	1,780	1,654	1,478	1,213	811
50 to 99 acres	1,371	1,291	1,157	1,048	864	657
100 to 179 acres	1,388*	1,279	1,200	1,103	953	771
180 to 259 acres	476*	517	493	487	464	414
260 to 499 acres	451	459	473	478	482	471
500 to 999 acres	160	164	174	182	192	200
1,000 acres and over	81	101	113	121	130	136
All census farms	6,289	6,097	5,859	5,382	4,782	3,704
Average size of farm (acres):						
All census farms	157	174	195	215	242	302
Commercial farms†	—‡	220	255	300	336	371

Source: Jackson V. McElveen, *Family Farms in a Changing Economy*, Agriculture Information Bulletin No. 171, Agricultural Research Service, USDA, March 1957, and Bureau of Census.

* Corrected for comparability with more recent census data.

† Census class I–IV farms, except that farms on which operator did 100 days or more of off-farm work or on which family nonfarm income exceeded farm sales were excluded from class V as well as class VI. Also excludes abnormal farms.

‡ Not available.

number of farms, and increase the per farm income quotient. Given knowledge of variables and relationships which enter into supply and equilibrium price, the structural answer also would seem simple: reduce inputs, contract output and improve prices and income. The Secretary's suggestion implies qualitatively these changes which might be suggested by economists.

Agriculture has made some very large structural adjustments since 1940. Some of these, as migration of labor from farms, have been truly remarkable but have not been great enough to arrest the downturn in income, or to cause real income to push upward to levels of important nonfarm sectors. The number of census farms declined by 2.2 million or around 40 percent between 1945 and 1959. However, as can be determined from Table 2.5, the greatest part of this decline has come from smaller farms, those of less than 179 acres in size. The number of farms larger than this has remained relatively constant in the last 15 years, with some reduction below 260 acres and an increase from those with larger acreage. The total product of American agriculture can still be produced with many fewer farms.

As Table 2.6 shows, less than 30 percent of farms fell in classes I, II and III in 1954 but produced nearly 80 percent of the value of agricultural products; adding class IV, 44 percent of all farms produced 91 percent of output. The 25 percent of commercial farms falling in classes V and VI and the 30.4 percent of part-time, residential and abnormal farms could easily disappear, with food needs of the nation being met because the latter produce such a small portion of output. But the bite

TABLE 2.6

ECONOMIC CLASSIFICATION OF FARMS, UNITED STATES, 1954

Economic Class	Sales Per Farm	Number of Farms (*thousands*)	Percentage of All Farms	Percentage of Value of Products Sold
"Commercial" farms				
Class I	$25,000 and over	134	2.8	31.3
Class II	$10,000 to $24,999	449	9.4	26.9
Class III	$ 5,000 to $ 9,999	707	14.8	20.5
Class IV	$ 2,500 to $ 4,999	812	17.0	12.1
Subtotal		2,102	44.0	90.8
Class V	$ 1,200 to $ 2,499	763	16.0	5.7
Class VI	$ 250 to $ 1,199*	462	9.7	1.4
Subtotal		1,225	25.7	7.1
All "commercial"		3,327	69.7	97.9
Part-time	$ 250 to $ 1,199*	575	12.0	1.4
Residential	Under $250	878	18.4	.3
Abnormal†		3	.1	.3
Subtotal		1,455	30.4	2.0
All farms		4,782	100.0	100.0

* Farms with sales from $250 to $1,199 are classified as part-time if the operator worked off the farm 100 days or more or if the family's nonfarm income exceeded the value of farm products sold.

† Public and private institutional farms, etc.

Source: 1954 Census of Agriculture.

could go much deeper. Scale economies and underemployed resources of typical commercial farms undoubtedly are great enough that a third of these 1.5 million farms could be removed from the scene, with the farm output produced abundantly by a remaining 1 million commercial farms. In 1959, 795,000 farms with sales over $10,000 (32.8 percent of commercial farms) had 71.9 percent of the sales of all farms. The 1,449,000 farms with sales over $5,000 (59.8 percent of commercial farms) had 97.1 percent of the sales of all farms.

There is still much slack in farm numbers and sizes, but withdrawal of small farms adds only slightly to income of true commercial farms. The resources and income of the former are small and add little but "magnitude of average" for large farms. The fact that the greatest decline has been in small farms magnifies the change in per acre size of commercial farms indicated in Table 2.5 between 1940 and 1959. Yet, it is still true that sizable changes in commercial farm size have taken place, especially in specialized grain producing and arid regions. This trend can continue because farms of typical size in corn and wheat regions especially have underemployed labor and machine resources and their high mechanization allows some further cost economies. Under pressure, American consumers could be fed, with some commodity exported and supply pressure still existing, with two million or fewer of all farms and a million of commercial farms.

Change in Labor Resources

Two of the more dramatic changes in American agriculture since 1940 have been a decline by a third in the total labor input and an increase of 50 percent in the total output. Obviously, some fairly marked reductions in the labor force have taken place without causing agricultural output to decline. As will be explained later, these changes were possible because of the great surplus capacity, or underemployment, of specific capital and labor resources in agriculture. In fact, if simple empirical inferences were to be drawn from trends of the past two decades, the conclusion would likely be that further reductions in the labor force and in the number of farms will take place while output of farm products will increase. Regression and correlation coefficients for the data of Figure 2.6 need not be derived to make such predictions. Figure 2.6 is not presented as a naive model containing all variables which explain increases in agricultural output. Obviously, numerous other

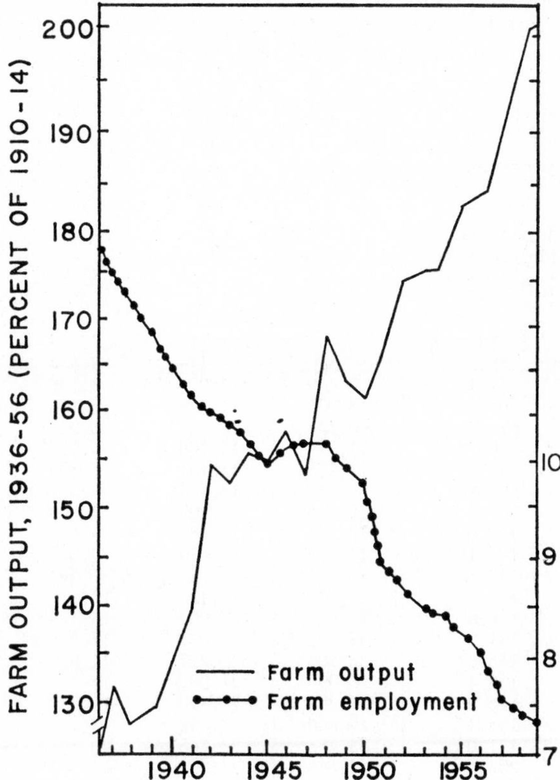

Fig. 2.6. Index Numbers of Farm Output and Total Farm Employment, United States, 1936–59.

variables affected output during the period. Two of importance were (1) greater inputs of certain capital items (representing known techniques) such as farm machinery, livestock numbers, fertilizer in particular areas, etc., and (2) inputs of particular capital items (representing newly developed techniques) such as the host of new crop varieties, insecticides, antibiotics, livestock breeds, and other innovations introduced during the period. But along with these changes other developments, (a) decreases in the farm population and labor force and (b) decrease in farm numbers and consequent increase in farm size, also allowed or brought about increased output.

It is well agreed that, relatively, income of agriculture is low because growth in output outpaced growth in demand during the 1950's. Furthermore, since agriculture obviously has a surplus labor force, it would seem that returns on resources in agriculture, in the long run, can be best put on a par with those in other industries by maintaining a growing number of nonfarm employment opportunities and by reducing the total farm labor input and population in agriculture. The solution of the agricultural problem, therefore, appears simple: Reduce the labor force, shrink output enough to equilibrate agricultural supply and food demand, and, as a consequence, raise resource returns.

This pat solution, in about the cause-effect sequence outlined, is re-

TABLE 2.7

VALUE OF FARM ASSETS, UNITED STATES AND PER FARM AVERAGE, 1940–58

Year	U.S. Value of Physical Farm Assets (current dollars in billions)	Value of Assets Used in Production			
		Per farm		Per worker	
		Current dollars	*1947–49 dollars*	*Current dollars*	*1947–49 dollars*
1940	$ 48.8	$ 6,094	$13,118	$ 3,413	$ 7,347
1941	50.3	6,340	13,444	3,634	7,706
1942	57.1	7,449	14,076	4,330	8,183
1943	65.8	8,934	14,748	5,176	8,549
1944	73.9	10,328	15,042	5,933	8,644
1945	80.2	11,346	15,100	6,625	8,817
1946	88.4	12,435	15,151	7,370	8,980
1947	92.6	14,154	15,364	8,072	8,762
1948	103.0	15,906	15,509	8,890	8,669
1949	109.0	17,144	16,480	9,466	9,100
1950	107.1	16,979	16,979	9,625	9,625
1951	124.8	20,434	17,742	11,394	9,893
1952	139.5	23,206	18,428	13,178	10,465
1953	136.0	22,946	19,009	13,313	11,028
1954	131.9	22,592	19,631	13,256	11,518
1955	135.8	23,806	20,287	14,018	11,957
1956	138.4	25,096	21,091	14,885	12,530
1957	146.0	27,203	22,499	16,880	13,363
1958	155.4	29,600	22,042	18,477	13,831
1959	171.0	33,455	23,165	20,598	14,229
1960	203.6	34,648	23,921	21,303	14,707

Source: USDA Statistics (Agricultural Outlook Charts, 1959 and 1960).

tailed widely, apparently as the immediate solution of the farm problem. We have no question about the long-run accuracy of the suggested adjustment and earlier-made similar suggestions.[5] There is, however, a question of whether the farm problem can be solved in a period of less than ten to fifteen years through this type of adjustment. Contrariwise, in important segments of American agriculture, a reduction per se in the farm population and total labor input promises to increase farm output.

The major structural change conventionally suggested for agriculture's problem, reduction in the labor force, is a long-run solution. It is not likely to solve the aggregate surplus problem of commercial farming in the next decade. Rapid progress towards a long-run objective of a labor force consistent with today's techniques and factor prices may well accentuate the very near-term surplus of farm products. Not only has farm employment declined greatly, but comparable changes have taken place in other aspects of the industry's resource structure and population. Capital per worker, measured in constant dollars, has nearly doubled since 1940. Although the situation differs by geographic region, capital assets per worker are about 50 percent greater in agriculture than in nonfarm industries. These changes represent some remarkable adjustments already in labor inputs and factor combinations for American agriculture. Still the rate and absolute magnitude of adjustment has not been great enough to lessen production or eliminate the farm problem.

Changes in Capital

Increase in input of certain capital items for agriculture has been even more extreme. Machinery and equipment used by 1960 were three times that of 1940. Livestock and auxiliary resources were four times, and fertilizer was 5.5 times the 1940 figure. Total cropland remained almost constant, partly because of space restraints. Value in current dollars of physical assets used in production (Table 2.7) tripled and value per farm increased more than fourfold. However, total inputs for agriculture increased by only 15 percent because the reduction in labor was only slightly less than the increase in capital.

The change in resource structure of individual farms has been greater than, and somewhat different from, that of the industry. While the industry had a decline of nearly a third in labor inputs between the periods 1930–39 and 1950–58, labor input per farm declined by only about 10 percent. And while the industry experienced no important change in the acreage of cropland, input per farm increased by 40 percent in this period.

The indices of selected categories of inputs in Table 2.8 further emphasize differences in change of resource structure by the industry and the individual farm. Aggregate inputs of the industry increased by only

[5] Cf. Earl O. Heady, *Economics of Agricultural Production and Resource Use*, Prentice-Hall, New York, 1952, Chaps. 24–25.

TABLE 2.8

TOTAL U.S. AGRICULTURAL INPUTS AND INPUTS PER FARM FOR SELECTED RESOURCES AND PERIODS

Item	Aggregate U.S. (Millions)				Average Per Farm			
	1930–39	1940–49	1950–58	1959	1930–39	1940–49	1950–58	1959
Cropland (acre)	477	470	472	470	71.2	78.2	92.6	102.2
All land in farms (acre)	919	1,005	1,042	1,045	137.2	167.5	204.3	227.2
Workers (number)	12.3	10.4	8.5	7.4	1.8	1.7	1.7	1.6
Man hours used (hrs.)*	21.7	18.9	13.0	11.1	3,239	3,150	2,549	2,413
Aggregate inputs‡	100	109	111	110†	100	122	146	160†
Farm real estate‡	100	103	112	112†	100	115	147	163†
Machinery and equipment‡	100	156	266	274†	100	174	376	399†
Fertilizer and lime‡	100	248	474	536†	100	278	624	780†
Feed, seed, and livestock services‡	100	205	313	381†	100	229	412	555†
Paid inputs‡	100	133	160	167†	100	149	238	243†
Unpaid inputs‡	100	86	71	65†	100	96	94	95†

* Billions for U.S.
†1958.
‡ Index.
Source: USDA Statistics.

10 percent over the 20 year period 1930–39 through 1950–58. While the increase in capital forms such as fertilizer, machinery and livestock were large, the decline in labor inputs and the relative constancy of the large input represented by land tempered the aggregate increase. But, again, because of the decrease in number of farms, total inputs per farm increased by 60 percent in this period. Real estate input per farm increased by 63 percent by 1958, while the increase for the industry was only 12 percent. As an average, per farm use of inputs such as fertilizer, machinery, feed and livestock services increased twice as much as industry use of these same inputs. Between the periods 1930–39 and 1950–58, per farm use of paid inputs increased by 138 percent. The comparable figure for the industry was only 60 percent. The index of unpaid inputs, mainly labor, declined by 31 percent for the industry but by only 5 percent for the average farm.

Quite obviously, then, individual farms have capital and financing problems which are greater than those of the industry. The trends pointed out above for the past two decades will certainly continue for the next two, and at an increased rate if relatively full employment and ample employment opportunities are maintained. Continuance of these conditions and increased communication among farm and urban communities will speed up the tempo at which occupational and spatial migration will take place, thus providing the opportunity for remaining farms to expand in land input and total capital assets. Upcoming technology for agriculture will certainly encourage this direction. But even in the absence of new technology, the full adjustment potential growing out of currently known technology and existing resource prices will directly carry typical farms in the direction emphasized by Table 2.8. Capital requirements for farming are now much greater than at any previous time in history. By 1960, typical or modal farms in various regions had these total investments: Cornbelt cash grain, $100,000; Northern Plains sheep ranches and Southern Plains wheat farms,

$85,000; Northeast dairy farms, $31,000; Southern Piedmont cotton farms, $17,000. Large-scale (but not extremely large) farms had investments of two or three times these amounts.

Trends in use of more resources per farm have been highly universal over the United States. As the data in Table 2.9 show, typical commercial family farms in various regions use considerably more land and capital but somewhat less labor. In most cases, reduction in per farm labor input, on these commercial units, has been much smaller than for agricultural industry, and increase in nonreal estate capital has been much greater than the national aggregate. However, considerable variation has existed among types. Increase in per farm use of nonreal estate capital has been lower for cotton and tobacco farms, with the latter having an effective price and quota program over the 20 year period, in the South than for Cornbelt and Great Plains farms and ranches. Similarly, typical dairy farms increased use of capital by a greater proportion than southern cotton and tobacco farms.

However, the cotton farms in the Southeast decreased labor inputs

TABLE 2.9

COMPARISON OF INPUTS, 1937–41 AND 1959, FOR SPECIFIED TYPES OF FARMS IN THE U.S.

Type of Farm and Location	Land (acres)		Labor (days)		Nonreal Estate Capital ($)	
	1937–41	1959	1937–41	1959	1937–41	1959
Cotton:						
So. Piedmont	158	183	526	370	$ 1,010	$ 3,120
High Plains (Tex.)	258	404	431	320	2,530	8,140
Delta (small)	53*	58	375*	274	1,540*	3,640
Peanut-cotton	122*	163	404*	332	1,820*	4,000
Cornbelt:						
Hog-steer	178	208	425	403	6,280	22,530
Cash-grain	209	234	380	329	4,910	17,560
Dairy farms:						
Central northeast	176	217	533	433	4,100	16,200
Southern Minn.	135	156	482	393	3,460	15,030
Tobacco:						
Kentucky	110	118	438	391	1,540	5,390
Coastal plain (large)	170*	170	1,084*	851	6,630*	7,830
Coastal plain (small)	50*	50	381*	320	1,900*	2,060
Wheat:						
No. plains (corn)	427	506	374	388	3,220	21,940
So. plains	586	732	272	312	2,860	13,140
Washington (pea)	416	555	389	349	6,600	29,270
Cattle Ranches:						
Northern plains	3,322	4,240	412	388	9,090	26,260
Inter-mountain	1,573	1,725	487	499	14,050	45,310
Southwest	8,316*	11,090	395	337	26,460	28,100

* 1947–49 (1937–41 not available).
Source: *Farm Costs and Returns*, Agr. Info. Bul. 176, USDA (rev. 1959).

by a larger proportion than other types of farms over the nation. While the increase in capital and land inputs per farm has not been as rapid for farms in the Southeast over the past two decades, the rate of change may well catch up over the next two decades. Change has been tardy in the Southeast because of (1) lower wage rates tending to discourage the substitution of high capacity machinery for labor, (2) the relatively less favorable initial capital position of farms in the Southeast, (3) poorer school facilities and lack of communication for occupational migration and improved farm management and (4) the tendency of many abandoned farms to move into forestry rather than into the farm consolidation process.

However, if national economic growth continues at a rapid rate, with relatively greater tempo in the Southeast than in the Midwest and Plains areas, factor prices will encourage a more rapid substitution of capital for labor. Economic stability and favorable incomes also can encourage a more rapid rate of farm consolidation and enlargement in the future than in the past. However, the rate of increase in land and capital inputs needed per farm must be much more rapid and of greater relative magnitude if the income gaps, between the Southeast and (1) nonfarm employment and (2) farming elsewhere in the nation, is to be closed. The changes needed are large, if returns on labor resources especially are to be brought to levels which Americans would currently term "decent." While the economic environment will allow these adjustments in the Southeast to be more rapid in the future, capital availability stands as a major obstacle in allowing per farm increases in land and capital inputs of the magnitudes needed.

Product and Resource Prices

Farm commodity prices have been depressed in the 1950's, enough to more than offset inflation and the rise in the general price level. Prices of all inputs have increased and farm profits in agriculture have declined. In response to this price and income complex, plus the relatively favorable returns to land and transfer of labor to nonfarm uses, capital inputs have increased, with land declining slightly and labor greatly for the industry as a whole. At first glance, it would appear that market forces, the prices of commodities relative to the prices of resources particularly, would cause the industry and firm to move in the same direction. Or, with scale economies associated with new technology still not fully exploited by individual firms, contrasting trends might be expected. Yet there also are other forces which have bearing on the quantity and mix of resources used by the firm, with contrasting adjustment of the industry.

New machine technology generally has served as a substitute for labor. One relationship between new machine technology and increased capital demand by the individual farm is reflected in the farm's cost curve or structure. However, the magnitude of the machine prices relative to the prices of other resources and to farm products is an important causal factor determining the amount of this specific form of capital which is used in agriculture. (Relative changes in the rate of substitution of machinery for other resources also are important in this respect.) Rather than discuss machinery alone within this framework, we turn our attention to capital resources in general. Resources such as fertilizer, feed additives, improved seeds and others have been used in increased quantities mainly because they have been priced favorably relative to the prices of farm products and because their marginal productivities have increased from technological discovery. Within this favorable environment, scale or cost economies have had little, if any, relationship to increased demand for such "biological" resources.

For the individual farm, capital items such as fertilizer, insecticides, fuel and seeds serve generally as complements with land. As more acres are operated, additional quantities of the capital items also are used. Similarly, with an increase in the number of animals and birds handled, the amount of feed and livestock services also increases. Technically, of course, other capital inputs can serve as substitutes for land and livestock, even for an individual farmer. He can produce a given output, for example, with more fertilizer and less land or vice versa. But in general practice and because of favorable price relatives, he either uses more fertilizer and other chemicals or inputs on a given acreage, or expands their use as he takes on a larger acreage. For the industry, however, fertilizer and similar materials serve more clearly as a substitute for land. With the large increase in fertilizer, insecticides, improved seeds and materials of other innovations, the nation's food output can now be produced with fewer acres devoted to the conventional mix of crops. Unfortunately, however, it has not been possible to withdraw or shift the excess land and surpluses still accumulate. But even if the national input of land were diminished to bring output into line with demand, individual farmers producing the particular commodity would not do so (in the absence of "across the board" control programs) but would continue to increase land and associated inputs, as long as price and marginal productivities of these resources are favorable relative to the prices of the commodities they produce.

The prices of factors used in production (Table 2.10) and the physical

TABLE 2.10

INDEX OF PRICES RECEIVED AND PRICES PAID FOR SELECTED INPUTS, 1935–59 (1935–39=100)

Index of	Period				
	1935–39	1940–44	1945–49	1950–54	1955–59
Prices received by farmers	100	144	231	252	221
Price of fertilizer	100	106	132	150	151
Price of machinery	100	102	130	173	191
Price of labor	100	178	333	395	455
Price of land (alone)	100	112	188	254	325
Price paid, all costs	100	122	184	220	229

Source: USDA.

TABLE 2.11

EXPECTED EFFECT OF CHANGES IN PRICE RATIOS AND MARGINAL PRODUCTIVITIES ON RESOURCE DEMAND (COMMODITY DEMAND FIXED)

Price Change	MPP Decrease	MPP Constant	MPP Increase
P_x/P increase	$X_n<X_0$	$X_n<X_0$	X_n ? X_0
P_x/P constant	$X_n<X_0$	$X_n=X_0$	$X_n>X_0$
P_x/P decrease	X_n ? X_0	$X_n>X_0$	$X_n>X_0$

magnitudes of their marginal productivities have favorably encouraged an increased demand by individual farmers for most major categories of inputs.[6] This has been true even in recent years when commodity prices have been depressed relative to factor prices generally. If marginal productivities are increased sufficiently through technical innovations, the farmer's demand for inputs can increase even under conditions of commodity prices which decline relative to factor prices.

Supposing that X_0 represents the original quantity of the resource, X_n is the new quantity, P is the price of the product and P_x is the price of the factor, we have the nine possible combinations of "developmental" changes represented by the cells of Table 2.11. The rows represent changes in the magnitude of the factor/product price ratio while the columns represent changes in magnitude of marginal physical productivity (MPP) of resources. Each cell indicates the expected change in factor demand by the individual farmer. For example, with the MPP and price ratio, P_x/P, both constant, no change would be expected in factor demand (the middle cell of the table). We can generally rule out the first column, except for situations such as extreme soil erosion. The middle column may apply to a few resources where technical innovation has been unimportant (for example, more so for range resources in the Inter-Mountain region than for farm resources elsewhere in the nation). However, the demand situation for most resources such as land, chemicals, machinery, livestock and feed is that characterized in the third column. The marginal productivities of the resources have increased due to technical research by the USDA, the land-grant colleges, private firms and farmer discovery and management. With the price ratio constant or decreasing, demand by individual farmers for the resources would increase. With the price ratio increasing, demand for resources would be expected to increase or decrease depending on whether the relative improvement in productivity of the resource is relatively greater or less than the increase in the price ratio. Evidently, for individual farmers in most regions of the country, the marginal physical productivities of resources have increased faster than the factor/product price ratio has increased in recent years. And in numerous occasions, the

[6] Against a 1910–14 base, indices of prices over the period 1950–59 were as follows: machinery, 349; operating expense items, 217; hired wage rate in agriculture, 642; land, 208; and building materials, 359.

specific resources (especially chemicals) have represented a situation such as the element connecting the third row and the third column.

Industry and Farm Differences Under Capital Limitations and Profit Depression

By resort to simple algebra, we illustrate how it can be profitable for an individual farmer, previously limited on resources but now able to acquire more because of capital gains in land through inflation or because of other reasons, to increase use of resources while prices and return to the industry in total decline. The demand equation is (2.1) where we substitute e for .4 and simply suppose, as in agriculture, the price elasticity is less than 1.0. The individual farm's production function is (2.2) except that we use elasticities of b and m and the industry production function, with n firms, is simply n times (2.2), in order to keep the example simple. We also suppose that b and m are each less than 1.0. While farmers are responsive to price, to be discussed later, we suppose that output in separate short-run periods is that forthcoming from a (fairly) fixed collection of resources in the period, a case to illustrate the logic but overly simplified for later analysis. (Hence, short-run supply equals the production function.) The amount of resources may be increased in a second period because farmers have the capital for acquisition and greater credit base as in the period 1940–60. Market demand and supply, in the first short-run period are equated in (2.14) and the equilibrium price thus derived is (2.15) where we set $r = e^{-1}$,

$$naX^bZ^m = cP^{-e} \tag{2.14}$$

$$P = c^r n^{-r} a^{-r} X^{-br} Z^{-mr} \tag{2.15}$$

which is a quantity greater than 1.0. The total value product, V, for the industry in this ultra-short-run equilibrium is (2.16) and will decline with any increase in magnitudes of inputs and input in a "next short-

$$V = (c^r n^{-r} a^{-r} X^{-br} Z^{-mr})(naX^bZ^m) = c^r n^{-u} a^{-u} X^{-v} Z^{-w} \tag{2.16}$$

run period" under the inelastic demand situation. Letting $1 - r = -u$, $b(1-r) = -v$ and $m(1-r) = -w$, and with these quantities all being negative, this decline is obvious in the marginal value productivities of (2.17) and (2.18).

$$\frac{\partial V}{\partial X} = \frac{-vc^r}{n^u a^u X^{v+1} Z^w} \tag{2.17}$$

$$\frac{\partial V}{\partial Z} = \frac{-wc^r}{n^u a^u X^v Z^{w+1}} \tag{2.18}$$

If the industry of farmers increases inputs and outputs, net revenue will decline (marginal value productivities are negative) if the resources have prices of zero or greater. If we suppose nonzero and positive prices of P_x and P_z for the two resources, this is still true for the industry but the outcome for the individual farm operator is different. Let us suppose that equity financing and risk aversion or credit rationing has restrained his purchase of resources such that their marginal products are greater than the two price ratios PP_x^{-1} and PP_z^{-1}. There are many experimental production function studies, linear programming and budgeting analyses and farm record summaries showing that the marginal returns on particular classes of resources have been much greater than their costs to individual farmers in postwar years. Even during the period of decline in feed grain prices, Iowa studies show that the return from fertilizer, at the rate at which farmers typically were using this resource, was over twice the cost of this resource. The same thing exists in respect to fertilizer use elsewhere over the nation, if one applies economic analysis to fertilizer response data.

Because of atomistic competition, demand for the product of individual farm is infinite at a constant product price of P. Total value product for the individual farmer is that in (2.19) while the marginal value products of resources are (2.20) and (2.21) where Q_p is as defined as n^{-1} proportion of the left-hand member of (2.14).

$$V = PaX^bZ^m \tag{2.19}$$

$$\frac{\partial V}{\partial X} = bQ_pPX^{-1} \tag{2.20}$$

$$\frac{\partial V}{\partial Z} = mQ_qPZ^{-1} \tag{2.21}$$

Total value product and marginal value productivities for an individual are not negative from the outset, as for the industry. Given a sufficient degree of capital limitations prior to a period such as 1940–60, marginal value quantities can be much larger than the factor prices for the individual farmer. If he has excess of income over expenditures and capital appreciation due to inflation or saving, providing him with added funds or credit base for purchasing resources beyond the original restraint levels, he can add to net income by using more resources, even though the industry cannot. He can profitably add resources (with the industry doing likewise but with price and aggregate net income declining) as long as the quantities in (2.20) and (2.21) for him are greater than factor prices.

For an important portion of the period following 1940, farmers used a big part of their increased incomes to pay off debts. But even so, individual farmers had added savings for purchase of more resources. Also, a smaller percentage debt on greater total assets still allowed a greater dollar or absolute amount of borrowing. While total inputs of the agricultural industry increased only modestly over the period 1940–59 under these conditions, there was a sharp rise in per farm use of resources. This differential change was possible because farmers remaining in the industry were in an advantageous resource purchasing position, able to acquire some resources otherwise used by migrating persons less well situated economically.

We have attempted to examine only one force: namely, the use of more resources by individual farmers in a depressed industry and illustrating that in an industry where greater inputs and output cause aggregate income to decline, individual farmers, previously limited in resource quantity by capital limitations, can still purchase more inputs and increase income relative to the group. But to do so they must increase their output by a larger percentage than the decline in price and/or attain certain other conditions in respect to costs. Farmers who cannot do so find themselves with depressed incomes, with the alternative of also increasing resources used or of leaving agriculture. Many followed the latter course over the past decade, with the conditions explained above allowing for individual farmers to remain in the industry. Industry net farm income declined in recent years, even while industry capital inputs were increasing. Because of fewer farms, income per farm has not fallen proportionately, although there is great difference among farms. Individuals increasing use of inputs by largest proportions and changing to profitable new technologies have partly offset the decline in prices by greater volume and lower unit costs. Some have increased their income by doing so, even while average income per farm declined. Other strata of farmers have experienced a sharp decline in income because capital and other forces have restrained their use of more resources and new technology.

Scale Returns and Cost Economies

Generally, however, the opportunity for individual farmers to in crease their use of resources, extend output and increase profits (or keep profits from declining when returns to the industry are depressed from greater output) rests on (1) increasing scale returns or cost economies associated with the prevailing or potential technology and/or (2) the relation of input prices to product prices.

On-the-farm scale returns or cost economies arise mainly from mechanical innovations such as those relating to power, machinery, equipment and buildings. They are only slightly, or not at all, related to such biological innovations as new seed varieties, fertilizer, insecticides and chemicals. Power units, field machines and harvesters of greater capacity and larger crop handling equipment have particularly increased the size or acreage range over which declining per unit costs prevail in cotton, corn, wheat and other field crop areas. Too, increased capacity and productivity of these machines has increased greatly the number of acres, animals and birds which can be handled by one man or the farm family. Since the fixed costs of these high capacity machines are greater than those of machines in prewar days, the curve of per unit costs declines more sharply over larger outputs. A greater gain in net returns per unit

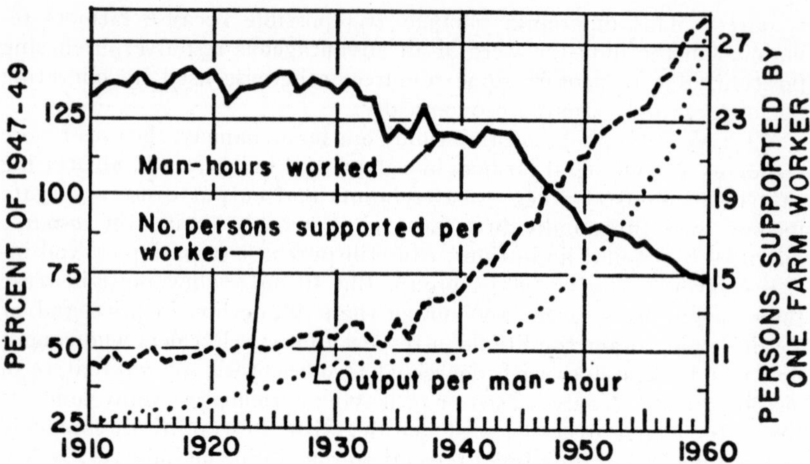

Fig. 2.7. Man-Hours worked, Man-Hour Productivity and Persons Supported Per Farm Worker.

as size increases is thus realized. For the same reason, the economic disadvantage extends more sharply to farms of small acreage. And, as pointed out in Chapter 14, they realize less relative gain from supply-restricting policies.

These recent and developing machine technologies increase the per farm demand for, or use of, several types of capital. First, of course, if they are going to be used, the investment in machinery and equipment itself is increased. But since the main cost advantages of these newer machines are realized only if their higher fixed costs are spread over more acres or animals, the latter categories of capital must be increased and the investment is augmented accordingly. Also, as implicit in (2.19) and (2.20), greater input of one factor increases the marginal value productivity and demand for others. In numerous types of production, investment in the added land or livestock, inputs necessary to allow attainment of the lower per unit costs from newer but more costly machines, is greater than the increase in machine investment.

PRODUCTIVITY AND OUTPUT OF LABOR

Adoption of new technology and the general structural change discussed above have greatly increased the physical productivity of U.S. farm labor. Value productivity per man has also increased, but by a much smaller proportion because price elasticity of demand is less than 1.0. Figure 2.7 indicates the magnitude of increase in physical productivity. Productivity per man hour increased by about 200 percent between 1940 and 1960 while productivity per person increased by 130 percent. The average number of persons supported per farm worker increased from 10.8 in 1940 to nearly 30 in 1960, compared to 7.1 in 1910 and 4.1 in 1820. In a developmental sense, these figures contrast with around 75 percent of the labor force used in agriculture in India and around 40 percent in Russia.

Resource Substitution Rates

Numerous factors have led to this remarkable increase in labor productivity. First, migration of persons from low productivity farms would increase the average of the industry, even if remaining farms did not increase labor productivity. However, other commercial farms have done so through use of mechanization and substitution of machines for labor and through the adoption of biological techniques generally. Innovations which increase yield per animal and acre do not increase labor requirements proportionately, and sometimes scarcely at all. Accordingly, productivity of labor is increased, just as it is when greater capacity in power and machinery is used to increase the number of animals and acres handled per man. Then, too, productivity of a particular resource is always increased, along a product isoquant, as input of one factor is decreased and another is increased.

Any development leading to an increase in labor productivity also tends to increase the rate at which capital substitutes for labor. Hence, fertilizer and improved seed, which increase yield per acre, and feed additives, which increase output per animal or feed unit, serve as substitutes, just as mechanization which replaces labor directly. With a fairly constant output desired by consumers at a particular time, and with prices favoring adoption of a technique, the greater productivity of land decreases the amount of both land and labor required to produce the nation's food. This point can be illustrated with either discrete type of innovations or continuous functions representing changes in technology. For example, suppose that fertilizer can be used on an acre of land to give a production function of typical form in (2.22) where Y is yield per acre and F is fertilizer per acre. (The same results prevail generally for any type of production function.) For a given soil type, supposing it is possible to obtain the same results for each acre, the aggregate

$$Y = f(F) = a + bF - cF^2 \tag{2.22}$$

$$Y^* = aA + bF - cF^2A^{-1} \tag{2.23}$$

production function in (2.23) exists where A, number of acres, is multiplied by the per acre production function in (2.22) and F in (2.22) is divided by A for (2.23). The "gross" marginal rate of substitution of fertilizer for land thus is defined in (2.24), derived from (2.22) and (2.23).[7]

---

[7] If we wish to express marginal rates of substitution for a particular output level, we can first define the isoquant in (a):

$$A = \frac{Y - bF \pm \sqrt{4acX^2 + (Y - bX)^2}}{2a} K. \tag{a}$$

It is the negative of marginal productivity of fertilizer divided by

$$\frac{\partial A}{\partial F} = \frac{2cFA^{-1} - b}{a + cF^2A^{-2}} \tag{2.24}$$

marginal productivity of land. If labor requirements per acre are constant regardless of yield, and land and labor are pure technical complements, we can substitute the appropriate term for A in (2.23). For example, if L is labor and r units of labor are required per acre, $L=rA$ and $A=r^{-1}L$, the same total function expressed in terms of labor is (2.25). The "gross" marginal rate of substitution of fertilizer for labor is

$$Y^* = ar^{-1}L + bF - crL^{-1}F^2 \tag{2.25}$$

$$\frac{\partial L}{\partial F} = \frac{2crL^{-1}F - b}{ar^{-1} + crL^{-2}F^2} \tag{2.26}$$

(2.26), a continuous function of the amount of fertilizer applied per acre and the number of acres fertilized.[8] However, the same general procedures specify the rate of substitution of other discrete practices or materials for labor, if we simply consider increments and replace ∂ with Δ. Roughly, as an average rate of substitution, it appears that each 20,000 bushel increase in corn production ($\Delta y^* = 20{,}000$) from new technology has allowed release of one worker for agriculture; each 10,000 bushel increase in wheat ($\Delta y^* = 10{,}000$) from new technology has released about one man. Recent estimates suggest that, for the 1960 level of food requirements, new technology has substituted for the equivalent of 60–80 million acres of cropland. Land is extremely immobile and various strata of farm labor highly so. Consequently, in the short run, land and labor have not been released physically and immediately from production. Instead they have tended to remain, producing an output which has not been constant in the product isoquant sense. Output has been increased, with consequent pressure on prices and income and movement of commodity into government storage.

With lagged or delayed action, labor has responded to this change by eventual transfer to business and industry. The migration has resulted both from the push of low incomes in agriculture and the pull of higher returns in other industries. However, because of its low reservation price, often for a particular commodity as wheat and cotton as compared to grass and trees, the quantity of cropland committed to agriculture has remained almost constant, covering 470 million acres in 1920–29 and in 1959. While land remained constant and labor decreased by around 40 percent in this period, total output has doubled. This is

[8] If labor requirements were considered to be a constant fixed amount, K per acre plus m quantity per unit of product (mY^* for total) and k per unit of fertilizer applied (kF for total), the equation can be modified accordingly. In (2.25), we have labor and land as technical complements so that r^{-1} acres of land are used with each value of L in the equation. Also, for each value of L in (2.26), r^{-1} acre of land also is replaced.

the type of change which less developed countries greatly desire; either to substitute other resources for land and be able to feed a growing population or to substitute resources for labor, freeing the latter for industrial expansion. In the United States, the rate at which farm commodity supply has increased and the tardiness with which labor and land have been withdrawn or shifted has not allowed realization of the developmental gains which other economies drive for, or which are probably preferred in the long run by U.S. society.

GENERAL RESOURCE TRANSFERS

National economies take long-run directions which conform largely to consumer preferences and national needs. In general, consumers with higher incomes place greater relative or marginal values on tertiary industries, representing services especially, than on secondary or fabricating and primary or extractive industries. In a broad sense, too, greater marginal value is placed on secondary than on primary industries. With technological improvement and economic growth, resources appear to respond well in the long run to these consumer preferences and, over time, are reallocated accordingly among industries. It is not apparent that there has been sufficient degree of monopoly in the U.S. economy, or that the extent of monopoly and nonprice competition which exists in the short run absolutely prevents this broad pattern in the long run.

Shifts specified by economic growth have not been unique to the agricultural industry but have applied equally to other primary and some secondary industries. (As Chapter 16 shows, productivity increases have been greater in nonfarm sectors than in agriculture.) Historically, changes in technology and demand have revolutionized the structure of some industries and diminished the relative magnitude of others. Capital has been substituted for labor, or workers have shifted from industries with low income elasticities of demand to those where they are higher. Table 2.12 indicates the general types of long-run adaptations which have taken place over an extended period in the United States. Relatively, shift of labor from agriculture has been large but no greater than for other primary industries.

The farm industry has faced all of the types of adjustments mentioned above. New technology in the form of mechanical and biological innovations have substituted for both farm labor and land. Low price and income elasticities of demand have not allowed output to expand as rapidly as for many other industries. The demand for farm labor has shrunk accordingly and migration has been necessary if (1) persons with limited opportunities in farming, because of lack of capital and managerial ability, are to take advantage of alternatives elsewhere in the economy where they can earn higher incomes and (2) those who remain in farming are able to operate with enough capital and land and on a scale which will provide their families with satisfactory incomes.

American society has had great gain from advance of agriculture.

TABLE 2.12

SHIFTS IN DISTRIBUTION OF U.S. LABOR FORCE AMONG INDUSTRIAL SECTORS, 1890 TO 1920 AND 1920 TO 1950

Industry	1890		1920		1950		Percent Change 1890–1920	Percent Change 1920–1950
	No.	%	*No.*	%	*No.*	%		
	(000)		(000)		(000)			
Farming	9,990	42	11,120	27	7,015	12	+ 11	− 37
Forestry and fishing	180	1	280	1	127	0	+ 56	− 55
Total primary	10,170	43	11,400	28	7,142	12	+ 12	− 37
Mining	480	2	1,230	3	1,035	2	+156	− 16
Manufacturing	4,750	20	10,880	27	15,930	27	+129	+ 46
Construction	1,440	6	2,170	7	3,940	7	+ 51	+ 82
Transportation and utilities	1,530	7	4,190	10	4,750	8	+174	+ 13
Total secondary	8,200	35	18,470	45	25,758	44	+125	+ 40
Trade and finance	1,990	8	4,860	12	12,650	22	+144	+160
Personal services	640	3	1,630	4	3,600	6	+155	+121
Other services	2,570	11	4,810	11	9,310	16	+ 87	+ 94
Total tertiary	5,200	22	11,300	27	25,560	44	+117	+126
All industries	23,570	100	41,170	100	58,460	100	+ 75	+ 42

Source: Solomon Fabricant, "The Changing Industrial Distribution of Gainful Workers," *Conference on Income and Wealth*, Vol. XI, National Bureau of Economic Research, Inc., New York. 1949; and George Stigler, *Trends in Employment in the Service Industries*, National Bureau of Economic Research, Inc., New York, 1956. Comparable data for primary, secondary and tertiary classification estimated from data in the U.S. Census of Population, 1950. Vol. II, Part I.

Between 1940 and 1960 alone, output increased by more than 50 percent while total inputs increased by only 6 percent as indicated in Table 2.13. (See also figures 16.1 and 16.2.) Consequently, the amount of resources or inputs (real costs) required per unit of output declined by almost a third in the 20 years. This degree of progress, an increase in ends from given means or reduction in means to attain a given end, has nearly kept pace with that in the economy generally in recent years. Agriculture has not, however, digested this change as rapidly as most other industries. Resources potentially released from food production by this process have remained in agriculture, and while many have been underemployed, they have not been unemployed. Greater productivity has been unleashed as much through greater output as through reduced inputs. With low price elasticity of demand, consumers simply will not take enough product so added to reward farm resources, in amounts retained by the industry, at the level of other economic sectors. But to understand why this condition prevails in a continuous series of short runs, each representing depressed incomes and resource returns, we must later examine the nature of product supply in agriculture; or more importantly, the structure of factor supply for the industry explaining why resources remain in the short run under returns which compare unfavorably with those of other groups.

MAGNITUDES AND EFFECTS OF COMPENSATION POLICIES

Technological improvement, in farming and nonfarm sectors, is the important source of economic progress and rising per capita incomes. Without improvements in technology, limits to the size of national income would soon be encountered. Or while national income might increase gradually with population and size of the labor force, per capita income would decline as population grew. Fortunately in the United States, particularly as a result of technological advance, capital accumulation and improved skill of people, national income has grown more rapidly than population, with a consequent rise in income per capita. Labor productivity has increased throughout the economy, as well as in farming. The nonfarm worker can obtain his family's food requirements with fewer hours of work than at any previous time in history. But also, because of technological progress in farming and other industries, farm people also can acquire nonfarm goods and services with a smaller outlay of labor than in previous decades—even though resource returns have been deeply depressed for a decade. (See Figure 3.5.)

This general type of progress, with more goods and services available with less human effort, is valued highly by United States and other societies. It is desired no less in farming than in other industries. Farming has contributed importantly to this process. Labor has been freed for use in other industries, capital requirements per unit of food production have been kept relatively low, and the real price of food has declined markedly.

But farming has also borne a burden or social cost of important magnitude as a result of its contribution to progress. It has contributed greatly to general progress but its rate of adaptation has been so slow

TABLE 2.13

INDICES OF FARM PRODUCTION AND RESOURCES USED, U.S., 1940–60
(1940=100)

Year	Total Farm Production	Total Farm Resource Inputs Used*	Resource Productivity	Resources Per Unit of Production
1940	100	100	100	100
1941	104	100	104	96
1942	117	104	112	90
1943	115	104	109	90
1944	118	104	113	89
1945	116	102	113	89
1946	120	102	117	85
1947	116	102	113	89
1948	127	103	122	81
1949	123	104	118	84
1950	123	104	118	84
1951	130	107	118	81
1952	132	107	122	81
1953	133	106	125	80
1954	133	106	126	80
1955	138	105	131	76
1956	140	105	132	75
1957	140	105	134	75
1958	152	103	145	68
1959	154	106	144	68
1960	158	106	149	67

* Taxes are included as inputs or costs in the "resource." Hence, the middle column differs slightly from the figures presented in Chapter 16.

Source: USDA.

that it has been penalized in income. Evidently as a compensation for this cost, and through the interest and pressure of farmers and related groups, society has generated numerous compensation policies for agriculture, such as those mentioned in the previous chapter. These policies have not, however, solved the basic problem of agriculture. In their effects, because of the particular variables which were manipulated, they have sometimes had the same outcome as developmental policies, favoring the use of more resources and the extension of output.

In general, policies of the 1950's have not solved the direct problems of supply and price, or the more fundamental problems of factor inputs and their returns. Policies have not arrested the rate of growth in output or the decline in relative income, even though these have been the immediate goals of recent policy. Public costs of programs have increased rapidly, with a greater proportion of price supported crop going under government loan and greater investment in carry-over of increasing stocks. Efforts in expanding demand through foreign and domestic disposal programs have not withdrawn large enough amounts for the domestic market to offset the increment in supply from technical improvement, immobile resources and policies which have had as much effect on the developmental as on the compensation side. In a nation where food supply is scant relative to demand and nutrition, an increase in P of equation (2.4) would be expected to increase the magnitude of Q_s, output. It would also increase cultivators' incomes. This would be accomplished if there were no restraint on X in (2.3). The equivalent of this increase in P and Q_s generally has been accomplished in U.S. farm policy since 1930 when the hope was to eliminate the surplus problem. Support prices have boosted P and modest and ineffective control on magnitude of land use have not restrained capital or X. (In the late 1950's, support prices were used and no input controls were exercised for corn.) As under economic development, income of farmers was supported, if not maintained, and output expanded, just as would be expected had the goal been one of developmental policy to expand output. In the backward nation, where agricultural supply is tardy, we also could pep it up by reducing the magnitude of P_x in (2.4) and increasing the magnitude of π and the elasticity in (2.3). This also has been accomplished in the United States by policies hoping to solve the farm problem; reduction in P_x being the same as (1) ACP payments to subsidize cost of resources and (2) reduced prices for credit resources; and enlargement of π or the elasticity coming about through technical improvement. Programs which have not had developmental effects, in the sense of encouraging even greater outputs, were those dealing with such coefficients as c and the elasticity in (2.1), including school lunch, foreign disposal and others. Government storage and eventual purchase of commodities, without requirement of input control to realize support price, is the equivalent of increasing the exponent of P in (2.1) to 1.0.

The effects of these several programs on commodity stocks and supply for three major categories of agricultural commodities during the

1950's is indicated in Table 2.14. By 1960, the total supply of wheat, including carry-over and production, had reached a level approaching five times the annual domestic food use of this commodity and more than twice the total domestic and export uses of a billion bushels (par of the latter being shipped under government subsidy with economic aid programs). Government stocks were equal to annual production. Total carry-over of feed grains were approaching half of annual uses. Even with price supports and government storage causing large increments in production to be held off the market, however, income from farming declined as indicated earlier. Prices of hogs and poultry products declined quite steadily during the 1950's. Cattle, hogs and poultry followed their normal cyclical price pattern; with the cycle for hogs being somewhat amplified by the rather fixed level of feed prices generated by government support.

Policies aimed at compensation of agriculture supplemented farm incomes but did not arrest the (1) sag in resources returns and (2) further increase in output and supply. This was true even though an important portion of labor resources had migrated from agriculture, farms were fewer and larger with much more capital per unit, and total input of resources and their services remained nearly constant over the decade. By 1960 the more general problem of inelastic factor and product supply functions, large output and depressed resource returns was not the pressing issue. A more immediate problem was disposal of mammoth government stocks requiring a large public outlay for their storage. An even more pressing problem was how to stop the buildup of stocks.

The U.S. public had made large investments in agriculture, just as

TABLE 2.14

STOCKS, PRODUCTION, FOOD SUPPLY OF SELECTED COMMODITIES, 1949–60

	Feed Grain (million tons)				Wheat (100 million bushels)			Cotton (million bales)		
Year	Govt. stocks	Other carry-over	Production	Total supply*	Govt. stocks	Production	Total supply*	Govt. stocks	Production	Total supply*
1949	15.3	15.1	120.1	175.5	3.6	11.0	14.1	3.8	15.9	21.5
1950	20.9	9.6	121.8	178.8	2.1	10.2	14.6	3.5	9.9	16.9
1951	14.8	13.8	113.1	169.2	1.6	9.9	14.2	.8	15.1	17.4
1952	9.0	11.1	119.7	167.7	4.9	13.1	15.8	.3	15.2	18.1
1953	16.6	10.4	117.5	172.2	8.5	11.7	17.8	2.0	16.4	22.1
1954	22.6	9.1	123.9	181.8	9.9	9.8	19.2	7.0	13.6	23.5
1955	29.7	9.4	130.9	196.9	9.8	9.4	19.8	8.1	14.7	26.0
1956	34.7	8.6	130.2	200.4	8.4	10.6	10.0	10.0	13.0	27.6
1957	40.8	8.1	142.9	219.5	8.5	9.5	18.7	5.2	10.9	22.4
1958	49.2	9.9	157.7	246.1	12.1	14.6	23.5	2.9	11.4	20.3
1959	57.0	10.0	167.1	264.2	12.6	11.3	24.3	7.0	14.6	23.6
1960	66.5	12.1	159.4	268.3	13.0	13.7	26.9	5.0	14.3	22.0

* Total does not equal columns on left due to: private carryover in wheat and cotton, by-products for feed grains and variation in definition of period. (Wheat and feed grain stocks also include CCC holdings acquired from private trade and farmer quantities held under nonrecourse loans.)

agriculture had made large contributions to national economic growth, but it had not solved the basic problems of the industry. If anything, the problems were more severe, even though policy mechanisms might have been employed to use the same or fewer funds to compensate agriculture equally (or more) while solving some of the more basic supply and resource problems. These policies were not initiated, probably because agriculture and the general public lacked sufficient understanding of the role of agriculture in a wealthy, rapidly growing economy. Or, perhaps more important was lack of agreement on the policy means to be used; these means taking the short-run character of ends or goals, with conflicts in values or economic interests among particular groups. As indicated in Chapter 14, the nation spent nearly 18 billion dollars on price and income supports over the period 1932–59, or 27 billion dollars if we add ACP direct payments and the cost of school lunch and other domestic food disposal programs. By 1959, these three programs were running to 2.8 billion dollars annually; an amount equal to 23 percent of the year's net farm income. The annual investment was large enough to make great inroads on the basic problems of developmental and poverty origin.

Low Income in Agriculture

Most major policies since 1940 have been aimed at commercial agriculture. The problems of this sector are of quite different degree, but of the same general nature (in terms of labor underemployment and low resource returns), as those of the chronically low income or poverty sectors of American agriculture. The latter had low incomes even in the more profitable era of commercial agriculture. In general, incomes in this sector of agriculture stem from initial conditions which placed little capital and education in the hands of the particular group of farm people. Farmers in this strata sell so little product and possess so few resources that policies of the 1950's could provide them with little income gain. Even had their incomes been supported or increased by as great a proportion as for all U.S. farmers, the increment would have been too small to take them near income levels Americans generally look upon as consistent with the nation's current state of economic development and wealth. While they are important in particular commodities, these farmers contribute little to the national farm output and are not part of the general supply problem. Over 44 percent of all farms had less than $2,500 in gross sales in 1959. This group is unimportant in total supply, producing only 7 percent of total output in 1954. Commercial agriculture has problems of human resource and family supplies which are large relative to the size of the market and the rewards consumers will provide them through a pure competition market. Low income agriculture has this same problem, but deeper in degree and for somewhat different historic and attached economic reasons.

Any industry has persons with low incomes resulting from age, illness and human hardship of various kinds. Agriculture has these, but they are not the basis of the widespread low income problem. The truly low income sector of agriculture is regionally concentrated in such areas as the South, the Appalachian Mountains and a few other scattered regions. In the South, 33 percent of farms had gross sales of less than $2,500 in 1954. They produced only 15 percent of the product in the region. Of the 1.2 million farms with sales of less than $2,500, nearly two-thirds were in the South. To explain the causes for this low income, we would need to delve deep into institutional, industrial and historic variables. Even if these problems were solved, the major problems of commercial agriculture would remain. Or, conversely, if the commercial farm problem were solved, the low income problem would remain. The task for the latter is, while allowing some to become commercial farmers, to give low income farm families, and particularly their children, the educational and occupational opportunities which are consistent with their abilities, human rights and growth opportunities in a wealthy and growing society. In this sense, many of them have been by-passed in economic and social legislation of recent decades.

3

Impact of Economic Development and Relative Factor Returns

THE FOCUS in the last chapter was of an intermediate period, reflecting neither the extreme short-run or transitory problems of income which attach to low price elasticity of demand or the more persistent, and almost permanent, secular lag of per capita income in the agricultural sector behind that of the industrial sector. The view was of American agriculture in an economic development setting of the years since World War I. While war-inspired increases in demand caused the agricultural sector to be profitable relative to the nonagricultural sector for short periods in this span of time, the general trend was toward increase in the supply function and depressed terms of trade of products in the agricultural sector for those in the nonagricultural sector.

But to better understand the economic problems of commercial agriculture, and the policy and institutional mechanisms appropriate for them, we need to turn in two directions: First we review the problems paramount in the short run because of low price elasticity of demand and fluctuations in commodity supply. Second, we make a broader analysis of the agricultural sector, examining its income performance in the greater dimensions of time, and economic development. Clearly, the first, low price elasticities of demand and cobweb fluctuations in production, calls for a specific agricultural policy. This is true because it stems from variables which are peculiar to production and decision-making processes for agricultural commodities. The second, however, more nearly calls for policy which is related to agriculture but which has its orientation in economic growth. Its variables relate more to interrelationships among national economic growth and the supply of factors, particularly of labor. Because it has been given detailed treatment elsewhere and is the least complex of the two, our treatment of the first is brief in this chapter. But it points up certain policy needs.

SHORT-RUN FLUCTUATIONS

Agriculture in nations well endowed with soil and climatic resources and favored by economic growth has experienced one type of stability; namely, ability for growth in supply to exceed growth in demand. But because sufficient capital also is present in agriculture under this setting, and agriculture is commercial, interyear stability in output of particular products tends to be low. Commodity output fluctuates greatly, in the absence of group or administrative control of price and production, between years or over short periods conforming roughly with the biological period of production. This inter-period instability in output and price arises because the elasticity of supply for individual commodities is relatively great. Coupled with a low price elasticity of demand and fluctuating output, the *high short-run elasticity of supply in respect to price for individual commodities* gives rise to a particular type of income problem in agriculture. It is in contrast to the income problem which arises from the *low short-run elasticity of supply in respect to price for agricultural commodities in aggregate.*

The high short-run supply elasticity for individual products gives rise to fluctuations well known as commodity cycles for potatoes, hogs, beef cattle, poultry and similar products. Fluctuations in output and hence price arise because of the somewhat discontinuous production period involved, the fact that output responds to expected or planned prices, because the production process per se is highly irreversible and because of the particular expectation models prevailing in agriculture.[1]

Consequently, planted acreages for crops such as soybeans, potatoes and fresh vegetables can change greatly between years. Similarly, the number of hogs, turkeys and chickens fluctuates considerably from one year to the next, with a somewhat similar and less explosive change for cattle, sheep and orchard crops over a longer period of time. In livestock particularly, several years are required for commodity cycles to build to peaks and troughs in market supply and price. The length of the period, from peak to peak, is inversely correlated with the intrayear elasticity of supply for the particular produce. If the elasticity is extremely high, in changing inputs and outputs between two years, and if the commodity does not represent an important resource in its own reproduction, output and price changes may be reversed in a single year. But where this is not true, and the commodity produced is withheld in important quantities from market supply to be used in extending output of later

[1] In respect to the latter, see Earl O. Heady, *Economics of Agricultural Production and Resource Use*, Prentice-Hall, New York, 1952, Chaps. 15–17.

periods, several years are required before a cycle in market supply and price is completed.

These fluctuations in commodity supply are but little related to the magnitude of consumer demand and national economic growth. They would occur if the consumer demand function for food grew at rapid rate, technological change did not take place and national economic growth were absent. Evidently the main expectation model employed in planning output for commodities with short-period cycles is one which extends the price of the current period, or recent trend into the future. Also, an aid to this cobweb reaction is pure competition and a supply function which has great intrayear elasticity. The supply path is highly reversible in the sense that output can recede, between production periods, down a particular function as easily as output is expanded along it.

Coupled with this planning basis for commodities with a longer cycle is a lagged distribution of response to price change. The distributed lag, arising because full adjustment to a price change cannot be made in one period, may stem from: (1)uncertainty with which expectations are held and discount of mean expectation of future prices; (2) price expectations which are a function both of "normal" prices and existing prices; (3) fixed costs and specialized equipment limiting short-run flexibility; (4) psychological restraint to sudden or large magnitude of change; and (5) a total complex which causes supply elasticity to increase with time but also causes the supply function to maintain an important degree of short-run irreversibility within production periods. In these two general cases, supply may fluctuate sharply between years as in the more volatile case of vegetables, or build up to peaks and decline to troughs more gradually as in the case of beef cattle.

In addition to the cyclical response of producers to price change phenomena, fluctuation in output and price also occur because of stochastic or random variables associated with climate and nature. These fluctuations are not importantly related to producer behavior, demand changes or economic growth. But because of low demand elasticities for major farm products, they have income effects paralleling the commodity cycles pointed out above. Hence, it is appropriate to consider the two together in this section. The particular or combined magnitudes of these two types of fluctuations are indicated in Table 3.1. Variations in output of both livestock and crops are high when we consider the small magnitude of price elasticities of demand; so great that the consequences in lowered income can be great. For the industry as a whole, a conservative picture since increases between years in one commodity offset decreases in another, variation in output is much greater than variation in input. This difference is due mainly to stochastic or random fluctuations which are not planned by farmers. The stochastic element also causes greater variance for crops than for livestock. The magnitude of change between years in input is major indication of

TABLE 3.1

INTER-YEAR VARIATION IN PRODUCTION. SELECTED FARM PRODUCTS, 1930–60

Commodity	Mean Percent Change Between Years	Commodity	Mean Percent Change Between Years
Hogs (no. farrowed)	9.8	Soybeans	22.6
Beef cattle (no. on farms)	3.6	Flax	39.4
Beef cattle (no. fed)	9.6	Wheat	14.0
Dairy production	1.7	Feed grains	15.1
Turkeys (no. produced)	10.3	Cotton	17.8
Chickens (no. produced)	4.9	Potatoes	10.5
Eggs (no. produced)	3.5	Tobacco	13.6
Corn	16.2	Oranges	8.9
Total farm inputs used	.5	Total farm output	4.0

planned change, although aggregate adjustment also obscures offsetting changes or substitutions among resources.

The income problem stemming from short-run fluctuations in farm output can be illustrated by means of a simple algebraic example where, for simplicity, we do not bother to include the effects of cross elasticities. Suppose again a demand function as in equation (2.1) where the price elasticity is of magnitude $-e$, a quantity smaller than 1.0. Also suppose that mean industry output is Q_m. By equating this supply, Q_m, with the demand in (2.1), the indicated equilibrium price for this output is (3.1) and gross revenue is (3.2) where we make the substitution $e^{-1}=r$ and r is greater than 1.0. However, if in individual years output or production takes on the value b_iQ_m, the equilibrium price in the ith year then is

$$P_m = c^r Q_m{}^{-r} \tag{3.1}$$

$$G_m = c^r Q_m{}^{1-r} \tag{3.2}$$

$$P_i = b_i{}^{-r} c^r Q_m{}^{-r} = b_i{}^{-r} P_m \tag{3.3}$$

$$G_i = b_i{}^{-r} P_m \cdot f_i Q_m = b_i{}^{1-r} G_m \tag{3.4}$$

(3.3) and gross revenue is (3.4) where equation (3.3) has been multiplied by output, b_iQ_m. Now with price elasticity of demand, e, less than unity, and with b_i greater than 1.0, G_i will be smaller than G_m. In other words, revenue in a year of a large crop will be smaller than that in a year of an average crop. This is true since G_m in (3.4) is multiplied by a quantity, $1/b_i$, smaller than 1 raised to a power which increases as elasticity decreases. Hence, if b_i is 1.2 and e is .5, revenue in (3.4) is only .83 proportion of that in (3.2), a decline in revenue due to an increase in output. If, however, b_i is less than 1.0, indicating a decline in output due to weather or similar variables, G_i will exceed G_m by the ratio b_i raised to the power $1-r$. Hence, with $b_i=.8$ and $e=.5$, G_i exceeds G_m by the ratio 1.25, an increase in revenue due to a smaller crop. This change in magnitude of revenue with large or small outputs would hold true for demand functions of other algebraic forms where elasticity is not held constant, given the low price elasticities for major farm commodities. Also, revenue from fluctuations can be less than that from constant production.[2] For, even if we consider cross elasticities and add the substitution effect, total revenue still decreases with greater output of major farm products.

At low price elasticities, revenue from an agricultural commodity fluctuates more than production, as weather and farmer planning procedures cause output to swing in contrary directions between years or production cycles.[3] Too, the relative magnitude of fluctuations in income, without countervailing force in farmer decision procedures or public mechanisms, stand to increase with time, as price elasticities decline due to further rise in per capita income and greater constancy in food intake. Hence, while output fluctuations are due to peculiarities of the agricultural production and decision making processes (aside from magnitude of consumer demand and per capita income growth) the relative magnitudes of the fluctuations in income are a function of economic growth and the demand environment. Under expected conditions outlined above, growth in magnitude of fluctuation with economic growth and decline in demand elasticity, average revenue will be depressed even more due to fluctuations in output. (See discussion in previous footnote.)

If the mean of income increments in years of small crops was greater than the mean decrement in years of large crops, fluctuating output would return more to agriculture than constant output, as an average over time. But with the opposite holding true, short-run output fluctuations will cause mean income over time to be less than under stable production. For example, with a constant price elasticity of .4, an increase of 10 percent in output will decrease price by 25 percent and decrease revenue by 17.5 percent; a decrease of 10 percent in output will increase price by 25 percent and increase revenue by 12.5 percent. In this case, average revenue from periods of increase and decrease in output by 10

---

[2] As a simple example using another algebraic form, suppose the demand function in (a) which, from equation with annual supply Q_m and solving for P, gives the equilibrium

(a) $Q_d = K - aP$ (b) $P = a^{-1}(K - Q_m)$

price in (b). Using the arithmetic quantities $K=7$, $a=.2$ and $Q_m=5$; the equilibrium price is $10, the price elasticity is $-.4$ and total revenue is $50. If production is b_iQ_m in a first year with $b_i=.8$, elasticity is $-.75$ and total revenue is $60. If then $b_i=1.2$ in a second year, equal absolute "deficits" and surpluses in the two years, elasticity drops to $-.17$ and revenue to $30. Under production at Q_m level each year, revenue averages $50 per annum. But if a series of three years gives production of Q_m, $.8Q_m$ and $1.3Q_m$, per annum revenue averages only $46.67.

[3] In our numerical example above, using a particular algebraic form, output ranges only between $.8Q_m$ and $1.2Q_m$ but gross revenue ranges between $.83\ G_m$ and $1.25G_m$. If the elasticity coefficient used were .2 instead of .5, output fluctuating between $.8Q_m$ and $1.2Q_m$, revenue would fluctuate between $.41G_m$ and $1.56G_m$. In the example of our previous footnote, output fluctuates only from 4 to 6, but revenue fluctuates from 30 to 60.

percent each will be smaller than if output were constant at the mean of periods. In the case above, gross revenue will be 2.5 percent less with fluctuations in output equal to plus or minus 10 percent, as compared to constant output among years. (Net revenue will be even smaller due to fixed costs within and between years.) It appears for major commodities that the decrements exceed the increments, in their effect on revenue and due alone to output fluctuations, for recent crops and periods without government price supports and storage.[4]

The income problem pointed out above does not rest on variables which call for modification of agricultural structure. It is true, of course, that the uncertainty and income instability created by the phenomenon cause farmers to use planning strategies which lower the efficiency of resource use.[5] The latter could be greatly lessened with elimination of the source of output variation, but the change in structure of agriculture would be modest. Modification is needed, instead, in market institutions to dampen annual fluctuations in quantities marketed and prices. Public storage policy to withhold the excess of bumper crops until years of small crops is needed to meet output fluctuations based on weather. Mechanisms for forward pricing and an altered environment for formulating price expectations, and education on decision procedures or strategies to accompany it, are needed for commodities with production cycles conforming to the cobweb pattern. We shall return to these and related policy propositions in a later chapter.

Equity in Distribution of Gains and Losses

But why should policy concern itself with fluctuations of the type mentioned above? Farm records and other data are available to prove that while farmers in aggregate may have less revenue under cobweb production response and commodity cycles, managers who are "on their toes" can actually gain from this instability. They, given knowledge of the cobweb structure, can increase their output in years of mass reduction and vice versa. Gain by some and loss by others does not, however, guarantee positive-sum utility outcomes for the aggregate community of farmers. Perhaps it could be true that a dollar of loss to a beginning farmer with low income involves less sacrifice in utility than the benefit to an experienced manager from a dollar of gain, but there is no interpersonal measurement available to prove it. Many would doubt it under these circumstances. Thus a problem of equity in the distribution of gains and losses from economic change and instability does arise. As in struc-

[4] We know too little here since demand estimates, like the example above, have most often been estimated in terms of average of arc elasticity. Hence, we still know little quantitatively about the magnitude by which elasticity increases or decreases as quantity decreases or increases respectively. As Table 3.1 indicates, the major short-term fluctuation is in output, and not in inputs. Hence, farmers do not compensate, in years of increased output and reduced revenue, by reducing costs. For this reason, fluctuation in net revenue is even greater than fluctuation in gross revenue.

[5] For example, see the discussion in Chapter 17 of Heady, *op. cit.*

tural problems of agriculture under economic growth, it is appropriate to examine policies which may better guarantee the positive-sum welfare outcomes or Pareto optima outlined in later chapters. These problems of equity in the distribution of gains and costs of change are almost everywhere the foundation in agricultural policy.

FUNCTIONING OF AGRICULTURE UNDER ECONOMIC GROWTH

The above section dealt with an aggregate problem of a commodity, and one of some importance to a major part of the industry where self-administered or public management of supply and price is absent. But it is a problem of a much shorter period than the one showing through the sketch of recent economic trends in Chapter 2. We now turn to the much more basic and long-run source of problems in relative income and factor rewards in agriculture. The phenomena to be examined is that of economic growth and agriculture's contributions to, and burdens from, it.

The Hens and the Egg

The interrelationship between agricultural development and national economic progress poses the problem of the hen and the egg. Which contributes mainly to the other? This question is still an extremely important one for some countries. What priority in allocation of public and private investment capital should be made for agricultural development as compared to industrial sectors? There is no standard answer to this question, even in nations where the public sector predominates and planning is largely by the state. The optimum current allocation of increments in development capital differs between India where food scarcity is a problem and Russia where food scarcity is near elimination; just as it does between Russia with less development and the United States with greater development and food surplus. It also differs between the U.S. economy of a century ago and that of the decades ahead. The question itself is now much less crucial and appropriate in the United States.

Before World War I, the U.S. agricultural sector employed a significant portion of the nation's labor force and total resources. Development of agriculture to save resources and free them for other sectors could contribute to the nonfarm sector, in magnitudes comparable to the gain of agriculture from economic development in other sectors. Development of agriculture still contributes to national development, but dependence of the national economic growth on agricultural development is now greatly diminished. This is true because the agricultural sector is a small and declining portion of the national economy and uses only a small fraction of nation's employed resources. While the hen couldn't exist without the egg, it has now hatched and can grow and produce its own surplus; the one egg of the product allocated to regeneration of the cycle being largely an insignificant diversion.

Growth Initiation in Agriculture

Starting from the other end in isolated and primitive societies, the story was quite different. General economic development depended unilaterally on agricultural development. Man's first task was to feed, shelter and reproduce himself. With no surplus product beyond that needed for these consumption activities, growth aside from primary subsistence could not be kindled. Only as development progressed to a point where labor produced a product in surplus of subsistence requirements could growth be initiated in another sector; or could another sector even exist. Development of agriculture effectively provided the capital allowing the initiation and growth of other sectors. As part of this process, it also produced food beyond subsistence of agricultural families, in order that population grew and a portion of food growth could be so utilized.

Initially, development in the primary sector went entirely to support population growth remaining in the sector, rather than for providing capital for initiation and growth of other sectors. Given the extreme postulated by Malthus, growth of other sectors could never have been initiated. But either through abstinence or primary development, growth of other sectors was initiated and the occupational trek from farm to town began. Initially, and for many centuries, growth of the nonfarm sector came about not by a direct diversion of labor and other resources from agriculture, but from simultaneous growth in labor and capital resources used in both sectors, with agriculture producing a surplus of labor and capital for diversion to development of the nonfarm sector. Problems in relative incomes and income distribution were nonexistent, even had there been statistics to allow their comparison, in periods when growth in agriculture not only paralleled that of other sectors but also agriculture dominated the total economy. Most persons born in agriculture remained in the sector and occupational transfer, and lagging income of agriculture was not an important issue.

This setting holds true and continues as long as the pace of development is slow, with growth in national income equal to, or meagerly in excess of, population growth. Populations then are kept so poor that their most urgent marginal want is still food and the central assignment of new members, representing additions to the labor force, is to produce their own food with only slight surplus. Frequently, this is the only choice open to them, since supply of employment opportunity in the nonfarm sector is too greatly restrained by slow growth rate. As long as the major effort of resources must go into food, growth in other sectors, starting from a small portion of the total economy, spreads thinly over the total. Growth in nonagricultural sectors has no appreciable effect on per capita incomes of the total population and, hence, on the pattern of demand.

Even after agriculture has developed to an extent allowing initiation of and progress in growth of nonfood sectors, the pace is slow and centuries-consuming. But even at minute initial pace in this growth process, the passage of sufficient time eventually brings capital and income to crucial levels. National product then allows important gain in per capita income and causes the pattern of demand to shift greatly, with the major part of consumer expenditures no longer allocated to food. Also at this point, allocation of the stream of population growth between the two sectors changes in relative proportions. This process is not, of course, as distinct as change in the seasons. It is so gradual that it is scarcely identified as it takes place, until it reaches a point where it is a "common place knowledge" of agriculturists that farming is a declining portion of national income—even though the turning point occurred far in the past.

AGRICULTURE IN ECONOMIC DEVELOPMENT

Agriculture has played an important role in economic growth for most nations up to and as they moved into the take-off stage towards maturity in development. This contribution often was less importantly that which might be indicated as "directly and biologically fundamental and obvious," and more that which was *indirect and less apparent.* In the primitive stage, of course, productivity of labor had to be increased to a point where some was freed from husbandry for other sectoral occupations. Workers could be released from food production to plant the first seeds of general economic progress only with development of agriculture. Too, food industry had to grow so that population, industry and commerce as well as agriculture could increase. But even in early stages, and later in nineteenth century America, the gain was as much the other way around. The rapid growth of population, supported particularly by commerce, industry and foreign trade, provided a market for the product of agriculture. It wasn't necessary that population exogenous to agriculture increase, but since it did, the role was as much that of social growth creating a market for farm products as that of farmers feeding city consumers so that they could keep alive.

Agriculture of nations in the future will never realize expansion in markets, from total growth in population and society, as rapidly as it did in the seventeenth and eighteenth century frontier regions of the world. Never will the U.S. agricultural sector have the same relative opportunity for capital gain, from general economic growth and activity quite apart from farming, as it did in the nineteenth century with land clearing and rising land prices. Contrast twentieth century India and nineteenth century North America. Economic growth in India cannot give comparable capital gains to Indian cultivators, which in turn can be used for improvement of farming. The only comparable periods, and then temporarily, of large capital gains to American agriculture from forces entirely outside the industry, were in two world wars of this century.

Social and economic growth obviously contributed much to agriculture in the United States during the 1800's. But agriculture also contributed to economic growth in a manner apart from the typically emphasized biological role of food. This contribution was of character realized in early growth stages for all nations. Agriculture provided an important amount of capital for general progress. Starting from an economy which is dominantly agricultural, the surplus and capital formation largely must be drawn from this industry. Employment in farming represented 72 percent of the U.S. work force in 1820. It was still 65 percent in 1850 and had only fallen to 50 percent in 1880.

In early regimes of landed nobles and serfs, or landlords and croppers, the surplus of income was practically all in the hands of the landowner. It was he, and not the serf or cropper with subsistence level of income, who could be taxed to provide funds for social investments. Still, in the development of nations such as the United States and Canada with owner-operators dominating, surplus or capital was drawn directly out of agriculture by property taxes. It gave rise to a type of social overhead capital represented by public schools, roads and other facilities of extreme importance to growth in the longer perspective. In a manner, agricultural resources contributed greatly to the development of railroads in the United States. Extension of this transportation was promoted through land grants, attractive as payment in kind largely because of the growing market for farm products.

Yet the most important syphon of surplus income from U.S. agriculture was by another source. It came about as population growth or labor supply in agriculture exceeded labor demand by the industry and net outmigration occurred. One source of capital transfer was in people per se. The agricultural sector invested capital in children, beyond its own labor demands. Capital so represented moved to the city with the laborer and nonfarm industries was not required to allocate a portion of income and capital to this portion of their labor force. But another source of capital transfer was also important. The inheritance customs prevailing in early times as well as now caused a distribution of capital gain and accumulation among all members of farm families, with a portion of the capital gain and income surplus eventually moving to the city with farm children who so migrated. This process still continues, but it is of much less relative importance than in early times.

Only in recent decades have numerous state economies passed this stage where a major portion of social capital was forthcoming from agriculture, and the intergeneration transfer of capital to city sectors became of minor importance. Agriculture has been the dominant sector of state economies within the last 50 years for most states west of the Mississippi River. Schools, roads and court houses were built mainly during the period prior to World War I in Iowa, Kansas, Oregon, Oklahoma and similar states with the exchange of products from original soil nutrients.

We have already mentioned another type of gain which accrues to general society from progress in agriculture. It occurs with technological progress and a relative increase in the commodity supply function, accompanied by a relative decrease in the factor demand function in agriculture. While the decline has been relative in the demand for the capital, it has been absolute for labor. The nonfarm labor force has been augmented by reduction in number of farm workers as well as by net outmigration from the continuous supply of youth entering the labor force. Through internal development, agriculture has freed resources to be used elsewhere in the economy, but not without some income lag due to the low mobility and supply elasticity of farm labor. Under these conditions, farmers simply accumulate less surplus income and capital to be transferred to nonfarm sectors. But by the same token, and because they need not make so large an outlay for food, food consumers can have greater surplus over income, allowing capital accumulation accordingly. A century hence, few will care whether capital for development arose more because food was abundant and consumers had greater savings, or because food was somewhat less abundant and farmers had greater surplus of income over consumption. In either case, the state of demand will lead to its eventual investment more in other sectors than in agriculture.

The question is more one of the present. Who should bear the sacrifice and who should realize the gains of this income and capital for development? In terms of numbers, one might now say that it is more essential that food consumers be given the opportunity; they outnumber food producers 11 to one. Yet there are no propositions in intergeneration or intrageneration welfare economics to prove that community utility over time is so maximized. Again, then, we are confronted with the foundation of agricultural policy problems; namely, equity in distribution of gains and losses, or of distribution which guarantees positive-sum outcomes in utility and welfare aggregated across all major economic sectors.

Agricultural Development for Social Capital

The demand setting to the turn of the current century was ideal for agricultural development policy, the variety of policy emphasized by the United States for the farm industry. It was ideal not only in the sense that the setting of demand elasticity allowed development of agriculture to bring greater revenue, but also in a Pareto-better sense. The Pareto-better condition, explained in detail later, was a product attainable by development of agriculture because two groups could be made better off: farm producers in greater revenue from farm products and consumers with lower real price of food and, effectively, more resources for economic growth. With direct focus on welfare of the agricultural industry, which was largely the whole of American society in terms of population, the demand for agricultural products allowed growth of the farm industry which outpaced the supply of labor arising in agriculture. Farming was expanding rapidly and drew upon supplies of labor outside the agricultural industry, particularly foreign emigrants and persons from settled farming regions. Income elasticities of demand were favorable and even, in the developing foreign market, price elasticity of demand for U.S. farm products blessed rapid shift in the supply function over much of the nineteenth century.

These conditions also were ideal for general society and progress. American society needed to build up its overhead capital, beyond that supplied by foreign investments and nonfarm sectors. It needed investments which provided "quick turnover." Public investments or aid in railroads, schools and general utilities of time required a much longer period for high payoff. Agriculture represented an opportunity for a much quicker payoff. Agriculture of the time rested mostly on land and labor, resources abundant in supply (land from within and labor from emigration), and but little on capital. By putting public land in the hands of cultivators who developed them commercially, a surplus of income over consumption was developed in a short period. Labor used to develop the land did not always drain on the capital of agriculture for rearing, because much of this cost or capital was provided by European countries. Labor came from these economies as "capital ready to go to work" in agriculture.[6] This surplus, in a relatively short time, provided a most important single source in capital formation leading to the rapid take-off in economic growth. Given the realized expansion in foreign markets during the 1800's and the availability of unsettled space around it, U.S. society could have found few other investments, leading to a quicker payoff and generation of further capital, so productive as investment in the Louisiana Purchase and its distribution to farmers and foresters.

A great deal said above also applies to the public decision which later led to social investment in research and knowledge communication for agriculture at a later time. While the gestation period in capital formation, or in capital input relative to its payoff, was a little longer, starting from the point of employing public scientists and building research facilities, it still was an investment which could give a large and relatively quick payoff. Once uncovered, improved seed varieties, improved husbandry, fertilization and better ration mixes require a short transformation period, as compared to canals, roads and alternative public investments which generate income only over a longer period of time. Hence, public policy to further aid development of agriculture, through socialized research facilities, was an appropriate decision in behalf of economic development. When initiated a century ago, demand conditions favored this as a quick payoff method for capital formation leading to economic development. Capital formation, as surplus of in-

[6] Each new region of agriculture fed on older settled regions similarly. Capital investment representing labor turned to the new regions came from families in the older regions of the United States, as well as from abroad, and had been accumulated in the rearing of persons over long investment period with no or little return. Most of the return on this human investment commenced immediately when the labor was used in the new region. In a similar vein, the total American economy realized quick return on investment made in human resources originating in European countries, and did not have to use part of its own product for these purposes.

come over consumption so derived, was drawn off partly by property taxes and the transfer of farm children to cities. However, a major payoff, in terms of resources released from food production, has come since 1920 from public research. This was a demand period in which the source of capital was less that of greater farm income, and hence surplus for eventual transfer to cities, and more that of abundant food at low cost and with fewer resources required to produce it. Undoubtedly the two major developmental policies, public pricing and distribution of land resources and public investment in research were viewed primarily as means of bolstering farm income. But, even if unwittingly, American society had made a profitable decision in investing in agricultural development as a means of promoting national economic growth. The setting was appropriate with a large proportion of the nation's resources in agriculture—a condition which is no longer true.

Other Market Feedbacks in Development

Agriculture and industry have simultaneously facilitated growth of each other. This has been true almost over the whole of the U.S. history. If the simultaneity was ever at a minimum, it is now when agriculture is small relative to the national economy. The nation was never truly faced with a Malthusian regime wherein increase in food supply was antecedent to increase in food demand (i.e., a population at subsistence equilibrium level with increase allowed only by greater food output). Dependence of increased food demand on existence of food supply has nearly held true in India and similar countries of population pressure and tardy food supply. But in the United States, growth in food demand almost always preceded greater food supply. Population increased nearly four times in the half century following 1800. It nearly tripled between 1850 and 1900. Consider the effects of an increase in demand at 8 percent per year, the rate of increase in population between 1800 and 1850; or of 4 percent per year as between 1850 and 1900. Population and income growth provided large opportunity for growth in food supply up to 1920. Whereas population increased by about 25 percent per decade between 1870 and 1920, it increased by only 15, 16, 7, 14 and 12 percent respectively in the five decades following. The population increase of 2.5 percent per year over the period 1870–1920 was greater than a 2.3 percent annual increase in agricultural production over the period 1920–1960, but the per annum population increase of 2.1 percent in the latter period was not.

We have explained the process by which capital generated in agriculture was diverted to investment in other sectors. But which was causal: the growth of American society which provided an expanding market for the product of agriculture, or the production of surplus labor and capital in agriculture which could help fill the growing resource of demand of industry? With agriculture as the broad foundation of early American society, its development provided the mass domestic market for initiation of industry. The farm demand for producers goods and durable consumption commodities, as small as it was in terms of current standards, helped to prime the pump for an infant industrial complex.

Still, if we view market interrelationships in another light, developing nonfarm industry provided a landing place (or a dumping ground) for some of the surplus labor which began to arise in agriculture shortly after the Civil War. While this was a developmental blessing to industry, it also was a windfall to agriculture. Had this surplus, of labor supply over labor demand in agriculture, had less outside employment opportunity and been turned back into farming, agricultural welfare would have been greatly depressed. With a greater labor supply, commodity supply would have pressed more on demand and lowered price. Labor returns would have been lower for this reason, and also because given income would have been divided among more persons. Competition for farming opportunity would have bid up the price of land, and resulted in more and smaller farms with higher unit costs. Thus, while each contributed to development of the other, it is not possible to say that net development of the U.S. economy in the nineteenth and early twentieth centuries depended on a one-way relationship between agriculture and industry sectors. Still if we use Rostow's point of take-off, in rapid economic development, with emphasis on industrialization, as about 1843–1860, agriculture was somewhat singularly important in providing preconditions for takeoff.[7] Given the stage of development, agricultural or natural resources and products were a chief source of the social capital accumulated up to that time. It also was important in contributing a source for capital import after the take-off point. Agriculture would have produced a surplus, to serve as capital and eventual transfer to the national economy, had it only been a domestic industry. However, this process and source of capital formation was greatly aided through the international aspects of U.S. agriculture. During the nineteenth century, agriculture contributed 80 percent of the value of U.S. exports. Exports represented a fifth of the value of the nation's farm production between 1850 and 1900.

The period in which agricultural and nonfarm economic development were so highly compatible and of relative equal contribution to each other no longer exists in manner of the period prior to 1925. Heading towards 1975, the farm sector is small relative to the total, and in capital and labor which can be generated in the industry for eventual transfer for development elsewhere. Expansion of the farm sector supply no longer meets a market of large demand elasticities for food. Expansion of the nonfarm sector does not bring with it, proportionately, as much increase in demand for food as it did in decades bygone.

It is important that this changed role and outcome of agriculture in economic development be understood. To an important extent, much recent policy and philosophy for U.S. agriculture has presupposed the developmental environment of the earlier economic regime. Policies

[7] W. W. Rostow, *The Stages of Economic Growth,* Cambridge University Press, New York, 1960, pp. 6–7.

since 1930 have had orientation towards overcoming short-term emergencies, as if the nation and agriculture were still attempting to erase the effects of the last major depression, rather than coming abreast of the stage of economic development and the functioning of institutions which is now fact. Many other nations, more tardy in both agricultural development and economic growth, still face a setting paralleling that of nineteenth-century America. They have problems of pushing food supply ahead with growing population and food demand, and of increasing productivity of agriculture in a manner to allow its commercialization and a greater transferable surplus for national economic growth. But typically, too, industrialization to absorb more of the farm population is needed in these economies.

Although the means is not entirely clear, further development of American agriculture may find its place as an aid in general economic progress of these much less developed nations. Agricultural progress may be relatively more important for these purposes than for promotion of domestic economic growth over the 1960's and 1970's. With capacity to produce our food in surplus for a decade, greater farm productivity has meaning for the domestic population largely in 1975 and 1990.

For purely internal developmental goal of the moment, an effective harnessing of current surplus resources and commodities of agriculture is more pressing than investment to increase current supply. Yet it would be unfortunate if our planning horizon was warped so closely to the present. Vision and an extended planning horizon led to investment in the Louisiana Purchase, the creation of the public school system, initial public participation in research for agriculture and others with large payoff over the last century and a half. Development is desired no less now than in the past. However, the role of agricultural progress in national economic development now is different, at least in relative contribution and in distribution of gain and cost over the contemporary farm generation.

Relative Allocation of Resources

In the 150 years from 1810 to 1960, the U.S. farm labor force dropped from over 75 percent to less than 10 percent of the nation's total labor force. Relative reallocation of this nature and magnitude does not at first, or necessarily ever, come with a sudden absolute shift of resources from agriculture and other primary industries to secondary and tertiary industries. In early stages of the relative reallocation, primary sectors grow in total quantities of resources used, but not at a rate as fast as sectors characterized by higher income elasticities of demand. A greater proportion of a nation's addition to labor force and capital supply simply is drawn into the more rapidly expanding industries.

Three conditions of inter-industry allocative patterns under economic growth can be postulated: In the *first*, wants for any product are far under the satiation level, and income elasticities of demand are equal for all commodities. With equal growth in supplies and productivity of resources, the relative allocation of resources would remain unchanged among industries. Resource employment in each sector would grow by the same proportion. Each sector would retain the historic proportion in national product and resource shares. Each sector could, in fact, absorb exactly the capital accumulation and population growth within it, supposing comparable intersector rates of saving and birth. If labor resources were like those of capital, without personal preference or utility attaching to different occupations, intersector exchange would be needed only in commodities and not in factors. Economic growth could be just as rapid under edicts preventing capital or labor arising in one sector from transferring to another, as where freedom of markets and resource flows are allowed and occur. The biological and psychological nature of consumers prevents this constancy of sector shares over time and under economic growth. It is not, however, unlike the model implicitly assumed in early U.S. educational policy, with education for farm youth largely oriented to their reentry into agriculture, or unlike the recently held thesis that all farm youth should have opportunity in farming.

Under the *second condition*, one encompassing most nations over the world, growth takes place in all major sectors, but at unequal rates. Preferences of consumers approach a satiation limit and marginal utility declines for particular goods. New consumer commodities are developed and income elasticities of demand take on varying magnitudes. With income elasticities greater than zero but having differential magnitudes for all sectors, a relative change in resource allocation necessarily takes place even if all sectors grow in magnitude of product and total resources employed. Resources are drawn, from capital accumulation and population increase, in sectors with lowest income elasticities to those with highest elasticities, although some additions to capital and labor remain in the former. Relative shares of particular sectors then change, in respect to both income and resources employed. If the transfers came from the *additions to capital stock and labor force* within sectors where demand for product grows less rapidly than supply of resources, the costs and difficulties of transfer could be small under certain conditions. The conditions required are, of course, rapid reflection of consumer desire (1) from commodities through resources, and (2) over spatial and industry boundaries, with consequent price effects to draw resources to them. Resources also must be highly mobile, without particular attachment or low reservation price for the sector of origin. With transfer coming from growth-generated additions to resource supplies, resources previously specialized to the particular sector could remain so, and with some growth rate, realize returns comparable to those of sectors expanding at greater relative rate even while the sector is absorbing more resources. Comparable factor returns could still prevail even if the sector of declining relative share has rates of capital accumulation, birth, and technological improvement greater than those of sectors increasing in relative share because of changing consumer expenditure patterns and high income elasticities under income growth; providing, of course, that markets are sufficiently alert in intersectoral reflection of demand and prices for factors and major shifts come from resources added to total supplies. This general condition, of absolute growth of agriculture and farm labor force but in decline of relative share, held true for U.S. agriculture up to 1915. (Also see Figures 16.1 and 16.2.)

Under the *third condition* of development, rates of growth vary greatly among sectors, because of either near-complete satiation of certain consumer wants or because substitute commodities are developed. Some sectors have rates of capital accumulation, technical progress and birth which exceed growth in demand for their product. These sectors then must decline in shares of income and resources. In these sectors, it also is necessary for some resources already employed, as well as those added to the supply, to transfer.

This has been the condition confronting American agriculture in respect to labor since 1920. While capital input has not been reduced, a part of savings and capital accumulation have been transferred to other industries, as an integral contribution to aggregate economic growth. Capital use has increased, but not in proportion to net family savings of agriculture over time. Transfer of both labor and capital surplus has been consistent with national economic growth and changing consumer preferences, and with maintaining incomes and resource returns in agriculture at more favorable levels. Had U.S. agriculture re-employed all of its additions to the labor force and saving, the industry would now be composed of a vast number of small-scale subsistent farms. Without transfer of labor from agriculture for over a century, a major source of labor force for industry, labor returns in agriculture would now be meagerly low while those in other sectors would be even greater. The same conditions also hold true in respect to capital. Evidently the industry employs sufficient capital to keep returns in aggregate at a level low relative to other industries. (See Chapter 5.) Had it absorbed entirely the surplus of income over consumption from the outset, given the current state of technology and low price elasticity of demand, capital return would now be approaching zero.

Condition one above unloads no burden on agriculture. Condition two would not do so under the degree of factor market communication and perfection mentioned earlier. But given any degree of imperfection and lack of communication, resources must pile up in the industry and earnings must decline relative to other sectors. The extent of decline depends on the degree by which the rate of increase in supply through capital accumulation or savings and birth rate within the industry exceeds the rate of growth in demand. Relative decline in factor earnings would be of important magnitude under condition two, but are of even greater extent under condition three. U.S. agriculture went through a long stage of condition two, an intermediate stage of economic development, with earnings in agriculture lagging those of other sectors. In recent decades, it has been under the more advanced stage of economic development, condition three. While the ratio of farm to nonfarm earnings has not declined continuously, difference in income among sectors has become of more critical public concern because communication science and statistical knowledge have improved so greatly. Farm people now know more about the lag of their income behind that of other sectors.

The United States is not the only country with growth rates sufficient to cause these differentials. These facets of growth are well illustrated with global figures. Practically all nations of the world now are developing under conditions two and three, although the exact stage of each differs greatly. Russian agriculture used 13 percent more man days of labor in 1950 than in 1929, although evidently reducing input by about 1 percent per year in the 1950's.[8] United States agriculture had a declining labor force in each of these periods. Many countries have had an increase in total agricultural employment since 1930, but the rate of increase has been less than for other sectors. Consequently, the surplus of births in agriculture has required a transfer of labor to other sectors. In nearly all countries approaching the U.S. level of economic growth and per capita income, agricultural employment has declined since 1940. Relative decline in agriculture, as in the recent history of practically all countries, can come alone from (1) national economic growth and (2) differential demand in elasticities of different sectors. It need not be a function of factor prices and resource substitution rates. But absolute decline in input of a resource, total output of the industry still increasing, must arise not only because of the differential rates of demand expansion which attach to economic growth but also because of relative changes in factor prices and substitution rates.

We can thus postulate a fourth pure condition or model wherein: population is constant, food is a commodity taken in limitational or fixed amount per person (demand elasticities are zero), knowledge of the production function is complete, factor prices remain in fixed ratio to each other and the current birth rate in agriculture just allows replacement of the farm population. Under these conditions, technology and resource mix in agriculture would remain constant, although agriculture's proportionate share in national employment would decline. But suppose that economic growth also causes differential changes in factor prices, with capital declining in relative price under excess of income over consumption and labor increasing in relative price as it is demanded more for service and tertiary industries. Under these conditions, the absolute, as well as relative, magnitude of labor share in agriculture will decline with

[8] A. Kahan, "Changes in Labor Inputs in Soviet Agriculture," *Jour. Pol. Econ.*, Vol. 57, p. 452.

economic development. Given a level of demand for food and complete knowledge of alternative technology, an isoquant of the nature in Figure 3.1 effectively exists for each country.[9] For the particular level of agricultural output, a least-cost technology, representing different mixes of labor and capital, exists under prevailing prices for capital and labor in all countries. For those at low stages of development, capital is high in price relative to labor. Technologies adapted are those which use large amounts of labor and little capital, as at points *a* and *b* in Figure 3.1.

Under the time path of economic development capital supply increases relative to labor and price of the former declines relative to price of the latter. Hence, the iso-outlay or budget lines decrease in slope. They are tangent lower on the isoquant in Figure 3.1, indicating resource mixes richer in capital and leaner in labor and calling for a large degree of mechanization, as at *d* and *e*. In optimum adjustment to factor prices, retention of larger labor supplies is specified at low stages of economic development. But with growth and relative change in labor and capital supplies and prices, diminished absolute input of labor becomes optimum. Thus, even if food demand and technical knowledge did not change, we would expect the capital-labor mix to change with economic development and decrease in price of capital relative to labor.

United States agriculture now falls somewhat in this category, with slight increases in capital to replace labor but with new technology still increasing the output/input ratio and dampening capital requirements while speeding the decline in labor requirements. In terms of relative shares of labor in agriculture, the general path described for Figure 3.1 will be reflected in other nations as economic progress reaches take-off stage or continues.

In summary, then, decline of income share by agriculture is a function of economic growth, as reflected in consumer preferences and differential income elasticities for various products. Decline of labor share is a function of this same phenomenon, and also of the relative change in factor supplies and prices under economic growth. The return to labor in agriculture would keep abreast of that in other sectors under conditions where the rate of population increase, rate of productivity increase and the income elasticities of demand for the products of all sectors are equal.

---

[9] Here we consider capital funds to be the resource input measured on the horizontal axis. The form of this capital is allowed to change as its magnitude is increased. Over the "whole" of a nation's agriculture, an isoquant of this type is likely to be continuous. But for an individual farm, it would better be represented by linear segments. More accurately, of course, we should include all factors (labor, tractors of different sizes, bullocks and other capital items being different resources) in our system and equate the quantities

$$\frac{\delta Y}{\delta X_i} = \frac{P_i}{P_y} \quad \text{and} \quad \frac{\delta X_i}{\delta X_j} = \frac{P_j}{P_i}$$

in reference to the production function in (7.13), specifying land, labor, machinery of various kinds, and other inputs simultaneously.

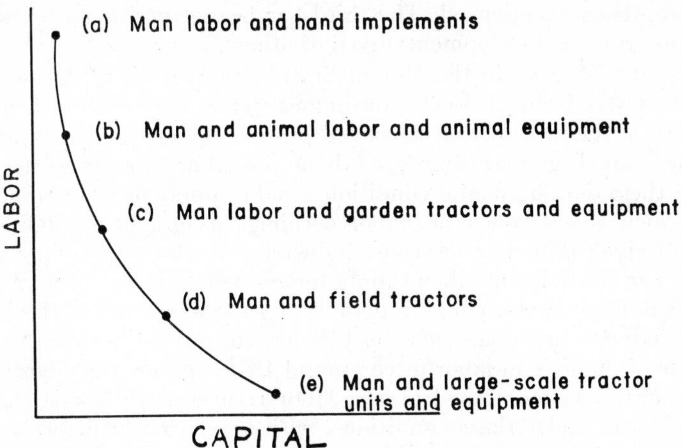

Fig. 3.1. Nature of Product Isoquants in Relation to Technology and Labor and Capital Inputs Under Economic Growth and Changing Factor Price Relatives.

However, with lower income elasticities, rates of population and productivity increase being the same, the demand for labor in agriculture will decline relative to nonagricultural sectors. Similarly, growth rate in agricultural labor productivity which exceeds that of other sectors, and a sharp rise in the marginal rate of substitution of capital for labor from new technology or rapid advance in the price of labor relative to capital, also will cause the relative demand for agricultural labor to decline if the supply of labor to agriculture is sufficiently elastic. Given the extreme case of an infinitely elastic supply function for labor in agriculture, returns to this resource would remain at a par with labor earnings in other industries, with differential due alone to living costs and occupational preference. But with low elasticity of supply of labor to agriculture, due to various mobility deterrents such as transportation costs and lack of knowledge, return to labor in agriculture will fall relative to that of other sectors.

Three Stages in Labor Demand and Supply

The United States has gone through three distinct stages in respect to development and demand and supply of labor in agriculture. In the first stage, total employment in agriculture increased faster than growth of labor force from farms. Labor was drawn into agriculture from outside the industry. In the second stage, total employment grew but at a slower rate than growth of labor force from families on farms. In the third stage, absolute decline in labor employment occurred. (See Figure 16.2.) In the history of agriculture in all countries, the first two stages have generally been experienced. The third has been experienced by a number, but still is a developmental goal of others.

Farm use of labor in the United States as a percent of national employment, has declined almost continuously since the birth of the nation. In much of the early period, however, growth of employment in agriculture was much greater than growth of the labor force in agriculture. Under these developmental conditions, and a supply of labor to agriculture which is highly elastic, labor earnings in agriculture should (for labor of given skill) parallel those industries which compete in employment. The elasticity of labor supply for the two sectors, farm and nonfarm, was likely about equal in periods of great migration to the United States. Growth in employment by U.S. agriculture fell behind the internal rate of increase in labor force around 1875, and net outmigration of labor began. As mentioned above, labor returns could equal those of other sectors under these conditions, with a sufficiently high elasticity of labor supply to agriculture. However, as is indicated later, this level of labor supply elasticity has never been the case. Under developmental conditions calling for net outmigration of labor from agriculture, returns are depressed in extent depending on supply elasticity of labor. Supposing alternative employment to be available, an obvious avenue for boosting labor returns is that of increasing its supply elasticity, an alternative discussed in later chapters.

While the United States passed from (1) a stage of growth in farm employment exceeding growth of the farm labor force within agriculture to (2) one requiring net outmigration around 1875, it passed from this stage to (3) one causing the absolute employment in agriculture to decline, around 1920. Hence, magnitude of labor supply elasticity to match outmigration requirements in the previous stage would have been too low in the second stage. Undoubtedly, the supply elasticity of labor to agriculture has increased since the period prior to 1875, and especially in recent decades. Yet the increase has not been great enough to draw labor earnings to the level of the nonfarm sector. An important question, then, is: does the complex of labor supply and food demand elasticities tend to worsen or improve the position of relative earnings in agriculture over time?

SHARES IN NATIONAL INCOME

We now review characteristics of national economic development as it relates to declining share of income to agriculture. The decline in share of agriculture in national income is universal, once minute degree of development occurs to allow some release of labor from pure pursuit of subsistence. The data used for examination of this phenomenon are those of Kuznets and refer to his A-sectors. While it includes agriculture, fisheries and forestry, we use the term agriculture since it dominates the sector. We present data for three periods or years, centering respectively on 1880, 1915, and 1950, from his estimates.[10]

Decline in proportion of income from agriculture has been especially great since 1950 in most countries. In the United States, net income from agriculture has fallen below 5 percent of national income in recent years. The proportion of agriculture in national economies will decline further with continued economic growth. Depression of agricultural earnings and return to farm labor would not occur under this relative change in sector shares if absolute growth of agriculture and in demand for food exceeded or was equal to growth in labor supply of agriculture; technology were constant and demand for labor in agriculture remained in constant proportion to output; or, without this condition, the supply of labor to agriculture were highly elastic. But generally one of these conditions is violated for all countries listed. In the United States, all are violated. We must, then examine how these conditions affect the returns to labor in agriculture relative to other industries. We wish, too, to determine whether economic progress has generally worsened the position of agriculture with time, supposing the relative decline in demand for labor to be great relative to growth in labor supply from farm families or, to decline in supply elasticity of agricultural labor. Or, conversely, we may try to determine, from the scanty data available, whether supply elasticity might have been increased sufficiently to offset other forces, thus causing improvement of relative earnings in agriculture.

Relative Share of Labor Employment in Agriculture

One basis for inference about supply elasticity for labor to agriculture is in relative share of the labor force in agriculture. With low supply elasticity, labor backs up in agriculture, causing share of the labor force to exceed share of income. Table 3.3 indicates the decline in percent of labor force in agriculture for countries which have experienced rather continuous economic growth since 1870. It also indicates the magnitude of labor force recently in agriculture for a number of countries with lower states of economic development, some only now reaching the "take off" stage. The percentage share of national labor force in agriculture has de-

[10] Various differences in data may cause some lack of comparability between time periods or countries for Tables 3.1 through 3.5. Differences likely arise because of: Classification of national labor force; inclusion or not of women and family workers in agriculture; change in composition of farm consumption between home-raised and purchased items; part-time employment of farmers; price of food at farm and non-farm sources; change in composition of labor force in different sectors; the period and method of national income accounting; etc. Some of these, as part-time farming and dependence more on purchased goods, cause the ratio for agriculture to appear either less or more favorable than long-term trends would indicate. But even with these difficulties in measurement and computation, it is certain that the income of agriculture does lag, and has for long periods, that of the aggregate nonfarm sector. This point is generally consistent with the interpretations of G. Bellerby (Agriculture and Industry: Relative Income. Macmillan. London, 1956), and E. Ojala (Agriculture and Economic Progress. Oxford University Press. London, 1952).

clined for countries experiencing growth of important magnitude. The rate of decline conforms roughly to the rate at which national economic growth has taken place. Or, stated in another way, the proportion of the labor force currently in agriculture corresponds approximately, but inversely, with the magnitude of income or consumer welfare per capita in the various countries.[11]

Comparison of Tables 3.2 and 3.3 suggest that supply elasticity of labor to agriculture has not been high enough to allow a decline in relative labor force of magnitude equal to the decline in relative income share. While the data of the two tables are not for identical periods and times, they indicate in all cases a greater decline in income share than in labor share. Under these conditions, and except in the case where labor productivity in agriculture outpaces that of nonagriculture, we should expect the difference to result in lower labor earnings in the agricultural sector. Again we do not have the refined data we wish, including marginal

TABLE 3.2

Relative Share of Agriculture in National Income for Selected Countries

Country	Early Period	Middle Period	Recent Period
Denmark	45	21	19
France	49	35	23
Germany	24	18	11
Netherlands	49	16	13
Norway	—	24	14
Sweden	40	25	13
U.K.	10	8	6
Italy	56	43	26
Hungary	49	49	—
Japan	54	34	24
Canada	43	26	14
United States	16	15	7
Australia	37	24	13

Source: S. Kuznets, *Quantitative Aspects of the Economic Growth of Nations*, II. Industrial Distribution of National Product and Labor Force (Economic Development and Cultural Change. Supplement to Vol. V, No. 4).

productivities of labor and returns of the resources imputed separately from those of capital. However, figures available are sufficient indication of long-term trends in ratios. For this analysis, we compare income in agriculture per worker with the comparable figure for nonagriculture as measured by Kuznets (with the A-sector being that explained above). Figures are presented in Table 3.4 for major countries of the world. The differences in real income are somewhat smaller than those suggested for money income since farmers consume more home-produced food at lower price and may have other slight advantages in living costs. How-

[11] For example, compare these figures with those of income in standardized units as indicated in Colin Clark, *Conditions of Economic Growth*, Macmillan Co., New York, 1957.

TABLE 3.3

LABOR FORCE IN AGRICULTURE (A-SECTOR) AS PERCENTAGE OF NATIONAL TOTAL FOR SPECIFIED COUNTRIES AND DATES

Country	1870	1900	1930	1950†
Algeria	—	—	—	81 ('48)
Australia	37	25	22	15 ('47)
Belgian Congo	—	—	—	85 ('52)
Belgium	25*	17	14	11 ('47)
Brazil	—	—	—	61
Canada	50	43	31	21
Denmark	51	41	30	23
Egypt	—	—	—	60
Finland	79†	72	57	47 ('40)
France	75	46	36	32
Germany	42*	35	17	13
Hungary	—	59	54	—
India	—	—	—	71
Ireland	41	44	48	31
Italy	62	59	47	41 ('54)
Japan	83	70	50	48
Mexico	—	70	70	58
Morocco	—	—	—	67 ('52)
Netherlands	—	—	21	19 ('47)
Norway	59	47	41	29
Pakistan	—	—	—	77 ('48)
Paraguay	—	—	—	55
Philippines	—	—	—	71 ('48)
Spain	—	67	53	49
Sweden	68	55	39	20
Switzerland	—	27	19	13
Turkey	—	—	—	86
United Kingdom	15	9	6	5
United States	50	37	22	12‡
USSR	—	—	58	45 ('53)

Source: Kuznets, *ibid.*
* Refers to 1880.
† Figure in parentheses indicates year other than 1950.
‡ Based on Colin Clark, *Conditions of Economic Progress*, Macmillan Co., New York, 1957, pp. 248–50.

ever, even with adjustment for these differences, an important difference in real income would still exist in most of the countries.[12]

The data of Table 3.4 indicate that decline in or lower relative income is not unique to U.S. agriculture. Income per worker in agriculture lagged that of income per worker in other sectors over the entire globe. The only exceptions to this statement for 1950 were countries such as the United Kingdom and Israel which were trying to develop agriculture for purposes of national defense or large scale immigration. Also, for the particular time indicated, income was relatively highest for countries where

[12] The figures used are "gross," in the sense that they represent all income of the two sectors divided by the number of workers (but represent income to all factors generally for all persons employed in the two aggregate sectors as explained elsewhere). Using more nearly "net return to labor," Bellerby, *ibid.*, shows the same general lag of farm income behind nonfarm income in his incentive income ratios.

TABLE 3.4

RATIO OF INCOME OF AGRICULTURE (A-SECTOR) PER WORKER TO INCOME OF NONAGRICULTURE FOR SELECTED COUNTRIES

(Labor Force of 1950)

Country*	Ratio A/non-A	Country*	Ratio A/non-A
Australia ('39)	.99	Israel	1.02
Austria ('51)	.40	Italy ('54)	.51
Belgian Congo ('52)	.09	Japan	.34
Belgium ('47)	.63	Mexico	.16
Bolivia	.48	Netherlands	.61
Brazil	.34	New Zealand ('51)	.88
Bulgaria ('34)	.18	Norway	.50
Canada ('51)	.63	Pakistan ('51)	.47
Ceylon ('46)	1.07	Paraguay	.74
Chile ('52)	.46	Philippines ('48)	.28
Denmark	.77	Portugal	.43
Ecuador	.68	Puerto Rico	.41
Egypt ('47)	.36	Sweden	.58
El Salvador	.66	Thailand ('47)	.21
Finland	.42	Turkey	.16
France ('46)	.36	U.K. ('51)	1.08
Germany	.44	United States	.56
Hungary ('41)	.56	USSR ('39)	.26
India ('51)	.42	Yugoslavia ('53)	.20
Ireland ('41)	.73		

Source: Kuznets, *ibid.*

* Figure in parentheses indicates year other than 1950. Figures are not entirely same as in Table 3.3 because of difference in year of measurement.

agriculture served to important extent as an export industry or in growing national market. Aside from these demand regimes, no definite international pattern exists; the ratio being high or low depending on status and rate of economic growth. Communication of employment knowledge, creation of nonfarm employment opportunities, education and labor mobility for agriculture is highest in countries with greatest economic growth. However, in these same countries, the rate of growth of agricultural productivity and the approach of per capita food to saturation level also are greatest, causing the demand for labor in agriculture to be dampened more severely and the demand for food to grow more slowly. Clearly, the income problem of agriculture is not a local problem; it is a world problem, and in relative magnitude, it is an economic growth problem. Only where societies are purely subsistence, or are in special developmental stage do we find a farm income per worker equal to or exceeding that of the nonfarm sector.

Ratio of Income in Agriculture and Other Sectors

But is this a problem only of modern day? Does the relative income problem of agriculture occur only in the last stages of development? Does it worsen with degree of economic development? To attempt answers for these questions, we again turn to data from Kuznets, the best currently available for these purposes. For our purposes and goals the data have, just as those in Table 3.4, these limitations: They are based on product per worker in the various industries. This product is due, of course, to capital as well as labor and an industry or country which used capital intensively would show a larger ratio of product or income per worker than one using a large proportion of labor to capital. However, the product of both labor and capital for such broad aggregates as agriculture and nonagriculture do provide the income of persons and families in these industries, the owners of both the labor and capital. Hence, income per worker or family corresponds roughly to the product per worker when based on these data, although the productivity imputed to a laborer need not.

Again, the data show no formal pattern. They do not increase or decline or decline consistently over time, even with depression periods excluded. If there is any tendency in these and other data, it is for the ratio to increase with time. Perhaps the best we can say is that the relative position of agriculture has not lessened in respect to time and economic growth. Or, comparing the relative depression of income in agriculture per worker with that of nonagriculture, it appears that agriculture generally has gained relatively as much from economic progress as the nonagricultural sector of countries experiencing economic growth. Certainly, farm families have not failed to realize gain from economic growth. Of course, with a growth in income for both sectors, with nonagriculture at a higher initial level, an equal growth rate over time means a greater absolute difference in money units or purchasing power. This fact, plus the greater communication among farm and nonfarm people and the fact that the goals of farm families now more nearly cause them to have the same level of consumption desires as other families, is still reason for concern, even though the relative position of agriculture has not been worsened by economic growth.

The position of U.S. agriculture appears particularly depressing if we view only the 1950's, for example, in Figure 3.2. And it is this and the 1960's which is of concern to current farm operators. The fact that their relative position is no worse in 1961 than that of their ancestor of 80 years ago is no particular comfort in a wealthy nation which has expressed, since 1930, some general objective of eliminating income disparities and their cause. Still, when we examine the data, for long-term perspective as in Table 3.5, there would appear to be definite improvement for U.S. agriculture in the long run.[13] Farm families have not been without some gain from economic growth; although, as mentioned earlier, an improvement in the income ratio of Table 3.6 still allows the absolute differential, in farm and nonfarm incomes, to grow wider as the level

[13] The figures for the more recent years are affected by government programs which transferred income to agriculture. The gain in magnitude of the ratio would have been somewhat less in absence of these public aids.

TABLE 3.5

RATIO OF INCOME OF AGRICULTURE (A-SECTOR) PER WORKER TO INCOME OF NONAGRICULTURE PER WORKER, SELECTED COUNTRIES AND PERIODS*

Country	1870–79	1900–09	1930–39	1950
Australia	—	1.05	.81	—
Canada	.72	.65	.33	.61
Denmark	.79	.58	.48	.79
France	.65	.75	.59	.58
Germany	.39	.43	.38	.41
Italy	.81	.58	.45	.51
Japan	.38	.42	.29	.34
Norway	—	.35	.28	.39
Sweden	.60	.53	.39	.59
United Kingdom	—	.65	.74	1.08
United States	.25	.35	.40	.56
USSR†	—	—	.83	.70

Source: Kuznets, *ibid.*

* Kuznets periods are not the same for each country. Hence, a period or year centering on the dates indicated is used. In the last column, most figures apply to 1950 or a few years in the early 1950's.

† Kahan, *op. cit.* Most recent figure is for 1953, 1955, 1957; earlier figure is for 1937, 1938, and 1940.

of all incomes increases. Being most optimistic, the present trend of Table 3.6, although other data do not show similar certainty of upward trend, would indicate that if we wait out time, the ratio of income in agriculture per worker should move up to that of nonagriculture.[14] The time involved is long, however, if we rest on the rates of improvement in

TABLE 3.6

RATIO OF MONEY INCOME IN AGRICULTURE PER WORKER TO INCOME OF NONAGRICULTURE PER WORKER, UNITED STATES

Year	Ratio
1870	.26
1880	.23
1890	.27
1900	.35
1910	.46
1920	.49
1930	.34
1940	.48
1950	.56
1960	.47

Source: Kuznets, *ibid.*, and agricultural outlook charts for 1960.

[14] Bellerby's (*op. cit.*) comparison of labor earnings for agriculture and industry show no upward trend after 1910, with the ratio average about the same in the late 1940's as in the period 1910–14. Thompson's (*Productivity of the Human Agent in Agriculture, an International Comparison*, Unpublished Ph.D. thesis, University of Chicago, 1951) figures, computed on a somewhat similar basis apparently show an upward trend somewhat paralleling that in Table 3.5. The figures for the United States in Table 3.6 overestimate the differential in terms of real income. For more adequate comparisons in this light, see Chapter 12.

the past, even such as those in Table 3.6. It would take over a century, at the indicated rate of improvement in the last 90 years, for the ratio to equal unity. Even if we adjusted the income figures for differences in purchasing power and capital costs, the time required for the ratio to equal unity at rates of improvement in the past, would still be great. It is desirable, in national growth objectives and welfare of farm families, that the gap be closed in even less than half a century. But, as mentioned before, U.S. policy issues stem not from trends of the last century, nor what they will be over the next century. Today's farmers naturally are concerned over the income drop of the 1950's and whether it will continue for the 1960's. The relative trends in Figure 3.2 provide the setting in which U.S. farm policy of the near future will be made. If we examine only this figure, it appears apparent that the ratio of real income per worker in agriculture has been declining rapidly relative to nonagriculture. If we view only this period, we do not get full interpretation of the long-run growth problems of agriculture. Similarly, if we view only the long run, we fail to interpret the urgency of the U.S. farm problem.

Long-Time Terms of Trade

We have examined a time span for agriculture which is long in terms of the interests of this generation of farmers, whose welfare is largely determined over three decades, or of public administrators who provide legislation to meet existing problems of food surplus or deficit. The span

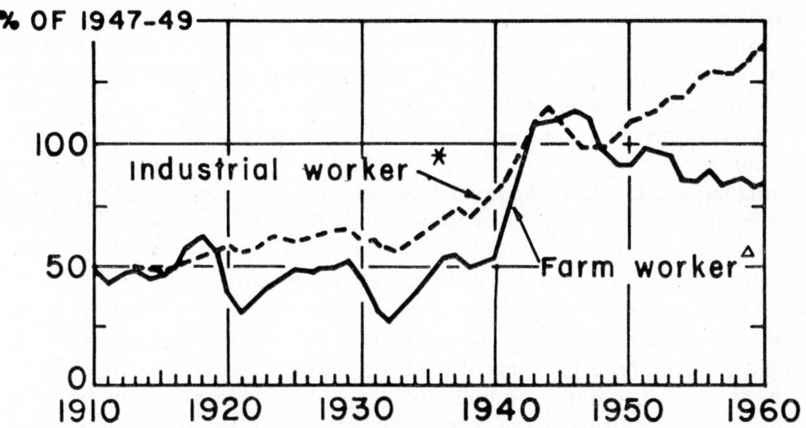

Fig. 3.2. Index of Real Income Per Farm and Industrial Worker, 1910–60.

examined is, of course, short in duration of agricultural and economic development. However, if we wished to better reflect all possible changes in the structure and fortunes of agriculture under economic growth, we would need to go back over a much longer period of time. Then we would not find a single trend expressing the fortune of agriculture in terms of trade or factor returns. The terms of trade and returns to resources would fluctuate absolutely and relatively, depending on the particular stage of economic growth and the nature of factor supply and mobility, for agriculture and other sectors at particular times. In an early society characterized by great population and demand growth from births or immigration, large income elasticities of demand for food, a labor supply internal to agriculture small relative to its growth and low supply elasticity of factors to farming, we would expect terms of trade and resource returns in agriculture to increase greatly. Given large supply elasticity of factors to agriculture, particularly for labor but also for capital, increase in terms of trade and factor rewards would be less, but likely positive. Under these same conditions, except for growth of labor supply in agriculture exceeding growth of labor demand in the industry, terms of trade and factor returns would bear no premium relative to other sectors; but they would not be depressed if factor supply elasticity to agriculture were infinitely elastic. Given extremely low factor supply elasticities, and a backing up of labor in the industry, both quantities would be depressed even under the otherwise favorable circumstances mentioned above. Transition to an economic growth stage with low rate of demand increase and small income elasticities for food need not dampen the fortunes of agriculture if supply elasticity of factors is high. But under conditions of labor supply typical of agriculture, birth rates greater than farm employment opportunities and a low relative mobility of labor, terms of trade must certainly be depressed. They will be depressed even more with technological progress exceeding growth in commodity demand and a strong leftward shift of the farm demand function for labor. The position of agriculture as an export or import industry also can alter the trend. Even with low internal food demand elasticities, terms of trade for agriculture can remain favorable if the industry is oriented to foreign markets and factor supply to agriculture, including knowledge and birth rate, has low elasticity. But increase factor supply elasticity under these conditions and premiums in terms of trade or factor rewards, will diminish.

Looking to the data, we find that long-term fluctuations in terms of trade for agriculture have very well expressed these developmental phases. A trend in relative prices or factor returns hardly exists, as a single regression line of positive or negative slope, for any nation. Apart from business cycle fluctuations, their magnitudes have moved upward or downward depending on the particular circumstances of economic growth and foreign trade. We illustrate this point with the long-run data from Britain, the United States and New Zealand. The data in Figure 3.3 provides expression of terms of trade for agriculture. They are prices of

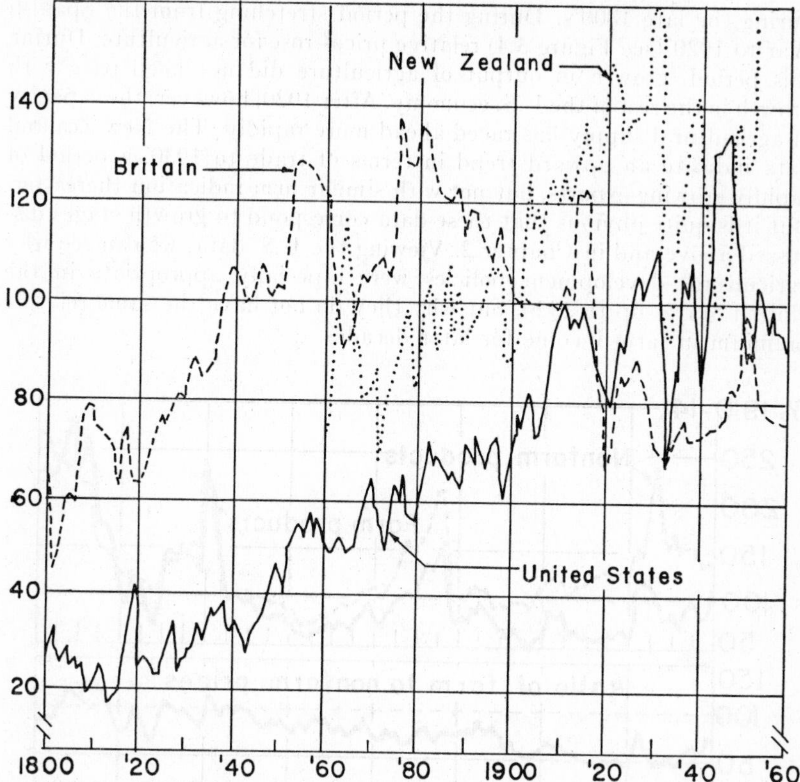

Fig. 3.3. Terms of Trade for Agricultural Commodities, 1800–1956, for Three Countries.

farm products divided by prices of manufactured products.[15] If we view British data only over the last 70 years, terms of trade for agriculture seem to have fallen, although in the 70 years of 1800–1870 they almost certainly were rising. They appear to move fairly regularly upward for the United States up to 1915, then give way to no particular direction, except for upward movement in war periods and downward movement in peace periods. During the period prior to 1915, American consumers grew rapidly in numbers and export markets for U.S. products had high price elasticity; farm products being the most important industrial aggregate in exports and amounting to as much as a fifth of foreign sales

[15] The source of these data are Theodore Morgan, "Long-Run Terms of Trade Between Agriculture and Manufacturing," *Economic and Cultural Development*, Vol. 8, no. 1, pp. 1–23. The series used are B for British and D for U.S. and New Zealand data. The price relatives, comparing only commodities and not factor returns, are not a sufficient indication of the real terms of trade because they do not account for changes in technology and input or cost for unit of output in the various sectors. Also, in recent decades, monetary costs have represented an increased proportion of farm prices.

during the late 1800's. During the period stretching from the Spanish War to 1920 (see Figure 3.4) relative prices rose for agriculture. During this period, growth in output of agriculture did not keep pace with growth in the rest of the U.S. economy. After 1920, however, the capacity of agricultural supply has raced ahead more rapidly. The New Zealand data indicate an upward trend in terms of trade to 1930, a period of rapidly growing exports, but not with similar firm indication thereafter. But it is quite obvious that these data correspond to growth stages discussed above and in Chapter 2. Viewing the U.S. data, we can see why agricultural development policies were especially appropriate in the United States up to 1920, but why they do not have the same relative premium in farm income for later decades.

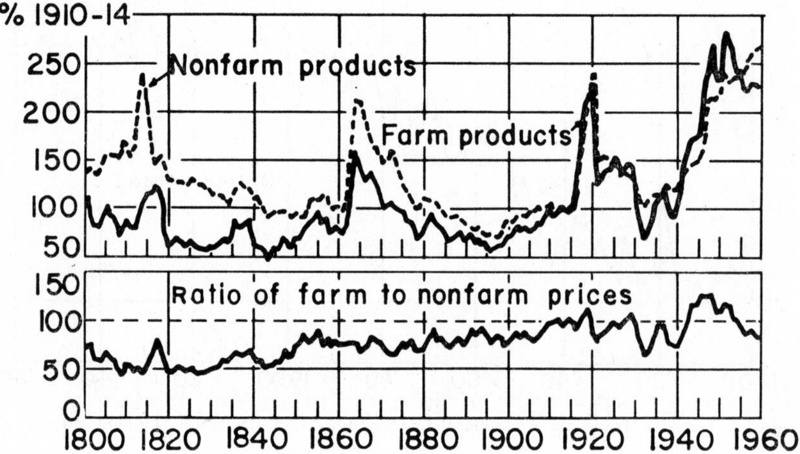

Fig. 3.4. Wholesale Prices of Farm and Nonfarm Products and Their Ratio, U.S., 1910–14 = 100 (Source: USDA).

Income and Transfer Problems

Left to the market in enterprise nations, and to planners in complete socialist countries, the relative income problem of agriculture is long-run and complex in nature. The United States, at the present level of per capita income, represents one extreme in development and the income problems attached to it. Not only is the level of per capita income so great that agriculture cannot grow at the rate of the nonfarm sector, but also the absolute demand for labor is declining. The supply elasticity of labor to agriculture has not been great enough to draw income per worker in agriculture to levels of the nonfarm sector. In most other nations, the same general growth pattern now exists, with income elasticities of demand being much less than unity and causing agriculture to grow at a slower rate than secondary and tertiary sectors. In many of these, the absolute demand for labor in agriculture has not declined, but additions to the labor force from the farm population exceeds replacements needed in farming. Hence, in these countries also, labor supply elasticity for agriculture has been too low to allow comparability of labor value productivity in farm and nonfarm sectors. The variables causing these differentials are long-run and growth-oriented. They are not likely to be turned back by temporary farm price or conventional compensation policy or increased technological progress in farming.

Productivity changes have, of course, taken place in the general economy as well as in agriculture. The annual rate of (percent) increase in productivity for the U.S. private domestic economy and for agriculture have been estimated as follows:[16]

Period	U.S. Private Domestic Economy	U.S. Agriculture
1889–1957	1.7	.76
1919–1957	2.1	1.16
1940–1957	2.3	1.62

Farm people have gained from productivity increase in the domestic private economy, just as consumers in general have gained from farm technological advance. In fact, as indicated above, the rate of productivity advance in the nonfarm economy is predicted to be greater than in agriculture. As for the U.S. economy in total, the real income of farm workers had a sharp rise after 1940. Economics-wise, as is illustrated in Figure 3.5, the war was an easy adaptation and real incomes were able to rise because of unemployed resources and an upsurge in economic growth rate. While farm real income jumped to a level equal to that of factory workers during the war as indicated in Figures 3.5 and 3.6, it sagged back to its historic comparison in postwar years. The gain in real income of farm workers during the two decades 1910–30 were much less than for factory workers; this being a beginning reflection of the less favored position of an agriculture in economic growth. The postwar upsurge in productivity and economic growth has not by-passed farm people. They now have much higher real incomes than in the prewar period. The income problem is more in relative terms, as explained elsewhere, and in an equitable sharing of agriculture in the productivity gains which it contributes to national economic growth. Loomis and Barton estimate that the real income of farm family workers dropped by 11 percent from 1947 to 1957, at a time when real income of factory workers increased by 22 percent. The real income of all unpaid resources in farming is predicted to have declined by 22 percent over the same period.[17]

[16] Based on S. Fabricant, *Basic Facts on Productivity Change*, Natl. Bur. Econ. Occas. Paper 49; and R. A. Loomis and G. T. Barton, *Productivity of Agriculture; United States, 1870–1958*, USDA Tech. Bul. 1238.

[17] Loomis and Barton, *ibid.*, p. 32.

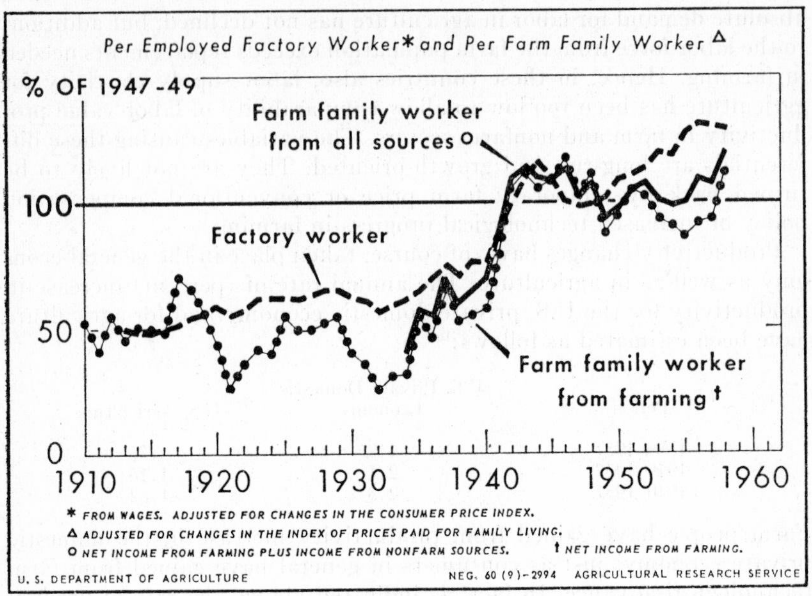

Fig. 3.5. Indexes in Real Income of Farm Family Workers and Factory Workers, U.S., 1910–60.

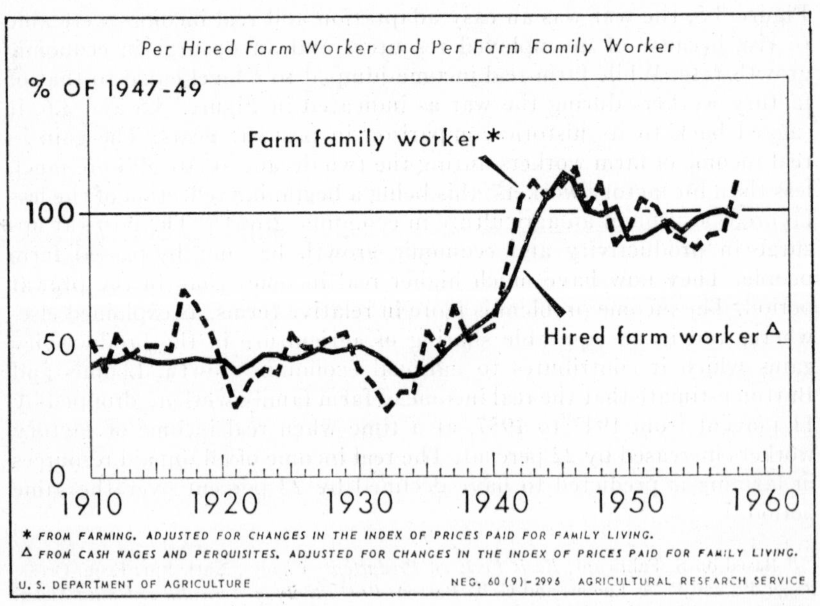

Fig. 3.6. Indexes of Real Income. Farm Family Workers and Hired Farm Workers, 1910–60.

Policies Appropriate to Income Problems

In this chapter we have outlined the two major income problems peculiar to commercial agriculture. One is of short-run nature and rests on high supply elasticities and low demand elasticities (both elasticities in respect to price) for individual products. The other is of long-run nature and rests particularly on low supply elasticity of labor to agriculture and low income elasticities of demand. The first has no important relationship to national economic growth. The second has its roots in this very complex. Both call for public policy, if they are to be solved readily and effectively. They need, however, quite different policies mechanisms and those appropriate for the first are not appropriate for the second, even if they have been so mixed in the United States.

4

Competitive Structure and Supply

THE COMPETITIVE STRUCTURE of agriculture is conducive to economic progress. U.S. agriculture has always been a competitive industry, just as is true of agricultures in other countries where decisions are made by masses of individual farmers and cultivators. In numbers of firms and homogeneity of product, it approaches the model of pure competition more than any other industry employing such large quantities of labor and capital. This competitive structure, under supplies of capital and technical knowledge with sufficient degree of elasticity, serves as both asset and liability. It is an asset in economic development, allowing gain to society generally and to farm families as part of the consumer sector. It is a liability in short-run level of profits for the industry since, given the supply inelasticity of certain resources, output presses continuously against a demand of low price elasticity.

Limitations in supply of knowledge and capital did restrain the rate at which the agricultural supply function increased in early periods of economic development in the United States. This restraint still applies in underdeveloped countries. Still, development of U.S. agriculture, in resources drawn in and products flowing out, was remarkable. It was aided by great elasticity of land and labor supply, with the public maintaining elasticity of the latter and encouraging more firms.

The competitive structure of agriculture no less encourages agricultural development today. The profit motive inspires progress in all industries, but in few more than agriculture's commercial sector where pure competition prevails and the individual firm has no measurable effect on industry output and price. Firms which compete in industries not characterized by pure competition do have short-run opportunity to establish price and to gear output to it. They can increase short-run profits through manipulations of prices, as well as through changes in technology, production structure and costs. This is possible especially for highly differentiated consumer products where a demand curve with slope much greater than zero faces the individual firm. It also is possible in producer's goods industries, such as steel, where the product is homogeneous but the small number of firms allows tacit management of price, with production being adjusted accordingly. Price is not given as datum to the firm or groups of firms in these cases. In 1960, for example, the steel industry produced at about 50 percent of capacity. While unit costs might have been lowered and steel output for economic development purposes might have been increased, had firms produced more at a lower price, the structure of the industry did not lead to this policy. Neither did competition among laborers cause them to sell more labor per week at a lower price, amidst unemployment, with demand for labor increased accordingly. These firm and industry policies, with price level highly fixed in the short run, are used to lessen the insecurity which would stem from dog-eat-dog competition. They do provide short-run stability in mass effect, as long as they do not lead to large unemployment. They do not, as pointed out previously, do away with competition.

Major competition still exists in development of new products, in adoption of new technology and in clamor for share of a total market at a given price. Over the long run, too, price does become flexible because of competition from other industry aggregates. Progress does occur in this competitive situation which is not pure. Incomes increase and security of degree prevails, although the major pulls of consumer preference and change continue. It is not, of course, inconsistent that firms, consumers and laborers simultaneously hold security, economic progress and level of income as goals. None of these goals, or others with which they compete and complement, is maximized, but an accepted combination has prevailed within these industries which are not pure competitive.

FIRM MOTIVATION IN PROGRESS

The firm in agriculture is not simply an inanimate complex of cost accounting and computers, generating short-run and long-run cost functions to establish the minima for the pure model. Typically, a household attaches to it. This household is the owner of resources, particularly labor of established skills, occupational preference and low short-run elasticity to the particular firm. It searches for technology which generates progress partly in order that it need not transfer its firm from the occupation. Since this firm-household complex has no control over price, it can increase profit or avert decline in income only by adopting new technology, a different mix of resources, to increase output by a greater proportion than costs. Or, it can try to reduce costs directly, without changing output, but techniques which reduce per unit costs subsequently serve to increase supply of the individual firm.

The individual firm in agriculture also can buy the services of more resources, increasing size and output, while retaining the same technology. The latter occurs continuously. However, at any given time more are searching for new technology, to increase output by a greater proportion than costs. The hope is simple: Increase in output, with price constant and the marginal cost of the resource less than its value return, will increase the individual's profit. But the constancy of price prevails only if most others do not follow a similar strategy. Whereas this is the hope for one farmer, it also is the hope of thousands of others. Consequently, price is not a constant for the industry. It declines absolutely, or lags behind upward movement of the general price level. This has been the history of U.S. agriculture from 1920 to the '60's. The competitive nature of the firm, in connection with low supply elasticities of factors in the short run, causes output to be high enough and price low enough that returns to factor are depressed below the nonfarm sector. While, in theory and fact, this should occur only in the short run, economic history is simply an interlocked sequence of short-run periods, with direction towards a distant long run which also is always changing in economic character. If we look back to Table 3.4 (page 100), and other data which can be marshalled for this purpose, one short run simply merges into another.

The search of farmers for techniques which increase input value by a smaller proportion than output has led to a continuous increase in supply. (See discussion of Figure 7.10 on page 298.) This is obvious in the data of Figure 2.4 and Table 2.13. Slight dips in output since 1920 have been mainly due to weather or extreme economic shocks usually for a single year. Run-of-the-mill decline of commodity price relative to resource price has not caused them. Increases in output came about under continual decline of this price ratio in the 1950's, not because farmers respond irrationally or are motivated only sociologically, but because new technology increased the marginal productivity of capital. More of capital representing new techniques thus can be used with increase in the resource/commodity price ratio. With increase in the price ratio, marginal productivity of resources must be kept higher, or the ratio of input to output must decline. And indeed this has happened since 1920. As Table 2.13 (page 71) indicates, there have been few years since 1940 in which input per unit of farm output has not declined. Measuring economic progress as the ratio of input to output, the consuming sector has indeed realized progress. With food produced under continuous per unit decline in aggregate input, and because of the burden of supply on inelastic demand, its real cost has declined.

The individual farmer's main hope for improving his income and welfare under the competitive structure of agriculture causes this progress to continue. This is true not because national economic progress is the primary goal in his decision making, but because the planning alternative open to him is one which leads to this end. He must be ever alert to find new technologies which allow him to increase output from a given collection of fixed resources. His hope is, as mentioned earlier, that with constant price he can increase output and revenue at a smaller increase in input costs. As most others do so too, total revenue declines under the inelastic demand for farm products. Still, the individual farmer would be worse off if he did not adopt new technology and increase his output, as long as the industry does so. A qualitative example and not a quantitative specification, is found in the demand and production functions in equations (2.1) and (2.2) and the equilibrium price in (2.6). The individual farmer has been producing q quantity of product. If he can increase his output to $1.2q$ and sell it at the price P_1, his revenue will be increased to the quantity $1.2qP_1$, or by 20 percent over the original quantity qP_1. Yet if all other farmers and the industry increase output from Q_1 to $1.2Q_1$, equilibrium price for the industry will fall to $.5P_1$. The individual farmer's revenue is then $1.2a \cdot .5P_1 = .6qP_1$, or a reduction of 40 percent. If however, he held output constant at q while the industry increased output to $1.2Q_1$ and price dropped to $.5P_1$, he is left with a revenue of only $.5qP_1$. His revenue declines by 40 percent if he increases output along with the industry, but by 50 percent if he does not do so. Hence, his "worse off" position is improved 20 percent if he too increases output, although it is less than the revenue which would have existed had both the individual and the mass held output constant. No single innovation or resource addition results in price and revenue declines of this relative magnitude, but this is the short-run qualitative effect of individual action under conditions of pure competition market and an inelastic demand. Over time, increase in output has accompanied increase in demand. But supply has shifted more rapidly than demand, causing agriculture's real terms of trade, reflected in resource returns, to decline or remain low relative to the nonfarm sector. Recent research shows the real income of nonpurchased inputs to have declined since 1947 and to have lagged factory worker real income since 1920.[1] The individual farmer is penalized if he innovates and adopts technologies leading to general economic progress, but the penalty is even greater if he does not do so. Progressive farmers who innovate before the masses realize net gain from progress, while the masses realize loss.(See discussion of equations (5.42) to (5.59) in the following chapter for a numerical example.)

While some farmers innovate and adopt new technology before others, the lag has become less as compared to decades of the past. Profits of innovation are relatively smaller and spread over less time than in earlier decades. In previous times, a new livestock ration or crop variety could be in existence for decades before it was adopted by the masses of farmers. Now, however, a new variety or feed additive is adopted by the majority of farmers in the course of two or three years.

[1] R. A. Loomis and G. T. Barton, *Productivity of Agriculture, 1870–1958*. USDA Tech. Bul. 1238, pp. 33–35.

Through developmental policy for agriculture, the American public provides a continuous flow of new technology to further this continuous and self-generating process of advance. It produces new techniques in the research services of the land-grant colleges and the USDA. It communicates this knowledge to farmers. With the high value which society places on progress, this will undoubtedly continue to be true, and the motives underlying innovation and change of the agricultural supply function will intensify as farm numbers continue to decline and the industry becomes increasingly commercialized.

Farmers have no choice in the timing and extent to which new technology will be introduced, in contrast to industries where the number of firms is small and individual firms guard technical developments with some secrecy. Not only does public production of innovations help assure progress in the sector, because of the competitive nature of agriculture, but this public investment also contributes greatly to maintenance of competition in farming. With knowledge of new technology freely available to all farmers, large or small, the advantages of extremely large-scale operations are partly nullified.

Increasingly, of course, private industry conducts research on new technology for agriculture. It does so in order to sell the materials of new technology and quickly presses this knowledge to farmers. As we indicate in a later chapter, this contribution of the private sector to innovation and technological progress of agriculture has increased greatly relative to the contribution of the public sector. (The public, therefore, has opportunity, as outlined in Chapter 16, to use more of its resources on research and education for adaptations of agriculture, which helps both the industry and general society to more readily and fully realize gains of economic progress.)

Competitive Structure and Economic Progress

The competitive structure and low price elasticity of food demand cause pressure on the individual to improve technology and increase output. Consequently, with magnitude of food demand tied closely to population, the strong trend is for each unit of output to be produced with fewer inputs, or at a lower real cost. Resources are thus saved, so that they can be diverted to other economic sectors where consumers desire larger growth as their incomes increase. With growing population, total food requirements or demand have increased, but it has been possible in recent times to produce this greater output with about the same total quantity of resource inputs (Tables 2.13 and 16.2).

As individual farmers use more capital resources and extend output against an inelastic demand, income per farm and person can be maintained only as there are fewer of both. This has been the main source of input or resource savings in agriculture over the years of 1940–59. Aggregatively, farmers remaining in the industry have, as an average, extended use of nonreal estate capital inputs by over 100 percent since 1940 (Table 2.8). These capital inputs represent both new technology and extension of existing technology. By individual categories, the percentage increase in inputs has been 135 for machinery, 142 for fertilizer and lime, 125 for feed and livestock and 37 for miscellaneous items. But at the same time, number of farms declined by 30 percent and farm labor by 47 percent. For the industry, increased value of nonreal estate capital inputs was approximately offset by the decline in labor inputs, with total value of inputs up only slightly while total output increased by 53 percent.

The drive by individual farmers to use new types of inputs, or extend use of nonland capital on the existing agricultural area, is a process which does not end, because the gains to the individual from extending output are partly or entirely dissipated as the masses follow this procedure and price and revenue are depressed in the manner explained above. The process becomes continuous as the individual perpetuates the search for methods to extend output and reduce unit costs, as a means for increasing profit through greater volume or greater profit per unit. But because of low demand elasticities, and in a growing economy where alternative resource employment is available at favorable rates, families with limited capital and managerial resources find they can increase income only or mainly by transfer to other industries. As they do so and income and resources are allocated to fewer remaining farms, economic gains to society are realized.

In general, labor inputs can decrease as capital is substituted for them. Too, with some surplus capacity of labor and machinery in major producing regions, farm consolidation can take place with a saving of inputs relative to total output. When two farms of 160 acres are consolidated, for example, the unit so created infrequently needs to duplicate the machinery of the previous two units. But even with a large decline in labor force and number of farms, the change in agricultural structure has not been great enough to bring factor returns in this broad sector up to the level of the aggregative nonfarm sector.

Factor Prices and Technical Improvement

Farmers adopt output-increasing technology not simply because of its discovery, but because it is profitable to do so, or unprofitable not to do so. Few, if any, adopt new techniques for the sake of being innovators. Largely they do so because of profit considerations. Profits can be increased through purchase of innovation materials only if their prices are favorable relative to commodities which they produce. And, aside from major depressions, this indeed has been the condition over recent decades (Table 2.10).

While all prices have increased due to inflation, prices of important categories of inputs did not increase as rapidly as farm commodities in postwar years. Accordingly, the real cost of these inputs decreased; their prices were lower relative to farm commodity prices than they were in prewar years. In general, too, the marginal physical productivity of capital increased because of technical discovery and adaptation.

The decline in real price of many capital inputs for agriculture is due to technological improvement and competition in firms and industries which produce these inputs. An outstanding example is that of fertilizer where a pound of nutrient had a much higher real price in 1935–39 than in 1955–59. It took only 70 percent as much farm product to buy a unit of fertilizer in the latter as compared to the former period, and its known marginal response was much greater. It was extremely profitable for the individual farmer to use much more of such inputs, even under an inelastic demand where greater aggregate output meant smaller industry revenue and less income per farm.

Technological improvement, in both agriculture and nonfarm sectors, is the important source of economic progress and rising per capita incomes. Without improvements in technology, limits to the size of national income would soon be encountered; or while national income might increase gradually with population and size of the labor force, per capita income would decline as population grew. Fortunately in the United States, particularly as a result of technological advance and improved skill of people, national income has grown more rapidly than population, with a consequent rise in real income per capita. Labor productivity has increased throughout the economy, as well as in agriculture. The nonfarm worker can obtain his family's food requirements with fewer hours of work than at any previous time in history. But also, because of technological progress in agriculture and other industries, farm people also can acquire nonfarm goods and services with a smaller outlay of labor than in previous decades.

This general type of progress, with more goods and services available with less human effort, is valued highly by American and other societies. It is desired no less in agriculture than in other industries. Agriculture has contributed importantly to this process, as labor has been freed for use in other industries and capital requirements per unit of food output have been kept relatively low.

The portion of gain in economic progress made to society by agriculture has not been made without sacrifice on the part of the latter. Other industries also contribute to the same process of economic progress and adjust labor and other resources accordingly. Down through history, changes in technology and demand have revolutionized the structure of some industries and diminished the absolute magnitude of others. Capital has been substituted for labor, or workers have shifted from industries with low income elasticities of demand to those where the elasticities are higher. (See Table 2.12).

With low price and income elasticities of demand, agriculture cannot expand as rapidly as others where income elasticities are higher. Because of low demand elasticities, a rate of growth in output which exceeds population growth (or expansion in foreign markets) severely depresses income. The demand for labor shrinks accordingly and migration must take place if (1) persons with limited opportunities in agriculture, because of lack of capital and managerial resources, are to take advantage of alternatives elsewhere in the economy which will reward their labor more bountifully and (2) those who remain in agriculture are able to operate with enough resources and on a scale which will provide satisfactory incomes. But this adjustment problem is extremely more difficult for farm people than for many industrial workers.

Especially important is the spatial nature of agriculture. It is more difficult for a Kansas wheat farmer, for example, to shift to employment in the electronics industry at San Francisco, than for a worker to shift between manufacturing or service industries within the city of Detroit. In the latter case, skills required in the two positions may be highly similar and the worker need not shift the location of his home. But the problem of facility in transfer of resources among alternatives under economic growth does not apply differentially only to labor. As mentioned in Chapter 1 for radios and hand washers, even capital resources and land have greater flexibility in most manufacturing industries than in farming. A firm producing button hooks and coffee grinders can somewhat readily shift its building and machine resources to thermostats and TV cabinets. A farmer cannot shift barns and cultivators so readily from crops to plastic bags or hi-fi sets. Decline in demand for a particular product is not of particular concern to the modern industrial firm; it expects as much and has a new product developed to replace it, using largely its existing labor force and plant. Plant and resources in agriculture are much more specialized to a particular product, and hence have low supply elasticity for it. Augmenting the short-run income effect of this low supply elasticity, again is the competitive structure of agriculture which prevents it from maintaining a price level and adjusting output to it. The constant quantity in the short run is more nearly output, with real price being variable. This is in contrast, as illustrated in Figure 4.1, to

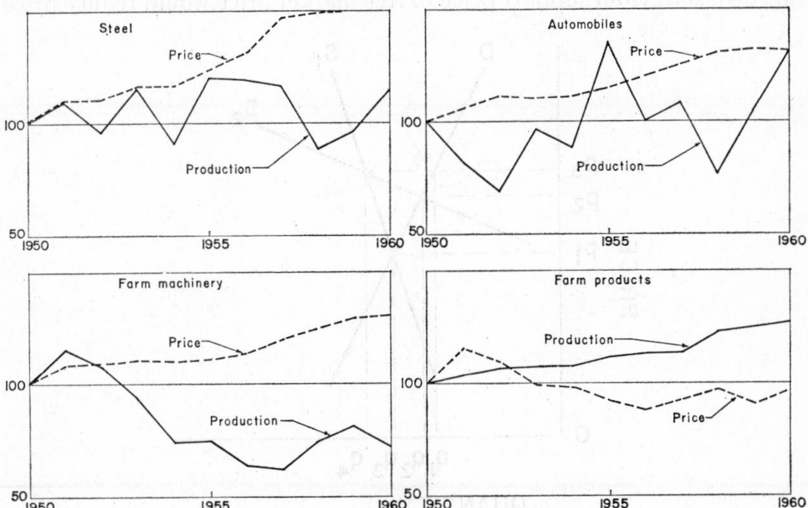

Fig. 4.1. Indices of Production and Price for Products of Four Industries, 1950–60 (1950 = 100).

certain other major industries where the extremely fluctuating short-run quantity is output, production being managed to maintain a desired price level.

AGRICULTURAL SUPPLY ELASTICITY

Superficially, the short-run income problems of agriculture are those of commodity supply elasticity. Much of public debate over American farm policy has hinged upon supposition of magnitudes of supply elasticity. American society has attempted to compensate agriculture for the income burden resulting from the constant contribution it makes to economic progress and low price elasticity of demand, through price supports greater than short-run market equilibrium prices. In both extended periods of price supports, the 1930's and since 1952, large public stocks accumulated and return to free market prices were posed as means of lessening these and their treasury costs.

A central issue of debate was how readily supply would adjust and how far prices would decline in a switch from support prices to free market prices. One proposition was that the process would be quite painless in the sense of a market price decline, an assumption of large price elasticity of supply. Another proposition was that it would be quite painful with a large price drop, an assumption of low elasticity. The significance of elasticity magnitude to extent of decline in production and price under this policy step is illustrated in Figure 4.2. Initially we have the demand curve D and the government support price of op_3, leading to annual output at level oq_4, with quantity oq_1 moving into consumption and q_1q_4 moving into storage. With great price elasticity of supply, expressed by curve S_1, shift from support price to free market price would reduce price

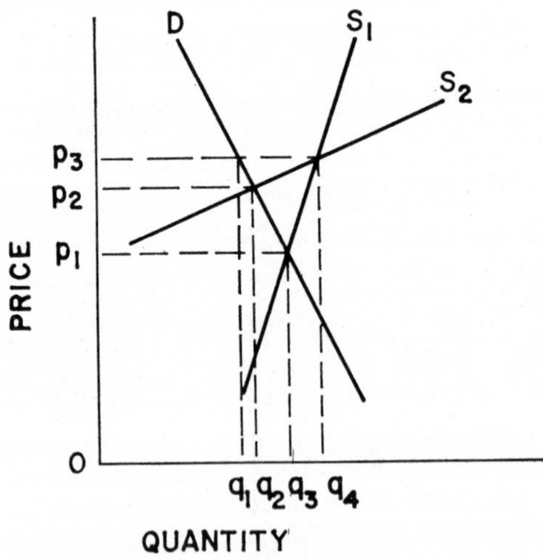

Fig. 4.2. Effects of Price Elasticity of Supply on Adjustment in Production and Price.

by a relatively small amount to op_2 and output by a relatively large amount to oq_2. With low supply elasticity, expressed by S_1, output would be reduced by a relatively small amount to oq_3 and price by a large amount to op_1. Obviously, then, supply elasticity has great relevance to policy mechanisms and magnitude of quantities important in farm income generation under a given demand regime.

Not only are supply elasticities important in policy questions such as the one posed above, but in ascertaining why supply presses so heavily on demand in the sequence of short runs which characterize the continuous adjustment of agriculture to a "moving long run" and a continuous depression of incomes and factor returns to levels below other major economic sectors. But the quantities involved are more than elasticity coefficients. They involve the entire structure and foundation of commodity supply in agriculture which we need to examine.

The problems of income are superficially those of commodity supply elasticity in the short run because elasticity itself is determined by other more fundamental quantities, namely, the elasticity of the production function and the elasticity of factor supply. Also, for short-run income problems, we also must understand how the supply function changes relative to the demand function and the relevant short-run elasticity quantities. But we should emphasize: the continuous short-run depression of income does not arise simply because the supply function moves to the right more rapidly than the demand function. Even under these conditions, income and resource returns could be maintained at some previous or comparable equilibrium level under particular regimes of factor supply and production function elasticities. We must eventually examine these more fundamental quantities. But before doing so, we must examine with less detail and formality the conditions of supply growth which can cause terms of trade and relative factor returns to be favorable to either agricultural producers or to food consumers.

Basis of Supply Elasticity

Again we turn to simple algebraic forms and static concepts for the industry in order to illustrate the dependence of supply elasticity on other quantities. (Other algebraic forms and decision environments lead to the same conclusions but are more difficult to manipulate.)[2]

$$Q_p = \pi X \tag{4.1}$$

$$X = sP_x^{.1} \tag{4.2}$$

$$X = \pi^{-1}Q_p \tag{4.3}$$

$$P_x = s^{-10}X^{10} \tag{4.4}$$

---

[2] See the footnote discussion of equation (1.1) to (1.5) for an explanation of the reason for the illustrative method which starts with the industry. We obtain the value $E,=.1$ in (4.8) because the value of Q_s is (4.7). Hence, substituting Q_s for $.909^{.1}\pi^{1.1}sP^{.1}$ in (4.8), we obtain $E_1=.1Q_sQ_s^{-1}=.1$

(4.5) $$C = K + P_x X = K + \pi^{-11} s^{-10} Q_p^{11}$$

(4.6) $$\frac{dC}{dQ_p} = 11\pi^{-11} s^{-10} Q_p^{10}$$

(4.7) $$Q_s = .991\pi^{1.1} s P^{.1}$$

(4.8) $$E_1 = .099\pi^{1.1} s P^{.1} Q_s^{-1} = .1$$

First, to examine the effect of factor supply elasticity upon commodity supply elasticity, we begin with the "higher elastic" or linear homogeneous production function in (4.1) and the factor supply function in (4.2). (We suppose π and s are larger than 1.0.) For the latter, a 10 percent change in price will cause quantity of factor to change by only 1 percent.

The amount of factor to produce a unit of commodity is (4.3) while factor supply price, the price of factor required for a given quantity of the factor, is (4.4). The total cost function is (4.5) where substitution of (4.4) for factor price and substitution of (4.3) for factor quantity gives the term at the right of (4.5). The corresponding marginal cost function is (4.6). By equating it to commodity price, P, and solving for quantity, the commodity supply function in (4.7) is obtained. Computation of

$$\frac{dQ_s}{dP}\frac{P}{Q_s} \quad \text{in} \quad (4.8),$$

the "own" price elasticity of commodity supply is indicated as E_1, a point directly evident from the power of P in equation (4.7). This is the coefficient when production has great elasticity (constant scale returns) and factor supply has low elasticity.

Now examine the case where the production function remains (4.1) but the factor supply elasticity is high as in (4.9). Derived as previously, the corresponding price elasticity of commodity supply E_2 is (4.10), a quantity much greater than (4.8) for low factor supply elasticity.[3]

(4.9) $$X = sP_x^{.8}$$

(4.10) $$E_2 = (.8)(.4444^{.8})\pi^{1.8} b P^{.8} Q_s^{-1} = .8$$

Now, using a given elasticity of factor supply, with the elasticity of production as the "variable" to be examined, we start with the extreme of factor supply equation in (4.11). The industry production function for comparison is one of low elasticity in (4.12). Its supply function is (4.13a), where the elasticity of supply is the power of P.

(4.11) $$X = sP_x$$

(4.12) $$Q_p = \pi X^{.1}$$

(4.13a) $$Q_s = 20^{-.053} s^{.053} \pi^{1.053} P^{.053}$$

(4.13b) $$E_3 = .053$$

[3] The value of .8 is derived in the manner of the numerical calculations outlined for equation (4.8) where $E_1 = .1$. In equation (4.10) the value of $.4444^8\, \pi^{1.8} b P^{.8}$ is equal to Q_s.

The corresponding elasticity of commodity supply in respect to price, E_3, is (4.13b). Now compare this with the price elasticity of commodity supply arising when the production function has greater elasticity as in (4.14).

$$Q_p = \pi X^{.8} \tag{4.14}$$

$$E_4 = .667 \tag{4.15}$$

Using the factor supply in (4.11) and the production function in (4.14) the derived price elasticity of supply for commodity, E_4, is (4.15).

In summary then, with a given elasticity of the production function (4.1), low elasticity of factor supply (4.2) gives a low price elasticity of commodity supply (4.8); high elasticity of factor supply (4.9) gives a high price elasticity of commodity (4.10). With elasticity of factor supply constant (4.11), low elasticity of the production function (4.12) gives low price elasticity of commodity supply (4.13), while high elasticity of production (4.14) gives high elasticity of commodity supply (4.15). At the very extreme of unit elasticity in production (4.1) and in factor supply (4.11), the elasticity of commodity supply would be infinite. Other algebraic forms would possess the same characteristics of commodity supply elasticity with respect to production and factor supply elasticity.

But the supply function has never remained fixed in U.S. agriculture. Developmental policy and market forces have continually shifted it to the right. It has most nearly been constant in countries lagging in economic development and with stagnant agricultural technologies. Hence both the elasticities and the changes in structure underlying commodity supply must be analyzed if we are to determine the effects and possibilities of population growth and economic development on real incomes to producers and food costs to consumers, or the policies necessary to modify either of these and still cause supply of farm product to be at levels deemed appropriate in agricultural or food policy. We discuss below the several supply environments which may exist, depending on shifts in the supply function and its elasticity.

Supply Function Constant

The supply function remains constant only if the production function and supply price of factors remains constant.[4] Supposing this to be true, we may have low commodity supply elasticity due to (1) low elasticity of the production function resulting from a fixed land area and no development of new techniques or resource forms or (2) low elasticity of factor supply because of restraint in land area and difficulty of attracting labor and capital into agriculture or in getting them to migrate from the industry.

Elasticity of commodity supply or demand in respect to price need not cause burden in family incomes and resource returns should certain con-

[4] To these two major conditions we should add that constancy in supply function exists only if institutions tenure and uncertainty remain constant. These points are discussed later.

ditions exist. Returns could be favorable, using various criteria, regardless of whether commodity supply elasticity were high or low. Unfortunately the necessary conditions are not attained in the short run for agriculture. Accordingly, real income tends to lag behind that of other economic sectors. One of the main conditions violated is that of factor supply elasticity. High elasticity of factor supply to agriculture could, of course, be attained with (1) great transferability of resources and (2) competitive conditions in other industries which do not restrict resource movement. The commodity supply function could shift to the right, with either high or low price elasticity, and resource returns could be maintained at a par with other industries if factor supply elasticities were sufficiently high. However, when factors become specialized to the industry they are much less adaptable to other industries and mobility and transfer is not accomplished as readily as the shift or reallocation of resources among manufacturing and service industries. Obviously, then, we must examine conditions of factor supply if we are to understand conditions of commodity supply and prices and incomes of agriculture. We do so in the next chapter.

Supply of commodity remains constant only if the production function and supply price of factors (perfectly elastic factor supply) remain constant. Either condition is highly unlikely, but is approached in underdeveloped countries where technology is more nearly static and an excess labor force exists without other employment opportunity. The supply function will change in the opposite environment: new knowledge of the production function; factor supply function less than perfectly elastic with growth in industries which compete in resources; and general change in the farm decision-making environment. The extent to which change in the commodity supply function of agriculture depresses prices and incomes depends on the rate of change in the supply structure relative to change in demand. Returns will be depressed, with rate of shift in supply function which exceeds that for demand function, not only if factor supply elasticity is low to agriculture but also if the noncompetitive conditions of other industries prevent flow of resources from agriculture. In the paragraphs that follow, we illustrate the effects of supply elasticity and rate of change in supply function on relative level of commodity price. (We will examine the effects of change in commodity supply and demand structure on factor returns subsequently.)

To illustrate these points, we use the simple "static" commodity supply and demand functions indicated in Table 4.1. Supply functions of both "high" (.8) and "low" (.1) own price elasticities are used. Similarly, "high" (.7) and low (.2) own price elasticities are used for demand. The value of r in the supply function can be looked upon as an "aggregation" of several of the right-hand terms in (4.7). Similarly, the c in the consumer demand function is derived from "aggregation" of effects of population, per capita income, etc. Functions of constant elasticity are used, not under the assumption that elasticity remains constant with time or quantity but to illustrate the qualitative impact of different elasticity magnitudes.

TABLE 4.1

EFFECT OF RELATIVE CHANGES IN SUPPLY AND DEMAND FUNCTIONS AND ELASTICITIES ON COMMODITY PRICE LEVEL

Supply Function	Demand Function	Equilibrium Price	Price Comparison
	Original functions		
(1) $Q_s=rP^{.8}$	$Q_d=cP^{-.7}$	$P_1=(cr^{-1})^{.67}$	
(2) $Q_s=rP^{.1}$	$Q_d=cP^{-.7}$	$P^2=(cr^{-1})^{1.25}$	
(3) $Q_s=rP^{.8}$	$Q_d=cP^{-.2}$	$P_3=cr^{-1}$	
(4) $Q_s=rP^{.1}$	$Q_d=cP^{-.2}$	$P_4=(cr^{-1})^{3.33}$	
	Shift in demand only		
(5) $Q_s=rP^{.8}$	$Q_d=\lambda cP^{-.7}$	$P_5=(\lambda cr^{-1})^{.67}$	$P_5=\lambda^{.67}P_1$
(6) $Q_s=\mathrm{r}\mathrm{P}^{.1}$	$Q_d=\lambda cP^{-.7}$	$P_6=(\lambda cr^{-1})^{1.25}$	$P_6=\lambda^{1.25}P_2$
(7) $Q_s=rP^{.8}$	$Q_d=\lambda cP^{-.2}$	$P_7=\lambda cr^{-1}$	$P_7=\lambda P_3$
(8) $Q_s=rP^{.1}$	$Q_d=\lambda cP^{-.2}$	$P_8=(\lambda cr^{-1})^{3.33}$	$P_8=\lambda^{3.33}P_4$
	Shift in demand and supply		
(9) $Q_s=\Gamma rP^{.8}$	$Q_a=\lambda cP^{-.7}$	$P_9=(\lambda\Gamma^{-1}cr^{-1})^{.67}$	$P_9=(\lambda\Gamma^{-1})^{.67}P_1$
(10) $Q_s=\Gamma rP^{.1}$	$Q_d=\lambda cP^{-.7}$	$P_{10}=(\lambda\Gamma^{-1}cr^{-1})^{1.25}$	$P_{10}=(\lambda\Gamma^{-1})^{1.25}P_2$
(11) $Q_s=\Gamma rP^{.8}$	$Q_d=\lambda cP^{-.2}$	$P_{11}=\lambda\Gamma^{-1}cr^{-1}$	$P_{11}=(\lambda\Gamma^{-1})P_3$
(12) $Q_s=\Gamma rP^{.1}$	$Q_d=\lambda cP^{-.2}$	$P_{12}=(\lambda\Gamma^{1}cr^{-1})^{3.33}$	$P_{12}=(\lambda\Gamma^{-1})^{3.33}P_4$

Starting with supply and demand functions of high elasticity on line 1, an increase in demand by proportion λ as on line 5 will change equilibrium price from P_1 to P_5, with the latter being $\lambda^{.67}$ times the former, an increase in commodity price of a smaller proportion than the shift in demand. In contrast, if we start with low supply elasticity and large demand elasticity as on line 2, an increase in demand by λ proportion on line 6 causes price in equilibrium to be $\lambda^{1.25}$ greater than the initial price for this setting, an increase for price greater than for demand. With the elasticity combination on line 3, the price increases by the same proportion as demand. But with initially low price elasticity for both supply and demand as on line 4, an increase in demand by λ proportion increases commodity price to $\lambda^{3.33}$ ratio of original price, a much greater proportion than the shift in demand. Quite obviously, then, with a fixed supply structure in agriculture, growth in demand will increase farm prices and food costs, in an amount depending on the elasticities of supply and demand (for other forms of functions as well as those used). Prices increase most under conditions of low elasticity of both functions. Of course, both functions change in growing economies, and we need to examine the bottom portion in Table 4.1 where changes in proportion of Γ for supply and λ for demand are assumed. With equal proportionate changes in supply and demand and elasticities remaining constant, the equilibrium price will not change irrespective of the magnitude of supply or demand elasticity. The magnitude of $(\lambda\Gamma^{-1})^n$ in the right-hand column is equal to 1.0 where $\lambda=\Gamma$. Hence, given an economy otherwise in static equilibrium and lacking changes in the price level due to inflation, commodity price will not decline if equal shifts in supply and demand prevail. If, however, changes in supply or demand are unequal, $\lambda \neq \Gamma$, commodity prices will not remain constant. If increase in demand exceeds increase in supply, equilibrium price will increase with the proportion depending on supply and demand elasticities. If Γ exceeds λ, as it has in the U.S. for the last decades, commodity price will decrease to the extent specified by price elasticities. Suppose, for the initial example on line 1, that demand increases to $\lambda = 1.08$ between two periods and supply to $\Gamma = 1.2$ that of the initial period on line 9. Equilibrium price in the second period then will decline to $(1.08/1.2)^{.67}$ or .931 proportion of the former price if supply and demand elasticity are at the high levels of .8 and .7 respectively and remain constant in the two periods. If supply elasticity is high (.8) and demand elasticity is low (.2) as on lines 3 and 11, the increase will cause price to decline even more, to (1.08/1.2) or .9 proportion of former price. The relative decline in price is even more, to $(1.08/1.2)^{3.33}$ or .704 proportion of former price where both elasticities are low (line 4) and remain of initial magnitudes (line 12). If demand shift exceeds supply shift, low elasticity of supply and demand will cause price to increase, more than if the elasticity coefficients were large. Suppose, for example, that $\lambda = 1.32$, $\Gamma = 1.2$ and $\lambda\Gamma^{-1} = 1.1$. With high original elasticities (line 1), price will change to $1.1^{.67}$ or 1.066 proportion of its original magnitude. But with low supply elasticity (line 2), it will increase to $1.1^{1.25}$ or 1.127 proportion of its original magnitude (line 10). Under low elasticities for both functions (line 4), it will increase to $1.1^{3.33}$ or 1.374 proportion of its original magnitude (line 12). Unfortunately from American agriculture, λ has been smaller than Γ.

More typically, supply and demand functions for farm commodities change in elasticity as economic growth and development occur. Price elasticity of demand declines as consumer income grows to allow abundance and variety in diets. Starting from a supply function based on "fixed land area and given technology," long-run supply elasticity itself is likely to increase under economic development, especially if elasticity of capital and labor supply can be made to grow. Within this framework, long-run elasticity may grow while short-run elasticity remains low. Let us examine outcomes under these possibilities. Starting with low supply elasticity and high demand elasticity (line 2) shift in supply exceeding that for demand and elasticities constant, the comparative results are lines 2 and 10. With $\Gamma = 1.2$ and $\lambda = 1.08$, the new equilibrium price, P_{10}, is only $.9^{1.25}$ or .888 proportion of the former price. However, if supply elasticity increases (from line 2) to .8 and demand elasticity declines to .2 as on line 11, with $\Gamma = 1.2$ and $\lambda = 1.08$, the elasticity changes may cushion or accentuate the drop in commodity price, depending on whether c is smaller or larger than r. The price resulting on line 11 is $P_{11} = .9c^{-.25}r^{.25}P_2$. Hence, whether the counteracting effects of increasing supply elasticity and decreasing demand elasticity cause price to decline more than if elasticities remained constant depends, in our example on the magnitudes of c and r, on the original multiplier of demand and supply, as well as on Γ and λ. If either Γ and c are large relative to λ and r, with elasticities changing in the magnitudes indicated, equilibrium price will decline.[5]

A somewhat parallel case is that in which demand function shifts to the right but its elasticity lessens, while the supply function shifts in similar direction but its elasticity remains constantly low. This is a hypothesis somewhat similar to one projected for U.S. agriculture.[6] Hence, suppose for our comparison the original situation is line 2 of Table 4.1. With change in supply and demand and decline in demand elasticity, the new situation is line 12. Price for the latter, P_{12}, is

$$\left(\frac{\lambda}{\Gamma}\right)^{3.33}\left(\frac{c}{r}\right)^{2.08}$$

proportion of the former, P_2. With Γ equal to λ, equal proportionate shifts in supply and demand and elasticity declining by the magnitude indicated, equilibrium price will decline if the original multiplier or coefficient of demand is low relative to supply, but increase if the opposite is true. For example, where c is less than r and $(c/r)^{2.08}$ is less than 1.0, equilibrium price will decline even if Γ is equal to λ; but even more if Γ is greater than λ. Obviously, then, all of the coefficients in supply and demand determine the extent to which commodity price will be maintained, increased or depressed as supply and demand functions shift to the right with the variables which change with time.

It is likely that while the supply function for the individual commodity may have increased in elasticity, with greater and more adaptable managerial skills and market orientation, the elasticity of the aggregate supply functions remains uniformly low in the short run as it moves rightward. Greater mobility or supply elasticity of labor, as evidenced in the great off-farm migration of labor in recent decades, alone should have the effect of increasing commodity supply elasticity. However, it also is likely that the dominating reservation prices and factor supply elasticities for aggregate supply elasticity in the very short run now are those of land and specialized capital. With families and labor withdrawn from agriculture, neighboring farmers take over their land and capital equivalent and retain them in production. Also, the supply and demand functions which exist at a given point in time are not, as in our example and as most frequently forced in empirical estimation, of constant elasticity. Hence, with rightward shift in the aggregate supply function at a greater rate than demand, equilibrium quantities increasingly fall at

[5] In the more general case, $P_{11}=\lambda\Gamma^{-1}c^{-.25}r^{.25}P_2$ while $P_{10}=(\lambda\Gamma^{-1})^{1.25}P_2$. Hence, P_{11} exceeds P_{10} if

$$\frac{\lambda r^{.25}}{\Gamma c^{.25}}>(\lambda\Gamma^{-1})^{1.25}\quad\text{or if}\quad\frac{\Gamma}{\lambda}>\frac{c}{r}\cdot$$

For our numerical example, P_{11} will be larger than P_{10} if c/r is less than 1.1 (i.e. less than $1.2\div1.08$). For a larger c/r ratio, P_{11} will be less than P_{10} when $\Gamma=1.2$ and $\lambda=1.08$.

[6] *Cf.* W. W. Cochrane, *Farm Prices, Myth or Reality*, University of Minnesota Press, Minneapolis, 1958, pp. 42–60.

points of lower price elasticity on the demand function. The relative speed in supply increase and lower demand elasticities both cause downward pressure on prices.

BASIS FOR CHANGE IN SUPPLY

Supply elasticity and rate of change in supply, given the demand function or its rate of change, determine the level of commodity price. Depressed commodity prices may or may not result in depressed resource returns and incomes, depending on factor supply elasticity. Hence, in later chapters, we must analyze further the relationships between supply elasticity for resource and commodity, and the relationships between commodity price and resource returns. Also, we must analyze the alternatives and prospects in change of demand structure. But before we do so, we continue with examination of change in the commodity supply function and elasticity since these are the quantities ordinarily given first attention in farm and food policy. The attempt in countries with a farm problem and relative decline in commodity price and factor return, aside from attempt to increase demand at more rapid rate, is to check rate of increase in supply. The hope of countries with a food problem and relative increase in food price and resource return, aside from checking population increase, is to speed the rate of increase in the supply function.

Static Setting

The two major supply shifters in a static economic setting, and similarly in a dynamic setting except for greater lag in response, are change in the productivity of particular resources and changes in factor prices relative to product prices. This point is readily apparent for any form of production function, but again is easily illustrated with the simple form in (1.1) where the corresponding resource requirements equation is (1.2). Substituting (1.2) for X in the total cost equation, taking the derivative to obtain marginal cost, equating this to product price and solving for quantity, the supply function becomes (1.4). Given the supply function in (1.4) output will increase with magnitude of commodity price, P. However, the supply function changes only with change in coefficients of the production function, π and b for (1.1), and with change in factor price, P_x, relative to product price.[7] The rate at which supply increases depends,

[7] We have illustrated with an algebraic form simple to follow. In a more general sense, the same statements apply to other forms of function. For example, the production function in (4.16) results in the static supply function in (4.17), where steps of equations (1.3) through (1.6) are used in derivation.

$$Q_p = a + bX - cX^2 \tag{4.16}$$

$$Q_s = a + .5c^{-1}b^2 - .5c^{-1}\sqrt{P_x P^{-1}} \tag{4.17}$$

Again in (4.17), it is obvious that any effort leading to increase in marginal resource productivity in (4.16), increasing a and b or decreasing c, or to decreasing in resource price will increase the supply function in the sense of greater output at given price. An increase in P alone, P_x and the production coefficients remaining constant, will increase output but will not change the supply function. In case $c=0$ for (4.16) or $b=1$ for (1.1), constant returns to scale exist and the production function has unit elasticity while the supply function has infinite elasticity.

then, on the rate at which the production coefficients are increased or factor price is lowered, for the simple production-supply environment indicated.

In the early years of agricultural development policy, the U.S. public caused supply to grow by increasing the quantity of a particular resource, X or land, and effectively increasing π in equation (1.1) by inflow of labor to agriculture. It also kept a factor price, P_x or land price low, sometimes causing it to decrease in real price. With a mammoth rate of population growth, real prices for food were kept low, although they were favorable to the economic development of agriculture. In the last half century, increase in the production coefficients, such as π and b in (1.1) have been brought about especially by public research to improve technology. The general nature of technological research can be indicated by the general production function in (4.18). A total of n resources enters into the production process and includes such specific factors as seed of one variety, nitrogen in a particular form, labor in June, labor in October, soil moisture from a previous period, moisture at the present, hand hoes, tractor plows of a given size, etc. At a given time, we know the existence and production coefficients or parameters for factors X_1 through X_g.

$$(4.18) \qquad Q_p = f(X_1, X_2, \cdots X_g, X_{g+1}, \cdots X_h, X_{h+1}, \cdots X_n)$$

Resources X_{g+1} through X_h are known but their production coefficients are not. Resources X_{h+1} through X_n are not yet known or cannot be controlled in quantity. Thus, prediction of the productivity parameters for resources in the category X_{g+1} through X_h allows their introduction into the production function in nonzero or larger quantities. Discovery of resources X_{h+1} through X_n or control of their magnitude serve similarly, once their productivity coefficients are established. Given favorable prices of these factors, their use has the effect of increasing the supply function, in the sense that they are the equivalent of increase in π or b in (1.1) and a or b in (4.16).[8]

The great revolution in structure and supply of U.S. agriculture over the last half century has come about through this process. Effectively, in the sense of (1.1), we have been able to make great strides in increasing the productivity coefficients so that magnitude of Q_s in (1.4) is increased for a given level of real commodity price. The rate of increase in the productivity coefficients has not been alone the result of market mechanisms. Importantly, it also has been a function of resources used in public

[8] More exactly, where we have functions such as

$$(4.19) \qquad Q_p = sX_1^{b_1}X_2^{b_2} \cdots X_n^{b_n}$$

$$(4.20) \qquad Q_p = a_{11}X_1 + a_{12}X_1^2 + \cdots a_{1m}X_1^m + \cdots a_{n1}X_n + \cdots a_{nm}X_n^m + \cdots b_{12}X_1X_2 + \cdots b_{n-1,} \quad {}_nX_{n-1}X_n$$

where π in (1.1) and a in (4.16) represent the effect of those resources which are present in nonzero and fixed quantity. The magnitudes π and a_{11} are increased as greater resources quantities are added to the collection. More particularly, however, productivity of a given resource is increased as suggested in (4.20) as new resources or their productivity are discovered and they are entered into the production function in nonzero quantities.

agricultural research institutions for this purpose. Increasingly, however, research in the private sector also has added to change in productivity supply coefficients. Discovery of a resource in the category $X_{h+1} \cdots X_n$, or discovery of the productivity effect of one in the class $X_{g+1} \cdots X_h$, allows, if its productivity is high enough relative to its price, an increase in demand for it. For example, if we start with the production function in (1.1), the total value function is formed by multiplying it by P, product price. Taking the derivative of the total value function, the marginal value productivity of the resource becomes (4.21).

$$MV = b\pi PX^{b-1} \tag{4.21}$$

$$X = (b\pi PP_x^{-1})^{1/(1-b)} \tag{4.22}$$

Setting the marginal value product in (4.21) equal to the factor price, P_x, and solving for X, we obtain the factor demand equation in (4.22). More of X will be used, aside from uncertainty and institutional effects or lack of knowledge, if commodity price is higher or the production coefficients, b and π, are larger. Factor demand also will grow if P_x, factor price, can be reduced. Accordingly, input-producing firms do invest in research to accomplish these discoveries of greater b and π or lower P_x.

While the motivation of scientific discovery in public institutions is only remotely related to the market, although directly related to the unknown realms of the production function, that of public firms is tied closely to the market and pricing system. If profit potential exists in the sense of high resource productivities in the yet-unknown realms of the agricultural production function, private firms will be drawn to conduct research in it. The profitability of this research depends quite largely on the marginal productivity of the resource to be discovered and the manufacturing production function and factor costs involved in its fabrication. Given the competitive nature of agriculture, efforts of researchers in public institutions and private firms to increase or discover productivity coefficients will result in increase of the agricultural supply function, if market conditions allow pricing of the resource represented at low level relative to its productivity. Private firms must balance investment in research directed towards greater knowledge of the agricultural production function against that of other economic sectors and products. Research workers in public agricultural institutions need not.

Role of Production Function and Public Sector

Public effort in shifting the supply function is quite apart from any predetermined or planned rate of change in agricultural output to attain a particular price level. U.S. public policy has only emphasized that the agricultural supply function be moved rightward. This decision was implicit in early agricultural developmental policy resting on land acquisition and distribution and more recently by investment in public research and education. Activity to shift the supply function has in no way been related to rate of shift in the demand function. The shift has not directly been managed at a particular rate, to feed growth in supply at a rate to maintain farm commodity prices at a particular level, or to push food prices down to a particular level. Once set in motion, aside from slight public excursions in decreasing supply to attain a particular price level through compensation policies, the process of supply increase stemming from technical discovery has been quite largely market oriented and dependent. With a population plagued by hunger and with economic development being a prime goal, a society would pursue this process with extreme vigor, uncovering new technologies and improving market mechanisms to cause rapid shift of the agricultural supply function. But in a well-fed society where greater food per capita has little marginal urgency, economic development as reflected in technical improvement should have no particular priority for agriculture over other industries.

The goal per se of general economic development, given abundance of food per capita, would be furthered equally by public concentration on technical development and shift of the supply function for nonfood commodities. It is not less important that labor productivity in building trades be increased, as compared to agriculture where society has served as an important catalyst to the market in increasing manpower productivity. Society also must make a choice, having succeeded in shifting the food supply function to an extent that the real price of food and the price elasticity of demand are low, whether it should pursue this investment alternative with greater vigor, or whether it should devote more investment to research and market improvements which extend length of life. In total welfare of society, is it more important to have fewer people who live fewer years amid a food surplus, or have more people live more years amid only ample food supplies?

Role of Factor Prices and Private Sector

The American public has taken responsibility for one set of variables which result in shift of the supply function, variables which relate to the production function. The private sector has had responsibility for the second general category of variables which similarly shift the supply function, namely, the price of resources which represent new farm technology. Had the input-furnishing industries been backwards or of sufficient monopolistic degree, increases in factor prices could have offset increase in productivity coefficients. Suppose, for example, in derivation of (1.4) from (1.1) and competitive factor price, an increase (multiplication) of the production function by Γ proportion and an increase in factor price by proportion β. If the increase in factor price is held to $\beta = \Gamma^{1/b}$, the supply function will remain constant. For $\beta > \Gamma^{1/b}$ the supply function will shift to the left regardless of technical improvement which increases marginal resource productivity. Factor prices need not remain constant or decrease to allow rightward shift in the supply function. They need only increase at a less rapid rate than productivity, in our case at a rate smaller than $\beta < \Gamma^{1/b}$.[9]

Factor prices have remained favorable relative to productivity changes in American agriculture. Evidently input industries have been sufficiently competitive (without being pure competition) for this, with the public sometimes stepping in to assure competition.[10] But perhaps equally or more important has been improvement per se in the production function involved in manufacturing inputs whose use represents improved farm technology. While inflation increased the price of all commodities from 1940–60, prices of hybrid corn, fertilizers, chemicals and similar inputs declined relative to the commodities they produce, after 1940, as compared to the period 1920–40. Even the price of machinery has been highly favorable relative to its productivity and farm product prices since 1940. (See Table 2.10). We discussed earlier the extent to which general economic development was financed by surplus of agriculture in earlier periods. To an important extent this function has shifted to the agricultural input industries, partly because they produce resources previously of farm origin, but also because an increasing proportion of the agricultural product must be imputed back to the resources so represented.

Role of Public Sector in Supply of Knowledge Resource

A supply function exists conceptually and effectively, for technical and other knowledge required in agricultural improvement. Knowledge can be obtained at a low price or cost to the farmer when it is produced and communicated by public agencies in magnitudes which bring it close at hand. However, it never has a zero real cost because time and other outlays are required to "go fetch it." The real cost increases as the supply is restricted and, relatively, is much greater in backward as compared to advanced agricultures. To obtain as much technical information as is available in the county seat to the U.S. farmer, the Indian farmer would have to travel far and at a much greater sacrifice in consumption. Transformation of it into understandable and usable form would add further to the real cost, relative to the U.S. farmer with his greater translating ability based on public investment in education.

The supply of technical knowledge is not restricted to that provided through public mechanisms, even in the United States. At a price, the farmer can buy newspapers, farm magazines, radios, books and television sets which provide him with knowledge. He can even hire a farm

---

[9] With b smaller than 1.0, the elasticity of factor demand in respect to its own price is always greater than unity. We do not propose this as a condition of agriculture, or that the relations of Γ and β above are those which must hold true. We use the function and example only because (1) we wish to show the interrelations between factor pricing and resource productivity in commodity supply and (2) the function used is simple to manipulate for this purpose (without devoting more lines and pages to more complex equations).

[10] For example see J. W. Markham, *The Fertilizer Industry*, Vanderbilt University Press, Nashville, Tenn., 1958.

management service. This also is true in Asia or Africa. Many of the same media are potentially available but at a much higher real price. The Indian villager could obtain technical knowledge for rice via television, but the price is that of an airline or ship ticket to Tokyo. Technical knowledge also is provided by private enterprise or markets in the U.S., but is much lacking in the underdeveloped agricultures. This source is currently of great importance in development of U.S. agriculture, perhaps even more important than knowledge supplied through the public sector. This source and its importance often is overlooked by the American agricultural expert who goes abroad and attempts to explain the rapid pace of technical progress in the U.S., or by the foreigner who comes here to identify the organism responsible for our upsurge in technology. Both emphasize that the "answer" is in the public facilities of our experiment stations and extension services. But if only these were duplicated in countries with backward agricultures, the result would not be increase in commodity supply of the U.S. magnitude because the public sector now provides only a portion of the total supply of technical knowledge.

The private sector in the U.S. provides knowledge as a joint product with the agricultural resources and materials which it produces and sells. It calls this knowledge, and its effects, to the attention of farmers through salesmen, newpaper and billboard advertising and investment in good will devices. The number, investment and variety of such "salesmen" is much higher in the private sector than in the public sector of knowledge supply in the United States. This knowledge is generally a joint product with the materials or resources produced by firms furnishing inputs to agriculture. Hence, it comes at a high or low real cost, depending on the price of its "joint material."

Knowledge of the production function and existence of favorable factor/product price ratios are necessary conditions for adoption of relevant technologies. But a sufficient condition also must be added; namely, the availability of capital for purchase of the inputs. One element of U.S. farm policy since 1920 has been to increase the supply and lower the cost of capital funds represented by credit. Certainly these were the main ingredients of the tremendous upsurge in U.S. agricultural technology from 1940 to 1960.

Knowledge was retailed to farmers in effective fashion by the public sector through extension education and by the private sector in advertising and salesmanship. Too, vocational agriculture, 4-H work and advanced education generally made the farmer of the 1960's, much more than his father, a "receptive" resource for use of this new knowledge.

The capital and equity position of farmers became more favorable than at any previous time in American history, as available statistical evidence proves. Then, as the data in Table 2.10 indicates, the relative prices of products and of factors representing new technology was extremely favorable in the post World War II period. Farmers reacted to these changes in price structure and knowledge just about as the economists would predict: machinery and other new technology substituted for labor; aggregatively, fertilizer and other chemical and biological inputs substituted for land, although public price and storage policies kept the effect from being fully realized. Individual farm operators increased their demand for the land, and farm size increased accordingly.

SHORT-RUN AND LONG-RUN SUPPLY ELASTICITY AND INCOME PROBLEMS

The major price and farm income problems of agriculture are not those of commodity supply functions and elasticities in the long run, but are those of the short run. While the long-run supply function may have large elasticity, farm income problems arise because the short-run supply function has low elasticity. One short run continually gives rise to another. Agriculture is faced with a continuous sequence of short runs, linked in important degree to each other, as they progress towards the long run. But equally important, change in national economic structure and in the production function and factor prices of agriculture gives rise continuously to new long runs. Had technology and factor prices remained constant at 1920 levels, American agriculture might now be well adapted to this setting. It would be prosperous, having to draw labor and other resources into it. However, even though outmigration was remarkable from 1940 to 1960 labor input has been no better adjusted to current farm technology and factor prices than it was in 1929, or even in 1950. This sequence of short runs and long runs, with supply elasticity at low level in each new short run, never allows labor returns of agriculture to catch up with other sectors, as indicated by the data of Chapter 3.

Long-Run Elasticity in Respect to the Production Function

Society has two alternatives in respect to farm price and income problems which arise because of low elasticity of commodity supply in the short run. It can push the supply function to the left, leaving short-run elasticity at low level; or it can attempt to increase the supply elasticity. A third major choice, one which does not rest on manipulation of the supply function, is increase in the demand function. All policies, direct and remote, which relate to attempt at improvement of commodity price and farm income fall in one of these three categories. We reserve the analysis of demand and alternatives for a later chapter.

Our discussion of equations (1.1) through (1.4) indicated the quantities and variables which must be manipulated if the supply function is to be managed in rate of shift to the left or right. We now examine more particularly the basis for differences in short-run and long-run supply elasticity and the variables of relevance in increasing output responsiveness. One set of basic phenomena involved is that of the production function. We illustrate the relevant quantities which differentiate short-run and long-run elasticity in this respect.

Returning to the production function in (1.1), we examine a long-run setting by letting $\pi = rZ^v$, where Z previously has had fixed value, and the long-run production function is (4.23).

$$Q_p = rX^bZ^v \tag{4.23}$$

$$X = v^{-1}bkZ \tag{4.24}$$

$$Z = \left[r^{-1} \left(\frac{v}{bk} \right)^b Q \right]^{1/(b+v)} \tag{4.25}$$

$$Q_s = [r(bP_x^{-1})^b(vP_z^{-1})^cP^{b+v}]^{1/(1-b-v)} \tag{4.26}$$

$$E_1 = \frac{b+v}{1-b-v} \tag{4.27}$$

$$E_s = \frac{b}{1-b} \tag{4.28}$$

Setting the marginal rate of factor substitution to equal the factor price ratio and solving for X in terms of Z, we obtain the isocline equation in (4.24). Substituting this value into (1.4) and solving for Z in terms of Q we obtain (4.25). With Z so obtained substituted into the total cost function where P_x and P_z are factor prices and P is commodity price, the long-run supply function is derived in (4.26). It compares with the short-run supply function in (1.4). The long-run elasticity thus is (4.27) and compared to the short-run elasticity in (4.28), derived from (1.4). Quite obviously, (4.27) is larger than (4.28) since $b+v$ is greater than b and $1-b-v$ is smaller than $1-b$. The long-run elasticity is much greater, as it would be for any form of function, than that of the short run, with both supply functions derived from a given long-run production function. In (1.3) the magnitude of Z is fixed, as is commonly the case of many multiperiod resources in agriculture. Obviously, then, supply elasticity grows as "variability of resources" increases.

One answer to problems of low supply elasticity due to the production functions involving fixed inputs would appear to be either (1) wait until the fixed resources is worn out or (2) transfer it out of agriculture. But neither of these attacks is very fruitful for resources specialized to agriculture in the short run. A fixed resource such as land hardly wears out, and many buildings last a half century. A machine may see a generation of men enter and leave agriculture. But even if the "wear out" period averaged only 10 or 20 years, farmers of the decade hardly relish depressed price and income because of low supply elasticity over the waiting period.

The transfer out is similarly clouded by time. The particular form of many specialized resources, even skills of labor, are not always adapted to employment in other industries. Barns in southern Ohio or crawler tractors in Kansas have little productivity in an electronics or food freezing plant. Accordingly, their value may be mainly that of scrap steel and lumber, or even kindling. These uses establish their reservation prices and they will remain in employment as long as their marginal value product is this high. Once committed to these forms for agriculture, supply of these resources is extremely inelastic (zero elasticity for returns down to this level) just as returns were high for Marshall stones.[11] It is this inflexibility and inelasticity of fixed factors that holds them in production, with level of output augmented and commodity supply elasticity lowered accordingly.

Price and income of agriculture then are depressed under the continuous march of short-run supply functions, at rates exceeding shift of the demand function (a point which we wish to examine in more detail in a later chapter). But even as the short run gives way to the long run, as resources of fixed form wear out or transfer and supply is changed accordingly, problems revolving around low short-run supply elasticity are not eliminated. New resources forms are added, but also are specialized and have low reservation prices. While horse-drawn cultivators eventually were worn out or sold for salvage, two-row tractor cultivators took their place and had low value outside of row cropping. Their replacements, four-row cultivators, serve similarly. Labor possesses similar qualities, although of smaller relative margin between reservation price based on opportunity in other industry and original price to agriculture. The particular problem is perhaps at a minimum for a multiperiod resource when the commodity or consumer value, as in the case of beef cows, establishes a rather high reservation price against the same resources used further in production.

Low Factor Supply Elasticity and Flexible Factor Prices

With the farm supply function moving rightward more rapidly than demand and the short-run supply function of low elasticity, commodity prices become depressed and resource returns are kept below levels of other sectors. But the inelasticity of commodity supply also can be overemphasized as a force leading to maintenance of agricultural output at levels which depress prices unduly in terms of level of factor returns. It is, in fact, possible for short-run commodity supply functions to have an important degree of price elasticity, yet have output maintained at a high level simply because factor prices are highly flexible and decline at about the same speed as commodity prices.

Flexibility in factor price of this extent arises in highly competitive markets where the short-run supply of factors has extremely low elasticity. One of its effects is maintenance of agricultural output at high or constant levels even with severe decline in commodity prices such as in major recession. The point is illustrated in Figure 4.3 where we assume the original demand function D_1. Now, if due to extended unemployment, a condition cushioned in effect on food demand by unemployment com-

[11] Alfred Marshall, *Principles of Economics* (Fifth Printing), Macmillan Co., New York, 1953, p. 423.

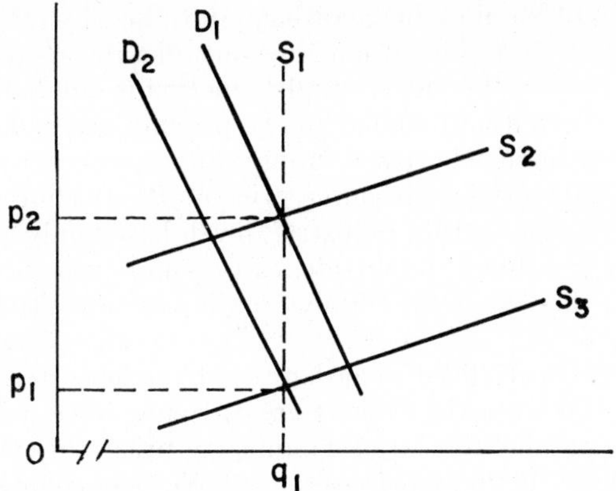

Fig. 4.3. Effect of Factor Price Flexibility.

pensation, the demand curve shrinks to D_2, we have these outcomes: If supply elasticity were zero, as denoted by S_1, output would be maintained at oq_1 level, even with decline of price from op_2 to op_1 level. However, these same quantities can occur even under high supply elasticity. Suppose, for example, that the initial supply function is S_2 and the demand function is D_1. Demand declines to D_2 but, without change in technology or the production function, supply changes to S_3 because of decline in factor prices. Shift in the supply function, due to decline in factor prices, causes output to be maintained at oq_1 even though price drops from op_2 to op_1. And this maintenance of output at reduced commodity price occurs under high price elasticity of commodity supply. We do not infer great short-run supply elasticity for U.S. agriculture in aggregate. Our emphasis is on the importance of supply elasticity for factors and factor price flexibility in causing maintenance of output and resource employment even under depressed farm prices and incomes.

In the absence of major recession, the picture is somewhat different from that in Figure 4.3, but of the same general character. Under population growth, demand moves continually to the right; but with low short-run elasticity of factor supply, rapid injection of technical change into the industry can result in greatly depressed prices, prices which are far below long-run equilibrium prices in level of resources return. This environment is best illustrated by resort to some simple algebra, rather than the geometry of Figure 4.3. Supposing the original production function to be (1.1), where X represents magnitude of services from a multiperiod resource, neglecting for the moment single-period resources and the extent of discount in inputs due to uncertainty and related phenomena. At original supply price of the multiperiod resource from nonfarm industry, the per unit price of resource service is P_x. But after the resource becomes specialized to agriculture, its reservation or sale price to outside industry becomes only βP_x, with β less than 1.0. Hence the new short-run supply function is (1.4), if the flow of services can be varied by period and are not absolute in quantity, multiplied by $\beta^{b/(b-1)}$. Since the exponent is negative (b is less than 1.0), output will be greater at a particular product price (the initial supply function is divided by a fraction smaller than 1.0). Without change in the production function and aside from change in demand, short-run supply shifts to the right, beyond that consistent with the original resource price of P_x. Decline of the supply price of resource to a "within industry" level, based only on reservation price and salvage value from outside, causes short-run supply elasticity to increase, but the shift in the supply function causes output to be maintained.

Since resources specialized to agriculture have low alternative return, they remain in the industry even at great decline in return. Return declines at a rate parallel to that of commodity prices, or even at a faster rate where nonproduction fixed costs are high. The competitive nature of agriculture causes the reservation price of these resources to be based largely on their value return, a quantity that fluctuates with commodity price. As in the case of Marshall's stones, they will take no less return than their alternative employment value in other industries (discounted for preferences, transportation costs, etc.). They will have no higher value or return than that representing the price at which they can be supplied from outside industries. But between these two extremes their return, or value based accordingly, can fluctuate up and down with commodity prices, the resources remaining in agriculture. The short-run supply function is shifted to the right accordingly and output is maintained at even declining price.

Land is an extreme example of a resource specialized to agriculture. Land prices were maintained or increased in the face of falling commodity prices during the 1950's mainly because of changed technology and extended cost economies in farm size. Farmers wishing to increase size for this reason could pay higher prices for acreage added, in terms of the net value return, than for their initial acreage. Operation of the large unit was typically allowed with fixed machinery and labor on hand and only purely operational costs contributed to marginal costs for the added unit. But an even broader market in land services is represented by rental prices, particularly share renting. Here the price of the resources service falls precisely as commodity prices fall. The ratio, to the tenant, of factor-price/commodity-price is maintained as the latter fluctuate.

Machines and buildings already in agriculture, in resource form having physical productivity mainly only in the industry, annually furnish a greater proportion of services than new units brought into agriculture. For buildings, the price is tied closely to land and fluctuates as above. For machinery and power, price of second-hand items fluctuates, between the extremes of salvage and new price, largely with farm prices and income. Feed prices, free from support and of major use as a resource in the industry, fluctuate with livestock prices. Breeding stock follows a similar pattern in respect to meat products. While labor is of more adaptable form than other multiperiod resources, even it has important degree of lag in transfer to other sectors, given a gap in returns between agriculture and other sectors. Prices for multiperiod resources already in agriculture thus are determined by commodity prices and factor productivities within the industry, and are little related to those of other economic sectors.

Resources transformed in single periods and supplied from outside agriculture have an entirely different short-run pricing structure (as do multiperiod resources supplied from outside in the long-run). Supply price then is based on resource productivities and prices in competing industries throughout the economy. Employment of these resources fluctuates more with commodity price than does employment, land, building and machine services. However, limits on short-run change in demand of these single-period resources exists for two reasons. Since their short-run supply price is determined mainly outside agriculture, a fairly constant return is imputed to them even under depression of commodity price, with the brunt of the diminished residual income falling mainly on the fixed or rentier multiperiod resources specialized to agriculture.

Many of these resources have high physical productivity and the individual farmer can use them in the face of price depression (i.e. the marginal productivity for the particular strata of resources outweighs price depression). An example is improved seeds and chemicals. During the 1950's, a period of decline in commodity prices, farmers could profitably add fertilizer not only because it was priced favorably but also because its physical productivity was extremely high. Few use a particular resource to a point where its value productivity touches its price, Cornbelt farmers realizing as much as a 200 percent return on the last margin of fertilizer used per acre. With commodity price cut in half, they could still use fertilizer profitably. (Empirical predictions show some temporary contraction with sharp breaks in price and income, although a general upward trend has existed even with declining terms of trade to agriculture.) Other single-period resources are extreme technical complements of multiperiod resources having low supply elasticity. If the relatively fixed supply of land and machines of any one year is to be used, tractor fuel and seed also must be used, but only if their return is as high as their outside supply price.

Because of this broad complex of low reservation prices and low supply elasticities of multiperiod resources, the agricultural plant remains highly fixed in output response. Withdrawal of individual firms need not cause the supply function to shift to the left in the short run; even the opposite being the likelihood. As a family abandons agriculture and withdraws its labor, other resources are not immediately withdrawn similarly. Its machinery and breeding stock are sold to be used by other farmers and its land is rented or purchased by a neighbor to extend his farm size.

Persons who leave agriculture typically are those with fewest managerial and capital abilities and greatest income disadvantage relative to employment in other industries. Those who remain and take over their resources apply more capital and management of particular forms, and attain an even greater output from the land and at lower real supply price. The latter is possible because of the existence of underemployed labor and machine resources in much of U.S. agriculture, with additions to farm size requiring costs marginal only to land, seed, etc. In fact, with this reorganization and change in agricultural structure, the change in capital may be more in its form than its amount. The remaining operator can invest more capital in improved seed and fertilizer than the transferring operator, but need not replace his machinery and labor where he has unused capacity of these.

An Iowa study illustrated that the shift in resource use under farm consolidation resulted in this very pattern.[12] Land market data of the 1950's also show that a major part of land purchases represent this general process of farm enlargement by remaining farmers. The immediate effect of labor and firm withdrawal from agriculture undoubtedly is to shift the short-run supply function to the right, with this shift per se being maintained until particular resources are depreciated or the distributed lag pattern of their transfer causes some rebound in the level of supply price.

Other Aspects of Distributed Lag in Output Response

There is no question that agriculture has long-run aggregate supply functions, each representing a point in the continuum of technologies or factor prices expressed over time, of less than infinite slope. Factors will be pulled into agriculture if consumer demand is high relatively, or ejected from the industry in the opposite case. Given 25 years and less of calendar time, output unquestionably could well be adapted to the economic environment. But income problems are still those of the short run, in either economic or calendar context.

The problem of supply response is in time required for a given short-run realm to completely shade into its corresponding long-run realm, with the complication that long-run realms also change. Fixed resources do not suddenly become exhausted of services, with supply short run changing to long run by the "suddenness" of lightning. Neither do all surplus labor resources with attachment to agriculture suddenly overthrow their immobility yoke and shift overnight to other industries. The process is gradual, with change less complete in the near-term and often being almost minute for buildings and land, and more complete in the long run.

A large category of adjustments in agriculture follow the time path of the function, illustrated in Figure 4.4A, with rate of change speeding up, under increase in general market communication and lessening of inflexibilities, but eventually dying away as extent of adjustment approaches its limit, Q^*. In empirical measurement for the individual, the time path may more nearly be approximated as Figure 4.4B. The varia-

[12] See Randall Hoffmann and Earl O. Heady, *Farm Consolidation in Southwest Iowa*, Iowa Agr. Exp. Sta. Bul. (forthcoming).

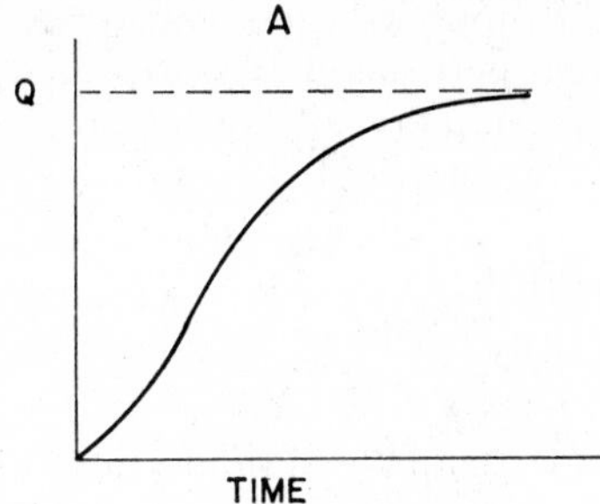

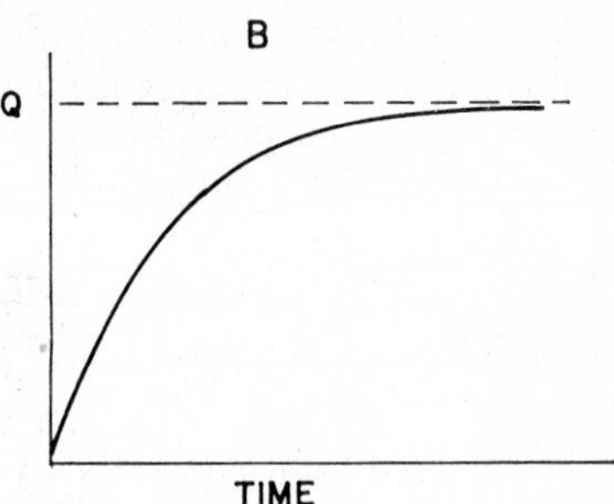

Fig. 4.4. Time Paths of Adjustment.

bles giving rise to this greater extent of adjustment in the long run are many, some already having been discussed.

A normal distribution in remaining life or unexhausted services of fixed resources would lead to the pattern in A for the industry, as would also the pure mechanics of communication, compounded with individual contacts at the outset but dying away later as the number of relevant individuals to be contacted declines. Given a permanent change in price or productivity, expectations may give rise to either type of time path, perhaps with B most appropriate if change conforms with expectations and the degree of uncertainty declines with time. The decision maker may "go only part of the way" in the first period with subsequent change in later periods. Capital restraints, psychological aversion to change or contractural and institutional restrictions may serve similarly. Likewise, the costs of rapid adjustment may be greater than those of delayed adjustment.[13] To an important extent, price change and elasticity of expectations, as well as the particular expectation model employed, also can lead to lag of adjustment, with change distributed over time in the manner above. In general form, the individual may react in the manner of B, while the industry reacts in the manner of A due to the pure communication mechanics mentioned above. In theory and quantitatively, it can be shown that the relative extent of response does change with time, the magnitude of elasticity growing between short run and long run, with long run distinguished as much by calendar time and transition between production periods as by distinction between fixed and variable resources in the classical sense. The formulation applies best to changes in prices and resource returns which are expected to be permanent in a particular direction and much less to repeated changes in opposite direction with complete reformulation of expectations required.[14]

[13] See Marc Nerlove and K. L. Bachman, "The Analysis of Changes in Agricultural Supply; Problems and Approaches," *Jour. Farm Econ.*, Vol. 42, p. 538.

[14] See Earl O. Heady, "Uses and Concepts in Supply Analysis," Heady, *et al.* (eds.), *Agricultural Supply Functions*, Iowa State University Press, Ames, 1961.

A logical illustration is as follows where the supply relation is expressed simply in (4.29), where Q_t is output in current period and P^* is expected price for the same period.[15] (The same relationship prevails for the previous period and the subscript $t-1$ need only be substituted for t.)

$$Q_t = a_0 + a_1 P_t^* \tag{4.29}$$

$$P_t^* - P_{t-1}^* = \beta(P_{t-1} - P_{t-1}^*) \tag{4.30}$$

It is expected that managers revise their expected price in proportion to the error made in predicting last year's price as illustrated in (4.30) where β is a coefficient of expectation. Thus, from (4.30), P^* can be expressed as (4.31).

$$P_t^* = \beta P_{t-1} + (1 - \beta) P_{t-1}^* \tag{4.31}$$

Or, following Koyck, we can illustrate the expected distributed lag in output response as follows, where we suppose a general supply model as in (4.32) where Q_t and P_t are output and prices at period t.

$$Q_t = a + b_0 P_t + b_1 P_{t-1} + b_2 P_{t-2} + \cdots b_n P_{t-n} \tag{4.32}$$

If the variables in (4.32) are in logarithmic form, the long-run elasticity of supply is (4.33) where b_t has the proportion to b_{t-1} in (4.34a).

$$E_1 = \sum_{i=0}^{\infty} b_i \tag{4.33}$$

$$b_t = \delta b_{t-1}, \qquad 0 < \delta < 1 \tag{4.34a}$$

As time passes, price converges geometrically as the relation of (4.34a) prevails. It follows from equations (4.32) and (4.34a) that output in period t is related to prices of previous periods as in (4.34b).

$$Q_t = a + b_0 P_t + b_0 \delta P_{t-1} + b_0 \delta^2 P_{t-2} + \cdots b_0 \delta^n P_{t-n} \tag{4.34b}$$

If equation (4.34b) is lagged by one period and multiplied by δ, the relation in (4.34c) for the previous period prevails.

$$\delta Q_{t-1} = a\delta + b_0 \delta P_{t-1} + b_0 \delta^2 P_{t-2} + \cdots \tag{4.34c}$$

By subtracting (4.34c) from (4.34b), the supply relation for the current period becomes (4.34f), where output now is a function of price in the period and output in the previous period.

---

[15] *Cf.* L. M. Koyck, *Distributed Lags and Investment Analysis*, North Holland Publishing Co., Amsterdam, 1954; M. Nerlove, "Distributed Lags and Estimation of Long-run Supply and Demand Elasticities," *Jour. Farm Econ.*, Vol. 40.

(4.34d) $$Q_t = a(1-\delta) + b_0P_t + \delta Q_{t-1}$$

In other words, δ is the adjustment coefficient, relating output of the current period to that of the previous period. Or, this logical distributed lag can be illustrated simply in the dynamic model of Nerlove in (4.34e) where Q_t is actual output in period t while Q_t^* is long-run equilibrium output in the same period (what output would be if "history could be overcome") and γ is a coefficient of adjustment relating output in the current (t) period to that of the previous ($t-1$) period.

(4.34e) $$Q_t - Q_{t-1} = \gamma(Q_t^* - Q_{t-1})$$

This relation supposes that in each period, producers adjust output in proportion, γ, to the difference between the actual output of the last period and the long-run equilibrium output. In other words, Q_t will differ from Q_{t-1} by an amount equal to γ times the difference between the "desired amount" this year and the actual amount last year. Under static expectations, the long-run supply quantity and relation is that in (4.34f).

(4.34f) $$Q_t^* = a + bP_t$$

(4.35) $$Q_t = a\gamma + b\gamma P_t + (1-\gamma)Q_{t-1}$$

By substituting equation (4.34f) into (4.34e), we obtain the supply equation in (4.35) which, in simple manner, specifies output in the current period to be a function of price in the period (or in relation to prices of previous periods as specified in earlier equations for b_t) and output of the previous period. Equation (4.35) has the same general form as (4.34f) if we substitute $\gamma = 1-\delta$ and $b\gamma = b_0$. With variables in logarithmic form, the value of $b\gamma$ is the short-run elasticity coefficient in respect to current period price, P_t. The value of $1-\gamma=\delta$, computed as a regression coefficient for Q_{t-1} and equal to δ for empirical analysis, can be used to compute b from $b\gamma$ as[16]

(4.36) $$b = \frac{b\gamma}{1-\delta} = E_1$$

where b also serves as the long-run elasticity coefficient of output in respect to its own price. The value of $b\gamma$ suggests the percentage by which output is expected to change with price in the short run, while b indicates the percentage change expected over "sufficient time for complete adjustment away from the past."

In summary, then, the models above provide logical basis for suggesting the distributed lag pattern of adjustment in output, given some ex-

[16] If $1-\gamma$ is estimated as a regression coefficient in (4.35) and is equal to .8, then $\gamma = 1 - .8 = .2 = \delta$. Then if $b\gamma = .4$, we have

$$b = \frac{.4}{.2} = \frac{b-\gamma}{\delta} = 2.0.$$

pectation of a long-run equilibrium price. It is expected that most adjustments in production structure follow some such path or modification of it, with change in one period related to that of previous periods and resource commitments, over a longer period of time and after the initial "shock" of large sudden changes (such as complete abandonment of price supports or a sharp recession) is overcome.

One problem in agricultural supply is to get a reasonably reliable expectation of future economic structure and price before farmers so that they can gauge decisions and adjustments accordingly. Too few farmers have come to understand the changing environment of agriculture under economic growth and the approximate equilibrium level of factor and product prices. But they have reason—their educational services have not informed them sufficiently. Accordingly, many who could commit resources in another direction have not done so under widespread lack in knowledge of long-run equilibrium structure. Even given this knowledge, adjustment in agricultural supply would still not be by "sudden stroke," with all problems of prices and income erased accordingly. Even given some accuracy in expectations, after initial impact of shocks turned loose in the market, adjustment of the majority of producers and the industry does not flash to approximation of equilibrium price consistent with changed economic structure. With expectation of an equilibrium price and corresponding long-run equilibrium output, Q^*, adjustment would still be gradual, as in Figure 4.4, for the individual. The change in output, Q_t, of a particular period towards the desired equilibrium output, Q^*, can only be gradual in agriculture. (Given the stock of services represented in many resources, the fact that their flow is a function of time and the fact that reservation prices of multiperiod capital resources are much lower than their new supply prices.)

The services given off by multiperiod resources representing the major capital agriculture (and the products they produce) are typically complementary among a restricted number of periods. The services are of flow nature, and if service and product is forthcoming this year, it also is forthcoming next year. This is true of a tractor, a dairy barn or a wheat drill, although a competitive component is expressed over a longer period of time. However, the competitive element is expressed only over longer periods. A two-year-old tractor is good for services in a third year regardless of services employed in the second year, although its life may be cut from 20 to 19.

Outputs in some periods are more clearly competitive, in such cases as fallow or continuous cropping of wheat in the Great Plains. Yet the services and products of the majority of capital in agriculture, including land, are complementary over a time span of a few years. This relationship, plus a low reservation price based on the particular form of capital resources, allows a short-run supply elasticity to be much less in a period of declining prices and contraction than in a period of improving prices and expansion. In expansion, output increases along a given short-run supply function and by movement from one to another supply function as a result of added capital and technology. During contraction, technology and the new or added resource inputs it represents holds the short-run supply function to the right, but the movement is dampened by slackened rate of general capital investment. Given the services which flow from a stock of resources specialized to agriculture, adjustment is down a highly inelastic short-run supply function, or in jump between supply functions which still shift to the right with reduction in factor price (Figure 4.3).

The forces towards dampened commodity prices from contraction along a given short-run supply function have never been great enough to consistently offset (1) the forces towards expansion through favorably priced new technology and (2) rightward shift of short-run supply functions from declining prices of resources already specialized to agriculture. Figure 4.5 illustrates this point quite clearly (the relation between prices paid and production is a distortion of true supply relationship, or response of output to price, because of similar trend in input prices due to inflation and in output due to technical improvement.)[17] The greatest deviations in output trend have been due to weather. While small reductions in output have lagged sharp breaks in price, extended periods of lower prices have not been accompanied by extended reduction in output.

With the extended decline in price relatives during the 1950's, output continued to grow as supply functions shifted rightward, overweighting

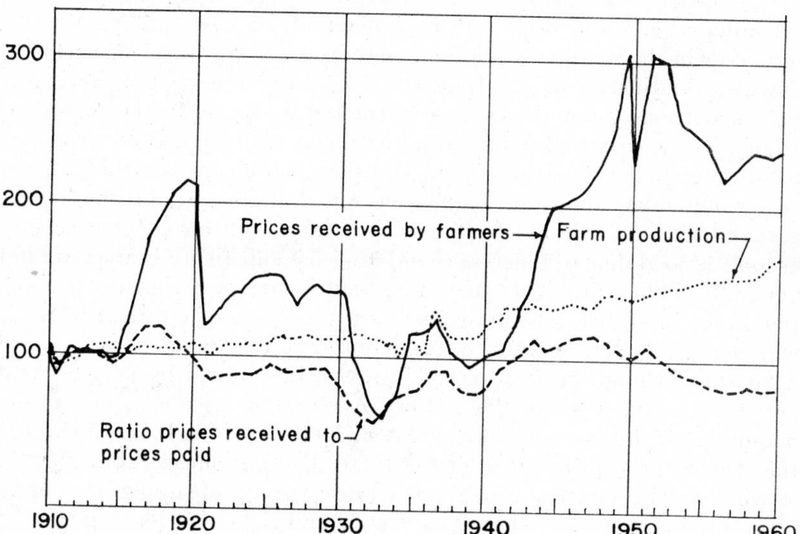

Fig. 4.5. Indices of Prices Received, Prices Paid and Total Farm Production, 1910–60 (1910–14 = 100).

[17] The ratio of prices received to prices paid does not include the implicit costs of resources already specialized to agriculture and is faulty, in a formal supply sense, for this reason. With implicit prices included, the ratio of price received to prices paid would follow quite a different path.

any tendency for production to be contracted along extremely inelastic particular supply function. The same was true during the 1920's and 1930's, aside from deviations due to drouth in the latter period. Of course, periods of depressed price relatives have not been long enough to specify how rate of output growth might be modified by tightened factor/product price ratios. U.S. agriculture still has tremendous slack in structure, allowing the supply function of regions to shift further. (As less efficient managers leave, farms grow larger and remaining operators use different resource mixes to lower per unit costs for a particular price regime.)

It appears possible that even though we exclude commercial farms of low output, such as those with gross income of less than $5,000 in Table 2.6, farm numbers may be decreased by as much as 40 percent, with the acreage so released operated by remaining farms with approximately the labor and machinery they had on farms in the 1950's. If farmers absorbing land area from migrating operators employed the same biological technology, with only difference in machine technology and fixed costs, the short-run supply functions would not change under consolidation. But where biological technology is different and gives higher per acre yields and lower unit costs, as is the typical case, the industry short-run supply function is shifted immediately through consolidation and increase in farm size.

U.S. agriculture has never gone through a long enough period of severe price depression and decline in food demand for possible long-run differentials in elasticities of supply to be reflected in contraction. Certainly downward adjustment in output would be great under a protracted period of extremely low prices and contracted food consumption. For example, if low-cost hydroponics and artificial photosynthesis developed to produce half the nation's food and prices adjusted accordingly, not only would labor and capital inputs decline, but also agriculture's aggregate output would diminish. But contraction in output is not necessary as long as food demand increases and low-cost substitute sources are not available. Policy problems arise, then, not in prospect that the production index in Figure 4.5 will decline, but in terms of the rate at which it will increase under favorable or unfavorable price ratios.

Growth in food output exceeded growth in demand by only a small percentage from 1940 to 1960. However, the low price elasticity of demand causes the excess to have great burden on prices. It is not evident that the reduced price ratios of the 1950's had any measurable effect in slowing down the rate of growth. The low elasticity of supply in a period of supply in a period as short as a decade and the forces leading to shift in short-run supply functions overrode lower prices. This is not to say that the elasticity is low over a long period, or that output cannot be affected within a period as short as a decade. By making the supply of technical knowledge more elastic, the public has caused short-run supply functions to shift rightward more rapidly. By making labor and capital resources more elastic to the industry (e.g. by "buying" specialized forms and diverting them from agriculture), it could similarly cause the short-run commodity supply function to be more elastic, with the rate of growth or magnitude of output in a particular calendar time period thus being less.

PROSPECTS IN OUTPUT AND SUPPLY

The tendency towards growth in output which exceeds growth in demand is predicted for U.S. agriculture in the 1960's. The basic question is not one of whether the nation can feed itself in the 1960's and '80's. It can do so easily, and, as indicated in Chapter 2, the prospect is that a sufficient stock of technical knowledge exists to carry output to 1975 consumption levels without strain.[18] Without new technological knowledge, but a greater average spread of that already in existence, 1975 food requirements of the nation still can be met.[19] Even if the production function remained constant, greater food could still be forthcoming. With no change in the aggregate production function and factor prices, the supply function would be constant. But a constant supply function does not mean constancy of output, except for a function of zero elasticity. The ultra short-run supply function of agriculture is highly inelastic. But the supply function involved when farm acreage is held constant, with more of resources in conventional technological form applied to it, certainly is not of zero elasticity.

More food could be produced, but at a lowered marginal productivity of conventional (already known) nonland resources and a higher equilibrium price of food. Resources could be pulled into agriculture and into industries producing more inputs of conventional form for agriculture. But the food could be produced. The difference is this: The current system of simultaneous growth in demand and change in the supply function through technological advance is similar to movement between lines 4 and 12 in Table 4.1. If supply did not change but demand did, the movement then would be the equivalent to a jump between lines 4 and 8. Equilibrium in food demand would still exist, "requirements" would be met, but food would be priced higher. With shift in demand but not shift in supply (line 8), food price would be the original price (line 4) increased by the ratio $\lambda^{3.33}$, a proportionate increase greater than for demand. If the future period (line 8) were near enough so that present owners of farm resources still existed, they would have greater profit with increase in price of food to $\lambda^{3.33}$ proportion of initial price. Food consumers would be worse off in (1) paying higher prices and a greater proportion of their incomes for food and (2) requiring more resources in agriculture and having fewer to produce other goods and services.

[18] Also see W. W. Wilcox, *Agriculture's Income and Adjustment Problem*, Economic Policies for Agriculture in the 1960's, Joint Economic Committee, U.S. Congress, Washington, D. C., 1960.

[19] *Cf.* O. R. Rogers and G. T. Barton, *Our Farm Production Potential, 1975*, Agr. Info. Bul. No. 233, USDA.

The nation could feed itself up to year 2000, even without technical improvement (an unlikely occurrence), but at an increasing real cost of food and with a large section of resources drawn into agriculture. The facts evidently are, however, that sufficient new technology exists, or can be more widely applied, to allow surpluses, in the sense of the 1950's, during the 1960's. Food for adequate nutrition and at low real cost can be readily attained up to 1975 on the basis of existing technology.[20] (Our current exports could be diverted to domestic use also.) Current investment in technological knowledge thus, in terms of potential of "food price squeeze," is for the consumers beyond 1980, perhaps the year 2000, even though a given supply function would allow them adequate nutrition, but at higher real food costs.

Fortunately, societies do invest with future generations in mind. The basic question is not whether these investments should be made for the future, but how those who suffer capital value and income losses, as supply of the near future is pressed against demand functions of low elasticity, can be treated equitably or compensated in appropriate amount to guarantee positive-sum utility outcome from this facet of economic growth. These are the basic problems of long-run supply complex in a society which prefers economic growth, or which requires it on basis of international sympathy or politics.

From our initial analysis of supply, the quantities which can be manipulated to affect price and income and welfare of farmers or consumers under growth become obvious. Attempt can be made to shift the demand function as or more rapidly than supply, opportunities which are analyzed in Chapter 6. The rate of shift in the supply function might be managed in a rate consistent with positive-sum outcome over farm income, consumer welfare and national progress goals. (See Chapter 16.) Or, after it has shifted, the supply function can be modified through legislative controls, such as legal restraints on particular outputs or inputs. Finally, the structure of supply can be affected by altering the structure of factor prices and supply. Which alternative should be selected depends on (1) the extent to which society has a particular set of over-all national objectives, (2) the extent to which market bargaining power in the hands of various economic groups requires offsetting policy for other groups to guarantee positive-sum utility outcomes over the entire community and (3) the extent to which compensation is publicly desired and is acceptable to redress the losses which fall on one group as a result of gains spread to society in total. These are points to be analyzed subsequently.

Optimum Supply Elasticity

An industry attempting to maximize revenue and income would try to establish the "optimum degree of supply elasticity." Neither the highest nor the lowest elasticity magnitude would be desirable, but a level which is consistent with demand conditions. If the land-grant colleges

---

[20] *Ibid.*

and the USDA, in their publicly financed research and education, had farm revenue as a single goal, an efficient framework for their activity would be to determine and bring about this optimum supply elasticity. We can illustrate it in both long-run and short-run context. In Figure 4.6 suppose that D_1 is the initial demand curve and I_2 is an isorevenue curve. At the point of tangency of the two, price elasticity of demand is unity. At output of oq_2 and price of op_1, revenue is maximized. A smaller or larger output (and larger or smaller price) would reduce revenue as indicated by isocurve I_1. (Points of intersection a and b both fall on the

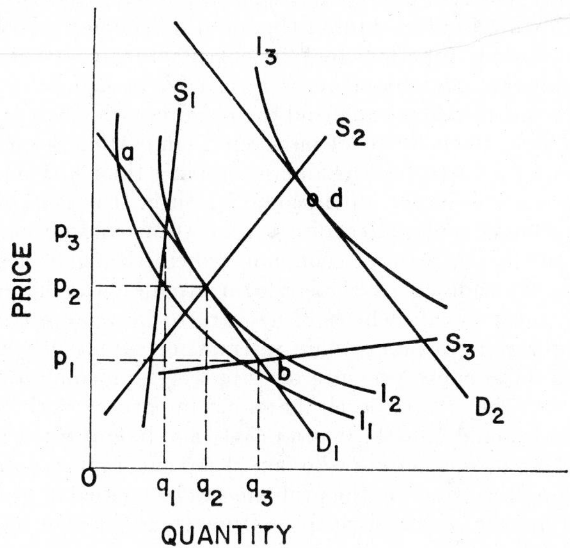

Fig. 4.6. Optimum Supply Elasticity.

smaller revenue curve I_2.) If the supply function is S_2, with output of oq_2 and price of op_2, revenue is maximized. If, however, supply is more elastic, as represented by S_3, the lower price of op_1 and greater output of oq_3 fetch smaller revenues. This also is true for less elastic supply functions such as S_1, where output of oq_1 and price of op_3 denote intersection of D_1 by revenue curves of smaller value than I_2. Even with an increase in demand, revenue will not necessarily increase most by causing supply to remain of low elasticity. For example, with increase in demand to D_2, revenue would be smaller if output followed along S_1 rather than S_2. In the new short run, a supply function is required which intersects point d if revenue is to be maximized.

Rate of Supply Modification

Nations faced with problems in modification of supply functions have two major sets of variables which can be altered: prices or supplies of factors and magnitudes of technical coefficients. In India the question is: How rapidly can supply elasticities be increased and functions shifted to the right to keep up with growth in population and to keep food prices at reasonable level for consumers? In the U.S. the question under surplus and high government support prices has been: How long is the period required before substitution of other mechanisms for high supports can draw the supply function back to level that prices and factor returns can be in magnitudes consistent with resource earnings in other sectors? A parallel question is: How low is the elasticity of the short-run food supply function and how drastically would prices fall, and how much time would be required for important recovery of prices, if control of commodity supply and resource commitment were relegated completely to the market? More fundamentally, the question is one of the extent and rate to which supply functions for particular factors in agriculture might be shifted leftward and/or made more elastic. It also is a question of the costs of relocation for people and the resources which attach to them. It is a problem of the persistence of resources in particular physical form to remain in agriculture and production during their life, because they have no other use of important monetary return. It is a set of problems readily solved over several decades or generations and perhaps of small concern in the long stream of economic growth. But it is a problem of important magnitude to particular farm families who have small resources and must decide whether they are to be among those in exit from the industry in bringing about restraint on supply or whether they are to remain and cause pressure on supply. The income increment or decrement that they realize in either case is important to them, if not to students of economic growth. It is a problem of important magnitude to farmers with greater resources who face sharp cuts in income and capital values. In the over-all sense, the problem can be tackled in cold scientific detachment as the small deviations from trend in centuries-directed economic development. Or it can be tackled in closer attachment to actual families with real aspirations and to human concerns. Both are required in the real world, whether the supply problems at hand arise in economics of low development such as India or high development such as the United States.

RATES AND TYPES OF SUPPLY CHANGE

The income problems of commodity cycles arise because the supply function of short runs are highly elastic for individual commodities. The industry income problems of agriculture under economic development arise because elasticities of short runs are low for agricultural output in aggregate. Short-run elasticity for the individual commodity is high because resources are easily adapted among individual enterprises and the supply function of resources to the product is highly elastic. Land, cultivators and manpower have great adaptability between corn and soybeans. Feed grains are readily shifted among livestock enterprises, and the elasticity of substitution of combines, soil and tractor fuel are highly constant between wheat and grain sorghum. The reward to land for growing corn cannot be lowered far before this resource and its technical complements will be shifted to soybeans. But just as the resources are highly adaptable and factor supply elasticity great for interproduct shift of resources within agriculture, the opposite holds true for agriculture in aggregate. The one problem exists because, given the expectation models used for products with discrete production periods, commodity supply has great elasticity; the other problem exists because commodity supply elasticity is so low.

The difference of adaptability of resources among commodities and between farm and nonfarm products can be better illustrated by this simple example. Suppose a production function for each of n commodities of the general form in (4.37), where Q_i is output of the ith commodity and X_i is the amount of given resource mix used for it. The corresponding resource requirements equation is (4.38).

$$Q_i = a_i X_i^{b_i} \tag{4.37}$$

$$X_i = a_i^{-1/b_i} Q_i^{1/b_i} \tag{4.38}$$

With $\overline{X}$ quantity of resource available, the production possibility curve is (4.39) for two commodities, and the marginal rate of product substitution is (4.40).

$$Q_1 = a_1 \overline{X}^{b_1} - a_1 a_2^{-b_1/b_2} Q_2^{b_1/b_2} \tag{4.39}$$

$$\frac{dQ_1}{dQ_2} = - b_1 b_2^{-1} a_1 a_2^{-b_1/b_2} Q_2^{b_1/b_2 - 1} \tag{4.40}$$

If the $b_i = 1.0$, the substitution rate will equal $a_1 a_2^{-1}$, a constant, with the magnitude depending on the two coefficients.[21] If $b_i \neq 1.0$, the rate of product substitution will not be constant and will change depending on the amount of the fixed collection of resources allocated to each product. But over farms and without major restraint on resource quantity, the derived production possibility curve has a form similar to that in Figure 4.7a for farm commodities which do not exhaust the land area adapted to them. It has form as in Figure 4.7c, where the area of adapted land is limited. (If it is extremely limited in particular soil type but other soils also can be used, the production possibility curve will have even greater curvature.) The production possibility curve for transfer of resources between agriculture and nonagricultural activity also can be constant over a wide range, but the marginal rate of substitution is low, as in Figure 4.7b, when it refers to machinery, buildings and land already in agriculture. In Figure 4.7a the reservation price ratio for product 1 is

---

[21] The statements applied to the particular form of production function apply similarly to any other form with

$$\frac{dQ_i}{dQ_j} = - \frac{dQ_i}{dX_j} \Big/ \frac{dQ_i}{dX_i}$$

represented by the slope of p_1p_2, the price of product 1 needing to be high enough relative to price of product 2 to cause the isorevenue line to have slope less than p_1p_2, before resources will be shifted to product 1. But for farm commodity against nonfarm commodity, the price of farm product needed to cause resources to be used for the former rather than for industrial product can be much lower. As indicated in Figure 4.7b, the isorevenue curve with slope greater than p_3p_4 is one with a low price of farm commodity relative to nonfarm commodity.[22]

Individual Commodity Supply Elasticity

Examination of supply functions for individual commodities, capable of empirical measurement without confounding of other structural changes as in long-run functions, indicates that farmers do respond to realized and expected commodity and factor prices and changes in the production function. Further, while short-run response to price change is relatively high, long-run elasticity is even higher, as expected from theory. For major commodities available, data allow estimation of response functions such as that in (4.41), after (4.32), where Q_t is U.S. spring hog farrowings in year t, and P_h, P_c and P_b are prices of hogs, corn and beef in year $t-1$.[23]

$$(4.41) \qquad Q_t = -3873 + 297P_h/P_c - 93P_b/P_h + .22\,Q_{t-1}$$

With observations in original quantities (millions), β in the equation is .78, and the direct short-run elasticity of hog farrowings in respect to price, computed at the arithmetic mean of the period 1938–56, is .65. Other commodities with longer production periods indicate similar elasticity of response, as against price of the commodity and other enter-

[22] If we were talking about resources as steel and lumber, rather than discs or farmers, the production possibility curve for Figure *b* would have much less slope, and a greater price of farm product relative to nonfarm product would be needed to bid their use to agriculture. We have used extreme examples of substitution, although the production possibility curve is linear over important ranges of interproduct allocation of resources. But considering different qualities of resources, and different products in aggregate sectors for which resources can be used, the production possibility curve in both cases will have some curvature as in *C*. As the curvature of production possibilities increases, the marginal rate of product substitution also changes more rapidly. The elasticity of supply of one commodity, against its own price, will be affected accordingly. This point perhaps should have been emphasized in text equations of supply functions of single commodities. However, we did not include price variables for competing commodities in order to keep the steps simple and to keep emphasis on the "aggregate farm product."

[23] See Gerald W. Dean and Earl O. Heady, *Changes in Supply Functions and Elasticities in Hog Production*, Iowa Agr. Sta. Bul. 471.

A similar function computed for eggs over the period 1924–59 is that below, where P_e is eggs price, P_f is feed price, R is an index of technical change and Q_t now refers to egg output for the U.S. The short-run elasticity in respect to P_e/P_f is .184 and the long-run elasticity is $.184 \div (1 - .752) = .737$ where observations are in logarithms.

$$Q_t = -.91 + \underset{(.063)}{.184}\,P_e/P_f + \underset{(.068)}{.229}\,(P_e/P_f)_{t-1} + \underset{(.068)}{.410}\,R + \underset{(.085)}{.752}\,Q_{t-1}$$

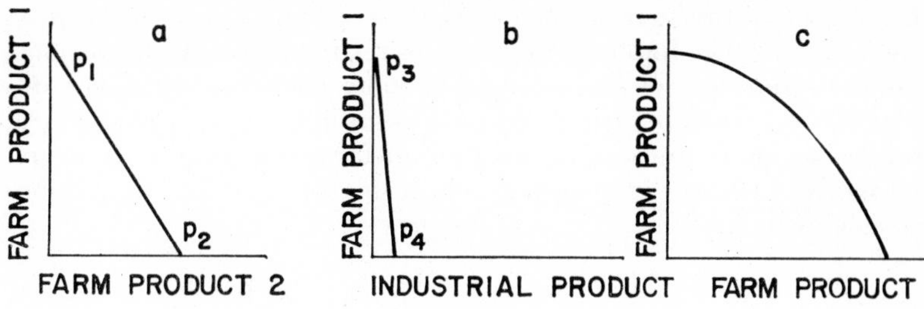

Fig. 4.7. Production Possibility Curves for Adjustment.

prises.[24] For example, Nekby found the short-run price elasticity (on own price) for animal food products to be .32. The corresponding long-run elasticity was 1.60. Against price of competing products, the short-run elasticity was −.14 and the long-run elasticity was −.68. There was less difference between short-run and long-run elasticities for fruits.[25] Farmers obviously are price and market oriented, even if less so than some corporation firms and the models of elementary texts. They reallocate resources with relative speed, depending on the production and payoff period dating from initial investment, among different commodities. And managerial acumen is increasing with greater market orientation. Regardless of increased scale of farm and product specialization, elasticity for the commodity is being maintained or increased. In the study cited above, for hots and the particular function, short-run supply elasticity to hog price increased from .46 to .65 between the periods 1924–37 to 1938–56.

Given the expectation models used so broadly by farmers, somewhat smaller elasticities of short-run supply response for individual commodities would lessen fluctuations in production, price and income. The extent of fluctuation in output and price for numerous commodities is too great for greatest benefit of both consumers and all producers. Particular types of price and storage policies would allow some of this instability to be removed, elasticities for individual commodities remaining high.

The Aggregate Function

The great adaptability of machines, buildings, land and labor, feed and other resources existing in agriculture among commodities, a cause of great supply elasticity for individual products, adds to the low elasticity of farm output in aggregate. This condition, and the fact that farm commodities are good substitutes in consumption for stomachs of limited capacity, causes surplus problems of one sector of agriculture soon to spill over into other sectors, or for supply, price and income problems to

[24] For example, see R. Barker, *Dairy Supply Functions*, Ph.D. Thesis, Iowa State University, Ames, 1960.

[25] B. Nekby, *The Structural Development of American Agriculture*, Ph.D. Thesis, Iowa State University, Ames, 1961. Also, see Marc Nerlove, *The Dynamics of Supply*, Johns Hopkins University Press, Baltimore, 1958.

be quite general to the industry rather than specific to the commodity. There are, of course, important exceptions resting on particular regional advantages and lack of substitutability among commodities. The difference which arises for various commodities is illustrated in Figure 4.8a, where S_a is a short-run supply function for farm commodities in aggregate, S_m is for a major crop such as wheat or corn and S_n is for a minor crop such as flax.[26]

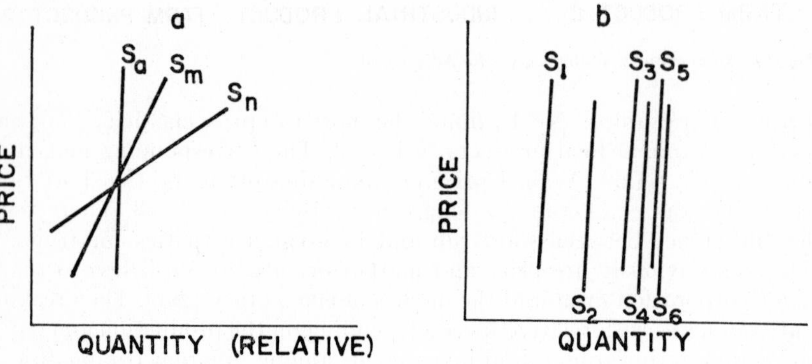

Fig. 4.8. Types of Short-Run Supply Functions.

In this setting, two price environments give response in output which causes the short-run aggregate supply function to appear to have zero elasticity or to be backward sloping. Both of these environments occur when a transitory increase in demand is withdrawn and farm commodity prices plummet relative to prices for factors from outside agriculture, but output is maintained or even increased. One has been experienced frequently following wars, with a parallel situation in major depressions. The other prevails, or might prevail, as governments withdraw or lower price supports, thus decreasing public demand for commodities in storage.

Again, if we look back to Figure 4.5, the major price decline in the early 1920's did not result in a commensurate decline in aggregate output if, in fact, output even declined as a result of price reduction. Neither did large price declines in the early 1930's, or in the 1950's, result in immediate or delayed downward trends in production. The effect of time in the immediate years of these periods was to cause output to follow the gradual upward trend. Under the usual formulation of supply models, lagged response of output to price decline is expected. But the lagged or delayed action of restrained production did not come about later in the 1920's, 1930's or 1950's. (The major declines in output were due to unfavorable weather and yields and not in planted acreage.) Production pushed upwards under less favorable price relatives even as labor inputs

[26] The same relative differences exist among commodities in extremely short-time spans when their production periods are different; with S_a referring to orchards, beef or range grass; S_m to beef, dairy or hogs; and S_n to broilers, peanuts or lettuce.

were decreased. This upward trend was due largely, of course, to new technology, or a remixing of the capital fund in agriculture, perhaps with a small substitution of present output for future output in the severe declines.

It appears that response to price had greater velocity, in expected direction, during periods of sharp upward swing in price, given sufficient lag for new investment and change in plans. An explanation behind the greater "upward" elasticity is provided in Figure 4.8b. With more favorable prices, or their expectation, farmers can bid more resources into agriculture from the input-furnishing industries, after sufficient lag to allow consolidation of investment decisions, to acquire or accumulate capital and to develop capital in the case of commodities such as beef or trees with longer transformation periods. The supply, for resources such as new tractors and similar physical items brought into agriculture, is relatively elastic. As a declining portion of the national economy, agriculture can easily bid more resources (as steel, tractors, lumber, barns, etc.) into the industry under favorable ratios, or readily slow down their acquisition under unfavorable prices. Since more resources can be drawn in with ease, short-run farm supply functions move rightward, with the speed or large jumps suggested by the difference among short-run aggregate supply functions S_1, S_2 and S_3. War periods especially have given demand and price spurts which were transitory. And agriculture has always shown great elasticity of supply during these expansion periods.

This was true in ancient times, with grasslands turned to grains in the twelfth century wars of England. It was equally true in the twentieth century wars of the U.S. where inputs were available for elastic expansion of output. But the contraction is a different problem. As prices turn unfavorably after demand decline, the multiperiod resources are already in agriculture. Their supply function has little elasticity. Hence, while new purchases are checked, used ones remain and output still expands as indicated by the smaller difference or jumps between S_3, S_4, S_5 and S_6. New technology in seeds, fertilizer and rations allows the addition; but so does the change in structure of agriculture growing out of decline in farm operators and labor force, the consolidation of farms and the market transfer of fixed resources into the hands of farmers with greater managerial and capital resources. Too, in this complex of rapid increase under favorable prices and continued (if slackened) shift under less favorable prices, capital accumulation and equity position favor it. With higher prices, farmers' savings and equity position increases, improving their capital position and lowering the degree of uncertainty so they can more readily add durable capital items and invest in new technology.[27] Too, those who remain after the initial impact of price decline are in capital position to apply better technology than those who release resources and leave the industry.

---

[27] For details on these points see Earl O. Heady, *Economics of Agriculture Production and Resource Use,* Prentice-Hall, New York, 1952, Chaps. 15 to 17.

Response to Price

Agriculture does respond to price in both directions. But the structure of production and supply functions for resource services and the changes in prices of these factor services cover up much of this response in the aggregate data under technological advance. (The resource service production function is one wherein services flow forth whether or not the factor is used, and cannot be captured at a later time if they are not used.) Farm employment has declined rapidly in confrontation with (1) declining farm income and favorable employment opportunity elsewhere and (2) favorable prices of farm machinery. Purchases of fertilizer have had temporary dips from the upward trend (a trend due to greater knowledge of response) in periods of highly unfavorable price relatives. The complex of commodity and resource prices within and outside agriculture caused the amount of land in farms to decrease by nearly a third between 1920 and 1960 in the four states of Massachusetts, Connecticut, Rhode Island and New York.

As mentioned previously, if technology brought low-cost and palatable substitutes for farm foods, with the real price of farm commodities dropping drastically, farm output and inputs would decline. But the extent of price decline and the length of time required for resources to withdraw in an extent allowing rebound of returns to levels of other economic sectors is the basic question of agricultural supply. It was obvious and necessary, under the rate of surplus accumulation and the mounting of public storage and program cost in the 1950's, that the price to which supply responds be geared closer to that corresponding with consumer preferences over the aggregate mix of goods in the economy. Price supports in the structure of the 1950's did not solve the problem of output to which they were directed; they only increased it, not only in the manner prescribed by theory in level of price, but also because they had an effect in increasing certainty of price expectations and farmers' willingness to commit resources to new technology. They did not come to grips with the basic problem of factor supply. Product supply in the short run would have been caused to increase in elasticity and decrease in magnitude more by public purchase of second-hand tractors, barns and labor services. (This is a possible compensation means consistent with the principles outlined in Chapters 8 to 11.) Supply elasticity and reservation prices of these resources to agriculture would then have increased.

While it is true that agriculture in aggregate does respond to price and that supply elasticity could be improved by certain market improvements and institutional changes, the competitive nature of the industry and the pressure for individual firms to innovate and adopt technical improvement, as their main control in income improvement, complicates the problem and represents a tempo not easily arrested. The historic persistence of low returns in agriculture relative to other industries, both worldwide and over many decades, underscores that the "length of run" is indeed lengthy. Land without industrial or urban employment opportunity will remain in agricultural use as long as its net marginal return is greater than zero (or greater than taxes), although it may shift to crops with smaller cash costs. In the short run, it even tends to hang in the same crop.

Two studies relate to the extent of inelasticity in short-run response and "shake down" in price which might be expected in a near future period, before sizeable response in output and resource structure could be realized. An Iowa study estimates that if price supports were withdrawn and surplus stocks were immobilized, the effect over two years would be price declines of around 40 percent for feed grains and livestock, with some increase in output under abandonment of production controls.[28] The two years would be a true "shake down" period, with prices, production and inputs recovering direction with some lag. Over a two-year period, from 1959–60 to 1962–63, hog prices were projected to decline from $15.70 to $11.00, beef cattle from $23.00 to $12.00, eggs from 31.50 to 28.3 cents, milk from $4.05 to $2.67, corn from $1.13 to .60, wheat from $1.72 to .74 and cotton from 35 to 21 cents. Prices existing in the latter period would be sub-equilibrium in the sense that they serve as "shake down" levels, with some adjustment taking place over a longer period of time. Income of agriculture would decline greatly since cash costs initially would remain near existing levels. Total cultivated acreage would adjust but little remaining nearly at levels of the earlier period. Income would drop also under the estimates explained below, except more farmers would have moved out and some improvement would take place in income per farm family.

Two joint committees of Congress suggest the extent of recovery in a period as long as five years.[29] Under these estimates, prices in 1965 would decline by the following percentage from 1959: hogs by 23, broilers by 30, corn by 38, wheat by 50, cotton by 35, rice by 30 and milk by 12. Supply would still be so large at these prices that, on average, returns to resources in agriculture would be lower than in 1959, and much lower than for other occupations, given the resource prices in agriculture at the outset. More needs to be known empirically about long-run supply elasticity, the above studies resting on projections of scant knowledge. However, belief of low elasticity in the short-run period is widespread.[30]

The burning policy question relating to these supply quantities is: How much time must elapse before supply and resource structure adjust "downward" to allow comparable resource returns? Accompanying questions of no less importance are: Which strata of agriculture would

[28] G. Shepherd, Arnold Paulson, *et al.*, *Production Price and Income Estimates and Projections for the Feed-Livestock Economy Under Specified Control and Market-Clearing Conditions*, Special Report No. 27, Iowa Agr. and Home Econ. Exp. Sta.

[29] See *Economic Policies for Agriculture in the 1960's, Implications of Four Selected Alternatives*, Joint Economic Committee of Congress, Washington, D.C., 1960, pp. 38–40. Also, see Senate Document 77, 86th Congress, 2nd Session, Jan. 20, 1960.

[30] *Cf.* M. R. Benedict and E. K. Bauer, *Farm Surpluses: U.S. Burden or World Asset*, Univ. of Calif. Div. of Agr. Sci., 1960, p. 90; and J. H. Alder, *Stabilization Policy in Primary Producing Countries*, Kyklos, Vol. 11, p. 157.

bear the cost of the "shake down?" To what extent, and in which manner, could they be compensated, equitably and acceptably? How could resources released be best guided to employment advantageous to themselves, and the preferences of consumers and national goals or responsibilities? The time period required for adjustment depends, of course, on the market and policy environment provided to guide adjustment. The policy question is not so much, given low short-run elasticity, whether elasticity of supply has sufficient long-run magnitude to bring resource use and output into rough conformance with consumer wishes, but rather one of how transition from a surplus situation such as that of the early 1960's might be made without throwing an inequitable portion of the cost of adjustment into the laps of particular farm families. To turn prices abruptly loose in the market would accomplish this transfer, but with bankruptcy of many families. The important social question is more nearly: Does a democratic society have other less painful means of solving a major structural maladjustment?

The basic U.S. problem in commercial agriculture cannot be solved by price, storage and production policies of the nature used over the three decades 1930–60. These suppose too nearly that the situation is temporary and the rate of increase in supply will slow down, to be overtaken by increase in demand. They are temporary in the sense that they could not be expected to be sensible for an agriculture with two decades ahead when it can extend supply beyond domestic demand. At the outset of this chapter we mentioned that commodity supply was only the superficial, the directly apparent, problem of agriculture. Problems of commodity supply are fundamentally those of resource supply. Hence, we turn in this direction for better understanding of the phenomena underlying the problems of commercial agriculture.

5

Supply, Market Power and Return of Resources

ANALYSIS OF GLOBAL AND HISTORIC DATA leads to the conclusion that return to agricultural labor remains more or less chronically depressed below that of other sectors under continued economic growth. We found this condition to prevail because of two major reasons: the tendency in highly developed economies for supply to grow more rapidly than food demand, and the low elasticity of short-run supply in respect to commodity price. But the commodity supply function doesn't "just happen." Its existence and nature rest almost entirely on resources: the nature of the (1) production function for resources, (2) resource supply functions, (3) price structures of resources and (4) technology representing transformation of resources into commodities. If the coefficients relating to these relationships of resources are known, then the commodity supply function is largely known, given the human agent and its goals and strategies in using resources.

We must examine the nature of resource production and supply functions and their pricing in order to take the step to commodity supply. Still, the path isn't "one way." Commodity supply, when put against commodity demand, leads to the marginal value productivity and demand for resources. Too, it thus relates to the return of resources. We must unravel this complex if we wish to prescribe commodity supply which does not cause persistent depression of factor returns in agriculture relative to other sectors. Supply which grows faster than food demand is not per se an unequivocal reason why resource returns must be low; neither is low elasticity of commodity supply. Resource returns could be as high under these conditions as under their opposite. The reason they are not rests on the structural or behavioral relations surrounding the resources themselves. Hence, our first task in this chapter is to "unravel the system," stretching from resource to commodity supply and back again to resource returns, with some degree of detail and refinement but not in degree of manipulation which overburdens the subject matter. Then we examine some of the particular supply conditions surrounding these resources, with emphasis on labor.

Laborers are farm operators and consumers—the reason that impact of economic growth on agriculture is of human concern. If all farm resources were inanimate, we could restrict analysis and policy to cold views of economic development in the long stretch of history and materials. We could concern ourselves only with quantities of resource, labor in this case, which might be manipulated. But for each labor input diminution or expansion involved, the decision or migration of a person and family is concerned. It isn't neutral or passive, as is the capital which serves as substitute or complement for it. Lack of communication between economists and people or politicians often arises for this reason. People who make up the magnitude of the X_i don't view it in this degree of abstraction. Even though they do react, in general, in the manner and approximate magnitude of coefficients which can be used for operation on the X_i, the change in the magnitude for a region or the U.S. requires tearing people loose from their moorings. To some, this is pleasant. And to some it is the opposite. We do turn to some abstractions, not in lack of sensitive regard for human resources which must shift to bring changes in marginal and price quantities, but to indicate the quantities important in earnings where resources may lack mobility or supply elasticity because of human or other attachment to occupation and location.

FACTOR SUPPLY IN RELATION TO RETURNS

The effect of factor immobility on its own price, and hence on the magnitude of the supply function and tendency towards constancy in output, was mentioned in the previous chapter. We now illustrate more precisely the path between resource supply elasticity and commodity price, and then back to resource return.

The marginal value productivity and money return of a resource can be maintained if resource quantity responds sufficiently to the conditions of commodity demand and factor pricing which surround it. As a first simple example illustrating these possible interrelationships, we use the production function in (1.1) and the commodity demand function in (5.1).

$$Q_d = cP^{-e} \tag{5.1}$$

$$Q_1 = \pi K^b \tag{5.2}$$

$$P_1 = (\pi^{-1} c K^{-b})^{e^{-1}} \tag{5.3}$$

$$MVP_1 = b(\pi^{e-1} c K^{eb-e-b})^{e^{-1}} \tag{5.4}$$

As an extreme in resource mobility or supply response, suppose that resource quantity is originally fixed at $X=K$. The corresponding supply or quantity of product then is (5.2), since we initially suppose supply elasticity of resources is zero, the resource used at whatever return realized. Hence, the commodity equilibrium price is (5.3) and the marginal value productivity of resources is (5.4), obtained by multiplying the price of (5.3) by the marginal physical product—the derivative of (1.1). If now demand increases to the proportion λ of original (5.1) and the production function is similarly increased by multiplying the original function by Γ, the corresponding static supply quantity and equilibrium commodity price are respectively (5.5) and (5.6). The new marginal value product then becomes that of (5.7).

$$Q_2 = \Gamma Q_1 \tag{5.5}$$

$$P_2 = \lambda^{1/e}\Gamma^{-1/e}P_1 \tag{5.6}$$

$$MVP_2 = \lambda^{1/e}\Gamma^{(e-1)/e}MVP_1 \tag{5.7}$$

The latter quantity will now decrease if the shifter for technology or the production function is great relative to the shifter for the demand function. Marginal value productivity of a given quantity of resources will remain at the previous level if the technology or production shifter is of the magnitude in (5.8). (See discussion of equation (7.8) where numerical elasticities are used.) If it is larger than this, marginal value productivity of the given quantity of resources will decline.

$$\Gamma = \lambda^{1/(1-e)} \tag{5.8}$$

$$X = (\lambda^{-1}\Gamma^{1-e})^{1/(eb-e-b)}K \tag{5.9}$$

Even though marginal value productivity for a given quantity of resources does decline, the marginal value product of resources can be maintained, of course, by decreasing their quantity.

How large must the quantity, X, of resources be after increase in demand and production functions, if the marginal value productivity of remaining resources is not to decline? It must decline to the magnitude or proportion of K, indicated in (5.9). Here, then, we have the proportion of resources to be retained in the industry as a function of commodity demand elasticity and the rate of increase in the demand and production functions.

Similarly, if the quantity of resources remains at K, the resulting value productivity or average resource returns also is a function of the elasticities and the supply and demand shifters. Table 5.1 includes, for the example under discussion, the (1) magnitude of marginal value product if resources remain at K quantity and (2) the proportion by which resource input must change if marginal value productivity is not to decline, for selected magnitudes of elasticities and structural shifters. For all of these situations we suppose the production elasticity in (5.2) to be .4, or $b=.4$. When the multipliers of the production and demand func-

TABLE 5.1

EFFECT OF PRICE ELASTICITY OF DEMAND AND SUPPLY AND DEMAND SHIFTS ON MARGINAL RESOURCE PRODUCTIVITY AND INPUT MAGNITUDE

Demand Elasticity (Price)	Magnitude of Marginal Value Product With Resources Input Constant at K		Magnitude of Resource Input To Maintain Marginal Value Product	
	$\Gamma=1.25, \lambda=1.25$ (Input$=K$)	$\Gamma=1.25, \lambda=1.18$ (Input$=K$)	$\Gamma=1.25, \lambda=1.25$	$\Gamma=1.25, \lambda=1.18$
.1	1.25 MVP_1	.70 MVP_1	1.05 K	.93 K
.2	1.25 MVP_1	.94 MVP_1	1.09 K	.97 K
.4	1.25 MVP_1	1.08 MVP_1	1.16 K	1.05 K

tions are equal, $\Gamma=\lambda$, the marginal value product for K quantity of resources increases to a corresponding magnitude of the original magnitude. For example, with Γ and λ both equal to 1.25, the new marginal value product is 1.25 proportion of the original marginal value productivity. The marginal value productivity increases because commodity price has remained constant but physical resource productivity has increased. However, when the production function is increased by 1.25 proportion but the demand functions by only 1.18 proportion, the marginal value productivity takes on different values, depending on demand elasticity. With a price elasticity of only .1, the marginal productivity of K magnitude of resource is only .7 as great as originally when production and demand functions were those in (5.1) and (5.2). With an elasticity of .2, the marginal value productivity of K inputs is only .94 of the original for $\Gamma=1.25$ and $\lambda=1.18$. But with demand elasticity at .4, marginal value productivity increases above the original level.

Now examining the magnitude of resource necessary, after shift of the production and supply functions, to maintain marginal value productivity at the original level, we find that input could actually increase regardless of demand elasticity when $\Gamma=\lambda$ or the two shifters are of the same magnitude. However, when the increase for the production function exceeds that for the demand function, the magnitude of input must be changed, if the marginal value productivity is to be equal to the original magnitude with input at K level. With demand elasticity of .1 and .2, input must decline to .93 K and .97 K levels respectively. Otherwise, if it remains at K level, the marginal value products drops to .70 or .94 proportions of original level respectively. If, however, demand elasticity is .4, the amount of resource can increase to 1.05 K level, marginal value product remaining at the original level. The latter increase is possible, even under an inelastic commodity demand and increase in production which is greater than increase in demand.

Obviously, from the above, the effect of structural change on resource returns, or the quantity of resources necessary to maintain a given return, depends upon the rate of change in technology, commodity demand and the relative elasticities attaching to these relationships. Evidently, in American agriculture, the marginal value productivity of resources "fixed to agriculture in the short run" has declined even with an increase in their physical productivity, due to the low price elasticity of demand and a rate of technical change which has been great relative to the change in demand. Even under these conditions, marginal value productivity could be maintained by a decrease in inputs. In Table 5.1, for example, with an increase in the production function to 1.25 proportion and in demand to 1.18 proportion with demand price elasticity at only .1 level, marginal productivity could be maintained if input declined to .93 proportion of original K level. This is, of course, the problem of broad sectors of American agriculture.

Rate of change in production and demand functions and magnitudes of elasticities were such that return on labor and specialized capital of inelastic supply began declining in the 1950's.[1] To maintain previous levels, or to keep returns moving up with those in other sectors under economic development, diminution in quantity becomes necessary unless compensation price policies are applied which offset the relative differences in increase of demand and supply and the inelasticity of factor supply. A policy of this nature can increase or maintain returns to resources, but it does not overcome the problem of low resource supply elasticity.

An alternative in maintaining resource returns is to increase elasticity of resource supply. The possibility here is illustrated in Table 5.2, where the production function is $Q_p=\pi X^{.4}$ and the demand function is $Q_d=cP^{-.4}$ for all situations, with these quantities being multiplied respectively by Γ and λ proportions to represent change for the bottom half of the table. We use four conditions of factor supply elasticity, with each being compared with itself before and after change. In the first case it is zero, with supply fixed at K. In two other cases, own price elasticity of resource supply is .1 and .5. In the final case, elasticity is infinite and the industry can obtain an unlimited quantity of resource at the economy-wide price of P_x. As the column of resource prices indicates, increase of technology by Γ and of demand by λ causes factor price to decline more for the situation where factor supply is less elastic, and to decline less in situations where factor supply is more elastic. In the case where factor supply is infinite, factor price is at level P_{x1} both before and after change in demand and technology. Conversely, the change in factor input where Γ is large relative to λ, is greatest for larger factor supply elasticity and smallest for lower elasticity. In the case of perfectly inelastic factor

[1] To keep the example simple, the Γ proportionate change in the production function was supposed without cost attached to it. Of course, technology does not change apart from costs. Had these costs been added in, as they are at a later point, the net value marginal productivities could be maintained only with resource adjustments somewhat larger than those suggested in the text example. Had we considered average return to the resource, the conditions would have been as follows for K quantity of resources and the functions of (5.1) and (5.2). The average return under the original situation is R_1 and under the change of production and demand functions is $R_2=(\Gamma^{\epsilon-1}\lambda)^{1/e}R_1$. Hence, the magnitude of change in resource input to maintain a given return per unit of resource is that indicated in the last column of Table 5.1 to maintain a given marginal productivity.

TABLE 5.2

EFFECT OF FACTOR SUPPLY ELASTICITY ON COMMODITY AND FACTOR PRICES AND FACTOR EMPLOYMENT

Factor Supply	Commodity Demand	Commodity Price	Factor Price	Factor Quantity
K	$cP^{-.4}$	$P_1 = \pi^{-2.5} c^{2.5} K^{-1}$	$P_{x1} = .4\pi^{-1.5} c^{2.5} K^{-1.6}$	$X_1 = K$
$wP_x^{.1}$	$cP^{-.4}$	$P_1 = 1.331 w^{-.8681} \pi^{-2.3707} c^{2.2845}$	$P_{x1} = .454\pi^{-1.2931} c^{2.1552} w^{-.7663}$	$X_1 = .962\pi^{-.1293} c^{.2155} w^{.8621}$
$wP_x^{.5}$	$cP^{-.4}$	$P_1 = 1.750 w^{-.5556} \pi^{-2.0833} c^{1.8056}$	$P_{x1} = .601\pi^{-.8334} c^{1.3889} w^{-.8889}$	$X_1 = .775\pi^{-.4167} c^{.6944} w^{.5556}$
∞	$cP^{-.4}$	$P_1 = 1.773\pi^{-1.5625} c^{.9375} P_x^{.6250}$	$P_{x1} = P_x$	$X_1 = .564\pi^{-.9375} c^{1.5625} P_x^{-.6250}$
K	$\lambda cP^{-.4}$	$P_2 = \Gamma^{-2.5} \lambda^{2.5} P_1$	$P_{x2} = \Gamma^{-1.5} \lambda^{2.5} P_{x1}$	$X_2 = X_1$
$wP_x^{.1}$	$\lambda cP^{-.4}$	$P_2 = \Gamma^{-2.3707} \lambda^{2.2845} P_1$	$P_{x2} = \Gamma^{-1.2931} \lambda^{2.1552} P_{x1}$	$X_2 = \Gamma^{-.1293} \lambda^{.2155} X_1$
$wP_x^{.5}$	$\lambda cP^{-.4}$	$P_2 = \Gamma^{-2.0833} \lambda^{1.8056} P_1$	$P_{x2} = \Gamma^{-.8334} \lambda^{1.3889} P_{x1}$	$X_2 = \Gamma^{-.4167} \lambda^{.6944} X_1$
∞	$\lambda cP^{-.4}$	$P_2 = \Gamma^{-1.5625} \lambda^{.9375} P_1$	$P_{x2} = P_{x1}$	$X_2 = \Gamma^{-.9375} \lambda^{1.5625} X_1$

supply, input remains at K, after change in both the production and demand functions by Γ and λ, and adjustment is in factor return or productivity. But in the opposite case, perfectly elastic factor supply at the economy-wide price, factor price remains at the same level and adjustment is in quantity of factor.

While the derived relationships are in the sense of static concepts, and for particular forms and magnitudes of relationships, they illustrate the possible and expected effect of factor supply elasticity upon the value return and magnitude of input. Too, it is evident that resource returns and employment in agriculture do parallel these conditions, with modification in time lag and other quantities relating to decisions and investment.

Magnitude of Input Under Change

Whether resources employed in an industry will expand or contract under economic growth depends particularly upon the demand elasticities for the commodity and the rate of technical or economic development within the industry. Looking back to Chapter 2, we see a tremendous increase in farm output over 30 years. Under constant technology, this increase would have required larger inputs of conventional form and would have favored high returns to them, with rewards in the short run greatest for resources with low supply elasticity. As Figure 2.8 illustrates, however, this greater output has come with a large decline in labor input, capital resources serving to substitute for labor. Input of particular capital forms has grown tremendously. However, as Table 2.13 indicates, the greater output of later periods has been possible with only a slight increase, or an almost constant quantity, of aggregate inputs.

These conditions, of a decline required in a particular input or of constancy in aggregate resource employment, do not favor high resource returns as would be true in the case where growth in commodity demand and slow rate of technical progress also required large increase in employment of resources. This is true especially when the resources which must be ejected from the industry lag in their response to price relatives and tend to be immobile in the short run. The immobility, as mentioned previously, causes supply to hang heavily over demand, depressing commodity prices and factor returns. In the food industry, this condition of low response elasticity of resources favors the consumer. Total expenditures for food at the farm level are less, under low price elasticities of commodity demand, than would hold true under great mobility of resources used for farming. In an undeveloped country where technical development of agriculture is tardy and population and per capita income are growing, growth in food demand would call for more resources in agriculture. If the elasticities of the production and factor supply functions were low, prices of food and expenditure on it at the farm level would grow. Resources would be drawn into agriculture and their real income would increase somewhat inversely to their supply elasticity.

As further illustration of the effect of economic development on resource employment and income in an industry such as agriculture, we refer again to the production function in (1.1) and the demand function in (5.1). The corresponding supply function is (5.10), where P_x is factor price and P is commodity price. The equilibrium price is (5.11) and the corresponding static equilibrium resource input is (5.12).

(5.10) $$Q_s = (b\pi^{b^{-1}} P_x^{-1} P)^{b/(1-b)}$$

(5.11) $$P = (b^{-b} c^{1-b} \pi^{-1} P_x^{b})^{1/(b+e-eb)}$$

(5.12) $$X_1 = (b^{e} c \pi^{e-1} P_x^{-e})^{1/(b+e-eb)}$$

If increase in supply amounts to multiplication of the production function by Γ and the demand function by λ, the new equilibrium in resource input, X_2, is that in (5.13).

(5.13) $$X_2 = (\Gamma^{e-1}\lambda)^{1/(b+e-eb)} X_1$$

Now, if under change in technology and shift in demand, input is not to decline, the multiple of the production function must bear the relationship in (5.8) to the demand shifter. Factor input must decline, with increase in demand and change in technology, if the technology shifter exceeds the demand shifter raised to the power $(1\text{-}e)^{-1}$. If e, demand elasticity, is large, the value of Γ can be great; if e is small, Γ must be smaller if input is not to decline under orthodox market equilibrium. Hence, under change of demand and economic development, the total quantity of resources to be retained will depend on the elasticity of demand as well as the rate at which demand and production shifts.

Table 5.3 indicates the effect of these magnitudes, for the particular functional forms, on the equilibrium quantity of resource after change in technology and demand. With a price elasticity of demand of only .1, the production function can shift only at the rate $\Gamma = 1.112$, if demand shifts at the rate $\lambda = 1.10$ and resource input is not to decline. For demand elasticity at .9, technology can shift at the rate 2.594 with $\lambda = 1.10$ and decline in resource employment does not occur. However, if Γ is greater than 2.594, with $\lambda = 1.10$, resource employment must decline if factor supply has some elasticity and return to the factor is not to decline. With a high rate of population and demand growth, $\lambda = 1.25$, and a large price elasticity, $e = .9$, the shifter for the production function could be as great as 9.313 without causing a diminution in resource employment. For values of Γ greater than 9.313, resources would be ejected from the industry, but for values of Γ smaller than 9.313 resources would be drawn into the industry. With values of Γ greater than that allowed by the demand elasticity and shifter, resources could be freed from the industry. Of course, if they are relatively immobile, the process of freeing them will cause them to be surplus in the industry, with a larger total output and a smaller marginal value product per unit of resources, as compared to a situation where their supply is highly elastic to the industry.

TABLE 5.3

EFFECT OF DEMAND ELASTICITY AND RATE OF DEMAND SHIFT ON STATIC EQUILIBRIUM OF RESOURCE INPUT (FIGURE IN CELL INDICATES VALUE FOR Γ IF INPUT IS TO REMAIN UNCHANGED)

Value of Demand Elasticity, e	Value of Demand Shifter, λ				
	1.05	1.10	1.15	1.20	1.25
.1	1.056	1.112	1.168	1.227	1.281
.3	1.073	1.146	1.221	1.298	1.376
.5	1.103	1.210	1.322	1.440	1.562
.7	1.176	1.373	1.592	1.835	2.102
.9	1.626	2.594	4.046	6.192	9.313

In an aggregate sense, change in technology of American agriculture has been fast enough, given the low price elasticity of commodity demand, to allow food "requirements" of a growing population to be met with almost a constant level of aggregate input over the years 1940–60. In fact, had labor withdrawn in the industry to an extent allowing returns equal to levels of nonfarm sectors, and to the extent of the farm organizational possibilities that exist, aggregate measure of input in Table 2.13 might show a clear-cut decline. But the underlying problem of American agriculture under economic growth is more than a rate of change in technology which exceeds the rate of growth in demand, or even of rates of changes wherein demand for aggregate inputs remains almost constant while output and commodity demand grows. It is one wherein requirements and demand for labor decline by large absolute amounts but labor supply elasticity to agriculture remains low in relation to rate of change in productivity. The problem is aggravated by the fact that technological improvement increases the marginal rate of substitution of capital for labor in agriculture, the change in substitution rate and the relative price of labor and capital both favoring the replacement of labor by capital over time.

These effects can be illustrated by the demand function in (5.1) where we assign the price elasticity of demand $e = .2$ and the industry production function is (5.14) where we suppose Z to be input of one resource and X to be input of another. (For explanation of the method see the footnote on page 21 referring to equations 1.1–1.5.)

$$(5.14) \qquad Q_p = rZ^{.4}X^{.4}$$

$$(5.15) \qquad Q_s = .0256r^5P_x^{-2}P_z^{-2}P^4$$

With P_x, P_z and P being the prices respectively for X, Z and commodity, the static supply function is (5.15).[2] The equilibrium price and

[2] Equation (5.15) has been derived by computing the isocline equation $Z = P_xP_z^{-1}X$ and substituting this into (5.16). X has then been derived as $X = r^{-1.25}P_x^{-.5}P_z^{.5}Q_p^{1.25}$. These values of X and Z are substituted into the cost function $C = P_xX + P_zZ$, to express cost as a function of output and derive supply accordingly.

TABLE 5.4

LEVELS OF PRICE, OUTPUT, INPUTS AND REVENUE AFTER CHANGE IN TECHNOLOGY AND DEMAND (WITH $c=.48$, $r=2$, $P_x=\$2$ and $P_z=\$4$)*

Value of:		Equilibrium Price	Equilibrium Output	Equilibrium Input of:		
Γ	λ	P	Q	Z	X	Revenue
1.0	1.0	2.370	.404	.096	.191	.957
1.2	1.1	2.082	.445	.092	.237	.926

* The first line refers to the original demand and production function in (5.14) where $\Gamma=1.0$ and $\lambda=1.0$ and both elasticities of production are .4. The second line refers to the new situation in (5.20) and (5.21) where $\Gamma=1.1$ and $\lambda=1.2$.

outputs are (5.16) and (5.17) while the equilibrium inputs are (5.18) and (5.19) respectively. Their values are in the first row of Table 5.4 for specified quantities of factor prices and coefficients. Now, if technology changes to give the production function in (5.20), the marginal productivity of both factors increases and the marginal rate of substitution of X for Z also increases.

$$P = 2.3933c^{.2381}r^{-1.1905}P_x^{.4762}P_z^{.4762} \tag{5.16}$$

$$Q_s = .8399c^{.9524}r^{.2308}P_x^{-.0952}P_z^{-.0952} \tag{5.17}$$

$$X = .8041c^{1.1950}r^{-.9525}P_x^{-.6190}P_z^{.3810} \tag{5.18}$$

$$Z = P_xP_z^{-1}X \tag{5.19}$$

$$Q_p = \Gamma r Z^{.4}X^{.5} \tag{5.20}$$

$$Q_d = \lambda c P^{-.2} \tag{5.21}$$

With an increase in demand to that in (5.21), a new set of equations for equilibrium prices, outputs and inputs arise and parallel those for (5.16) through (5.19). The new quantities are expressed in the second row of Table 5.4 in numerical example where we have arbitrarily used the values $c=.48$, $r=2$, $P_x=\$2$ and $P_z=\$4$. For all cases we suppose that demand increases to $\lambda=1.1$, but technology improves to $\Gamma=1.2$ with the elasticity of X increasing to .5 as in (5.20). With the rate of "growth" in technology twice that of demand, the equilibrium price declines from 2.370 to 2.082 and output grows from .404 to .445. Input of Z declines from .096 to .092 while input of X increases from .191 to .237. The decline in magnitude of Z arises because both (1) the rate of increase in transformation of resources is large against an inelastic demand which increases at a smaller rate and (2) the marginal rate of substitution between factors has changed.

This is roughly the situation which has held true in U.S. agriculture, with labor input being comparable to Z and capital comparable to X. In addition, and in contrast to the example where factor prices are the same before and after the change, the price of labor has risen relative to capital items (Table 2.10), further encouraging the substitution of capital for labor. As in our example, not only has price and input of Z

declined, but total revenue is also less. In our illustration, however, we have supposed supply of Z to be sufficiently elastic that its marginal value productivity can remain at market price of the factor.

Unfortunately, elasticity is not this great in agriculture and labor returns tend to remain depressed. As our example shows, however, it would be possible for factor to maintain marginal productivity at "outside wage rate or price," even under inelastic demand, technology increasing faster than demand and marginal rate of substitution of capital for labor increasing. Even with decline in industry price and revenue, this would be possible if factor supply were sufficiently elastic.

FACTOR SUPPLY ELASTICITY, MONOPOLY POLICY, INPUT MAGNITUDE AND RESOURCE RETURNS

Level of commodity price is not a gauge of farm problems because it fails to take into account the rate at which resources are transformed into product or the prices of resources. Commodity prices can be low without an income problem to producers or an allocative problem to society, if transformation rates are large and factor prices are low. Conversely, an income and allocative problem can exist under high commodity price if transformation rates are low and factor prices are high.

We have seen that rates of increase in resource productivity which exceed rates of increase in demand need not lead to low resource returns. Even though it is necessary for resources to be ejected from an industry, as labor from agriculture, level of resource return can be maintained at the level of other industries if the rate of outflow is great or rapid enough. The outflow rate, of course, gives rise to a problem because, as noted before, people are not passive resources with lack of values and orientation to particular communities and occupations. It is this low elasticity of factor supply which causes commodity prices to fall to levels causing continuous short-run depression of resource return.

The problems of supply elasticity and low resource return have importance particularly in respect to labor. As noted previously, capital resources also take on low supply elasticity and remain in the industry at low returns once they have been committed to material forms unique to agricultural production. Still, if there were great enough flexibility in labor, the problem of low short-run supply elasticity for capital would be less critical. If reduction of labor input were of sufficient magnitude, output could be diminished and return to capital resources increased. As we have seen, such adaptation in short duration of time would require a drastic uprooting of labor in agriculture. Too, it is unlikely that the more normal rates of migration can easily lead to any prolonged reduction in output if, in fact, reduction is ever realized. Yet it is true that where problems of producer income and national allocative patterns revolve around the magnitude of resources employed in an industry, demand inelastic and given at a fairly stable level, the income problem has only two basic solutions: a reduction in product from the resources or a reduction in the quantity of resources. The first supposes some type of supply management or monopolistic production policy applied to the industry while the second supposes an attack on the mobility and supply elasticity of relevant resources. If all industries were organized optimally in terms of consumer sovereignty and free market equilibrium, monopolistic production policy would be consistent with greater farm income, but inconsistent with maximum consumer welfare. If, however, an important degree of monopolistic pricing and production policy exists elsewhere in the economy, consumer welfare need not be diminished by solution of low farm incomes and large resource commitment by use of monopolistic production policy. This is true only if resort to supply management and monopolistic production policy in agriculture causes resources to be allocated more nearly in the same productivity terms as other industries and if resources can remain fully employed.

If resources are allocated to and within agriculture in terms of marginal quantities based on average price or revenue and marginal physical productivity, while they are allocated to and within other sectors in terms of marginal quantities based on marginal revenue and marginal physical productivity, supply management or monopolistic production policy in agriculture could cause resource allocation to conform more nearly to consumer preference, providing, of course, that the same total level of resource employment is maintained. Hence, before final judgment can be made about the relevance of production control policy for agriculture, the extent of monopoly and its effect on resource employment in the rest of the economy must be gauged.

Agriculture is not the only industry with resource supplies of low elasticity. A parallel situation exists for petroleum and other industries, especially those with activity based on natural resource endowments. For example, the amount of petroleum available for exploitation, the supply quantity, is highly stable over a wide range of crude oil prices. The petroleum industry has tried to solve its problem of low factor supply elasticity, not by making petroleum deposits or supplies more elastic and causing them to "go away," but by certain formal and informal controls on resource inputs and commodity outputs.

The other avenue for solving income and allocative problems based on low factor supply elasticity, increasing the mobility of the resources, is consistent with general consumer welfare but may be inconsistent with the values and welfare of particular farm people. The extent to which this avenue is more relevant than monopoly policy for agriculture depends on (1) the magnitude of any conflict in utility attainment which may exist between these two groups, (2) the extent to which resource allocation in general is based on monopolistic or competitive pricing and (3) the extent to which compensation mechanisms are appropriate and acceptable in application so that while consumers in general gain, farm groups can be guaranteed against utility sacrifice.

We shall return to analysis of these alternatives in a later chapter. Meanwhile we continue our analysis of unique causes of low supply elasticity and return of agricultural resources. Thus far we have emphasized one cause of low factor supply elasticity, namely, conditions endogenous to the industry and relating to the unique physical, sociological and psychological attachments of farm resources. But resource commitment in a particular industry also may be large for reasons exogenous to the industry, and even in the face of high factor supply elasticity. This possibility would exist where major resource-employing sectors use monopoly pricing and production policies, while a minor part of the economy rests on competitive policy and must absorb resources excluded from monopoly sectors.

Monopoly and Competitive Effects in Resource Allocation and Returns

An exodus of labor has occurred in agriculture and will continue because of the three main reasons mentioned previously; (1) the rate at which resources are transformed into product has increased more rapidly than demand, (2) the production function has changed to increase the marginal rate of substitution of capital for labor and (3) the price of labor has increased relative to the price of capital, favoring substitution. Directly, people have moved out of agriculture because their incomes were low relative to possibilities from the same resources in other industries. But underneath, and while indirect but more fundamental, has been the complex of forces mentioned above. These forces, put against the low supply elasticity of labor to agriculture—relative to the demand for labor in farming—have caused price and resource incomes to be depressed below orthodox long-run equilibrium levels and to be less favorable than in other industries.

If the attack in solving the basic farm income problem is to be that of increased factor supply elasticity, another question must also be raised. Can other economic sectors absorb displaced farm labor as rapidly as it must be ejected from agriculture? The answer depends on the rate of economic growth and the extent of monopoly organization in nonfarm industry. Even with existence of some monopolistic organization, or oligopolistic structure leading to the same end, the rate of absorption of displaced farm labor could be high enough to boost resource returns in agriculture to comparable levels of other industries if rate of economic growth and employment creation were rapid enough. As we point out later, and over a longer period of time, the rate of national growth has particular importance to agriculture in future decades.

But let us return to the possible effect of monopoly and competitive structure on the level of resource prices and returns. To do so, let us suppose each of two industries with a commodity demand function defined by the price equation in (5.22), where Q is quantity and P is price of commodity. The production function of both industries also is identical as in (5.23). The marginal revenue equation, the derivative of the product of the price function and quantity, is (5.24).

$$P = a - .01Q \tag{5.22}$$

$$Q = 5X \tag{5.23}$$

$$MR = a - .02Q \tag{5.24}$$

$$\frac{dQ}{dX} = 5 \tag{5.25}$$

$$X_m = 10a - 2P_x \tag{5.26}$$

$$X_c = 20a - 4P_x \tag{5.27}$$

Multiplying marginal revenue (5.24) by marginal physical product (5.25), equating this quantity to P_x or resource price and solving for X, we obtain the monopoly industry resource demand function in (5.26). Multiplying average revenue (5.22) by (5.25) and proceeding similarly, we define resource demand for the competitive industry in (5.27). The total resource demand function, (5.26) plus (5.27), is (5.28).

$$X_t = 30a - 6P_x \tag{5.28}$$

$$X_s = 4P_x - 5a \tag{5.29}$$

$$P_x = 3.5a \tag{5.30}$$

With the factor supply equation in (5.29), we can equate supply and demand and solve for resource price as in (5.30).

With equilibrium price of $3.5a$ substituted into the factor demand equations, resource employment is $9a$ total, with $3a$ in the monopoly and $6a$ in the competitive industry. Hence, under these conditions, the resource would be priced at equal level to the two industries. It would, however, have an entirely different level of return. The average return per unit of resource is $3.5a$ in the competitive industry and $4.25a$ in the monopoly industry. The marginal value productivity of resources differs even more, being at level of $3.5a$ in the monopoly industry and $2a$ in the competitive industry. If both industries were competitive, the total factor demand equation would be (5.31) and equilibrium factor price would be at the higher level of $3.75a$.

$$\overline{X}_t = 40a - 8P_x \tag{5.31}$$

$$\pi = PQ - P_xX = 12.75a^2 - 10.5a^2 \tag{5.32}$$

The equilibrium input also would be larger, totaling $10a$, with $5a$ to each industry. Average and marginal revenue would be the same in both industries, amounting respectively to $3.75a$ and $2.5a$ per resource unit. Resource employment in the competitive industry would decrease between the two situations, from $6a$ to $5a$. Employment in the monopoly industry would increase from $3a$ to $5a$, and output would decline from $30a$

to $25a$. Average return in the competitive industry would increase from $3.5a$ to $3.75a$ while marginal return would increase from $2a$ to $2.5a$. At the same time average resource return is raised in the competitive industry, it would be lowered in the monopoly industry, with intersector comparability in resource returns brought about from change in both directions. There would be no pure profit in the competitive industry, its gross return being just equal to the quantity of resources multiplied by their market value. In contrast, the monopoly industry would have in the original situation, based on the profit equation of (5.32), a net or monopoly profit of $2.25a^2$, gross revenue exceeding the value of resources by this amount, with resources rewarded at the aggregate market rate.

We have examined a second set of economic phenomena which may cause resource employment to be large and returns to be low in an industry of pure competition, such as agriculture. Clearly the relatively lower returns and large employment of resources in the competitive sector under equations (5.27) and (5.29) are not due to low supply elasticity of resources in the competitive sector. For the equilibrium resource price of $3.5a$ and total resource quantity of $6a$, with return lower in the competitive sector, supply elasticity computed from (5.29) is 2.33, denoting a 2.33 percent change in quantity supplied for a 1 percent change in resource price. Accordingly, it is necessary that the possible role of industry organization be analyzed along with factor supply elasticity, in our attempt to explain the quantity and returns of resources in a competitive industry such as agriculture. Before we do so, however, we may ask whether, under mixed economic organization including both monopoly and competitive industries, transformation of the competitive industry into one of monopoly would solve the problem of resource return and input magnitude.

Returning to the example in equations (5.22) through (5.29), with an industry at each extreme of organization, we have this outcome. Transformation of the competitive industry to monopoly would give rise to two industries, each with the resource demand function in (5.26). The total resource demand then would be (5.33).

$$X_t = 20a - 4P_x \tag{5.33}$$

When equated with the factor supply equation, the resulting equilibrium price for factor is $3.125a$, an amount smaller than under-mixed organization because many fewer resources are employed. Total resource employment, with both industries organized as monopolies, is $7.5a$ with $3.75a$ in each industry. The industry marginal value product of resources is $3.125a$, now higher than originally ($2a$) for the otherwise competitive industry, but lower for the original monopoly industry. The average return per unit of resource, 4.06, is higher than the original quantity of $3.5a$ for the competitive industry and lower than the original $4.25a$ for the initial monopoly industry. There are, of course, fewer resources employed at this average return rate, $1.5a$ or 16.7 percent less. If we are concerned with total product, and aggregate the products of the two industries on equal basis, the original product under mixed organization is

45*a*, while it is 37.5*a* where both are organized as monopoly. Hence, an appropriate question is: Would the initial problem of relative resource employment and return in the two industries be better solved by converting the monopoly sector to competition, rather than the opposite? Converting both to competition would give average revenue of 3.5*a* to all resource units and result in 50*a* of total product. If, of course, it is impossible to convert the monopoly industry to competition, or if doing so brings about instability and firms too small for progress, the decision might then be otherwise.

We discussed an example where factor supply had high "own" price elasticity, mainly to show that level of resource employment and return also can present a problem even where factor quantity responds readily to price. Let us now examine the opposite, the same form of demand function where elasticity is at the other extreme as X_s in Figure 5.1. We again suppose two industries with identical demand curves for their products and with identical production functions. The marginal and average value productivities of resources for each industry are respectively X_m and X_c in Figure 5.1. In this case X_m is the demand function for resources by a monopoly industry; X_c is the demand curve under competition. We might suppose the factor to represent a resource such as labor which is largely fixed in short-run quantity and whose price is flexible.

If one industry is organized as monopoly and the other as competitive, total factor demand is X_1 (mixed organization), with employment at ox_2 in the monopoly industry and ox_4 in competitive industry. Average resource return is ov_4 in the former and ov_2 in the latter. Transformation of both to competition will expand total factor demand to X_2 (all industries competitive), with employment increasing to ox_3 in the previously monopolistic industry and decreasing to ox_3 in the original competitive industry. Average return per unit of resources will decline from ov_4 to ov_3 in the former monopoly industry, but increase from ov_2 to ov_3 in the original competitive industry.

Transforming both industries to monopoly pricing and production policy provides a total resource demand function X_c (all industries monopoly), with ox_3 resources employed in each industry, the same allocation as if both were converted to competitive. The average revenue also will be ov_3 for both, the same level as if both were competitive. Similarly, the marginal value productivity of resources will be the same, ov_1, if both industries are competitive, the same as if both were monopoly. The average return of the original competitive industry will be raised from ov_2 to ov_3 level, by converting all industries to either competition or monopoly. Similarly, resources employed in the original competitive industry will decline from ox_4 to ox_3 regardless of whether all industries are converted to pure monopoly or to pure competition. While the marginal value productivity of resources is ov_0 for the competitive industry under mixed organization, it rises to ov_1 under monopoly or competitive organization of all industries.

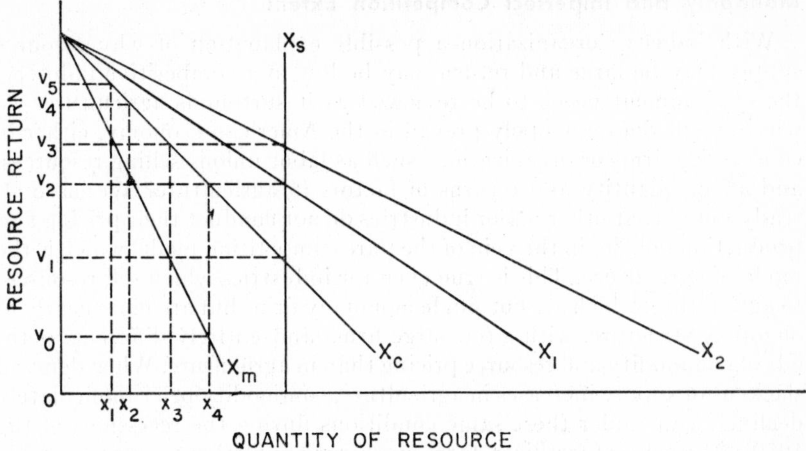

Fig. 5.1. Relation of Industry Organization to Resource Employment and Return.

Clearly, in the case of inelastic resource supplies as perhaps for labor in the short run, an allocation more consistent with consumer preference, as indicated by equality of marginal and average resource returns among industries, can be created by transforming a mixed industry organization into one of either pure competition or pure monopoly. The aggregate product would be equal under the two extremes of all monopoly or all competition, and larger than with mixed competition and monopoly. In mixed organization, marginal value productivity is ov_0 for the competitive industry but at ov_2 level for the monopoly industry. Under complete monopoly or complete competition for both industries, it is at ov_1 level for both, denoting a maximum aggregate product with full employment of resources. If one group of persons owned resources and another or different group purchased them, a major difference would still exist. Under mixed organization, resource return or price is ov_2, while it is only ov_1 under complete monopoly but at the higher level of ov_3 under complete competition.

Resource supplies do not in general fall in either of the elasticity categories discussed above. Some are highly elastic and others are of low elasticity in the short run. Even labor supply has elasticity in the short run, although the peculiar institutional and sociological attachments cause the short-run elasticity to differ greatly among industries and among sectors of agriculture. The low elasticity of farm labor supply, to the industry relative to magnitude of demand for labor in farming, has little impact on supply elasticity for a labor sector where employment opportunity is highly restricted to union membership; but the low elasticity in the union sector, protected from outside supply, could have important impact in causing supply to remain large and of low elasticity in sectors of competitive labor.

Monopoly and Imperfect Competition Extent

With industry organization a possible explanation of why resource supply may be large and return may be low in a competitive industry, the environment needs to be reviewed as it surrounds agriculture. To what extent does monopoly prevail in the American economy, either in commodity firms or organizations such as labor unions selling resources, and affect quantity and returns of factors in agriculture? We have already noted that other major industries do not conduct their pricing and production policies in the vein of the pure competition model which is the mode of agriculture. This is true even for industries which sell resources to agriculture, which are not single monopoly firms but are more nearly of oligopoly structure, with a few large firms and entirely different methods of commodity and resource pricing than in agriculture. When demand slackens or supply increases in agriculture, commodity price immediately declines. But under these same conditions during the recessions of the 1950's, the price of fertilizer, farm machinery and other resources outside of agriculture generally did not decline as producing capacity and supplies pushed against demand. Instead, prices were maintained, and sometimes increased, while output was curtailed. Firms did not "in general break out of the flock," producing more and selling it at a lower price. Certainly, competition generally does exist in such industries, but not in respect to short-run price in the extent of agriculture. Competition perhaps is more in (1) gaining share of the market at a general schedule of prices, although the price line is not easily or always held, (2) in developing new products and new technology and (3) other activities of the latter nature which do lead to progress. Galbraith perhaps would suggest that the level of affluence of American society might well lessen urgency to produce more and allow some luxury of monopolistic-bent pricing and production policy, to provide greater security and stability.[3]

There is not firm agreement on extent of monopoly in U.S. economy. A few studies have suggested that it does not prevail widely. Other persons claim that it is of important magnitude. Harberger suggests, as measured by magnitude of profit, the extent and importance is not large.[4] The data he explores are quite aged, the extent of monopoly influence being subject to increase with time, or to curtailment with federal antitrust action. Too, existence of monopoly is not adequately measured by profit or rate of return, where the latter may be capitalized into resources or facilities, the apparency of pure profit then disappearing in income statements and balance sheets.

Using profit rate on equity as one indication of degree of monopoly, Bain presents the figures in Table 5.5.[5] Agriculture has the lowest return,

[3] J. K. Galbraith, *The Affluent Society*, Houghton Mifflin Co., Boston, 1958, pp. 127–32.

[4] Arnold C. Harberger, "Monopoly and Resource Allocation," *Amer. Econ. Rev.*, Vol. 44.

[5] Joe S. Bain, *Industrial Organization*, John Wiley and Sons, New York, 1959, pp. 384–85. He points out (Chap. 10) the chronic maladjustment in unconcentrated, excessively competitive industries such as agriculture.

TABLE 5.5

AVERAGE PROFIT IN EQUITY FOR SELECTED SECTORS IN 1953

Sector	Average Profit Rate (After Tax)
Finance	10.1
Manufacturing	8.1
Construction	7.8
Services	5.9
Wholesale and retail trade	5.7
Public utilities	5.1
Mining and quarrying	4.5
Agriculture, fisheries and forestry	2.9

as would be expected for a competitive industry surrounded by monopoly sectors. However, we must also recognize that low factor supply elasticity for particular industries also can contribute to similar disparities in profit rate. Such broad sectors, of course, aggregate some unlike products and industry organizations. Using smaller aggregates, Bain found the 1953 profit rate to be 12.9 for motor vehicles and equipment, 10.9 for electrical equipment, 9.5 for chemicals and 8.7 for tobacco manufacture. For the four largest firms in particular sectors, over the period 1947–51, he found profit rate of 23.9 for automobiles, 18.6 for distilled liquor, 15.8 for soap, 12.6 for cigarettes, 11.2 for steel, 9.8 for canned goods and 5.1 for meat packing.

Kaysen and Turner examine industrial structure in terms of oligopolistic markets, with oligopolies defined to have a market share of sufficient magnitude to cause interaction between behavior of individual firms.[6] They conclude that structural oligopoly is the numerically dominant form of market organization in manufacturing. Heflebower expresses the belief that competition outweighs monopoly by a wide margin in the American economy, citing as evidence that the economy is large enough so several firms and industries can operate at maximum efficiency, competition exists between firms due to rivalry of managers, and public opinion is unfriendly to monopoly.[7] He does not, however, provide empirical evidence of his own.

The degree of market concentration and the trend is suggested in summary Table 5.6 from the Report of the Subcommittee on Anti-Trust and Monopoly.[8] That output control is sufficient to give important degree of stability and certainty in price for important sectors of the economy is suggested when only 200 firms account for 37 percent of total value added in all manufacture. To this can be added the ability of even smaller

[6] C. Kaysen and D. F. Turner, *Antitrust Policy*, Harvard University Press, Cambridge, Mass., 1958, Chap. 2.

[7] R. B. Heflebower and G. W. Stocking, *Readings in Industrial Organization and Public Policy*, Richard D. Irwin, Inc., Homewood, Ill., 1958.

[8] United States Senate, 85th Cong., 1st Sess., 1957. "Concentration in American Industry," Report of the Subcommittee on Anti-Trust and Monopoly to the Committee on the Judiciary, p. 11.

TABLE 5.6

SHARE OF TOTAL VALUE ADDED BY MANUFACTURE ACCOUNTED FOR BY LARGEST MANUFACTURING COMPANIES IN 1954 COMPARED TO THOSE IN 1947

Company Rankings in Respective Year	1954	1947
Largest 50 companies	23	17
Largest 100 companies	30	23
Largest 150 companies	34	27
Largest 200 companies	37	30

firms, when a few represent the majority of a sector, to serve effectively in price determination.

Nutter stated the extent of monopoly to be inconclusive to 1939.[9] His criterion was based on a concentration ratio of .5 or larger by the four largest firms in particular industries. His estimates showed 21 percent of national income in 1937 produced by monopoly industries, using the definition above. However, for particular industries, he found 100 percent of anthracite mining to be produced by monopolistic groups. The comparable figures were 64 percent for metal mining, 68 percent for rubber products, 37 percent for iron and steel, 93 percent for transportation equipment, 34 percent for chemical and 39 percent for miscellaneous products. His figures also showed 78.2 percent of value of manufactured products to be produced by the largest 10 percent of establishments in 1939. For the same year he uses Stigler's estimates, indicating 55 percent of income to be produced under competitive conditions and 24 percent under monopoly conditions.[10] For the same year, Stigler estimated 28.7 million persons to be employed under competitive industry, 1.4 million under compulsory cartel, 7.4 million under monopoly and 8.5 million under nonallocable industry. The relative employment of labor in these various categories may be more significant for agricultural supply than proportion of national income produced by monopoly industries.

Galbraith implies the major price-making forces, as well as important elements leading to technical progress, to rest in monopoly or oligopoly industries. His figures indicate that in 1947 the largest three producers accounted for two-thirds or more of the output in motor vehicles, farm machinery, tires, cigarettes, aluminum, liquor, meat products, tin containers and office machinery. The largest six accounted for two-thirds of volume in steel, glass, industrial chemicals and dairy products. He looks upon the negative outcome of monopoly power to be less a shortage of product and extreme of price and to be more that of excessive employ-

[9] G. W. Nutter, *The Extent of Enterprise Monopoly in the United States, 1899–1939, A Quantitative Study of Some Aspects of Monopoly,* University of Chicago Press, Chicago, 1951.

[10] G. J. Stigler, *Five Lectures on Economic Problems,* the London School of Economics and Political Science, The Macmillan Co., New York, 1950.

ment in competitive industries.[11] He also emphasizes the social concerns of mixed economic organization in a wealthy society to be less that of inefficiency of production and more that of inequality of income distribution, with the extreme fortunes of leading families having come from monopolistic industries such as oil, steel and copper and never from competitive industries such as agriculture.

MONOPOLY IN LABOR MARKETS

Sufficient monopoly in sectors of the labor markets would also strain the supply of labor in agriculture, causing it to back up on farms and produce a larger product for the market and at a lower return for itself. It is known, of course, that extreme cases of monopoly unions exist, with great featherbedding to spread supported wage levels to more labor resources which qualify under the restraints of entry to the union or craft. Yet monopoly in labor supplying by unions itself cannot have a dominating effect in backing labor up on farms. Too many persons migrated from farms from 1940 to 1960 for this to have been a deterrent of significant effect. During major spans of the period, even more could have migrated geographically and occupationally to receive greater resource returns than in farming. Other off-farm factors, such as information, housing and schools, probably were restraints more than was lack of nonfarm job opportunity; and these were probably less important than particular attachment to agriculture or knowledge lacks, in holding labor in agriculture. Also, an important portion of the U.S. labor force is not unionized, with farm labor having equal footing in these sectors. Finally, scattered empirical data available suggest that migrants from farms find, upon entry to the nonfarm labor force, employment equal or comparable to persons of nonfarm origin with the same skills and abilities.[12]

Exclusion for opportunity in nonfarm job opportunity is important in isolated areas in maintaining a surplus of labor in agriculture. It is most important in respect to Negro labor. Even here, a substitute for nonfarm employment in the community is the same at a different location where the similar institutional restrictions do not apply (but obviously one of a higher monetary and knowledge cost in transfer). In this sense, widespread existence of intensive pure-type monopoly is prevented by the presence of many substitutes, just as in the case of products where one fuel, metal or transportation method is a substitute for another, or where products of foreign producers serve as substitutes preventing the classbook terrors of monopoly (although foreign products do not use surplus labor from competitive industries in the U.S.).

Undoubtedly the monopoly power of unions acts as some restraint to the migration from agriculture, particularly in movement to specific in-

[11] J. K. Galbraith, *American Capitalism,* Houghton Mifflin Co., Boston, 1956, pp. 103–4 and Chap. 7.

[12] D. Gale Johnson, "Functioning of the Labor Market," *Jour. Farm Econ.*, Vol. 33.

dustries. However, empirical evidence which exists is too meager and inconclusive for quantitative statements. Union restrictions are most important during periods when some unemployment persists, as in the period following 1957, and less important in periods of full employment and labor scarcity. The latter characterized much of the decade following World War II and probably caused monopoly power of unions to be ineffective in restraining migration from farms. Still, with an important degree of chronic unemployment, such as that arising after 1957, union restrictions and seniority restraints became much more effective in excluding farm labor from opportunity. With surplus of labor, and that from other sectors having the first claim, farm labor is more nearly pushed to the point of "taking the second-best," or of obtaining employment only after "first claimants." While it may have return as high as others of the class where it does obtain employment, it can be greatly excluded from other employment sectors of higher return.

But with the array outlined above, U.S. industry is not competitive in the sense of agriculture's pure model, the latter being entirely a "price taker" with no ability to restrict output to an established price. Not even the corner druggists in the farm town are thus. Neither is U.S. industry monopolistic in sufficient extent to stifle progress, diminish national product to important degree and cause extreme poverty for the masses.

Noncompetition in respect to short-run price does not, as we have pointed out previously, mean lack of competition. Competition is sufficient in other respects to generate progress. As Galbraith has suggested, countervailing power and economic progress has prevented negative-sum outcome to the national community. Perhaps, too, as he suggests, the visible effects of monopoly on efficiency are negligible, given the opulence of the American economy. If resources were allocated more efficiently throughout the economy, through reduction of monopoly power, and given the exotic nature of the product mix which has already been attained, the outcome would be more zippers for cigarette packages and larger tail fins, although certainly the nation has important missions and goals which could absorb added manpower and capital. But even more of these could, of course, provide added employment opportunities for surplus labor from agriculture or other competitive industry. Or, given the mixed industry organization of the U.S. economy, economic growth of sufficient magnitude would still provide employment opportunity for labor released from agriculture.

With the present organizational mix projected into the future, reemployment of surplus labor from agriculture depends almost entirely on economic growth. This is likely the dominant prospect and stands to be more important than elimination of monopoly structure in allowing labor released from agriculture to be absorbed in other economic sectors.[13]

---

[13] For further discussion and bibliography relating to monopoly power and industry organization, see R. B. Heflebower and G. W. Stocking (eds.), *Readings in Industrial Organization and Public Policy*, Richard D. Irwin, Inc., Homewood, Ill., 1958.

While an important portion of production capacity often goes underutilized, in adjustment of monopolized industries to a given demand and price potential, general underemployment has been, at least until recent years, more a short-lived function of recession than of monopoly expanse. Even in the existence of some monopoly, or noncompetitive industry organization, economic growth in post World War II years generally was ample to absorb labor migrating from farms. The relatively large percentage of unemployment maintained after the 1957 recession, however, is burdensome particularly for an industry such as agriculture which has to send out part of its labor force.

The crucial questions of monopoly and managed production and prices in respect to agriculture perhaps are less the effect of the latter in backing labor up on farms, thus causing returns to be low, but more this: To what extent should and can the managed policies of other industries be used in agriculture, to put it on the same control footing as major nonfarm sectors, to convert an industry of pure competition and low demand elasticities to greater stability, to solve its basic capacity problems and to provide means in equity whereby it can retain some positive share of gains from its contribution to economic progress? We come back to these points in a later chapter. Even if agriculture is to gain market or bargaining power as in other industries, which model will be used: the pure monopoly model, the steel industry, telephone communication, grocery stores, the textile industry or drugs? None of these are pure competition, but they differ greatly in their monopoly extent.[14]

Even if it were certain that monopoly industry dominated other industries and caused labor of low return to back up importantly in farming, an attack on industry monopoly to solve the farm problem would have little prospect of success. Why? Because it is unlikely that agriculturally oriented policy could gain the strength and momentum to upset and change the industry organization of the dominating sectors of the economy and convert them all to pure competition. Agriculture doesn't have this amount of political strength. Other industries probably would rather subsidize agriculture than have their organizational structure upset to solve farm ills.

---

[14] For some concepts and other indications of monopoly and competition, see E. S. Mason, *Economic Concentration and the Monopoly Problem*, Harvard University Press, Cambridge, Mass., 1957; M. A. Adelman, *A and P: A Study in Price-Cost Behavior and Public Policy*, Harvard University Press, Cambridge, Mass., 1959; A. D. H. Kaplan *et al.*, *Pricing in Big Business*, Brookings Institute, Washington, D.C., 1958; J. Downie, *The Competitive Process*, Duckworth, London, 1958; S. M. Loescher, *Collusion in the Cement Industry*, Harvard University Press, Cambridge, Mass., 1959; J. W. Markham, *The Fertilizer Industry*, Vanderbilt University Press, Nashville, Tenn., 1958. Also, for suggestion of competition over "monopolistic" industries, see J. A. Schumpeter, *Capitalism, Socialism and Democracy*, Harper & Brothers, New York, 1947, pp. 84–85. He indicates that the important competition involves new technology and new products even in "less competitive" industries.

CAUSES OF VARYING FACTOR SUPPLY ELASTICITY

Having examined an "outside force" with possible effect on size of and return to farm labor, we now return to the "inside forces." Low factor supply elasticity does not cause low resource returns and prices under every circumstance. When demand increases faster than farm technology, low factor supply elasticity causes premium returns to resources. Instances in less developed countries where supply of capital and technical knowledge are of low elasticity have typically led to high real prices of food and high prices for borrowed capital and land. Under the sudden demand bursts attached to war, similar circumstances have surrounded U.S. agriculture. Its supply being inelastic, land has had a much greater, or a sharp increase in, return imputed to it during these periods, with resulting inflation of values such as occurred following World Wars I and II. Return and price of capital items of low supply elasticity, such as secondhand farm machinery, also increased greatly, often above the controlled price of new items. These spurts in returns provided capital gain in land and other assets, improving the equity position of farmers and the base for more new technology and farm size expansion.[15]

The variables important in causing depression of farm prices, incomes and resource returns, during a normal period of favorable national economic growth and rising real incomes of the nonfarm population, are not alone those relating to the supply elasticity of resources such as land and labor or capital in dollar value. Even where resources have low elasticity in the short run, their return can be maintained or increased if improvement in productivity is held in check against increase in demand. The problem of agriculture over the last century, with returns below those of nonfarm sectors, has been caused partly by high birth rates. Labor born in agriculture has always had to migrate, even at times when employment in agriculture was increasing. But once the rate of technical advance becomes accelerated, with the productivity of resources growing more rapidly than demand for them in agriculture, the situation is aggravated. Under these circumstances, with rapid increase in substitutability of capital for labor, not only does surplus farm labor need to migrate, but also total employment must decline if returns are to be maintained. The historic tendency of labor to hang back in agriculture thus gives an exodus too small to draw returns in agriculture nearer levels of the nonfarm economy, particularly when the rate of technological improvement exceeds growth in food demand.

Low supply elasticity for some factors would be unimportant in causing lag of returns if it were not true that elasticity of other resources is

---

[15] Land values, after the great postwar demand burst had eased and the supply of capital items became more elastic for substitution with land, were importantly supported as operators with capital gains bid for land to expand their units. With the high fixed costs representing modern machine technology, acreage added typically had greater net marginal value productivity than that already owned. This phenomenon, plus the emerging structure of agriculture based on technology and factor prices favoring specialization and substitution of machinery for labor, greatly increased capital requirements, at the very time commodity prices became depressed and general resource returns declined.

high. As emphasized several times herein, returns to resources of inelastic supply could actually grow with population and food demand if the rate of technological improvement were sufficiently restrained, or of sufficiently low elasticity in supply. Quite obviously, then, high supply elasticity and low price of knowledge representing technical improvement, taken as a resource along with the new forms of capital it represents, causes a problem to grow as reflected in rapid technological change and low short-run supply elasticity of land, labor and capital resources committed in form to earlier technologies. The high supply elasticity of one set of resources, knowledge and the capital forms it represents, causes problems to stem especially from the low supply elasticity of other resources (and the tardy rates at which they adjust to changes in the production function and price relatives).

Conceptually and factually, it is easy to illustrate how increase in supply elasticity, or decrease in supply price, of some factors may depress returns to resources of inelastic supply. Using an extreme case for illustration, we use the commodity demand function in (5.1) with the elasticity $e = .2$ and the industry production function in (5.14). (See footnote discussion for equations 1.1–1.5) Further, for the extreme illustration, we suppose that price elasticities of supply are zero for Z factor but nonzero for X. Expressing commodity price from (5.1) as a function of Q, substituting the value of Q from (5.14) into this equation and multiplying by the marginal physical products of (5.14), the marginal value products of resources represented by Z and X respectively are (5.34) and (5.35). We have substituted the values in (5.36) and (5.37)[16] into the original equations or marginal value productivities in expressing (5.34) and (5.35), since Z is fixed in magnitude along with price and productivity parameters.

(5.34) $$MVP_z = K_1 X^{-1.6}$$

(5.35) $$MVP_x = K_2 X^{-2.6}$$

(5.36) $$K_1 = .4c^5 r^{-4} Z^{-2.6}$$

(5.37) $$K_2 = .4c^5 r^{-4} Z^{-1.6}$$

With the factor supply equation in (5.38), the factor "supply price" equation is (5.39). Equating factor price in (5.39) and marginal value productivity in (5.35) for X factor in a competitive industry, the static equilibrium demand quantity for the variable resource is (5.40) where the terms making up K_2 dominate w.

(5.38) $$X = wP_x^{\,s}$$

(5.39) $$P_x = w^{-1/s} X^{1/s}$$

(5.40) $$X = (w^{1/s} K_2)^{s/(1+2.6s)}$$

[16] In other words, $P = c^5 Q^{-5} = c^5 r^{-5} Z^{-2} X^{-2}$ where $e = .2$ in (5.1) defining magnitude of commodity price in terms of inputs. The marginal value product $P \cdot (\partial Q/\partial X_i)$, using X as

$$MVP_x = (c^5 r^{-5} Z^{-2} X^{-2})(.4rZ^{.4} X^{-.6})$$

Obviously, if the price elasticity of factor supply, s, is increased in magnitude, input of X also will be increased as indicated by (5.40), but for our particular function in asymptotic limit. Substituting the magnitude of X in (5.40) into the marginal value productivity of Z in (5.34), the latter can be expressed as (5.41).

$$(5.41) \quad MVP_z = K_1(w^{1/s}K_2)^{-1.6/(1+2.6s)} = K_1(w^{1/s}K_2)^{-s/(.625+1.625s)}$$

Hence, it is obvious that an increase in supply elasticity, s, for X will reduce the marginal value productivity of Z if the latter remains fixed in quantity.[17] Obviously, too, if supply price of X is reduced by increase in magnitude of w, factor supply elasticity remaining fixed, magnitude of X also will increase and marginal value productivity of Z resource, in its fixed magnitude, will decline. As a general case for any form of functions, industry total revenue will always decline with increase in price elasticity and reduction in supply price for X and greater use of this factor with Z at fixed value and with a price elasticity of demand for the commodity of less than 1.0. Net return in total to the industry and per unit of Z will always decline where price elasticity of demand for X is greater than 1.0, a condition depending on the magnitude of parameters in the production function, and increased expenditures on this factor results. It also will decrease if the decline in industry total revenue is greater than reduction in expenditure on X, where supply price of the latter declines but its price elasticity of demand is less than 1.0.

Again, with the marginal productivity of Z resource of magnitude in (5.34) or (5.41), its marginal value productivity, or even net return per unit, can be restored to original magnitude (or other level) by decreasing the quantity of this input, as already illustrated for change in the production function relative to Table 5.1 and as being forced on U.S. agriculture by the pressures of the market. But as explained previously, the rate of decline in labor and land devoted to particular commodities in agriculture has not been sufficient to maintain level of return in the market, or even in the presence of price supports.

DIFFERENTIAL STRATA OF AGRICULTURE

Changes in technology and supply price of resources need not reduce, or change in similar directions and magnitudes, the income of all strata of farms and farm resources, even where reduced income is the outcome for the industry and price elasticity of demand for food in aggregate is inelastic. On a first possible category of exception are a few commodities with high price and income elasticities of demand, where change in demand and technology at particular rates may allow increase in net sector income and resource returns. Falling most nearly in this category are commodities of greatest exotic nature, such as selected fruits and vegetables. The regions best described by these conditions largely are favored

[17] The value of $-s(.625+1.625s)^{-1}$ increases absolutely with s, but towards the limit mentioned previously. The value of wK_2 raised to this power will also increase. However, since wK_2 is in the denominator, the marginal value productivity of Z will decline as value assigned to s increases.

by unique climate or soil conditions which limit the growing area and restrain the supply function accordingly. Localities of the Southwest and Southeast suited to crops such as artichokes, lemons and similar products are examples, although means (e.g. market orders) other than the free market and magnitude of unique soil and climatic inputs are sometimes necessary (or used) to hold gains of technical advances in agriculture and input industries for growers.

A second category of conditions allows some farmers to gain while others sacrifice in income as supply price of commodity declines under inelastic demand. If some strata increase output by a greater percentage than the decline in commodity price, their revenue will increase, as that for the industry and for strata which increase output by a smaller percentage than the decline in price diminishes. This possibility can be illustrated simply by supposing the industry demand function in (5.42) where Q_d is quantity of commodity and P is price. We also have two strata of farms, each originally with the supply function in (5.43). Summing supply for the two strata, the industry supply is (5.44).

$$Q_d = a - cP \tag{5.42}$$

$$S_i = .75cP - .1a \tag{5.43}$$

$$S_t = 1.5cP - .2a \tag{5.44}$$

Now equating demand (5.42) and total supply (5.44) and solving for P, we obtain the static equilibrium price in (5.45). Output of each stratum is (5.46) and revenue to each is (5.47).

$$P = .48ac^{-1} \tag{5.45}$$

$$Q_i = .26a \tag{5.46}$$

$$R_i = .1248a^2c^{-1} \tag{5.47}$$

Now suppose that supply for the first stratum changes to (5.48), through technical advance or a more favorable price for a resource such as capital, while that for the second stratum changes to (5.49). The second stratum realizes greater productivity gains from technical change or more favorable prices for factors than the first stratum. The total supply function now is (5.50) and the new static equilibrium price is (5.51).

$$S_1 = .9cP - .12a \tag{5.48}$$

$$S_2 = 1.05cP - .14a \tag{5.49}$$

$$S_t' = 1.95cP - .26a \tag{5.50}$$

$$P' = .4278ac^{-1} \tag{5.51}$$

$$Q_1 = .265a \tag{5.52}$$

$$Q_2 = .3092a \tag{5.53}$$

$$R_1 = .1135a^2c^{-1} \tag{5.54}$$

$$R_2 = .1323a^2c^{-1} \tag{5.55}$$

Outputs of the two strata are (5.52) and (5.53). Revenue for the stratum with the smaller change in supply function declines from (5.47) to (5.54) while revenue for the other stratum increases from (5.47) to (5.55). Technical change and supply increase have been realized by both stratum, but one gains and the other sacrifices in revenue because of differential rate of change. While total revenue for the industry, including both sectors, decreases, revenue of the second stratum is improved. Changes in net income among groups generally will be in the same directions as for gross revenue, although it will be modified by the resource demand elasticity of each stratum.

A third category of conditions, similar to that presented above, also can allow return to the industry to decline, while some strata gain and others sacrifice in income. This is the case where one stratum cannot expand output because of lack of resources. For example, suppose that our first stratum of farms has output restrained to $.25a$ because of capital limitations while the second stratum originally has the supply function in (5.43). Industry supply is (5.56), and with demand in (5.42), static equilibrium price is $.4857ac^{-1}$. Revenue of the first stratum, with $.25a$ output, is $.1214a^2c^{-1}$.

$$S_T = .75cP + .15a \tag{5.56}$$

$$S_T' = 1.05cP + .11a \tag{5.57}$$

Revenue for the second stratum, with $.2643a$ output, is $.1284a^2c^{-1}$. Now if the supply function of the second changes to (5.49) and output of the first remains at $.25a$, due to lack of resources, total supply becomes (5.57) and equilibrium price falls to $.4341ac^{-1}$. Revenue of the first stratum, with $.25a$ output, will decline to $.1085a^2c^{-1}$ while that for the second stratum, with $.3158a$ output, will increase to $.1371a^2c^{-1}$.

Economic development in an industry of inelastic commodity demand and factors of low elasticity need not, then, cause all producers to sacrifice. Some strata may gain, along with society in general, from development while the sacrifice of advance falls more intensely on a smaller group. This differential impact on income applies among groups which are separated by both geographic region and capital availability. Public and private actions which increase the supply elasticity or lower the supply price of resources such as knowledge and capital items do not apply equally to all groups. This gives rise to major policy issues, with groups sacrificing from aggregate change often expressing preference for policy differing from those who gain from the over-all change. More particularly it gives rise to, or need for, policies which redress the costs of some as others gain from progress, or for framework which better guarantees positive-sum utility outcomes where progress rewards in the market are not distributed symmetrically.

The same differential income outcome applies similarly among commodities where the cross elasticities of demand are sufficiently large (i.e., the commodities are "close" substitutes in consumption or in further production) and supply function for one commodity is lowered more than for another. Since the same general outcome applies among substitute commodities, policy conflict again tends to arise. Wheat producers favor control programs and are willing to restrict wheat output if they can shift resources to grain sorghums, and corn farmers required to restrict corn output are willing to do so if they can shift to wheat or beans, etc. Even if grain output did increase slightly under control mechanisms, one group of farmers who can increase output greatly can gain at the sacrifice of those who are more restrained by control mechanisms. This complex has generally led to control programs which have an escape route among substitute commodities for resources freed from particular commodities in the various regions, with the result that aggregate output is affected but little.

RESOURCES OF HIGH SHORT-RUN SUPPLY AND DEMAND ELASTICITY

The important capital resources of elastic supply which substitute for labor and land of low short-run elasticity are largely new machinery, chemicals for fertilizer and pest control and biological forms which represent new varieties and breeds and improved nutrition. If their supply price is kept low, incentive for substitution is great and will cause the rewards to factors with low supply elasticity to continue in depressed state. This depression of income will occur, of course, only if the aggregate supply function shifts rapidly relative to the demand function. Even with substitutes, the short-term rewards to labor and land would still increase if growth rate for demand was sufficiently greater than aggregate commodity supply. The prices of these "more variable" capital items have been kept low since 1940, causing continuous pressure on labor and land except as cushioned by temporary demand spurt and support prices, evidently because the degree of competition and the extent of technological research within industries furnishing inputs to agriculture have been sufficiently great.

In addition to the evidence contained in Table 2.10, Figure 5.2a illustrates how an important input, fertilizer, has maintained a favorable price relative to crop prices since 1940. During the sharper break in farm price depressions, due to the structure of pure competition in agriculture, and a smaller degree of competition in the fertilizer industry as expressed in price constancy, the price of fertilizer rose relative to crop prices. The industry structure of the cluster of firms making up the fertilizer sector does not provide the same short-run price flexibility as farm prices do under recession and demand curtailment. The structure of pricing in the chemical industry has not been one of *pure competition*.[18] Yet *competition* since 1940 *has been sufficient* to keep fertilizer prices low

---

[18] For a discussion of anti-trust legislation relative to the fertilizer industry, see J. W. Markham, *The Fertilizer Industry*, Vanderbilt University Press, Nashville, Tenn. 1958.

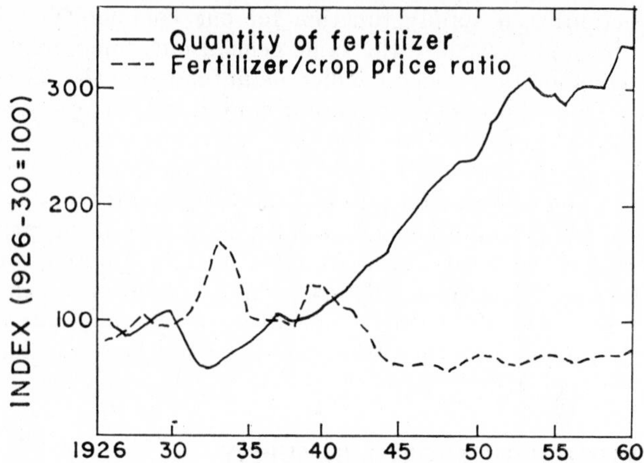

Fig. 5.2a. Total Demand or Use of Fertilizer and Fertilizer/Crop Price Ratio. U.S. 1926–30 = 100.

relative to farm product prices. Fertilizer prices not only have been kept at low real level because of sufficient competition, although not of the pure type with prices breaking sharply when demand slackens relative to capacity (fertilizer prices have sometimes increased after farm demand for fertilizer declines following reduced farm income), but also because of technological developments relating to the manufacture and analysis of fertilizer.

Increasingly, as capital items come to dominate agricultural inputs, research in and relative to the input-furnishing industries has importance in changing commodity supply in agriculture. Decline in the real supply price of farm capital items would not, of course, result in the use of (the demand for) new technology if the supply of knowledge were not also great. As mentioned previously, the level of supply price for both of these technical complements is important in farm development. It is not possible, even in the case of fertilizer where quantities are more readily quantified, to separate the proportion of increase in fertilizer demand or use which can be attributed to either (1) the relative pricing or (2) knowledge increase since 1930. Both scientists and farmers know more about fertilizer productivity than they did at that time. But ability to quantify the effect of knowledge supply on response currently cannot be extended much beyond the general magnitude in equation (5.58).

$$\log Y_t = 10.677 - \underset{(.201)}{.490} \log X_1 + \underset{(.054)}{.637} \log X_2 - \underset{(.615)}{1.082} \log X_3 + \underset{(.022)}{.076} \log X_4 \qquad (5.58)$$

In this demand equation from our Iowa study, predicted for the period 1926–56, Y_t refers to U.S. fertilizer use in the current year, X_1 is the

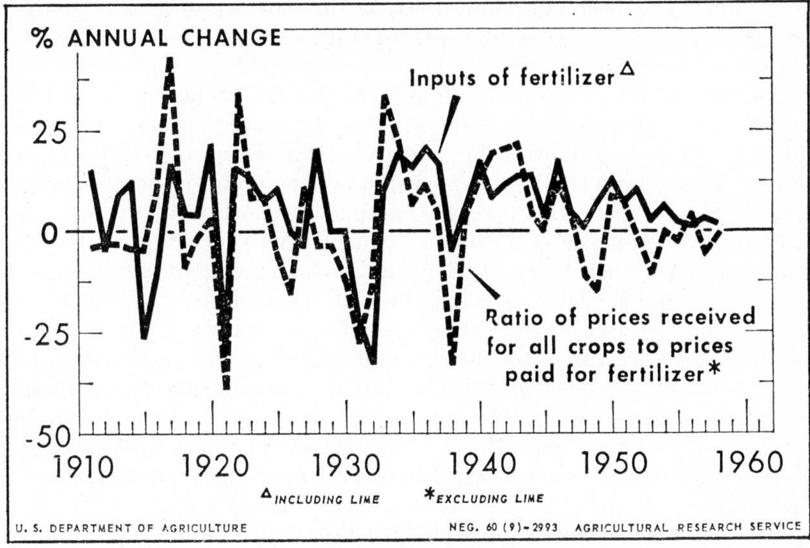

Fig. 5.2. Percent Annual Change in Commercial Fertilizer Inputs and Relative Prices. U.S. 1910–60.

fertilizer/crop price ratio at planting time, X_2 is gross cash receipts from farming in the previous year, X_3 is total acreage of cropland and X_4 is time. This equation, with a coefficient of determination of .99 (standard errors in parentheses below regression coefficients), uses X_4 as a "gross measure" of knowledge (and other variables related to it) in expressing the effect of time on use of the fertilizer resource. The elasticity of the fertilizer/crop price ratio in this short-run equation is $-.49$; indicating both (1) the quantitative effect of a decline in the real price of fertilizer and (2) that farmers are short-run price responsive in the use of resources whose supply is not fixed to agriculture.[19] This same short-run responsiveness is illustrated in Figure 5.2.

The situation is similar for other new capital forms where the degree of competition and technical research in the input industry, applying both to processing of a resource and in predicting the productivity effect, keeps the real price of the factor low and more of it is "demanded," as a substitute for other resources. Hybrid corn, improved seeds generally and other capital items have been similarly priced at favorable levels relative to farm product prices. Of course, the price ratio is only one magnitude expected to cause greater use of a resource with elastic supply.

[19] A corresponding long-run model applied to the same data is (5.59) where the lagged value of fertilizer demand is used to predict short-run and long-run elasticities.

$$\log Y = 2.602 - \underset{(.246)}{.352} \log X_1 + \underset{(.048)}{.094} \log X_4 + \underset{(.164)}{.715} \log Y_{t-1} \quad (5.59)$$

This equation, with an R^2 of .95, predicts a short-run elasticity of fertilizer use in respect to the fertilizer/crop price ratio of $-.35$. The comparable long-run elasticity computed from the equation is -1.23.

Its productivity is equally important, and research, both by the private and public sectors, has caused these magnitudes, or knowledge surrounding them, to grow.

As mentioned before, input firms and industries can be expected to extend research at both levels, that related to the processing of inputs keeping their supply price favorable and that related to productivity of inputs on farms, both leading to expansion in demand for resources of nonfarm origin. Since agriculture uses a small proportion of the nation's capital, these inputs can continue to be furnished to agriculture with high degree of supply elasticity. Agriculture's relative magnitude alone will not give rise to increasing costs in industries of chemicals, steel and drugs. This setting, along with the pure competition structure of agriculture, is indeed conducive to continued economic development in the farm industry. Given the level of demand and its inelastic nature for major farm products, however, this complex is not likely to lead to greater total revenue of the agricultural industry, except as brought forth by general inflation, a condition wherein real income of agriculture may still decline.

The net effect of high supply elasticity for capital items representing new technology and tendency of real price of these resources to remain low is to allow physical productivity of land and labor in agriculture to increase, thereby reducing the amount of either required to produce conventional products at the rate of demand growth being experienced. To the extent that the pricing mechanism is used to promote economic development and allocate resources, this complex leads to reduced returns for resources which come into surplus relative to consumer preferences. The important policy questions, then, supposing the pricing mechanism to be the major gauge for intra-sector resource allocation and continued economic development, are these: How can the pricing mechanism or its equivalent be used to suggest or implement the change implied by economic growth without causing owners of surplus resources to bear unreasonably the gross social costs of change? Can extra-market mechanisms be used equitably to bring compensation to these resource owners while still allowing net social gains from economic development? Or, can market mechanisms be modified to allow simultaneous accomplishment of these two goals in sufficient degree?

Capital Substitution and Prices for Land and Labor

As productivity of capital items representing new technology is predicted, the demand function for them generally moves to the right, even where they are used for commodities of inelastic demand. Reduction in their real supply price also causes increase in their use. The individual farmer does not directly substitute items such as fertilizer and improved strains for land and labor; he simply uses more of them with a given input of land and labor, although he may substitute machinery for labor under favorable price and productivity ratios. In aggregate, however, a given quantity of food can be produced with less labor and land as new technology is used to increase output per unit of land, feed or animal. In an economy dominated entirely by competition and the market, these technological advances would cause labor, and especially land used at the margin of profitability, to shift more rapidly, but still with lag, to other uses as the commodity supply function shifts more rapidly than demand.

Policy mechanisms which support prices at previous levels tend to retard this reallocation, especially for land. Land prices since World War II have increased, seemingly a contradiction to part of the above analysis. A large portion of this increase came, however, in the period when foreign demand was greater and resource productivity was somewhat smaller.[20] In the absence of price support and public storage programs, a realignment of land prices would take place. Under the forces of the free market the problem of "comparable resource returns" largely would be solved by a reduction in land values, plus some further migration of labor.

Whereas farmers in aggregate have received a lower return on their capital investment than nonfarm industry, if market wage rates are imputed to labor, the return generally would be as high—if land values were reduced. For example, disregarding scale economies possible from expansion, a farmer with 200 acres priced at $200 and with net of $6 per acre, after expenses and imputation of market return to labor and other capital, will realize 3 percent on land investment. (This level of return, or lower, has been typical on many farms even under price supports, and would be even more widespread in the absence of price supports.) If, however, land prices were to decline to $100 per acre, the same investment would support 400 acres. The return of $6 per acre, supposing scale economies offset addition of some nonfamily labor, would amount to 6 percent on investment, a level more nearly comparable with industrial investment. Hence, we have a second major "market specified mechanism" for remedying the problem of rate of return in agriculture. The first "market specified mechanism" was: increase the supply elasticity of particular resources to agriculture with emphasis on labor. The second "market specified mechanism," like the first, has psychological and economic blocks for particular persons and groups.

While a decline in land prices, accompanying freer markets for commodities and decline in their price level, would help solve the "rate of return problem" in the manner illustrated above, it would still require a

---

[20] Prices continued to move up because of the cost economies of modern machine technology and specialization, the net marginal value productivity of land for farm size expansion being greater than for the original unit, as noted earlier. Too, for individual operators, capital items representing new technology serve in a complementary manner with land, although the two serve as substitutes in the aggregate. The potential gain to the industrial operator from improved seed or fertilizer is limited to the number of acres under operation. By adding more acres, he can realize more gain from new technologies. Finally, inflation and price support policies have maintained levels of land price in the face of surpluses and depressed income for particular commodity sectors.

capital loss for landowners. If a farmer could withdraw his investment before decline from the $200 price and hold it for reinvestment after decline to the $100 per acre price, capital loss would be averted. This procedure is impossible, of course, on a net basis. Accordingly, farmers do not recommend it as desired policy. An alternative policy mechanism which might serve as the equivalent, requiring smaller public investment than an infinite time span of subsidies in price supports and commodity storage, would be public compensation to offset decline in resource values. In the above examples, compensation of $100 per acre, to cover the capital loss, would allow the farmer to expand acreage to 400. Still a "catch" arises. One could expand only if another withdrew from agriture, and agreement among farmers in respect to "who should stay and who should leave" would not be easy. The answer to this conflict is not given among industrial firms who, not always competing on a quoted price basis, use ingenuity in a competitive attempt to expand at sacrifice to each other for a given demand quantity.

The "market specified mechanism" would cause the aggregate substitution of capital in new technology for land to be more fully and quickly realized. Under policy mechanisms of the last several decades, land clings fairly well to its conventional uses, with new technology used on it and the growing surplus channeled into public storage. Under the free market, however, that at the margin would gradually shrink away from its conventional farm uses, being replaced by the capital of new technology used on land of greater comparative advantage remaining in production.

This substitution of technology capital for land and labor is one of the social gains of economic development. Had not the resources of auto and plane production been allowed to substitute for those of buggy and trains, or the public power line for the kerosene lamp, farmers and other consumers would now find life less convenient. In fact, aside from the characteristics of pure competition and public investment in development, the major problems of agriculture have been widely experienced in other industries. Resources for farm machinery replaced those of harness producers, and even blacksmiths. Petroleum and other energy sources have substituted for labor and capital specialized to coal production. The technology and capital investment adapted to supermarkets caused the neighborhood grocery to be replaced, much in the vein that modern technology and capital requirements in farming bring fewer firms, a different spatial concentration of firms and the displacement of particular labor and building resources.

As a single sector, agriculture does represent more persons and resources than other distinct industries. But the aggregate of change and substitution in several industries has involved as many resources and persons as that of agriculture. Why, then, is specific public policy to cushion change and modify its effects of greater importance for agriculture than for aggregates of industry? Or, alternatively, if policies to modify the social costs of change are important for agriculture, why are they not equally relevant for other sectors? Agriculture and other sectors have had somewhat similar mechanisms to lessen income losses from change growing out of economic development. Labor displaced by technological change in nonfarm industry has had unemployment compensation to help bridge the income gap *in shifts among occupations.* Agriculture has had support prices to lessen the income burden, but only for resources *which remain in agriculture.* Mechanisms for both sectors lessen the pain to the individual of adjustment to technological change, but the mechanisms for agriculture are much less consistent with economic development. The mechanisms which provide cushion of unemployment are not intermixed with the mechanisms possessed by labor, a sector which otherwise would be as competitive as agriculture, to provide stability and bargaining power. Policy to provide stability in farming is curiously mixed with that which might be termed compensation for the sacrifices which fall on agriculture as a result of its contribution to economic progress.

BASIS OF LOW FACTOR SUPPLY ELASTICITY

In the scheme of impersonal economic analysis, large supply and low price for farm commodities and low returns of resources can be attributed to the low supply elasticity of certain factors. If these resources flowed more rapidly from agriculture, the marginal productivity of those remaining would be enlarged. Resource return would be increased especially if reduction in inputs lowered commodity output in magnitude to raise price sufficiently. But without reduction in output, or even with small increase, the average return of human effort would be increased greatly by migration of many more persons with low capital and income. The average would be raised through the simple mechanics of arithmetic: division of the product among fewer laborers. It also would increase the amount of capital per remaining person, allowing fuller and more complete use of much underemployed labor. By the same arithmetic, net income per farm would increase if low income families left agriculture, even with their resources remaining idle.

Manipulation of resources to raise averages and margins is a simple process for inanimate resources. They have no personal feelings in respect to which are withdrawn or which are left. To raise the average and marginal product of fertilizer, the process is simple: withdraw some units of fertilizer from each acre, the particular units being of no concern. The labor return and family income problem is not so simply solved because "it does matter" to these resources. Most farmers actively engaged in the occupation would like to stay, a psychological factor which goes a long way in explaining why short-run labor supply elasticity is low to agriculture, at least in relation to rates of change in commodity demand and technology.

LABOR MOBILITY

Supply elasticity is highly synonymous with factor mobility, especially for labor. Farm labor has been mobile, with the number of workers declining by nearly half since 1920. But decline in number of workers underestimates the real extent that labor has shifted from agriculture. This is true since it does not reflect the great increase in farm persons employed part or full time in other industries. Mobility has not been small in absolute terms, but only relative to the magnitude of change in technology and supply capacity of agriculture. Even with large absolute reduction, farm labor has been in surplus because the rate of technical advance has been much more rapid than the rate of demand growth.

We need to explore, then, not so much why agricultural labor has lacked mobility, but why it has not been more mobile. One important reason has already been mentioned: the attachment of a person or consumer to the labor unit. But the consumer is guided in preferences and flexibility by other quantities we must examine. In a sense, the question is one of why a certain stratum of the farm population has low mobility relative to change around it. Mobility varies greatly among geographic, age and income strata of farmers. As Figure 5.3 indicates, migration is highest in the 15 to 25 age group, representing those first entering the labor force. It is lowest in the 30 to 49 age group, representing those who are actively engaged in farm operation, and next lowest in the 25 to 29 and 50 to 54 groups. This selectivity in migration has shifted a greater proportion of the farm population into the age group beyond 45 and under 15 years. Consequently, the potential in mobility rate at conventional level of income and wage variables would be expected to decline if the shift

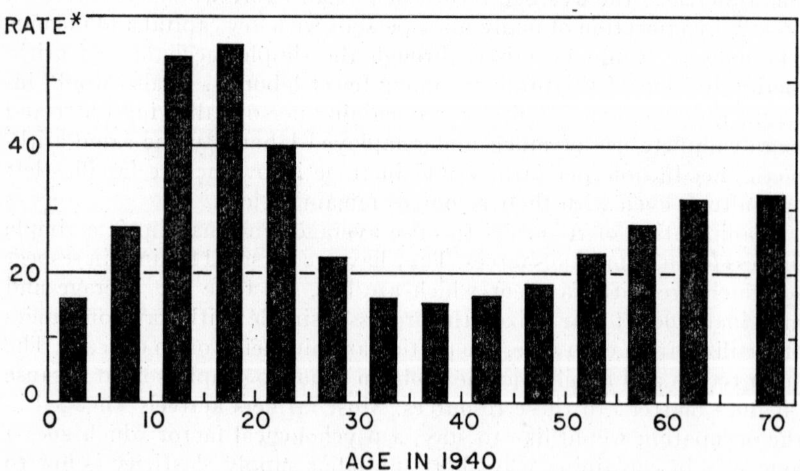

Fig. 5.3. Net Migration From Farms, U.S. 1920–58. (Source: A.M.S.)

continued long enough. However, the relative shift of population to older groups itself serves to reduce the size of the farm labor force more rapidly. Fewer young persons are attached to farming to enter the industry and a greater proportion of laborers are retiring.

The migration of nonwhite labor has been greater than for whites, a likely function of income level, amounting to 42.2 per 1,000 population for the former and 28.8 for the latter in the decade 1940–50.[21] Bowles found the migration rate to be as high as 36.9 in extremely low income areas, as compared to 28.0 for medium and high income areas. Further increase in migration rates for those groups highest in the past is needed particularly to increase their own economic outlook and opportunity. It is needed for young persons so that more will have a greater income potential under economic growth. It is needed for nonwhite and low income families particularly where their resources and outlook in farming are meager and their incomes could be raised substantially from nonfarm employment. Yet these groups produce only a small fraction of the total farm product and their basic land resources could be operated by many fewer remaining operators. Hence, the migration rate within these groups could be considerably greater without causing material reduction in the commercial farm problem as it is conventionally defined for basic commodities. Large outmigration of low income and nonwhite operators in the mountain areas and Southeast would not solve the problems of surpluses in wheat and feed grains, just as supply control for the latter would not solve the poverty problems of the former.

A considerable step-up in migration rates would be needed to close the gap between farm and nonfarm labor earnings. The large outmigration over the last several decades did not close the relative income gap. Farm persons have realized about the same proportionate gain in real income per capita as the nonfarm population as an average over the period since 1945. But the relative gap has been maintained, indicating that it was necessary for farm labor to decline almost a third to hold its own in a relative sense. Too, real income of agriculture declined in the 1950's. This rate of outmigration might well continue in the 1960's and 1970's with agriculture only holding its own in respect to per capita income. To be sure, its absolute income would increase, but per capita farm income as a percent of nonfarm might well remain at current levels. Johnson estimates that this could be possible, with farm labor declining by as much as 35 percent in the period 1956–75, without improvement in the relative return per capita.[22] The possible offsetting forces would be slow-down in rate of technical advance or large increase in foreign demand. Without these modifications, a deep bite in the labor force of commercial farms, beyond that needed to improve economic outlook of young and low in-

[21] Gladys K. Bowles, *Farm Population—Net Migration From the Rural Farm Population, 1940–50*, AMS Stat. Bul. No. 176, Washington, D.C., 1956.

[22] D. Gale Johnson, "Labor Mobility and Agricultural Adjustment," *In* Earl O. Heady *et al.* (eds.), *Agricultural Adjustment Problems in a Growing Economy*, Iowa State University Press, Ames, 1956.

come persons, would be needed in the next decade if labor returns were to be boosted to the comparable nonfarm level solely through the market mechanism. As a step in gauging these possibilities it is useful to examine variables which cause supply elasticity of labor in farming to be low relatively.

Anticipation and Communication

As mentioned previously, migration rate is lowest for established farm operators. They are experienced in the occupation, generally have values oriented to a rural community and generally have preferences for remaining in agriculture. Partly, however, this preference arises because of expectations in respect to the farm industry and lack of sufficient knowledge about economic growth and its relation to agriculture.

In respect to expectations, established farmers up to the 1950's have known that agriculture, as other industries, "has its ups and downs in economic conditions." In their limited knowledge, depression of income was only temporary, as it had always been in the past, with eventual restoration to some normal level. Agricultural economists led them to the firm belief, during the last major depression, that solution of the farm problem rested on full employment. The war and postwar period seemed to confirm this proposition. Then as temporary demand melted away, the illusion disappeared. National and per capita income grew to record levels, but farm income declined and continued in depressed state.

Still farmers knew so little of structural relationships, both in agriculture and the national economy, that many held to the belief that "improved economic weather will be back as soon as the demand drouth is over." But why should they know otherwise? This generally had been true during periods of "ups and downs" for their fathers and grandfathers. Then, too, their educational institutions did not provide them with knowledge of basic economic structure, even though knowledge of structure and intersectional outlook was crucial information to them in planning such important matters as future of their children and their own occupational directions and investment. They were provided information of fertilizer response, next year's hog prices, new varieties and similar important physical and economic data. But the meaning and magnitude of income elasticities of demand were not explained to them generally. Neither were they instructed in the relative premiums and penalties which attach to different industries through economic growth. While slight improvements have been made in this situation, it still predominates. Extension programs have been mercifully weak in presenting the broad picture of economic structure to farmers. Farmers and their children have suffered in income and opportunity accordingly, even though hogs and hens have been better off because of the intensive education devoted to improvement of their menus and housing. Certainly more farmers would have shifted resources to other occupations had economic structure been communicated more effectively to them. Even more would have altered plans in respect to on-farm investments.

Inflexibility and Location of Skills

Flexibility in the human resource is greatest before it has been committed to an occupation, as is reflected in mobility rates among age groups. Dip in income of resources owned by middle-aged operators can be considerable before they are convinced to change occupations. The response is indeed one of distributed lag pattern, of the general nature illustrated in Chapter 4. Partly, they have persisted in farming under hopes and expectations that "things will improve," but also because it takes time for reorientation of plans and values. Farmers generally have established preferences for their occupation, tied as it is to a particular type of community and method of living. Also, while the inherent abilities of a 48-year-old Kansas wheat farmer and an electronics worker in Massachusetts may be equal, their skills are no longer so. Even if the Kansas wheat farmer is realizing only $2500 for his labor, he is not likely to receive the return of the electronics worker if he shifts occupations. Not only do his skills become less flexible with time but also his personal preference and value orientation become highly fixed. The complex provides a much greater obstacle to occupational migration than for the skilled worker who may shift readily to another industry as it provides greater return. Not only are the latter's skills more easily transferred, but also he continues to live in a community of the type to which he is accustomed, even if he moves across the nation. With high outmigration by young people, the major component of low labor supply elasticity to agriculture is in the age groups representing established farmers. Since labor in farm operation, for the individual entrepreneur, is complementary with capital and land, the latter resources remain with him in low out-response to depressed returns.

Flexibility in human capacities and value orientations could be higher than at the present, although it has been growing with economic development and increased communication. However, a society truly pressed in scarcity of resources, and extremely concerned about welfare of persons with depressed incomes, would find means of increasing flexibility of skills and elasticity of factor supply to particular industries. Not only would it gather up the steel in obsolete and surplus farm machines and forge it into other tools; it also would provide equivalent facilities, in adult education and redirection of skills, for agricultural labor.

Market Communication of Occupational Outlook and Resource Returns

The free market does not work perfectly in reflecting expectation of prices to all producers and resource owners. It serves best for the market of a particular day at a particular location. It is less perfect in reflecting price and return at a future time and distant location. To help overcome these imperfections, the USDA and land-grant colleges established outlook services for commodities. These aids have been useful to farmers in planning use of their resources on farms. They have been developed to the extent that if a sow could read the morning paper, she could learn her worth at Chicago or Denver. Similarly, a calf on the ranges of Wyoming could acquire expectations of his worth as a vealer next month or as a bull four years hence. But a farm boy has not been provided equal facilities for acquiring expectations of his worth in different occupations and locations. This is true even though no commodities produced in agriculture have greater social importance than persons.

These historic imperfections of the market in reflecting price outlook of resources in various occupations and locations have been extremely important in causing resources to remain in agriculture at lower return than in other occupations. The burden falls more on agriculture than other industries because of the tendency of agriculture to be geographically separated from other occupations and to concentrate in restricted communities. Lipset found, in his analysis of social mobility in California, that the smaller the community of orientation, the greater the chance that the person would spend his career in manual occupations.[23] With larger community orientation, the status of the job and upward mobility increased.

While a variety of manufacturing and service industries exist side-by-side in most industrial complexes of the nation, agriculture typically is not geographically mixed with nonfarm occupations. This separation of markets has impact on both farm youth and operators who have already committed resources to agriculture. Youth groups in school have greater occupational homogeneity and less opportunity to learn about alternative employments and returns from their companions. In the same vein and for the same reason, schools in rural communities have provided much less in the way of vocational guidance and counseling. Because of pure knowledge lack, the farm youth has had a lower reservation price to the occupation in which he was born than his city counterpart.[24]

But this is also true of the established farm operators. Because of the geographical separation of farm and industrial concentration, he is poorly informed both of the existence of employment alternatives and of the rate of resource remuneration. Even the newpaper he reads seldom has a page of advertisements for labor in different industries, as is true for his city counterpart, because it has a particular geographic and occupational focus. The worker or businessman in the industrial complex is generally much better acquainted with developments in other fields about him, partly because he is not separated from them in the same geographic and informational sense. The geography itself presents a psychological barrier. Reynolds found that shift "to the unknown" and breaking ties with friends and relatives served to restrict occupational mobility of urban

---

[23] S. M. Lipset, "Social Mobility and Urbanization," *Rural Soc.*, Vol. 20.

[24] C. N. Hamilton ("Educational Selectivity of Migration From Rural to Urban Communities," *Amer. Soc. Proc.*, 1960) found migration to be greatest among the most highly educated farm youth and lowest among those who completed only eight grades.

workers.[25] These factors would be expected to serve more strongly in agriculture where the changed cultural environment must be added to these shift obstacles.

This informational void is not lacking for on-the-spot commodity prices of agriculture. Major commodity exchanges exist to reflect the value of wheat, cotton and similar resources to every part of the country. They do so not only in averages but in specific and refined grades of these commodities and resources. The USDA and land-grant colleges invest in further defining these grades so that refinement and detail are extended. Market communication of comparable refinement and geographic and quality coverage of the agricultural commodity exchanges does not extend to the basic resources of agriculture. If comparable market information were developed for human resources, geographic isolation would much less keep the supply elasticity and reservation price of labor to agriculture at such low levels. It is this communication void, rather than industrialization per se, which causes the extremes in lag of adjustment in agriculture to economic development. Schultz attributes the differential adjustment of agricultural resources and income to what he terms "locational matrices," with these being oriented to industrial-urban development.[26]

Quite obviously, nations with rapid economic development have advanced far in income beyond those experiencing only meager progress. The result could not be otherwise. But in respect to rate of adaptation of agricultural communities, to generate higher farm incomes and higher resource returns, location in respect to industrialization is only a superficial relation. The important and basic variables are those related to communication of market quantities and conditions for resources. They are also those relating to investment in social overhead capital, with its effect on knowledge, skills and mobility of people. It is true that if a large industrial plant is located in an isolated farming area in South Dakota, farm labor and resources nearest the plant will adjust to the new employment opportunity more quickly and completely than those more distant. But this need not be true. The adaptation of wheat resources, to the growing of the commodity or the time of the marketing of the raw material, does not vary between locations in Kansas nearer or further from the central markets and processing centers. Similarity exists in the adaptation of these wheat resources relating not to location, but to communication of market information and investments to effect their transfer as readily at one as the other location. It is not the location, in orientation of a resource or commodity to a particular price or income, but the degree of perfection in market reflection which does so.

One can find illustrations of more rapid and complete adaptations of

---

[25] L. G. Reynolds, *Structure of Labor Markets*, Harper and Brothers, New York, 1951, pp. 76–112.

[26] T. W. Schultz, "Reflections on Poverty Within Agriculture," *Jour. Farm Econ.*, Vol. 33.

TABLE 5.7

PERCENT CHANGE IN FARM POPULATION AND EMPLOYMENT BY DECADES (ALL FIGURES REPRESENT DECLINE UNLESS OTHERWISE INDICATED)

Region	Farm Population					Farm Employment				
	1920–30	1930–40	1940–50	1950–60	1920–60	1920–30	1930–40	1940–50	1950–60	1920–60
New England	4.2	+ 8.4	20.7	12.6	31.8	10.0	13.0	23.8	14.0	48.7
Mid Atlantic	10.1	+ 4.4	10.4	7.5	22.2	16.1	1.7	13.8	29.6	50.0
East North Central	9.1	+ 3.0	11.8	8.5	24.4	16.3	1.8	12.7	11.4	36.4
West North Central	2.4	7.3	16.9	18.4	38.7	4.1	13.3	5.5	20.1	37.2
South Atlantic	9.0	+ 2.5	16.6	15.2	34.0	11.7	8.7	19.1	25.3	51.3
East South Central	2.8	+ 3.4	18.3	19.4	33.8	2.2	16.7	15.8	39.6	58.6
West South Central	+ .6	5.3	32.3	24.5	51.4	3.2	25.7	25.9	18.4	26.5
Mountain	3.1	2.2	17.1	16.6	34.4	+ .9	13.5	13.7	16.6	37.2
Pacific	+11.1	+10.2	2.6	3.0	+15.6	+11.1	+ 7.1	.8	5.1	+12.1
U.S.	4.5	+ .1	18.0	15.5	33.8	7.0	12.1	14.9	22.0	45.7

Source: *Agricultural Marketing Service.*

farm resources to development along a particular vector of a locational matrix; but equally, the variance to this structure exists, with greater adaptation of resource use and returns in regions distant from centers of industrialization than in areas of closer attachment. The difference either way is to be explained in income, communication and market reflection rather than in location. Market communication is more fundamental than location, per se. In some cases other variables are fundamental to communication. Income and phenomena surrounding it, such as schools and travel, explain why some pockets of labor in agriculture are ill-informed and less mobile in respect to job opportunities.[27] In other cases, lowness of income in agriculture itself has encouraged exodus regardless of vector in the locational matrix.

Expressing differential relating to this more complete structure during the decade 1940–50, the farm population declined 35 percent in North Dakota, 38 percent in Montana and 43 percent in Oklahoma. These are states without industrial development of important magnitude and great distance to the "industrial matrices" of the nation. The decline was only 15 percent in Pennsylvania where per capita commercial farm incomes averaged less than for the states cited above and industrial concentration is much greater. It was much lower than for these Plains states in areas of the Southeast where industrial development has been substantially greater and farm incomes are lower. While the groupings in Table 5.7 are too aggregative for reflection of important detail and difference, they do indicate rates of migration and labor reduction which have been especially high in areas distant from urban development centers and in areas of lowest farm income. (Also see Figure 12.1.)

In a more restricted geographic comparison and along a different comparative vein in economic development, we find higher labor returns in farming in north central Iowa than in parts of southern Iowa closer to industrial areas such as Des Moines or St. Louis. We find higher labor

[27] Gladys Bowles (*Farm Population and Migration From Rural Farm Population,* AMS Stat. Bul. 176) shows that the rate of migration from low income areas is about a fifth greater than that for agriculture as a whole.

returns on wheat farms in northeast Colorado or in Montana than for farms near a rapidly growing industrial complex in North Carolina. For example, in 1959 the average value of real estate per farm was around $65,000 in Phillips County, Colorado, a county without industrial development and of considerable distance from major industrial center. The value of products produced per farm laborer approached $10,000. In contrast, Paulding County, Georgia, had a per farm value of real estate of around $6,000. The value of product produced per farm laborer was around $600. Yet Paulding County falls in locational orientation and proximity to a rapidly developing industrial complex. The farm population of these two counties declined by nearly equal proportions from 1920 to 1959. The locational matrix per se fails to explain the greater degree of farm development and income in Phillips County as compared to Paulding County. These contrasts in agricultural adjustment and development stem more from mobility characteristics relating to farm income and market communication than to particular locational matrices related to industrialization. The same is true for the higher rate of development of farms in upper Illinois near industrial development as compared to those of western Arkansas which are more distant from development.[28]

The exact cause and extent of poverty or degree of economic development cannot be traced to a single original cause. As Myrdal points out, it is perhaps useless to look for one predominant explanation.[29] Still, if we were pressed for one, we would indicate it as lack of a community's ability to invest in the necessary social overhead capital, developing the characteristics of human resources which allow them to adjust to employment opportunities wherever they exist in the economy.

While the South lacks resources to make this investment on scale of other regions, this has not always been true. Even at earlier times when it possessed more wealth and development per head, it did not invest in the social overhead capital necessary to produce attributes of human resources for the purpose under discussion. This was true in comparison with newer regions of the West which were purely agriculture and with little commerce and which did invest more heavily in social overhead capital. Douglas C. North indicates that the South showed but little concern for widespread education of both whites and nonwhites before 1860, even though it had relatively more resources for this purpose than newly developed regions.[30] The complex of human opportunity and return cer-

---

[28] Also see Gladys Bowles ("Migration Patterns of Rural Farm Population," *Rural Soc.*, Vol. 22) for added explanations of migration patterns over geographic areas. For differences among regions, she emphasizes level of fertility, productivity of farming and farm income level, etc. Finally, the relation of demand and supply in labor rather than space and locational matrix per se, becomes important in the manner outlined by W. E. Hendrix, "Income Improvements in Low-Income Areas," *Jour. Farm. Econ.*, Vol. 41, pp. 1072–73.

[29] Gunnar Myrdal, *Rich Lands and Poor*, Harper and Brothers, New York, 1953.

[30] Douglas C. North, *Economic History of the United States to 1860*, Prentice-Hall, New York, 1961.

tainly revolves around this type of investment more than any other thing, although wealthier and more industrialized communities can best afford the investment. Quoting from North, we believe the following to explain much of the difference in human productivity and mobility outlined above.[31]

> Investment in human capital in the South was conspicuously lower than the other two regions. The ratio of pupils to white population in 1840 was 5.72 percent . . . compared to 18.41 percent in the non-slave holding states. . . . Even more significant were the attitudes of the dominant planter class, who could see little return to them in investment in human capital. . . . To educate the large percentage of white Southerners who were outside the plantation system was something they vigorously opposed. . . . The attitude of the West towards investment in skills, training and education led to an early willingness of Westerners to devote tax money for education and training . . . tax money devoted to public education all show a great difference of the West over the South. The Westerner looked upon education as a capital investment with a high rate of return . . . invested heavily in spreading skills, knowledge and technology. . . .

Capital for Transfer

The cost of transfer among locations is lower within an urban complex which includes a variety of industries and services than in transfer from farming at one location to nonfarm employment several hundred or a thousand miles distant. Accordingly, reservation price of industrial labor in one industry is near the return of competing industries which use similar labor at the same location. True, the cost of bus transportation, or gasoline for a cheap auto, is of small magnitude for long-distance travel. Without other commitments and investments, this relatively low direct cost allows great mobility among young persons and raises their reservation price and supply elasticity to agriculture. The real costs of transfer are considerably greater, however, for an established farmer with family commitments and farm investment. Liquidation of assets requires period of income loss for farms built around dairying or other fairly stable commodity flow. The period required for employment and housing contacts, and the living attached to it, also boosts costs for this group. In the sense of expectations and uncertainty, knowledge lack also results in a greater degree of discounting of possible returns at other locations and in other employment, as compared to the young or urban worker. We are moving, however, to a time when lack of capital and funds is much less a deterrrent to mobility than lack of market knowledge and skill flexibility. For many farm families in the poverty class, however, it is still an obstacle of magnitude equal to communication void.

Education and Training

No larger occupational group has had immobility forced on it through educational facilities as much as has agriculture. Not only are educational facilities generally of lowest quality in rural communities but also they have been oriented towards turning farm children back into agriculture. Vocational agricultural training has dominated in rural communities,

[31] *Ibid.*, pp. 133 and 155.

often being the only type of vocation training offered aside from home economics. As stated before, investment in occupational guidance also has been smallest in rural communities. Auxiliary educational and guidance facilities have supposed farm youth to be unique agricultural resources to be driven back into the industry to produce more farm products. Extension youth and 4-H efforts had this as their near single focus up to recent times, and in most states this is still true. (See the allocations of vocational education funds indicated in Chapter 13.) These concentrations have tended to help hold the supply elasticity of labor to agriculture at relatively low levels, although farm youth have increasingly been saved from extreme oversupply to agriculture because of the growing mass of communication stemming from economic development. Study by the Freedmans emphasizes the effect of education which tends to turn youth back into the same occupation.[32] They found that farm-reared youths are over-represented in low status position, whether status is measured in occupation or income. The farm reared generally held low-status jobs and received low incomes, the findings applying regardless of sex, color or region of residence. (Also see Table 13.1.)

Many rural communities do not have the resources for education and guidance facilities which will produce labor resources of quality and skill to mesh with opportunity in growing nonfarm industries of other states. It is unfortunate that the individual community has so long been expected to do so. The public in other states and locations make investments for improved agricultural resource use (e.g. research on new crop varieties, fertilizer response, etc.) in a particular agricultural county, in order that consumers in distant urban centers will gain from price, quantity and quality of farm commodity. Mechanisms to accomplish the same improvement and flexibility in the human product of agriculture also exist and are no more "unworldly," whether they be obtained by state and federal aid to schools or by other means.

Miscellaneous Attachments

Numerous other phenomena cause labor to remain attached to agriculture and receive income lower than in alternative occupations. Historically, the higher birth rate on farms than in cities has caused a large labor supply oriented to agriculture. Origin of large quantities of labor in agriculture is not per se a reason why its supply elasticity and reservation price to the industry should be low enough to cause depressed resource returns. However, it is only this fact in connection with the variables mentioned previously which causes the situation to prevail. Combine high birth rates with low incomes, inadequate education, lack of market information, inverse vocational guidance and lack of alternative economic opportunity and insufficient investment in social overhead generally, however, and the supply situation will be intensified. The

---

[32] Ronald and Deborah Freedman, "Farm Boy in the City," In *Principles of Sociology*, Henry Holt, New York, 1956.

opposite of these conditions and high birth rates are not a basic cause of low factor supply elasticity, large commodity output and low product and resource prices in any industry.

Difference in living costs in farm and city occupations provides a basis for difference in money income, but not in real income. The persistent intersector gap in money income cannot be explained fully by difference in price of consumer goods and services. Analysis by Koffsky and Reid suggests that purchasing power of farm and nonfarm income has important gaps even when price and tax differentials are considered.[33] Johnson suggests that per capita money income of farm people equal to around 70 percent of that of nonfarm people is necessary to give equal real income to comparable labor. This takes into consideration price differentials and composition of labor force by sex, age, capacity and dependency.[34]

The data of Table 2.4 indicate that important increase in per capita farm income is still necessary to provide comparable real income. Indirectly and somewhat remotely, we must also attribute some degree of low mobility and elasticity of farm labor supply to low elasticity of credit and capital to agriculture. The supply of credit is highly elastic, up to a restraint based on the equity of the operator. Beyond this, response of capital supply to him is relatively low at high prices. This factor market condition has implication to labor supply especially in the low income and poverty sectors of agriculture. If capital supply were of higher elasticity over a greater credit range, more operators could expand farm size and improve income. Consequently, low income and inadequate communication and related restraints on mobility would be lessened for their children, and not infrequently for themselves. For some established operators, ejection would come as greater capital supply allowed others to expand and bid away their resources.

To some extent, but in much less degree than sometimes proposed, government compensation policies have held labor in agriculture in the extreme short run. Undoubtedly the positive empirical effect of these payments has been much less important than the quantitative effect of the small public investments in appropriate job communication, economic outlook, education and training and vocational guidance towards nonfarm development. As in tobacco, subsidies and control effects on income have been largely capitalized into land values. Return to a farmer with fewer acres and higher land values is not materially greater than it would be in the absence of extra-market policy and more acres at lower price per acre. On the large number of low-income farms, an increment of $100 to $200 from government programs is not the crucial factor

[33] N. Koffsky, "Farm and Urban Purchasing Power. Studies in Income and Wealth," Vol. 11, *Nat. Bur. Econ. Res.*, 1949. Also see discussion by Margaret Reid.

[34] D. Gale Johnson, "Labor Mobility and Agricultural Adjustment," *In* Earl O. Heady *et al.* (eds.), *Agricultural Adjustment Problems in a Growing Economy*, Iowa State University Press, Ames, 1958.

Fig. 5.4. Rate of Outmigration From the Farm Population, 1940–50. (Source: USDA.)

in holding labor of a family in agriculture, particularly youth entering the labor force, when the unit has income equal to less than half that of comparable nonfarm labor.

Subsidies cannot explain the century-long and world-wide persistence of labor remaining in agriculture to the extent that incomes have trailed other sectors. The years 1940–60 in the U.S., with out-movement being very great, provide no positive indication that farm subsidies have been an important long-run deterrent to migration from farms. Logically, one would expect the rate of migration to be a function of income disadvantage in agriculture and off-farm job opportunities. Indeed it is, particularly at extremes as suggested by the stoppage or great reduction in migration during depressions such as that of 1929 or recessions of magnitude in the 1950's. (See Figure 5.4.) Even during 1954, following the 1953–54 recession, net migration from agriculture dropped to zero. But with job opportunities, the level of farm income and the effect of subsidies therein appear to have had little effect. People have migrated more rapidly in periods of high farm income than in periods of lower income, given the opportunity of employment. (Lack of nonfarm employment opportunity does, of course, give a zero ratio of nonfarm to farm return.) Neither have values oriented to agriculture acted to deter farm youth. The majority evidently prefer urban life and migrate accordingly. At even labor returns, many would still do so, given current day communication and orientation towards urban life.[35]

[35] See Larry Sjaastad, "Trends in Occupational Structure and Migration Patterns in the U.S." (Center for Agricultural and Economic Adjustment, *Labor Mobility*. Iowa State University, Nov., 1960). His regressions show magnitude of employment opportunity to be dominant over farm/nonfarm income ratio. Similarly, C. E. Bishop (same publication), found net migration to be positively regressed on level of farm prices, with farm prices and incomes also being positively correlated. His regressions also suggest a higher elasticity of migration with respect to nonfarm employment opportunity than with ratio of farm to nonfarm income of labor.

Supply and Demand of Farm Labor

Some quantitative indication of variables relating to U.S. farm labor supply is given by our Iowa study: in regression equations (5.60) estimated from original data in a two-equation, just-identified model, and (5.61), estimated as deviation from means by a single equation, the former for hired labor and the latter for family labor over the period 1929–57.

$$(5.60) \quad Y_h = 22.87 + .815Y_{t-1} + .176X_1 - .365X_2 - .104X_3$$

$$(5.61) \quad Y_f = \underset{(.136)}{.774Y_{t-1}} + \underset{(.059)}{.132X_1} - \underset{(.153)}{.405X_2} + \underset{(.078)}{.149Z_1} - \underset{(.103)}{.135Z_2}$$

While estimated by somewhat different technique and based on time series data which are not completely comparable, the relationships show, however, farm labor supply to be responsive with respect to price magnitudes within and outside agriculture.[36] For hired labor, the mean short-run supply elasticity in respect to farm wage rate is .13, the long-run supply elasticity being .71. The cross elasticity of hired labor supply with respect to nonfarm wage rate is predicted as .057 for the short run and .31 for the long run, all of these quantities being perhaps low for the future. While the results are not entirely comparable and the findings may have greater qualitative than quantitative importance, the family labor supply to agriculture shows positive response to magnitude of market labor return in agriculture and negative response to magnitude of nonfarm wage rate and percent unemployment.

The quantity of labor on farms also is a function of demand for this resource. Hence, we have estimated separate demand functions for hired and family labor. The U.S. demand function (5.62), estimated for hired labor over the period 1910–57, indicates demand for this resource to be responsive to changes in price of both labor and agricultural products.[37] Furthermore, the level of response of demand to a sustained price change was higher in the war and postwar period than in the depression period.

---

[36] For additional detail see Stanley Johnson, *Labor Supply and Demand in Agriculture*, Ph.D. thesis, Iowa State University, Ames. For both functions, labor supply is measured in millions and the variables have the meanings: Y_{t-1} is lagged magnitude of supply, X_1 is composite deflated farm wage rate, X_2 is time, X_3 is a composite nonfarm wage rate and employment indicator defined as $A(1\text{-}5U)$ where A is average wage rate and U is percent unemployment, Z_1 is a composite deflated nonfarm wage rate, Z_2 is percent unemployment. The figures in parentheses are standard errors. The hired labor equation was estimated by a simultaneous equation model and the family labor equation by a least-squares model.

[37] The demand function presented for hired labor and assumed to be the most efficient in estimation was a "simultaneously estimated autoregressive" least-squares equation with a distributed lag where: X_1 is the aggregate hired farm wage rate, X_2 is the index of prices received by farmers for all commodities, X_3 is time as a trend variable, X_4 is an aggregate value of farm machinery and equipment, and Y_{t-1} is the total number of hired farm workers lagged one year. The numbers below the regression coefficients in parentheses are the standard errors.

$$Y = 116.3 - .341X_1 + .243X_2 - .687X_3 + .206Y_{t-1} \quad (5.62)$$
$$(.122) \quad (.112) \quad (.523) \quad (.195)$$

These results indicate that hired farm labor demand response is related to the period of the business cycle. The estimated short-run price elasticity of demand for (5.62) is −.26. The computed long-run elasticity is −.32. Demand functions computed in our study for various census regions provide the elasticities in Table 5.8 for hired labor. These estimates, provided as means over the period 1910–57 by a distributed-lag regression model, indicate the elasticity of demand in respect to wage or price for hired labor resources to be considerably greater in the long run for all regions. Although there is some "tendency" for the elasticities to be highest in such "less industrialized" areas as the Cornbelt and Great Plains and in regions of lowest family incomes, we can make no probability statements about the pattern. The hired labor demand elasticities in respect to the parity ratio, prices received divided by prices paid, also are much greater in the long run. Among the regions for which we have computed the latter, no differential pattern can be expressed between short-run and long-run response. But the data clearly indicate a decline in demand for labor with an increase in its price and with a decrease in farm commodities relative to farm input costs. Empirical demand functions also were derived for family labor, both for the U.S. and by regions. The specification of the models was the same as that used for hired labor. Nationally, the regression results indicate a significant response in demand for family labor in relation to farm wage rate and farm income. However, "demand" is not unrelated to "supply" for family labor, and additional quantitative analysis is needed before differential effect of relative resource returns and farm commodity prices can be specified in demand for labor.

TABLE 5.8

ELASTICITIES OF DEMAND FOR HIRED FARM LABOR, 1929–57*

Region	Elasticities in Respect to Farm Wage Rate		Elasticities in Respect to the Parity Ratio	
	Short run	Long run	Short run	Long run
Northeast	−.05	−.17		
Mid Atlantic	−.19	−.75	.16	.64
East North Central	−.15	−.90		
West North Central	−.51	−.71	.36	.50
South Atlantic	−.12	−.32		
East South Central	−.35	−.82	.29	.68
West Central	−.26	−.67	.19	.50
Mountain	−.11	−.18		
Pacific	−.19	−.27		

* Functions for the West North Central and Mountain regions are for 1940–57. Those for the Pacific region are for 1947–57, a period too short to provide elasticities of comparability.

We have been discussing reasons why net migration and labor supply elasticity have not been greater—great enough to solve the farm price and resource income problem of agriculture. The analysis is in a relative sense to this magnitude of adjustment and not in terms of absolute migration. Numbers of persons migrating have been great relative to job opportunities on average, and in particular years. More persons would move if the job opportunities were closely available and they had this information. Certainly the elasticity of migration in respect to nonfarm returns is increasing. But it is not clearly apparent that migration can solve the capacity and commodity supply problems of commercial agriculture in the 1960's, except to the extent that capital losses of important magnitude are taken for land and more of this resource moves into less intensive uses such as forestry, grass and recreation. The degree of intensity, level of applying fertilizer and other technology inputs, is not likely to decline greatly at commodity prices of considerably lower level. This is true because many farmers do not use resources per acre at levels to equate marginal revenue and cost, as more large-scale operators with sufficient capital would do, and because the agricultural supply function so represented is based on a production function which has low elasticity in these reaches.

SHORT-RUN LAND SUPPLY FOR PARTICULAR USES

Land supply to agriculture is of much lower elasticity than labor supply. This is true because of its extreme lack of nonfarm employment opportunity. It responds readily to price stimuli in moving into urban and similar employment where the opportunity exists. This demand, however, is small relative to the total supply. More important to farm income and surplus problems is the magnitude of elasticity to particular farm uses, rather than to agriculture in aggregate. If land had shifted from corn, cotton and wheat to grass, trees and recreation as rapidly as knowledge and factor prices have allowed new technology capital to substitute for it, surpluses in these commodities would not have risen and their prices would have been higher, although prices of the alternative products would have been somewhat lower. Even if labor mobility were increased greatly, response of land would lag behind because of the tendency for remaining farmers to take it over and retain it in current uses.

Land in aggregate does respond to price stimuli in the longer run, even though the tendency of total plowland to persist at nearly 470 million acres for several decades would suggest other hypothesis. Yet if we examine land in farms and crops in regions such as New England and the Southeast, we do have evidence. In Table 5.9, for example, the long-run supply response of land to agriculture is suggested to be considerable for most of the states indicated. The magnitude implied is more nearly the cross elasticity of land for farms relative to the nonfarm price for land (or of land for farming relative to nonfarm return) rather than for

TABLE 5.9

LAND IN FARMS FOR SELECTED STATES AND REGIONS (1,000 ACRES)

State or Region	1900	1920	1940	1955
Masachusetts	3,147	2,494	1,938	1,439
Connecticut	2,312	1,899	1,512	1,138
New York	22,648	20,633	17,170	15,071
Pennsylvania	19,371	17,658	14,594	13,162
Virginia	19,908	18,561	16,445	14,686
West Virginia	10,655	9,570	8,909	7,352
North Carolina	22,749	20,022	18,845	18,260
Tennessee	20,342	19,511	18,493	17,654
New England	20,549	16,991	13,371	11,121
Mid Atlantic	44,860	40,573	33,639	29,898
South Atlantic	104,298	97,775	92,555	90,259

Source: U. S. Bureau of Census, *Statistical Abstract of the United States*, Vols. 44, 63, 71 and 81.

farm land with respect to farm prices. Yet the ratio of prices, nonfarm/farm, is the crucial quantity whether computed from a base of high or low farm prices. Given a low level of farm prices relative to the prices of land services for nonfarm uses, even where the latter are near zero, land would shift similarly out of agriculture over the long run in other agricultural regions of the nation. While some of the land withdrawal indicated in Table 5.9 has gone into urban uses, a greater proportion has gone into forestry and other less intensive uses as labor has migrated from agriculture. The level of returns in nonfarm relative to farm uses for both land and labor thus are crucial quantities in relation to land supplied for farm uses.

Labor mobility has never been great enough to cause noticeable slackening of land intensity over most of the nation. The rate of migration has to be considerably greater than it was during the 1950's, relative to the magnitude of the remaining labor force, to cause any extensive shift of land from the conventional product mix. The reservation price for land to agriculture in aggregate, except where it has urban opportunity, is in the neighborhood of tax levels and can even drop below this for short periods. For particular commodities in surplus, the reservation price also is low. The return from grazing is so much lower than for wheat over most of the Great Plains that commodity price would need to fall more than 50 percent from 1955 to 1959 levels before much of it would shift to grass. The same is even more true for cropland held in the hands of farmers which could be shifted to trees in the Southeast. With capital shortage and high discount rate, the present value of a forest product harvested 20 to 40 years in the future is extremely low for the individual. Under these conditions, most forest uses cannot compete easily with an alternative employment which returns $2 net per acre each year.[38] More

[38] See Earl O. Heady and Harald R. Jensen, *Farm Management Economics*, Prentice-Hall, New York, 1954, Chap. 8.

frequently, for the individual operator in the Southeast, forest crops have risen because the operator lacked capital for annual crops, with trees springing up under favorable climate and being too expensive to clear after establishment.

Clearly, an important degree of low supply elasticity for land in particular uses stems from labor elasticity and mobility. An abundance of persons have remained to till the land left by those who migrate from it in concentrated crop areas of feed grains, wheat and cotton. But also, low elasticity of capital and credit supply has caused land strongly to resist change in employment. As capital in committed form, machines can hang on for some time before their repair and replacement costs cause large numbers of farmers to crimp use of land. Low elasticity of credit supply to the individual operator, in the quantity extending beyond the highly elastic range tied to equity, acts to prevent shift of land to grass and trees with their longer waiting period. The discount rate for most farmers is not the market rate of interest. Few use variable capital to the level of marginal return (although the level is frequently lower over prolonged periods for fixed capital) because of uncertainty and captial market conventions.[39] The discount rate thus becomes an internal earning level of capital, compounded further because of uncertainty. Even in terms of intertemporal consideration alone, the present value of $1 in even 10 years is small (12 cents) for a farmer whose discount rate is 20 percent as illustrated in (5.63), with V being present value and I being income in the ith year.

$$V = \frac{I_i}{(1+r)^i} = \frac{1}{(1+.20)^{10}} = \frac{1}{8.183} = .12 \tag{5.63}$$

Ten years is a period approached in shift of wheat to grass. For 20 years at this rate, a period approached for pulpwood, $1 of future income has a present value of only 2 cents, compared with 83 cents for an annual crop marketed in a year. The capital restraint may operate more practically in the sense of the prolonged period required for family living expenses, before income of any magnitude is generated from investment in livestock under shift to grass. The problem of deferred income and living expenses is even more extreme in forest production. Added to these effects are institutional conditions tending to prevent shift, such as sharecropping and the dependence of landlords retired from farming on income of annual crops.

Government subsidies have undoubtedly been more important in holding land to the current product mix of agriculture than in holding labor to agriculture. This is especially true of policy mechanisms which provided price supports but did not require output restraints, or for those production control programs which allowed shift in each region from one to an-

[39] For some of these, see Earl O. Heady, *Economics of Agricultural Production and Resource Use*, Prentice-Hall, New York, 1952, Chaps. 16 and 17.

other surplus commodity. Still, cessation of price supports and turn to free market prices of agricultural commodities would not cause land to shift greatly in agricultural employment in the span of two years, or even in four years, although a start in this direction would come about. A much greater thinning of population and labor force, expansion of farm size and acquisition of capital per operator would be necessary before the allocation of land among products would change greatly.

CAPITAL INFLEXIBILITY

The reasons for low supply elasticity of agricultural capital already existing in forms for farm production have been explained in some detail. The fact that the "fixed forms" of capital serve in complementary capacity with land, over a large range, helps hold the latter resource to its current uses. Agricultural machines have no less transferability to other industries than obsolete airplanes. Unfortunately, however, they are attached to an industry rewarded less by economic growth than air transportation. While the rate of obsolescence is high in air transportation, growth in air freight has absorbed yesterday's equipment at prices relatively higher than scrap metal price (although this is less true for obsolete railroad equipment, with exodus of labor from passenger transportation).

The supply of capital services in farm forms can be illustrated as in Figure 5.5 where the supply price differs, depending on whether the demand for the particular capital forms is increasing or decreasing. Line *AP* represents a general nature of supply function traced when demand is increasing relative to new technology and the stock of capital items on hand. But during a period of decline in demand, the supply of capital services does not retrace *AP* segment, but rather *PB* until it falls to scrap value or similar reservation price as suggested by *SB* segment. (The relationship may be nonlinear, and without corners, even intersecting the

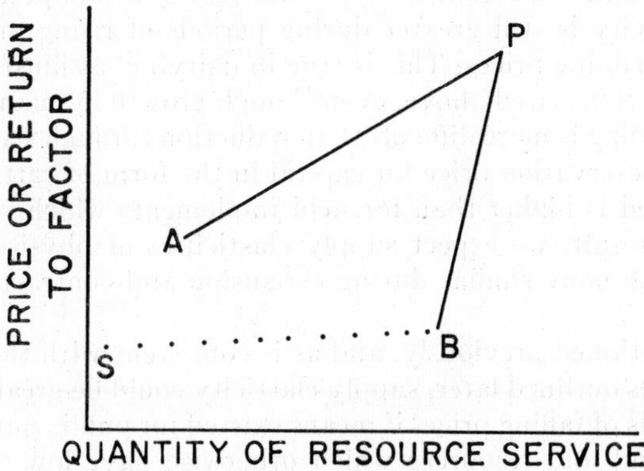

Fig. 5.5. Supply of Capital or Services in Periods of Expansion and Contraction of Return.

horizontal axis for the segment representing decline in commodity demand and price.) That the commodity supply function parallels this nature suggested for resources has been given some quantitative basis as indicated in Table 5.10. Four dairy supply functions, with observations in logarithms, were fitted to years of rising or falling trend and annual prices. While the number of observations is not large for each situation and additional refinement in analysis is desired, the data indicate supply elasticities in respect to price ratio which are lower under falling than under rising prices. Too, differences in elasticities under rising and falling

TABLE 5.10

ELASTICITIES OF MILK SUPPLY RESPONSE FOR LAKE STATES WITH RESPECT TO TIME AND MILK-FEED PRICE RATIO

Price Situation	Years	R^2	Elasticity in Respect to:	
			Time	Milk/feed price ratio
Rising trend and rising annual......	12	.97	.0057 (.0004)	.349 (.136)
Falling trend and falling annual.....	5	.99	.0054 (.0002)	.254 (.042)
Rising trend and falling annual.....	9	.94	.0053 (.0008)	.239 (.108)
Falling trend and rising annual......	7	.99	.0045 (.0003)	.134 (.114)

Source: Randolph Barker, *Milk Supply Functions for Lake States*, Ph.D. thesis, Iowa State University, Ames. (Figures in parentheses are standard errors.)

prices are expected to be less for products such as cattle or orchards, where resources such as machines and buildings can be supplied from outside but new stock must be supplied from within the sector, than for annual crops such as wheat and cotton. Low elasticity of supply for capital funds serves similarly to check expansion during rising prices.

The extreme difference between the Southeast and Southwest in change in structure and commercialization of farms is partly a reflection of variance in credit and capital supply elasticity. But even with these types of restraints on resource supply during expansion periods, product supply elasticity is still greater during periods of rising prices than in periods of declining prices. This is true in dairying, as illustrated by the response functions cited above, even though growth in quantity of stock through breeding is more difficult than reduction through slaughter. Too, the relative reservation price for capital in the form of cattle which can be slaughtered is higher than for field implements which serve only as scrap. As a result, we expect supply elasticities of physical capital to dairying to be more similar during expansion and contraction than for field crops.

As we mentioned previously, and as is consistent with the compensation principles outlined later, supply elasticity could be greatly increased during periods of falling prices if means existed for public purchase of the machines, land and resources which otherwise have low "downward" reservation prices.

6

Expenditure Patterns and Demand Potential

THE THREE MAJOR STRUCTURAL ADJUSTMENTS which exist as potentials for lessening the income burden in agriculture have been mentioned. In orthodox economics supposition of competitive conditions throughout the economy, one alternative is that of increasing the supply elasticity of resources. With migration of labor and land from agricultural uses, smaller inputs should result in larger marginal returns. Fewer and larger farms, with more capital per worker and less underemployment, should provide a larger net income per worker. Changes in this vein have been taking place, especially in labor input and farm size. But even while large, this change has not been enough to bring real resource returns to the nonfarm level. U.S. farm policy has never focused on this alternative, however. More frequently it has had opposite orientation, in training farm youth only for return to agriculture. Hence, a second alternative has been employed. It partly assumes that competitive structure is not the dominant form of nonfarm industry organization and that agriculture might appropriately be given mechanisms to control supply and apply price policy in the manner of other sectors. This alternative also assumes that the outmovement of labor cannot be great enough, or is sufficiently inconsistent with the values of rural area citizens, to attain goals of comparable resource returns. Supply and production controls thus have been used, in an attempt to increase commodity prices and factor returns. They have, however, been largely unsuccessful at the national level, apart from commodity storage and nonrecourse loans, because they have failed to control output.

Farmers and farm representatives thus have long looked to demand improvement, the third major alternative, as means or hope for eliminating the price and income problems of agriculture. Review of literature over the past two decades indicates that many agricultural scientists also rest their hopes on this expectation, particularly in respect to the population variable. Quite common is the exhortation by agricultural scientists to themselves: speed the supply of commodities before population increases to the Malthusian subsistence level. It is apparent, of course, that a society as wealthy as the United States will not and need not allow economic retrogression to the level where food is again its first concern. It need not do so because even should the stream of new technical knowledge diminish near zero, resources could be transferred from de luxe trim and zippers—if not from automobiles and clothing—to production of irrigation equipment, fertilizers and other resources representing existing production functions; allowing a greater output from conventional input types. It could use calorie sources of lower cost, both in money and resources. Also, it could manage population magnitude to levels consistent with food supply. More nearly, the task of a wealthy and progressing economy is to see that farm technology progresses so that large quantities of resources need not be diverted from other industries, or that it can use high-cost rather than low-cost calories and proteins rather than to prevent starvation.

Still it is true that demand expansion is the most popular major means of solving the farm problem. It also has widest political acceptance. This is true even if the demand expansion means has to be foreign surplus disposed only a step or two removed from dumping. Demand expansion is popular because it does not require persons to move out of agriculture when their values are otherwise; or does not interfere with the free market in farmers' decisions, where this mechanism is valued as an end per se (although the means to increase demand is likely to involve "nonmarket tampering" with particular quantities), or does not restrict opportunity for individuals to reflect their ability to initiate progress with greater vigor than other farmers. The popularity of this alternative is quantified in the many resolutions of farm groups and the documents of legislative committees, pressing for industrial utilization of farm products, improved nutrition of the American consumer, improvement of food quality, distribution of food to the underprivileged, foreign surplus disposal and improvement of the marketing system to lower costs and expand consumption. The Agricultural Marketing Act of 1947 had orientation in solving the farm problem through demand improvement. Even those provisions for research on improved marketing efficiently implicitly assumed that a reduction in processing costs would be effective in expanding demand and farm income. The fulfillment of these assumptions rests, of course, on (1) competition in food processing and retailing to an extent that cost savings would be reflected in higher prices at the farm level or (2) price elasticities of demand of sufficient magnitude that cost savings extending to consumers would cause sufficient increase in consumption to improve farm revenue.

The efficacy of demand improvement in increasing farm prices and income has been well illustrated in periods of sudden spurts in market expanse. Two recent examples which stick in the minds of farm people and their representatives are those of World Wars I and II. These periods of demand expansion were particularly effective because they were of short duration and supply elasticity of resources was sufficiently small. Accordingly, supply of commodity was sufficiently restrained to cause premium prices and factor returns. But given greater expanse of time and increased factor supply elasticity for new resources drawn into farming, commodity supply expanded sufficiently in both cases, even against the nontransitory elements of demand increase, to eventually cause major decline in farm prices and incomes.

While demand represents the one blade of the Marshallian scissors, determining level of price and resource return, it is not the sole phenomenon relating to these quantities. The world, and particular countries in it, have experienced periods of rapid increase in food demand.[1] This was particularly true of the eighteenth and nineteenth centuries, especially in the United States. Still, the rapid increase in demand did not remove the chronic disparities in relative farm returns illustrated by the global and historic quantities of Chapter 3. Change in consumer demand without parallel and consistent change in factor supply and structure causes an income problem to remain. But equally, sufficient change in demand can lessen the burden of resource adjustment. It is appropriate, therefore, that the potential in demand expansion be examined as a means of alleviating the income and resource returns problems of agriculture. Solution through this avenue is largely the hope of the more commercial segment of agriculture in respect to its secular income problem. It bears little promise for lifting incomes of the poverty segment of the industry to income levels consistent with the growth status of U.S. society. Families in this strata own so few resources that doubling of food demand would still leave family incomes at meager levels. Neither is it the appropriate solution to instability of output and price for individual commodities; problems which rest on high short-run supply elasticity and relatively constant marginal rates of substitution for resources transferred among products.

MAJOR DOMESTIC VARIABLES

Taking food as an aggregate product, the major variables determining magnitude of its consumption and demand are its own price, the level of per capita income and the size of the population. The relative preferences and the eating habits of consumers, the cross elasticity of demand of one food in respect to price of another, also could be mentioned. However, these explain mainly the mix of food products used, and much less the

---

[1] For examples of varying rates of growth in a European country see Jan Marczewski, "Some Aspects of Economic Growth in France," *Economic Development and Cultural Change,* Vol. 9.

aggregate food intake. True, food demand would increase if obesity came into high style in economies such as the United States, or if per capita income were to rise sharply in economies such as India. Neither of these alone promise to erase the domestic farm problem of the United States before 1970.

We mention "own price," because it is the elasticity of demand for food in respect to its own price which is the crucial quantity in respect to income crises created by rapid expansion of food output, or by cobweb fluctuations in commodity production. Own price is a crucial quantity because in an economy as wealthy as the United States the cross elasticity of food demand with respect to prices of nonfood consumer goods is insignificant in respect to aggregate food intake. Even in the realm where farm commodities can serve as resources, with potential substitution for resources of nonfarm resources, the cross elasticity of demand in respect to price of industrial substitutes has little near-at-hand importance. As we point out later, farm products must be priced much lower than 1960 prices before they have great potential industrial use as resources. Corn price, as an example, would have to fall to around 40 cents, in the 1960 price environment, before it would be substituted in significant quantities for other resources used in production of motor fuels. When corn declines to this price level, the farm problem will more nearly be solved through exodus of labor and land from agriculture, than through industrial utilization of farm products.

Population growth brings mouths to be fed and is the main source of domestic food demand increase in a wealthy society such as the United States. This magnitude, plus per capita income and related demand elasticities, provides a fragrant future for firms and industries which produce goods of greatest marginal urgency in a wealthy society. In India, considering both the underemployed workers in agriculture and in Bombay, Calcutta and many other towns, goods of high marginal urgency are those whose lack burdens the life of the consumer—food, shelter and primitive medicines. But in the United States and much of the Western world, the opportunity beyond population increase, domestic markets only considered, is not great for food. Marginal consumer urgency is greatest for those services which appeal to psychological wants related to time freed from work, rather than to biological needs in lessening misery. For nonfarm firms and industries, research and resources can be shifted continuously to the complex of developing urgencies or demands which arise less with population and more with level of income; although population growth also allows more consumers with demands rooted in affluence. Agriculture, given its geographic and climatic orientation, is not similarly adapted to continuous shift of resources and production from commodities which fall increasingly in the category of commonplace, to those which have more exotic attraction. Still, it is true that demand elasticities vary among farm commodities. And a review of these magnitudes is necessary in any analysis explaining possible structure and policy for agriculture.

THE PRICE ELASTICITIES

Agriculturists in public research and educational institutions conventionally have looked to greater output of the individual farm as a major means of income improvement. Price elasticity for the firm is infinite, as is true for any industry of pure competition. But what is true for the firm does not hold for the industry, and farmers in aggregate action are confronted with demand functions having price elasticities much less than unity. Consequently, increased output decreases aggregate revenue, as well as income for the individual who cannot increase output by a greater proportion than the decline in price. As mentioned in Chapter 3, this environment is highly conducive to economic growth, largely because the individual farmer, while realizing less income from greater industry output, is penalized even more by not advancing technology.

That price elasticities for major crops and food in aggregate are low (less than 1.0 with the result that revenue from greater output is less than that from smaller output) has been recognized for several decades by farm leaders and legislative bodies. This knowledge has been reflected in attempts at output control and supply management through public legislation and action of cooperatives and marketing organizations. The hope of production-control legislation has been to reduce output and thus increase farm income, as would certainly have been the case had supply actually been restricted. Supply control has been popular because output for the past decade has exceeded utilization, if we consider some foreign disposal as "surplus," only by around 6–8 percent annually.[2] But because output is so hard to control, given the political strength and logrolling practices of the various commodity, regional and income groups, demand expansion through advertising and promotion industrial utilization, distribution of food to the needy and others have been popular. To know the effect of these various schemes on individual commodities and food in aggregate, we need to examine the elasticities which relate to the major variables affecting expansion in food consumption.

Farm and Retail Elasticities

Price or income elasticity is lower at the farm level than at the retail level. This point can be illustrated with the two simple and hypothetical price-quantity demand equations in (6.1) and (6.2) for retail and farm level respectively.

$$P_r = a - 2Q_r \qquad (6.1)$$

$$P_f = .8a - 2Q_f \qquad (6.2)$$

[2] For example, J. D. Black and J. Bonnen (*A Balanced United States Agriculture in 1965*, Special Report No. 2, National Planning Association, Washington, 1956) placed it at 4 to 6 percent; R. G. Bressler ("Farm Technology and the Race with Population," *Jour. Farm Econ.*, Vol. 39.) placed it at 5 percent in 1954 and 1955; N. Koffsky ("Long-Term Price Outlook and its Impact on American Agriculture," *Jour. Farm Econ.*, Vol. 36) placed it at 8 percent of total production in 1953. Given the magnitude of output in the latter 1950's, excess production appears to be more nearly 8 percent in recent years.

Here, for purposes of simplicity, we suppose a constant marketing margin regardless of quantity. With quantity dependent, the two equations become (6.3) and (6.4). Taking the derivative of quantity with respect to price and multiplying by the price/quantity ratio, we obtain the two elasticities in (6.5) and (6.6). The elasticity at farm level is considerably less than that at retail level. For example, if we let $a=30$ and $Q=10$,

$$Q_r = .5a - .5P \tag{6.3}$$

$$Q_f = .4a - .5P_f \tag{6.4}$$

$$E_r = 1 - .5aQ_r^{-1} \tag{6.5}$$

$$E_f = 1 - .4aQ_f^{-1} \tag{6.6}$$

elasticity at retail level is $-.5$ and elasticity at farm level is $-.2$. (Similarly, other equation forms provide differences in elasticities at the two levels, aside from those which force a given elasticity.) The elasticity at retail level is the significant figure for analyses concerned with consumer expenditures and outlays; that at farm level for interpretations concerned with farm income. The two arithmetic quantities cited above represent about the same relative difference we find in price elasticities at farm and retail levels, with the magnitudes of the example being approximately equal to both the absolute and relative differences found for income elasticities.

Elasticity Magnitudes

Elasticity magnitudes, as well as rate of population increase, during the first century of U.S. society caused developmental policies to be more consistent with growing farm income than in the first half of the twentieth century. We have few measurements of these elasticity magnitudes, except calculations such as those of Engel leading to qualitative indications for consumers and nations in general. Intensive demand analysis for farm commodities conducted first by Henry Schultz indicated price elasticities generally to be low; sufficiently less than unity so that increased output was expected to be accompanied with diminished revenue in the short run.[3] More recent models and estimating techniques, such as distributed lag and simultaneous equation approaches, would provide estimates of short-run and long-run elasticities differing from these of Schultz. However, recent estimates are consistent with those of Schultz in the important sense; namely, price elasticities are sufficiently low that increase in supply which exceeds shift in demand function will give rise to income problems in agriculture.

The relative magnitudes of price elasticities have particular importance in determining how resources within agriculture might be best allocated as differential rate of technical change and supply increase takes

[3] H. Schultz, *The Theory and Measurement of Demand*, University of Chicago Press, Chicago, 1938.

place. However, for purposes of general farm policy, it is not exceedingly important whether the average price elasticity for a particular commodity is −.1 or −.25. The important knowledge is: it is much less than 1.0 and is low. Even for specific policy aimed at reducing output to bring price to a certain level, the variables on the supply side are too elusive in exact quantification and control to cause great needs in reducing the standard error of estimate for the demand elasticities by 20 percent. In this sense, Schultz's quantities, tentatively forthcoming in the 1920's provided forewarning of farm price and income problems to come. Average price elasticities computed by Schultz for three periods approximating 1875–95, 1896–1914 and 1915–29 were respectively −.38, −.27 and −.31 for sugar; −.71, −.61 and −.53 for corn; −.51, −.25 and −.12 for cotton; −.03, −0.15 and −.18 for wheat (but as a more reliable estimate, $-.2 \pm .04$ for 1921–34 with seed excluded);[4] and −.68, −.54 and −.32 for potatoes.

More significant than the exact magnitudes of these elasticities is the fact that they are less than unity and declining with time. The latter is expected in a rich society, growing wealthier amidst an abundance of food; where per capita food consumption is limited by physical restraint of the consumer, medical considerations and concepts in beauty which lead away from obesity. Looking upon food as an aggregate commodity, as is appropriate where substitution takes place largely within the aggregation and hardly at all with nonfood commodities, Cochrane indicates the price elasticity of farm product also to decline with time.[5] He estimates price elasticity for food in aggregate, at the mean of the periods, to have been −.31 for 1922–41, −.23 for 1929–49, with 1943–46 excluded, and −.10 for 1929–56, with 1943–46 excluded. Other estimates substantiate decline for individual commodities.[6] Based on this trend, a given excess in rate of supply increase over rate of demand increase brings a growing income depression as time progresses. Similarly, the commodity cycle causes a sharper depression in income during the period of large output and a widening relative swing in price and income as supply fluctuates in cobweb fashion.[7] Knowledge that demand elasticities tend to decline with time and income growth is also important for proper interpretation of the coefficients which follow. Most have been computed as average

---

[4] Schultz (*ibid.*, p. 400) compares his estimate of $-.24 \pm .04$ for the period 1921–35 with that of Working ("The Elasticity of Demand for Wheat," *Econometrica*, Vol. 5, pp. 185–86), $-24 \pm .09$, for the period 1921–34. He also indicates that the demand curve for wheat was already shifting downward in the period 1896–1913.

[5] Willard W. Cochrane, *Farm Prices, Myth and Reality*, University of Minnesota Press, Minneapolis, 1957, p. 38.

[6] For example, see G. W. Dean and Earl O. Heady, "Changes in Supply Response and Elasticity for Hogs," *Jour. Farm Econ.*, Vol. 40, p. 858; G. S. Shepherd, *et al.*, *Economic Analysis in Trends for Beef Cattle and Hog Prices*, Iowa Agr. Exp. Sta. Bul. 405, p. 737; F. V. Waugh, *Graphic Analysis in Agricultural Economics*, USDA Handbook No. 128, p. 30–31.

[7] See Earl O. Heady and G. W. Dean, *Changes in Supply Functions and Supply Elasticities in Hog Production*, Iowa Agr. Exp. Sta. Bul. 471.

elasticities from time series data. Accordingly, they overestimate the elasticities currently existing, or those which will determine the magnitude of income and adjustment problems of the future.

Recent Estimates of Price Elasticities

The magnitude of elasticities estimated for farm products varies, depending on the period of the time series observations used, the estimating technique and the income level (mean or otherwise) for which they are derived. Hence, for fuller examination and knowledge of these quantities it is essential to examine several sets of more recent estimates, both to find values towards which these converge and to estimate general level to which they decline with time. One of the more recent sets of estimates for livestock products at the farm level are those of Brandow in Table 6.1.[8] The negative elements along the diagonal of the matrix indicate elasticities on the commodity's own price; others represent cross elasticities in respect to the commodity indicated. Except for calves, sheep and vegetable oils, variations likely growing out of "flukes" in the sense of multicollinearity in data for the livestock, all own elasticities are less than unity. This denotes that, other things remainining equal or all commodities increasing jointly in quantity, revenue from the livestock product declines with output. Eggs show an own elasticity of about −.23, indicating a 4.4 percent decline in price for a 1 percent increase in output. Hogs, with an own elasticity of −.46, indicate a 2.2 percent decline in price for a 1 percent increase in output; although the net effect of increased hog production can be determined only by consideration of the cross elasticities. On the basis of own elasticity alone, cattle price is estimated to decline by 1.5 percent for each 1 percent increase in output. With its more recent popularity and holiday characteristic, turkey has an own price elasticity of −.92, while soybean and cottonseed oil, commodities of wide opportunity in substitution with other oils, are indicated to have own elasticities respectively of −3.99 and −6.92. The last column suggests the rate at which demand for each commodity increases with time (population and change in consumption habits due to income and occupational status being the dominant variables of time). Both eggs and lard show a declining demand with time.

A Minnesota study synthesized elasticity coefficients at retail for the somewhat more aggregative groups of commodities shown in Table 6.2.[9] The estimates are based on past empirical studies, theory and judgment and are "updated" to a 1955 point in time. Fruits in aggregate are estimated to have an own price elasticity as high as unity. Meat products, estimated as 36 percent of expenditures, have an elasticity of only −.60

[8] See George Brandow, *Economic Policies for Agriculture in the 1960's*, Implications of Four Selected Alternatives, Joint Economic Committee of the United States, 86th Congress, 2nd Session, Washington, 1960.

[9] J. M. Wetmore, *et al.*, *Policies for Expanding the Demand for Farm Products in the U.S.*, University of Minnesota Tech. Bul. 231.

TABLE 6.1

FARM-LEVEL PRICE ELASTICITIES OF DEMAND AND TREND TERMS FOR LIVESTOCK PRODUCTS AND FATS AND OILS

Quantity Demanded of—	Farm Prices of:											
	Cattle	Calves	Hogs	Sheep and lambs	All chickens	Turkeys	Eggs	All milk	Soy-bean oil*	Cotton-seed oil*	Lard*	Time†
Cattle	−0.684	0.039	0.060	0.030	0.048	0.005	0.003	0.005	‡	‡	—	3.808
Calves	.256	−1.082	.110	.055	.087	.009	.003	.005	‡	‡	—	1.665
Hogs	.091	.025	− .458	.026	.042	.005	.003	.005	‡	‡	—	1.680
Sheep and lambs	.421	.116	.247	−1.782	.136	.014	.003	.005	‡	‡	—	.110
All chickens	.157	.043	.092	.032	− .737	.081	.003	.005	‡	‡	—	1.678
Turkeys	.066	.018	.039	.014	.317	− .924	.003	.005	‡	‡	—	1.703
Eggs	.011	.002	.006§	.001	.003	.001	− .233	.006	‡	‡	‡	− .331
All milk	.009	.002	.004§	.001	.002	.001	.002	− .416	0.016	0.010	0.004	1.180
Soybean oil	.007	.001	.003§	.001	.002	.001	.001	.143	−3.988	2.736	.131	4.040
Cottonseed oil	.008	.001	.004§	.001	.002	.001	.001	.176	5.577	−6.921	.136	4.191
Lard	.008	.001	.004§	.001	.002	.001	.001	.046	.181	.094	− .540	− .146

* Wholesale price.
† Percentage change in quantity demanded per year at constant prices.
‡ Less than 0.0005.
§ Effect of pork price.

TABLE 6.2

RETAIL PRICE ELASTICITIES OF DEMAND FOR SELECTED COMMODITY GROUPS

Demand Equation for:	Proportion of Expenditure*	Retail Price					
		Meat	Dairy products	Eggs	Fruits	Vegeta-bles	"Other"
Meat...........	.363	−.60	.10	.04	.08	.06	.03
Dairy products...	.171	.21	−.50	.02	0	.06	.03
Eggs............	.045	.29	.08	−.58	0	0	.05
Fruits...........	.088	.33	0	0	−1.00	.20	.03
Vegetables.......	.098	.22	.10	0	.18	−.70	.02
"Other".........	.235	.05	.02	.01	.01	.01	−.10

* Proportion of total expenditure on commodity group indicated.

while "other" commodities, accounting for 24 percent, are estimated to have an elasticity of only −.10; both elasticities suggesting a very large decline in price for each unit increase in output. As also suggested by Table 6.1, these data indicate small cross elasticities among commodity categories. Hence, greater technical efficiency in production or processing of one commodity, to lower its price and draw demand away from its competing products, promises only meager gains to producers. A similar set of synthesized farm level quantities are presented in Table 6.3.[10] Like those of Table 6.2, they are useful in the sense that they draw together the most logical estimates from numerous demand studies based on different techniques and periods, although they perhaps refer best to the demand regime of the past two decades. In contrast to previous tables, the elasticity coefficients have been converted to a form showing the percent by which price is estimated to decline at farm level, as the quantity of output of the particular commodity or competing commodities is increased. In this case, the aggregate indicated as "competing commodity" is large enough that increase in the magnitude would lessen price of the

TABLE 6.3

EFFECT OF ONE PERCENT INCREASE IN OUTPUT OF COMMODITIES ON PRICES (PERCENT)

Commodity	Response of Price to a 1 Percent Increase in Output of:	
	Particular commodity	Competing commodities
Beef and veal..................	−1.7	−.5
Pork..........................	−2.5	−.4
Lamb and mutton...............	−1.7	−.7
Poultry meat..................	−1.7	−1.0
Eggs..........................	−5.0	−1.5
Dairy products................	−3.3	−.3

[10] G. S. Shepherd, *et al.*, Price and Income Projections Under Free Market Conditions for Feed Grains. Iowa State University Center for Agricultural and Economic Adjustment, Special Report.

particular commodity by important extent. Computed from these figures, for example, the own price elasticity of pork is estimated as (1) ÷ (−2.5) = −.40.

As noted, the figures presented above are consistent with others estimated for time series data of the '30's, '40's and '50's. Fox obtained own price elasticity of −.41 for all food livestock products (1922–41) and −.62 for meat (1922–41) by least-squares methods at the farm level.[11] At the retail level, Shepherd obtained −.74 for meat by least-squares (1920–41); Tintner obtained −.79 by reduced form equation (1919–41) and Working obtained −.67 by diagonal regression (1922–41).[12] At farm level, Fox obtained (1922–41) −.84 for beef, −.65 for pork and −.34 for eggs by least-squares.[13] At retail level, Wahby[14] obtained −.77 (1922–41) for beef by reduced form, and Judge[15] obtained (1921–41) −.29 by reduced form and −.58 by limited information, for eggs. Using a distributed lag model for meat (1922–41), Ladd and Tedford did not establish own price elasticity for meat at retail to be materially higher in the longrun than in the shortrun, although this type of response is generally expected for price change.[16] Learn, using single equations with observations in first differences (1924–54 with 1942–46 excluded), obtained own price elasticities at farm level of −.73 for beef, −.55 for pork, −.86 for poultry, −.41 for eggs and −.38 for dairy products.[17] Maki, estimating by first differences over quarters for the period July, 1947 to December, 1956, derived own price elasticity at market level of −.55 for beef and −.59 for pork.[18] However, distributed lag response might again be expected for periods of this duration. Rojko provides own price elasticities at retail of −.27 for fluid milk and cream, −.25 for butter and −.74 for manufactured dairy products, using first difference and least-squares (1924–41).[19] Using his model II, Gerra obtained (1931–41, 1946–54) own price elasticities for eggs at retail ranging from −.11 to −.40 respectively, using single and simultaneous equation estimates.[20] Judge, using alternative techniques and periods between 1921 to 1950, obtained own retail

[11] K. Fox, "Factors Affecting Farm Income, Prices and Food Consumption," *Agr. Econ. Res.*, Vol. 3.

[12] G. S. Shepherd, *Changes in Demand for Meat and Poultry Products*, Iowa Agr. Exp. Sta. Bul. 368; G. Tintner, "Static Econometric Models," *Metroeconomica*, Vol. 2; and Elmer Working, *Demand for Meat*, Institute of Meat Packing, Univ. of Chicago, Chicago, 1954.

[13] Fox, *loc. cit.*

[14] O. Wahby, "Econometric Analysis of the Demands for Pork, Beef and Poultry," *Econometrica*, Vol. 20.

[15] G. Judge, *Econometric Analysis of the Demand for Eggs*, Ph.D. Thesis, Iowa State Univ., Ames, Iowa, 1952.

[16] G. W. Ladd and G. R. Tedford, "Generalization of the Working Method for Estimating Long-Run Elasticities," *Jour. Farm Econ.* Vol. 41.

[17] E. W. Learn, "Demand for Livestock at the Farm Level," *Jour. Farm Econ.*, Vol. 38.

[18] W. Maki, "Economic Effect of Short-Run Changes in Demand," *Govt. Farm Econ.*, Vol. 39.

[19] S. A. Rojko, "Econometric Model for the Dairy Industry," *Jour. Farm Econ.*, Vol. 39.

[20] M. J. Gerra, *Demand, Supply and Price Structure of Eggs*, USDA Tech. Bul. 1204.

TABLE 6.4

Price Elasticities (own) of Demand at Farm Level From Mehren for 1949

Commodity	Elasticity
Dairy products	−.60
Whole milk (Mfgr.)	−.60
Hogs	−.80
Lamb and mutton	−.80
Beef	−.80
Eggs	−.42
Butterfat	−.75
Chickens	−.89
Turkeys	−.55
Wheat	−.41
Beans, dry	−.12
Potatoes	−.15
Peanuts	−.40
Cotton	−.60
Soybeans	−.60
Burley tobacco	−.20
Flue tobacco	−.45
Barley	−.51
Corn	−.69
Grain sorghum	−.38
Oats	−.55
Rice	−.40

price elasticities for eggs ranging from −.30 to −.60.[21] Using his own estimates and those of other studies, Mehren summarized the price elasticities at farm level for prices at 1949 magnitude, included in Table 6.4.[22] These data, like most others cited, are based on time series data of an earlier period in supply, per capita income and location in the price-quantity vector. However, the elasticities are predicted by Mehren to exceed long-run elasticities because demand was so favorable in 1949.

Demand analysts have concentrated their efforts on livestock products. However, those studies available generally indicate inelastic demand for field crops. Meinken, again using an earlier time period (1921–29 and 1931–38) estimated domestic food wheat price elasticity, at Kansas City price, to be −.04; a quantity extremely near zero.[23] For domestic consumption as feed, he estimated the own price elasticity of wheat to range from −.33 to −.40, depending on the estimating procedure. His estimates for feed grains (1922–41) were −.63 for corn, −.49 for oats and −.41 for barley.[24] The Iowa study assumes an elasticity of −.40 at farm

[21] G. G. Judge, *Econometric Analysis of the Demand and Supply for Eggs*, University of Conn. Agr. Exp. Sta. Bul. 307.

[22] G. L. Mehren, "Comparative Costs of Agricultural Price Support in 1949," *Amer. Econ. Rev.*, Vol. 41.

[23] K. W. Meinken, *Demand and Price Structure for Wheat*, USDA Tech. Bul. 1136.

[24] K. W. Meinken, *Demand and Price Structure for Oats, Barley and Sorghum Grains*, USDA Tech. Bul. 1080. Also see G. A. King, *Demand and Price Structure for By-Product Feeds*, USDA Tech. Bul. 1183. His limited information estimate gives −.68 for feed grains in aggregate.

level for feed grains as a more current estimate.[25] An own price elasticity of −.5 at farm level has been projected as a current estimate for rice.[26] Fox summarizes the data in Table 6.5 for miscellaneous fruits and vegetables at farm level.[27] Again, these indications of own price elasticities are for mean price, quantity, income and time of period, 1922–41. Current elasticities and those of relevance for the next decade are expected to be considerably lower. Quantitatively, the important reflection of these data are the differences in price elasticities among commodities.

TABLE 6.5

PERCENT PRICE CHANGES ASSOCIATED WITH 1 PERCENT CHANGE IN PRODUCTION, SELECTED VEGETABLES AND FRUITS

Commodity	Percent Price Change	Commodity	Percent Price Change
Potatoes	−3.51	Oranges	−1.61
Onions (summer)	−2.90	All citrus	−1.32
Lemons (summer)	−2.48	Winter vegetables	−1.13
Onions (all)	−2.27	Spring vegetables	− .95
Grapefruit	−1.77	Apples	− .79
Summer vegetables	−1.72	All deciduous fruit	− .68
Fall vegetables	−1.67	Peaches	− .67

Aggregate Food Elasticity

Numerous studies have estimated price elasticity for food in aggregate. The elasticity coefficients, estimated largely for the period 1920–41, with quantities referring to expenditures at retail level, again vary some depending on the estimating technique used. These tend to concentrate on a magnitude −.20 to −.25 at retail level, suggesting a percentage price decline from four to five times a percentage output increase under given conditions. This is the magnitude suggested as most likely by Wetmore.[28] However, numerous studies provide elasticities which are higher for the retail level, perhaps averaging nearer −.40 for all time series studies completed to date, but the distribution of coefficients is skewed in direction of quantities smaller than this.[29] Even on the basis of this magnitude,

[25] Shepherd, *loc. cit.*

[26] Brandow, *loc. cit.*

[27] K. A. Fox, *Econometric Analysis of Public Policy*, Iowa State University Press, Ames, Iowa, 1958, p. 105.

[28] Wetmore, *loc. cit.*

[29] See such studies as the following: M. A. Girshick, and T. Haavelmo, "Statistical Analysis of Demand for Food," *Econometrica*, Vol. 15; I. Tobin, "Statistical Demand Function for Food in the U. S.," *Jour. Royal Stat. Soc.* Series A, 1B; G. Kuznets, "Measurement of Market Demand for Food," *Jour. Farm Econ.*, Vol. 35; L. N. Shores, *Structural Equations Defining Demand for Food*, M. A. Thesis, Univ. of Chicago, Chicago, 1946; M. C. Burk, "Changes in Demand for Food from 1941–50," *Four Farm Econ.*, Vol. 33; W. W. Cochrane, *Analysis of Farm Price Behavior*, Penn. State Univ. Progress Report No. 50.

assuming no decline with time, a price decline of 2.5 percent for each 1 percent increase in output, is implied for a particular environment in respect to population, time and income.

Even if we accepted the mean of these estimates of food price elasticity for the prewar period, the span of nearly all estimates, it would overestimate future elasticity when consumers have higher incomes and food abundance has driven consumption to lower points on the demand curve. It should be noted that the elasticity coefficients quoted are almost entirely mean estimates in respect to time, income and food consumption over the time period 1920–41. In this sense, an estimate of −.25 or less is a more realistic estimate of the current retail price elasticity of food, and even this magnitude is likely on the upper side. Barton and Daly estimate a price elasticity of −.15 to −.20 at the farm level and Daly's estimate is below −.15.[30] Food production in aggregate over the next decade is more likely to "bump against" a price elasticity at farm level of −.15 than of −.4. (The price elasticity of food in aggregate is much lower than for commodities which make up the aggregate because substitution among foods is not then possible.)

In any case, elements of developmental policy to shift supply to the right (whether based on public investment in technical research, lower capital costs or subsidies to encourage improved practices under the guise of soil conservation payments), are likely to have negative effect on farm revenue. Given the price elasticities cited above, rapid shifts in the supply function obviously stand to benefit the consumer rather than the producer, allowing him to acquire his food basket with smaller outlay. This in itself is a noble purpose. Everyone, including farmers, is a consumer. The significant policy questions are whether this transfer of benefits to consumers can be accomplished equitably without undue burden or sacrifice to producers, or whether the rate of change should be managed in order that farm families might better share in the progress which they help to create.

These elasticity figures also suggest the futility of coaxing the American consumer to "eat up the surplus," even if he were willing to abandon a smaller waistline. With consumer food outlay at about 60 billion dollars, a 3 percent increase in aggregate (1.8 billion constant dollars) consumption would entail a price decline of 7.5 percent and a 4.5 billion dollar decline in expenditure at retail (with a price elasticity even as great as −.4). The public of consumers would not be likely to subsidize itself to

[30] G. T. Barton, and R. F. Daly, "Prospects for Agriculture in a Growing Economy," *Problems and Policies of American Agriculture*, Center for Agriculture and Economic Adjustment, Iowa State Univ. Press, Ames, 1959, p. 32. Koffsky and Daly, ("Potential Demand for Farm Products over the Next 25 Years," *Dynamics of Land Use*, Center for Agricultural and Economic Adjustment, Iowa State Univ. Press, Ames, 1961) summarize the price elasticities for broad groups as follows: meat animals, −.30; dairy products, −.05; poultry, −.50; eggs, −.10; fruits and vegetables, −.06; cereals, potatoes and beans, −.002; other crops outside of imports, −.02. Daly, ("Demand for Farm Products at Farm and Retail Level," *Jour. Amer. Stat. Assoc.*, 1958, pp. 656–658.) indicates farm level elasticities in respect to income of less than .15 for farm products in aggregate.

this amount, simply to coax itself to greater feasting (i.e., it would consume the added food only at the outlay reduction, then would have to compensate farmers for roughly 40 percent of the reduction.)

INCOME ELASTICITIES

A substantial rise in per capita income would surely increase both physical intake of food and expenditure on foods, given population and point in time, in such nations as Peru, Nicaragua, Bolivia, Jordan, Iran, Tunisia, Libya, Korea, Ceylon, Indonesia, Philippines, India, Pakistan and China (see Figure 17.2). Starting from low levels of income, income elasticity of demand stands to be quite high, particularly for livestock products and less common grains and vegetables, but even for food in aggregate. Commodities with large elasticities in economies of high per capita income fall largely outside the food category, however. Investors searching out growth stocks for investment turn rather to recreational commodities, appliances, travel services, amusement and services or conveniences incorporated with foods, rather than to food production per se. Physical intake of food per capita has declined slightly in the United States since 1920, although the grocery mix now includes commodities of higher quality and greater caloric and resource cost.[31] Decline in intake has come about with shift to occupations requiring lower physical exertion, a greater proportion of older persons in the population and a set of values placing premium on "slimness and longer life."

GROWTH OPPORTUNITY

Consumer expenditures do show some expansion with income growth, even in wealthy societies. However, this rise in expenditure is reflected in purchase of higher quality or more exotic foods and on the services which can be incorporated with foods, rather on aggregate farm products per se. This growing expenditure per capita on food in the United States has been especially concentrated on freezing, packaging and preparation of foods. It also finds allocation in important magnitude to meals away from home, with meals in exotic atmosphere having higher income elasticity than ordinary lunchroom meals. An estimate based on cross-sectional data of urban families in the spring of 1948 showed an elasticity of expenditure in respect to income of .42 for all food, .29 for food consumed at home and 1.14 for that consumed away from home.[32]

In general, the major elements of positive income elasticity expressed in the data which follow are for the services and quality of food, rather

[31] In contrast, demand elasticity for consumer items such as automobiles has been high. Chou (*Demand for Automobiles in the U.S.*, North Holland Publishing Co., Amsterdam, 1957, pp. 68–71, 81–83) reviews price and income elasticities of around −1.5 and −2.1 respectively.

[32] K. A. Fox, "Factors Affecting Farm Income, Prices and Food Consumption," *Agr. Econ. Res.*, Vol. 3.

than for food itself. The income elasticity for food in aggregate and physical form is so near zero in the United States that further growth in per capita income bears no promise for prosperity in the farm industry paralleling that of sectors designated as growth industries by the stockbroker, or even in comparison with the average of the U.S. industry. It is for this reason that the food processing industry grows more rapidly than the food industry, or that the spread between farmer and consumer, the marketing margin, widens with time.

As with price elasticities, those for income vary with the estimating technique used, the period of observation and algebraic form and techniques used in deriving coefficients. A summary of income elasticities has been prepared by Daly, to provide a basis for projecting demand to future points in time.[33] These are included in Table 6.6 and presumably refer to response in farm commodity rather than expenditure at retail.

TABLE 6.6

INCOME ELASTICITIES OF DEMAND FOR PROJECTING PER CAPITA CONSUMPTION

Commodity	Elasticity	Commodity	Elasticity
Citrus fruits	.65	Pork	.20
Beef	.40	Eggs	.15
Tomatoes	.40	Other fruits	.13
All fruits	.32	Fluid milk and cream	.12
Chicken and turkey	.30	Total milk equiv.	.10
Fresh green and yellow vegetables	.25	Sugar	−.07
All meat	.25	Wheat and flour	−.20
All vegetables	.25	Dry beans and peas	−.20
Other vegetables	.20	Potatoes	−.25
		Melons	−.40

As denoted by the negative coefficients, per capita consumption declines with per capita income growth for commodities such as potatoes, wheat products, and dry beans and peas. Income elasticities are also predicted to be less than zero, with the same implications, for specific products within groups of Table 6.6. This is true for lard, fats and oils, nuts and similar inferior goods, with physical food intake per person declining with income level for this group of inferior goods. Waite and Trelogen estimated the elasticities for particular commodities shown in Table 6.7.[34]

[33] R. F. Daly, "The Long-Run Demand for Farm Products," *Agr. Econ. Res.*, July, 1956. In a parallel set of coefficients based on time series, single equation estimates and presented by Barton and Daly (*ibid.*) include the following income elasticities for expenditure at the farm level: .48 for meat animals, .62 for poultry, .62 for poultry, .47 for eggs, .09 for dairy products, −.24 for grains and dry beans, .16 for all fruits and vegetables and .16 for all other foods. For a somewhat different aggregation of commodities, Koffsky and Daly (*ibid.*) provide the following predictions of income (expenditure) elasticities: Meat animals, .48; Dairy products, .09; Poultry, .62; Eggs, .04; Fruits and vegetables, .16; Cereals, potatoes and beans, −.23; and other crops, .16.

[34] W. C. Waite and H. C. Trelogen, *Introduction to Agricultural Prices*, Burgess Publishing Co., Minneapolis, 1948, p. 25.

TABLE 6.7

INCOME ELASTICITIES OF DEMAND FOR SPECIFIC COMMODITIES

Commodity	Elasticity	Commodity	Elasticity
Lamb and mutton	1.77	Vegetable shortening	.32
Tomato juice	1.38	Uncooked cereal	.25
Beef sirloin	1.32	Round steak	.21
Asparagus	1.14	Canned beans	.09
Cream	1.12	Canned peas	.03
Chocolate	1.04	White potatoes	−.04
Fresh peas	.90	Chuck roast	−.04
Prepared cereal	.77	Rice	−.10
Fresh carrots	.68	Evaporated milk	−.13
Sliced ham	.61	Salt side	−.19
Pork chops	.52	Boiling roast	−.21
Cheese	.50	White flour	−.24
Milk	.50	Lard	−.30
Orange	.43	Canned tomatoes	−.37

These estimates, based on 1935–36 cross-sectional expenditure data for households in the North and West are somewhat obsolete for the current demand regime, but do indicate the variance existing among individual food products. Numerous of the products in the inferior goods category, such as wheat and dry beans with negative elasticities, are grown independently. However, others of low elasticity are produced as technical complements with those of high elasticities. Examples are lard, sliced ham and bacon or chuck roast, hamburger and beef sirloin. Hence, the long-term outlook is not as good for beef cattle and hogs as it is for sirloin and sliced ham respectively.

Other income elasticities for cross-sectional studies based on later time periods are shown in Table 6.8. Those by Heifner for 1955 and by Fox for 1948 are compared with the cross-sectional estimates based on a prior period of approximately 1922–41. (Also see the income elasticities shown in Table 17.3.) These data emphasize both the overestimation of economic growth on demand at the farm level when elasticities are measured in consumer expenditure and in earlier period before the tremendous postwar upsurge in income growth.

The data in Table 6.8 partly suggest why supply and price problems have been particularly great for individual commodities in postwar years. Extreme surplus problems have existed at times for wheat, potatoes and eggs—commodities with extremely low price and income elasticities of demand. While agriculture in total could not grow as rapidly as the nonfarm economy, because of general consumer well-being and hence lower income elasticities for food, farm commodities with low demand elasticities could not absorb technical change as readily as those with high elasticities. Too, commodities such as eggs, potatoes and wheat use a relatively small proportion of the feed and soil resources adapted to them. A double threat in surplus thus exists because of supply potential, low income elasticities and slow demand expansion.

TABLE 6.8

ESTIMATES OF INCOME ELASTICITIES BASED ON CROSS-SECTIONAL AND TIME-SERIES DATA

Commodity	Heifner (1955)* Quantity	Fox (1948)† Expenditure	Fox (1948)† Quantity	Time Series (1922–41) Expenditure
Milk and milk products	.01	.32	.23	.16‡
Meat, poultry, fish	.19	.36	.23	—
All meat	.17	—	—	.56§
Beef	.26	—	—	.80‖
Pork	.09	—	—	.84‖
Lamb and mutton	.53	—	—	
All poultry	.25	—	—	.53**
Chickens	.23	—	—	
Eggs	.13	.22	.20	.38††
Veal	.35	—	—	—
All livestock products	—	.36	.23	—
Fruits and vegetables	—	.42	.33	—
Green, yellow vegetables	—	.37	.21	—
Citrus	—	.41	.42	—
Grain products	—	.02	−.21	—
Fats and oils	—	.13	−.04	—
Dry beans and peas	—	−.07	−.33	—
Potatoes	—	.05	−.05	—

* R. Heifner, Unpublished Estimates of Weighted Average Income Elasticities from 1955 Consumer Budget Study, Ames, Iowa, 1959.

† Fox, *op. cit.* (with estimates for 1948 urban families)

‡ Rojko, *loc. cit.*

§ Average of estimates by Shepherd, Tintner and Working in the publications cited earlier.

‖ Average of estimates by Fox and Wahby in publications cited previously.

** J. A. Nordin, *et al. Application of Econometric Procedures to Demand for Agricultural Products*, Iowa Agr. Exp. Sta. Bul. 410.

‡‡ Mean of estimates by Fox and Judge in publications cited previously.

In similar form, problems of surplus have been less in such commodities as beef and citrus where income elasticities are higher and national economic growth has been accompanied with a fairly large increment in demand and sharp rise in per capita consumption for these commodities. Neither of the latter commodities have had the benefit of public price support and production control and have prospered relative to farm commodities in general. However, marketing orders have led to some stability for citrus.

The income elasticities suggest the relative direction in which agricultural resources will need to be reallocated under economic growth in future decades if technical progress is to continue and consumer preference is to serve as the basis for allocation. First, income elasticities are much greater for nonfarm goods and services where consumer satiation is much less near than for foods. In the total food complex, even more resources will be drawn into the services attaching to foods, with relatively more invested in the processing and marketing process. Even within agriculture, the relative shape of resource allocation will be away from products with low income elasticities in those with higher elasticities. In this view, direction is given for research in the experiment stations, such as continued emphasis in shifting the mix of products making up a hog away from lard as an inferior good towards ham and loin with higher income elasticities of demand. This statement applies broadly to farm commodities. Demand elasticities are certainly greater for the quality than for the quantity aspects of agricultural products but historically research facilities have been concentrated on the former.

Aggregate Commodity

Individual foods can serve as close substitutes, but food in aggregate is a poor substitute for other goods of an affluent consumer society. Hence, the net growth opportunity for agriculture is best expressed in the income elasticity of demand for food in aggregate. Numerous studies have been made from time series data, mainly for prewar years, suggesting the magnitude of income elasticity with respect to expenditure on food at the retail level. Some of these estimates are summarized below.[35] As the coefficients based on time series data are average elasticities with respect to income over the period included and overestimate elasticity at higher income levels of recent time. Where elasticity is in terms of expenditures at the retail level, they overestimate demand potential at the farm level, apart from processing and marketing services incorporated with food. Girschick and Haavelmo computed elasticities (1922–41) for expenditure averaging .29 for current income and .05 for lagged income.[36] Burke estimated an expenditure elasticity of .24 (1922–41) for current income. Tobin obtained an expenditure elasticity (1913–41) of .45 by one least-squares model and .27 by another at retail. Stone obtained, for prewar years, an elasticity at retail of .59.[37] Fox, using urban family budget data for 1948, obtained a coefficient of .25 for current income with respect to expenditure at point of farm sales, .28 for food consumption based on the BAE index and .42 for food expenditures. The coefficient for farm sales is the best indication of demand potential for farm products since it includes only the shift to higher class and quality of food product with greater income; whereas food expenditure also reflects services incorporated with food. Barton and Daly estimate the income elasticity for expenditure on food at the farm level to be from .15 to .20.[38] In terms of physical quantity of food alone, without consideration of greater expenditure due to shift in quality of food mix, USDA figures for the period 1909–49 indicate an elasticity of zero.[39]

Estimates for current time suggest that the income elasticity coefficient of expenditure for food at the farm level, approximates .15. This

---

[35] All references cited are the same as those listed previously for price and income elasticities unless otherwise noted.

[36] All references are the same as those cited previously, unless otherwise indicated.

[37] Richard Stone, "The Analysis of Market Demand," *Jour. Roy. Stat. Soc.*, Vol. 107. His estimate for tobacco alone was .32. His figure for household equipment was 2.07 and for automobiles, 4.16.

[38] Barton and Daly, *loc. cit.*

[39] U.S. Department of Agricultural Economies, *Consumption of Food in the United States*, 1909–48, BAE Misc. Publ. 691.

magnitude is listed by Wetmore and Fox.[40] The 1955 survey of nonfarm families by the Agricultural Marketing survey showed an income elasticity in respect to expenditure on food of .20.[41] Converting this to food purchase only would reduce the elasticity coefficient to .15 or lower. In fact, when the 1955 survey was stratified into income thirds, the elasticity in respect to expenditures for the lower group was .25. The corresponding figures for the middle and upper income groups were .20 and .15 respectively.

Our conclusion is, in terms of demand expansion through the normal domestic market mechanism, that output of the agricultural industry can grow largely at the rate of population growth. More efficient production and lower supply price of farm commodities, against a given income and population, bears little promise in absorbing large supply increase at favorable income since price must decline by four to five times the increase in quantity. Further per capita income growth, given population, will not increase the aggregate physical demand for food but can increase expenditure on foods at the farm level by around .15 percent for each 1 percent increase in income. Agriculture as a shrinking portion of the national economy is thus the prospect for the decades ahead, and the pull on farm children and labor force will be accordingly.

CHANGES IN UTILIZATION

At stages of economic growth and in particular countries where per capita incomes are low, human energy and hunger satisfaction is derived largely from calories of low-cost sources. The percentage of calories derived from cereals and root crops—low-cost sources of calories—is highly correlated with per capita incomes over the world. In low income countries, it amounts to 60–85 percent of total caloric intake; in advanced countries, only 25–40 percent.[42] At higher income levels, diets shift to calorie sources of plant oils and animal fats which are more expensive in consumer outlay and resource requirements. Should food demand or requirements ever press supply in advanced countries, rise in real cost of diet and minimum nutrition requirements could be attained with some shift back to lower cost calorie sources, with perhaps a windfall in health from lower cholestrol intake.

Utilization of farm products in the United States has changed in line with the elasticities summarized above and with the changing occupational and age structure of the population. These magnitudes, plus the size of the population, will determine the structure of domestic food demand over future decades. Consumption will trend in the direction of

---

[40] Wetmore, *op. cit.*; K. A. Fox, *Demand Expansion and Agricultural Adjustment*, Center for Agricultural and Economic Adjustment, Report 2, Iowa State Univ., Ames, 1950, p. 133. Fox estimates an elasticity of .14 for both quantity of food purchased and product mix, the latter reflecting shift among commodities.

[41] Agr. Marketing Service, USDA, *Food Consumption of Households in the United States*, Report No. 1, Household Food Consumption Survey, 1955.

[42] M. K. Bennett, *The World's Food*, Harper and Brothers, New York, 1954, pp. 212–213.

TABLE 6.9

SOURCES OF CALORIES BY MAJOR FOOD GROUPS FOR U.S. SPECIFIED PERIODS AND RELATIVE RETAIL COST PER CALORIE AT 1947–49 PRICES

Group	Percent of Calorie Intake From Food Group			Relative Calorie Cost at 1947–49 Prices (Average = 100)
	1909–13	1947–49	1960	
Potatoes, dry beans and peas	7.5	6.6	6.3	70
Flour and cereals	37.2	23.8	21.1	30
Sugar, fats and oils	27.5	34.6	36.2	40
Meat, poultry, fish	13.5	15.2	16.4	240
Dairy products	9.6	13.5	13.9	120
Fruits and vegetables	4.7	6.3	6.1	300
Total	100.0	100.0	100.0	100.0

food commodities which are more expensive in both cost at retail and farm resources required to produce them. Table 6.9 illustrates how the mix of products has changed in approximately 40 years, the criterion of proportions being caloric content. These data roughly indicate the relative reallocation consumers have made in their diet among major food groups. The shift has been away from foods of low caloric cost to those of higher cost. However, the greater cost of the latter is not represented mainly by greater input requirements of farm resources, but as much by the larger processing and marketing inputs required for meats, vegetables and fruits.

The absolute rise and decline in per capita consumption of different product groups is indicated in Figure 6.1. It is not likely that the same relative shift will occur in the next three decades. Change will still occur, but at a lower rate than over the past three decades. Smaller opportunity for the excess of farm resources to be absorbed in the upgrading or higher cost of diets exists in the future than in the past. In other words, if technical change runs as far ahead of domestic demand as in the 1940's and 1950's, problems of potential surplus would be expected to grow because relatively less productive power could be diverted to foods with higher resource requirements. Income elasticity of expenditure for products at the "farm gate" have come almost entirely from shifts among commodities. With income elasticity for food in aggregate now approximating .15 and declining further with economic growth, the potential for gain from economic development is small. The trend lines in Figure 6.1 already show a "slowing down" and approach to mathematical limit in the rate of shift, as compared to the earliest decade shown. Further findings on health and longevity might, of course, reverse some of these trends, particularly to the extent that diets of lower cholestrol content might be encouraged.

Population Distribution

One of the more important dynamic elements in the postwar U.S. economy has been the rate of population growth. This variable of demand has been more important for agriculture than for other industries which gain from higher income elasticities, as well as from a greater number of

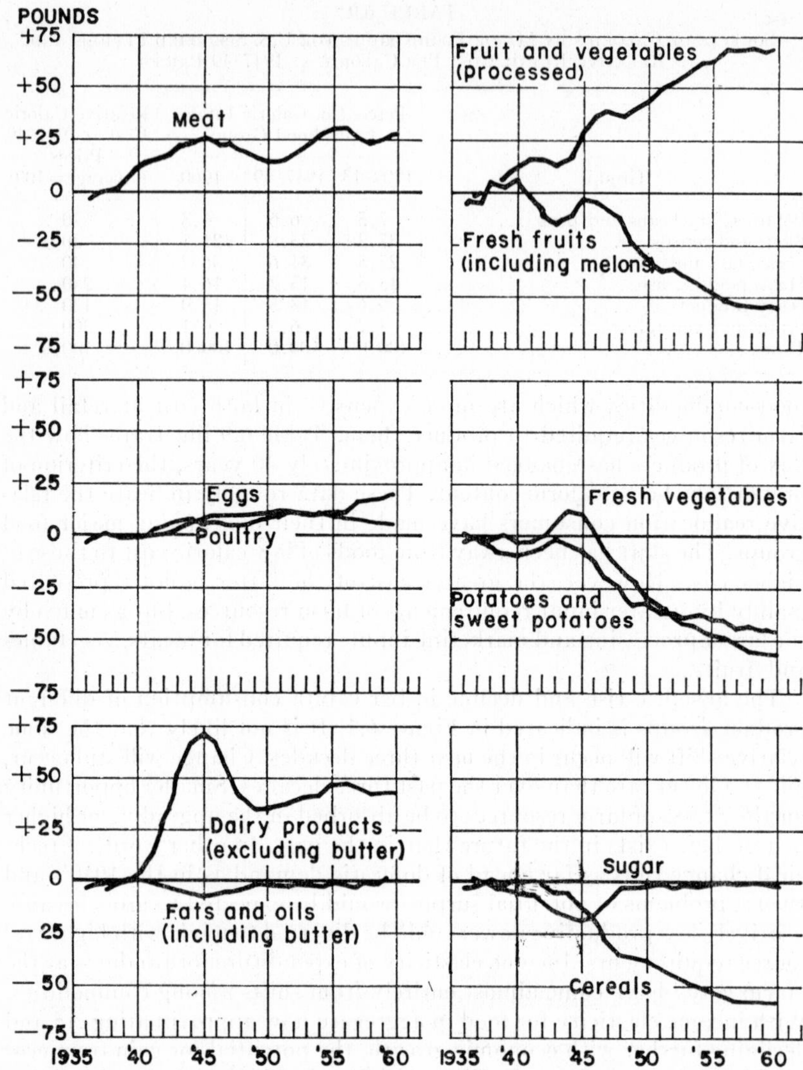

Fig. 6.1. Change in Per Capita Consumption of Particular Food Groups, 1935-60. (Source: Agricultural Marketing Service, USDA.)

consumers. With variance in birth rate between periods separated by the wars and due to improvements in human medicines and health, the age distribution of the population has been changing and is projected to change further as illustrated in Table 6.10. Shift, however, is into age groups both under 19 and over 55 with the net effect of larger caloric requirements for the first group to be offset by lower requirements for the second group. Computed as weighted averages for the various age groups, requirements for 1950, 1960 and 1970 projected amount to 2,340,

TABLE 6.10

POPULATION DISTRIBUTION AND RECOMMENDED DIETARY ALLOWANCES

Age Group	Population Number*			Population Percent			Recommended Daily Dietary Allowances†	
	1950	1960	1970	1950	1960	1970	Calories	Protein
	(mil)	*(mil)*	*(mil)*	(%)	(%)	(%)	*(Number)*	*(Grams)*
All ages......	150.7	180.1	213.8	100.0	100.0	100.0	—	—
0–4.........	16.2	20.0	24.2	10.7	11.1	11.3	1,000	40
5–9.........	13.2	19.2	22.1	8.8	10.7	10.3	1,800	55
10–14........	11.1	17.2	20.9	7.4	9.6	9.8	2,600	75
15–19........	10.6	13.4	19.3	7.0	7.4	9.0	3,000	85
20–34........	35.2	34.1	42.6	23.4	18.9	19.9	2,800	60
35–54........	38.8	44.8	46.6	25.7	24.9	21.7	2,500	60
55 and over..	25.6	31.4	38.5	17.0	17.4	18.0	2,200	60

* *Statistical Abstract of the United States*, 1959, p. 27.
† *Recommended Dietary Allowances*, Nat. Res. Counc. Pub. 302, 1953, p. 22.

2,310 and 2,319 calories respectively. (The National Research Council has provided somewhat higher requirements.) Protein requirements computed similarly as a "very minimum" are 60, 61 and 61 respectively. (A more common estimate for the population at large is 65 grams.) On the basis of these data, it again appears that the major coefficient attaching to the population variable, in respect to demand growth, is still magnitude of population itself.

Nutritional Level

The plane of nutrition in the United States has been upgraded greatly since 1940, due to education and improved knowledge and greater income. This is true even though the public invests considerably more in research and education on animal nutrition than on human diets. Few, if any, U.S. consumers are or need to be hungry. Nutrition surveys indicate the diet in all income classes is sufficient in bulk and calories. Even in crude protein content, this is generally true. Nutritionists and medical experts, if they were to make a blanket recommendation to the nation's consumers, would recommend a smaller, rather than larger, total food intake. They would, of course, recommend less caloric food and more of the essential nutrients. Annual per capita consumption in the U.S. well exceeded 3,000 calories in 1955, against average requirement of 2,640 calories. This compares with the approximately 2,100 calories consumed per person as an average for Asia and the Middle East.

The 1955 Household Food Consumption survey provides fairly current indication of the extent of nutritional deficiencies in U.S. consumer diets. Percentages of families with deficiencies in each of eight nutrient categories is indicated in Table 6.11 by income class and location of dwelling.[43] The figures show the percentage of households falling in the particular

[43] *Food Consumption and Dietary Levels of Households in the United States*, Reports 7–10, Household Food Consumption Survey, 1955, Agr. Marketing Service, USDA.

TABLE 6.11

PERCENT OF HOUSEHOLDS WITH DIETS NOT PROVIDING RECOMMENDED AMOUNTS OF EIGHT NUTRIENTS; BY URBANIZATION AND INCOME GROUP—U.S. 1955

Nutrient	Recommended Daily Allowances Per Nutrition Unit	Family Incomes of Households of Two or More Persons						
		Under $1,000	$1,000 to $1,999	$2,000 to $2,999	$3,000 to $3,999	$4,000 to $4,999	$5,000 to $5,999	$6,000 and over
		Total U.S. percent						
Protein	75 gr.	23	15	10	6	3	3	3
Calcium	0.8 gr.	37	41	34	31	25	23	22
Iron	12 mg.	15	16	10	9	7	6	7
Vitamin A	5,000 I.U.	36	30	18	18	12	11	9
Thiamine	1.5 mg.	17	19	16	16	13	16	16
Riboflavin	1.9 mg.	32	30	25	17	15	12	14
Niacin	15 mg.	17	13	9	6	4	4	3
Ascorbic acid	75 mg.	51	41	30	26	21	19	12
		U.S. nonfarm percent						
Protein	75 gr.	27	17	11	6	4	3	3
Calcium	0.8 gr.	43	46	36	32	25	23	22
Iron	12 mg.	17	19	11	9	7	6	8
Vitamin A	5,000 I.U.	37	31	17	18	12	11	8
Thiamine	1.5 mg.	20	23	17	16	14	16	17
Riboflavin	1.9 mg.	37	34	27	18	16	12	14
Niacin	15 mg.	20	15	9	6	4	4	4
Ascorbic acid	75 mg.	52	42	31	26	21	19	12
		U.S. farm percent						
Protein	75 gr.	18	9	7	6	3	8	3
Calcium	0.8 gr.	28	23	25	22	24	16	21
Iron	12 mg.	10	6	4	4	2	4	3
Vitamin A	5,000 I.U.	35	25	23	17	13	17	13
Thiamine	1.5 mg.	12	8	9	9	5	10	7
Riboflavin	1.9 mg.	25	17	17	14	11	12	10
Niacin	15 mg.	13	8	7	6	0	4	2
Ascorbic acid	75 mg.	49	35	29	28	20	23	15

income and location group with diets containing less than recommended daily allowances of each nutrient. They do not indicate the percent by which the nutrient is deficient for the particular group. The data show diets to be lowest in calcium, riboflavin and ascorbic acid. Too, deficiencies decline with level of income. Average per family income exceeded $5,000 in 1955 and the skewed stratification of the table by income groups tends to suggest greater deficiencies than actually exist. Actually, only about three in ten of all households had less calcium than was required, and one in four had less ascorbic acid (vitamin C) than was required. Even deficient households used some of these nutrients, often near the prescribed level. The percentage deficiency in these nutrients is much smaller than the percentage of families with a nutritional deficiency. Thus the national deficiency, as measured from the same source and by the same method, is small. Summary of national deficiencies, at 1955 time, is provided in Table 6.12. (Data in Table 6.11 refers largely to percentages of families with shortage of nutrients. Many consumers have intake exceeding daily requirements of all nutrients.)

TABLE 6.12

DEFICIENCY OF EIGHT NUTRIENTS IN DIETS AS PERCENTAGE OF U.S. TOTAL NUTRIENT CONSUMPTION, 1955

Nutrient	Percent Deficiency of U.S. Total
Protein	1.1
Calcium	5.9
Iron	1.4
Vitamin A	2.8
Thiamine	2.8
Riboflavin	4.0
Niacin	1.0
Ascorbic Acid	5.4

Any one of these deficiencies could be brought to the prescribed level without absorbing the equivalent of resources which has gone into the 6–8 percent surplus of aggregate production over consumption in the past decade. Just as a relatively small proportion of U.S. consumers uses too little of some nutrients, a greater proportion uses more than requirements of these or others. Some deficiencies exist in all income classes, due to consumer preferences or lack of knowledge of dietary requirements. However, by 1941, average calories available or produced per consumer was 3,408, against daily requirements of 2,640. At the same time, protein available (produced as food) per person was 98 grams—against daily requirement of 65 grams. Even as early as 1930, food supplies in the United States provided an amount of all essential nutrients well exceeding average daily requirements.[44] It has been estimated that less than 10 percent of U.S. households have seriously deficient diets,[45] and these diets are not deficient in calories. U.S. families probably have an "overage" of calorie intake against medical recommendations. The 1958 average daily caloric intake per person was estimated at 3,220 for the U.S.[46] While about 10 percent of the households do not meet the NRC

[44] For discussion of the abundance of food nutrients against requrements, see H. K. Stiebeling, *Family Food Consumption and Dietary Improvement*, Bureau of Human Nutrition and Home Economics, USDA, Oct. 1949. Also see R. P. Christenson, *Efficient Use of Food Resources in the United States*, USDA Tech. Bul. 963.

[45] Willard W. Cochrane, "Demand Expansion Opportunities and Limitations," in *Problems and Policies of Agriculture*, Iowa State Univ. Press, Ames, 1959.

[46] *World Food Deficit, A First Approximation,* Foreign Agricultural Service, USDA, March, 1961.

recommendations for noncalorie nutrients, the deficiency is very small as indicated in Table 6.12.

These data provide sufficient indication that the excess of supply or production capacity over domestic demand of conventional food mix cannot be absorbed by bringing all diets to levels of adequate nutrition. To make these changes in Asia or the Middle East would have large relative effect on food and resource quantity. This is not true in the United States, however, because high per capita incomes allow consumers to attain these levels, if their preferences and knowledge lead them to do so. Because of the wide range of food substitutes available for meeting dietary requirements, most families could do so within the restraints of their present budgets for food.

To test this hypothesis, a Minnesota study derived three diet plans; low cost, moderate cost and liberal cost, with each attaining dietary requirements.[47] Supposing that all persons were shifted to the low cost diet, total national food use, in aggregate value, would decline 21.8 percent. Shifting all consumers to the moderate cost diet would reduce aggregate food intake by 5.5 percent. These declines would come from lower caloric intake or shift in sources, rather than from downgrading of the diet. Use of the liberal cost diet by all consumers would increase all food consumption by 2.3 percent. Again, the latter increase would be too small to absorb the resources represented by the 6–8 percent surplus production over the 1950's. Summary of changes for some individual products is given below under each of the three diets:

Product	Low Cost	Moderate Cost	Liberal Cost
Milk products	+ 2.3	+ 4.1	+11.1
Meat	−43.1	− .6	+11.7
Citrus fruits and tomatoes	−17.2	+ 3.2	+19.9
Eggs	−18.1	− 4.7	− 2.3
Grain products	− .1	−10.4	−15.9
Potatoes	+21.4	+ 6.1	− 5.1
Green and yellow vegetables	+ 6.6	+12.5	+14.1
Dry beans and peas	+13.3	−34.0	−42.3
All food	−21.8	− 5.5	+ 2.3

The Minnesota study group estimated changes in resource requirements if all consumers were to be shifted to each of the three diets specified above. The estimates are given in Table 6.13. The low cost diet, with all consumers shifted to it, would reduce total resource requirements in U.S. agriculture by 21.6 percent, with individual decreases of 27.5 percent for land and 18.0 percent for labor. It is not likely, given the level of affluence and desire for the "more exotic" that consumers would prefer this shift, however. Shift to the moderate cost diet would reduce total resource inputs by .4 percent, with land decreased by .8 percent and labor increased by .8 percent. For the liberal cost diet, but one not all households would wish to buy, total resource requirements would be increased by 7.6 percent, including a 8.6 percent increase in land and a 9.1 percent

[47] Wetmore, *et al.*, *op. cit.*

TABLE 6.13
CHANGE IN RESOURCE REQUIREMENTS TO MEET THREE MINNESOTA DIETS MEETING NUTRITIONAL REQUIREMENTS

Resource and Product	Low Cost Diet	Moderate Cost Diet	Liberal Cost Diet
Total resources to:	−21.6	−0.4	7.6
Livestock and products	−26.4	0.3	9.8
Fruits	−15.5	−0.4	12.3
Vegetables	− 6.3	5.6	14.1
Other foods	5.9	−9.2	−16.3
Land to:	−27.5	−0.8	8.6
Feed grains	−31.2	−0.3	9.5
Fruits	−16.3	−0.2	12.5
Vegetables	− 8.6	3.5	12.5
Other foods	1.5	−11.4	−17.3
Labor to:	−18.0	0.8	9.1
Livestock and products	−15.9	1.3	9.3
Fruits	−15.8	−0.3	12.4
Vegetables	− 8.5	3.4	12.9
Other foods	9.0	−6.9	−15.1
Feed grains	−33.5	−0.4	9.7

Source: Wetmore, *et al.*, *ibid.*

in labor. Total resources to livestock and products decline under the low cost diet, increase by .3 percent under the moderate cost diet and increase by 9.8 percent under the liberal cost diet. Land to feed grains would decrease by 31.2 percent under the low cost diet and increase by 9.5 percent under the high cost.

Actually, the average American diet lies somewhere between the medium and high cost diets specified by the Minnesota group. Largely, the data indicate that the problem of surplus capacity will not be solved during the 1960's by shifting the entire population to the latter dietary level, or that the population will all shift to this diet. Estimates current in 1960 indicated that at least 10 percent of cropland could be diverted to soil bank or other purposes, simply to "break even" on output and utilization and keep prices from further decline. Underemployment of labor in agriculture approached a third of the farm labor force. The data are more assurance that U.S. consumers need not soon go hungry as their numbers increase, if they should shift to a diet of lower calorie and resource cost, than that the surplus capacity problem can soon be solved through dietary improvement—although the latter would help erase surplus capacity problems.

Production and Consumption Potential

As variances in the estimates discussed previously indicate, it is not possible to predict all demand parameters with certainty. Life would be dull and drab were it possible to do so, since then life of the individual would be purely mechanistic and physical, and perhaps even static, in the sense of the equilibrium of the jungle where some plants emerge and some die but the average shape and magnitude is the same. Still, even though quantification cannot be perfect, economists feel fairly firm about their ability to forecast demand quantities.

Much less knowledge and predicting ability rests on the side of supply, particularly if we wish to quantify the effect of each behavioral variable related to decisions to produce and invest. If the goal is less that of structural knowledge in motivation and more of forecasting, projections can be made with some degree of confidence. Aside from weather variations, projection of time trends for limited spans can be made in a positive manner. Perhaps more useful are normative projections which indicate possible production in light of present knowledge and technology.

Barton and Daly provide us with estimates of the latter nature, with our confidence quite firm in the sense that they conform quite closely with the trends discussed in Chapter 2.[48] Using estimates of demand parameters outlined above and with projection of the structural variables to 1975, they compared potential demand with potential of production. Demand potential does not consider growth due to industrial utilization, advertising, promotion, etc. Production estimates are in terms of that possible under present knowledge of technology, without consideration of supply functions in the conventional sense or of new technology which might be generated to 1975, the future point of reference. Their projections of farm product utilization are given in Table 6.14.

Total domestic utilization of farm products in this earlier study was predicted to increase by 50 percent over 1956–57 while total output needed for this demand increase is 41 percent. Utilization of livestock products is predicted to increase 52 percent for domestic food purpose, and output increase needed to meet this is 45 percent. Output increases, based on the earlier estimates, needed for crops amount to 32 percent by 1975. Barton and Daly estimate that if only currently known technique were used to best advantage, yield per acre could increase by 50 percent in 1975 over 1956–57. Feed conversion rates also could increase by 10 percent; these two improvements allowing attainment of increased demand or requirements with ease. In a later study, using 1956–58 as a base, Rogers and Barton project a 35 percent increase in volume of farm products to meet domestic demand in 1975, with a 25 percent increase needed for crop production and a 45 percent increase needed in livestock production.[49] Even supposing some limitations on management and economically attainable use of present known technology, Barton and Daly predict that yield per acre could increase by more than 25 percent—an increase coupled with improved conversion rate for all feed which would allow attainment of 1975 food requirements.

It is expected, of course, that new technology will be uncovered and put to use. On this basis, Barton and Daly's estimates would forewarn of supply problems of 1960 magnitude through 1970 in the absence of government policy or market pressure towards alteration of the supply

[48] G. T. Barton, and R. F. Daly, *op. cit.*

[49] R. O. Rogers, and G. T. Barton, *Our Farm Production Potential, 1975*, Agr. Info. Bul. No. 233, USDA.

TABLE 6.14

FARM PRODUCT UTILIZATION AND OUTPUT, 1925–29, 1935–39, 1956–57 AND 1975 PROJECTED (INDICES, 1947–49 = 100)

Item	Average 1925–29	Average 1935–39	Average 1956–57	1975	1975 Change From 1956–57
					(Percent)
Population	81	88	116	157	35
Per capita real income	71	69	118	165	40
Utilization of farm products					
Livestock products					
Food, domestic	72	75	122	186	52
Meat animals	73	75	124	197	59
Poultry	59	64	162	268	65
Nonfood, domestic	102	103	87	105	21
Exports	72	26	163	105	−36
Imports	80	67	93	155	67
Output	75	77	120	174	45
Crops					
Food	80	88	106	148	40
Cereals and potatoes	104	99	102	122	20
Fruits and vegetables	74	84	103	155	50
Nonfood (excl. feed and seed)	69	78	104	165	59
Feed and seed	88	80	109	146	34
Exports	90	55	136	135	− 1
Imports	88	99	112	160	43
Output	80	77	106	140	32
Total domestic use	74	78	115	172	50
Food	74	79	117	174	49
Nonfood	69	76	99	155	57
Exports, total	87	50	140	130	− 7
Imports, total	87	93	109	160	47
Output, total	72	74	115	162	41

structure in agriculture. Another alternative which would remove the burden from supply structure would be developments leading to change in the demand structure. On the basis of statistics presented thus far, change in demand structure of sufficient magnitude to accomplish this end is not apparent in the domestic economy. If it is to be accomplished, it must come from the outside or world market, from unexpected "break throughs" in lowering the cost of farm products as resources in industrial utilization, or from other "wishing wells." Otherwise, demand for farm products will expand at about the rate of the domestic population variable. This is the 1960 market variable of best prediction, for farmers making decisions in respect to long-term investment and education of their offspring.

OTHER QUESTS IN DEMAND

Farm products per se provide little grist for the mills of advertising agencies. When consumers are short in supply of food, they are hungry and need no one to tell them that they should eat. Once their stomachs are full, they listen but little to one who tells them to eat more. This is in contrast to many other goods and services, including those which go with food, which appear in the market as new phenomena, with the consumer convinced of his desire by the most efficient applied psychology known. To add to the weight of cars and housing owned, or of intercontinental travel, suggests to the community that one is affluent and intelligent. But to add to one's own weight tells the community that one is sloppy and destined for early death.

This complex thwarts those who would solve the commercial farm problem through advertising and promotion. The marginal rate of substitution of food in aggregate for other commodities is too near zero, given the vector in consumption space defining diets of U.S. consumers, to allow greatly increased consumption at other than disasterously low and unprofitable food prices. The aggregate farm problem cannot be solved in the 1960's through this approach to demand expansion. The cross elasticities among important commodity groups are large enough that one group of producers might make sizeable inroads into the market of another through lower supply price of a particular product. Developments in broiler productions and utilization over postwar years provide an excellent example. But the investment required to change consumer values and the configuration of the U.S. consumption surface to substitute food for nonfood commodities must be extremely great and of low return, particularly where it does not recognize the main shifter in this process to be per capita income. Mostly it is not an answer to the aggregate farm supply and resource problem because of the inelasticity of the human stomach and the rigid desires of the consumer in respect to weight. Increase input of one food and another is replaced. Advertise one food, and the same is required for another, if it is to "hold its own." Advertising and promotion by state and commodity "improvement groups" thus become neutralized. The return in food demand expansion would likely be greater if these advertising funds, invested in exhorting the consumer to "eat more pork," "eat more beef," and "eat more poultry," were donated to impoverished nations as subsidy in food consumption or for promotion of economic development and human enlightenment.

Walsh[50] estimates the total advertising investment relating to processing and retail of farm commodities and beverages to exceed three billion dollars in 1958, an amount equal to a quarter of annual net income from farming over the period 1956–60. Of course, a major portion of this advertising had objective of increasing demand for a particular brand and retailer of food or other commodity. Its effect was more in respect to this complex, than in increasing demand for food in aggregate. Even at the elementary level, wheat from Wyoming is a perfect substitute for wheat from Kansas and the New York consumer isn't concerned about the source of ingredients for her prepared cake mix. This evidently has not always been apparent to state groups who invest in advertising to increase sales of their local product.

---

[50] R. M. Walsh, *Increasing Domestic Demand for Farm Products by Advertising and Promotion*, Center for Agricultural and Economic Adjustment, Report No. 2, Iowa State Univ., Ames, 1959.

Advertising or promotion can have two related goals: (1) to shift the demand curve to the right and (2) to make it less elastic. Causing the demand function to decline in elasticity is a main desire for producers of differentiated products. Farm groups probably have had in mind shift of the demand functions, with less concern for changing its elasticity. However, successful commodity advertising would help accomplish the goal of reducing demand elasticity for one product, and allow less inroad from the decrease in supply price and advertising of competing products. Advertising of new products such as frozen orange juice and concentrated lemonade has undoubtedly increased the demand for the farm product resource, citrus fruit, going into them. Research shows that advertisement of other new products such as potato flakes and precooked rice has caused demand for the particular processed product to grow rapidly.[51] In this case, however, gain for potatoes consumed in flake form is loss for potatoes consumed in raw and various other states of preparation. Gain is largely to the producers of services going into production and marketing of flakes, rather than to producers of potatoes.

Advertisement and promotion of some farm commodities undoubtedly has had important effects in improving consumer knowledge of nutritional requirements and possibilities. This was true particularly at lower stages of income and affluence in American society, as consumers were made aware of presence of vitamins and other nutrients of particular foods. It is less so in stage of development where consumers are better educated and informed on nutrition, and income level has allowed them to attain higher cost diets. Hence, the prospective marginal return from investment in advertising and promotion is less in 1960, with product measured both in human well-being and magnitude of farm demand, than it was in 1940.

There is no doubt about the ability of advertisement and special promotion to shift demand from one brand of corn flakes to another, or demand for beef from one store to another. But there is no evidence to indicate that the advertisement for these purposes increases the permanent demand for corn or cattle. The effect from advertising and promotion in the future will be more nearly that of shifting demand elasticities among products, or in shifting demand for one particular form of a product to another processed form of the same product. Also, it will have concentrated effect in shifting demand from one differentiated processed brand to another. It will have little effect in boosting the demand for food in aggregate because of the low marginal rate of substitution of food for nonfood goods and services.

Quality Improvement

The income elasticity of demand for special services and qualities incorporated into food sold at retail is much higher than the elasticity for

[51] See the following publications: "Potato Flakes, A New Form of Dehydrated Mashed Potatoes. Market Position and Consumer Acceptance in Binghampton, Endicott and Johnson City, New York," Agr. Marketing Service, MR Report No. 186; Super Valu Study, *Progressive Grocer*, New York, 1957, pp. 17–32.

food itself. Food increasingly is a bundle of services, rather than food alone. Part of the services of food, such as prepreparation, is a substitute for other labor in the household and economy; the so-called "built-in maid" being an example. Also, one set of tastes and characteristics of a food item has been substituted for another. For example, consumers substitute the taste and characteristic of frozen peas for canned or dried peas or that of canned fruits for fresh fruits. The quantity of farm product, as the resource leading to the food commodity, itself remains highly constant in this substitution; with the increased consumer demand and expenditure diverted to more of the new characteristic and less of the old, the farm product input remaining constant.

Greater quality and service is desired by the consumer as his income increases and saturation level is approached in commodities which serve mainly a biological function in life. Given this state in economic development, shift of the relative allocation of resources in this direction is consistent with both greater consumer welfare and producer income. The trend has been expressed by the tremendous growth in service industries, and even in the adornment of automobiles and cigarette packages with conveniences and gadgets relating to their psychological appeal rather than their mechanical and biological performance.

With this growing demand and greater income elasticity for services attached to the basic commodity, relative to the basic product itself, it is logical that the economy be adapted in this direction. Public agricultural research institutions could well adapt their activities accordingly. Demand elasticities with respect to quantity per se being low relative to those for quality and services of food, research and education in the experiment stations should be reoriented accordingly (see Chapter 16). This is a logical and realistic step for public investment pointed to increased welfare of food consumers and producers. But while this is true in economic development logic, we need to determine whether it can solve the problem of price and income in agriculture.

Changes in market structure, ranging from vertical integration to other connecting links between farm producer and retailers, are partially a reflection of trend in demand intensity towards quality. The gravitation of farms towards production of market specified qualities will continue, with agriculture becoming more specialized and commercialized. Farm numbers are likely to decline and sizes are likely to increase as a result of this process. In itself, the process is not the answer to the income problem of small commercial farms and poverty groups with meager resources.

The extent to which agriculture in general, given its existing structure, can benefit from the higher income elasticities for products and services represented by food quality depends on the magnitude in which these products can be produced in the farm sector. Many, perhaps the majority, of these qualities and services can be produced more appropriately and at lower cost under factory than under farm conditions. Peas of appropriate size and form are needed for freezing, and farm producers who adapt their resources accordingly can benefit. However, the main inputs and return from producing frozen peas must come from off-farm production processes. Frozen peas are a direct substitute for canned peas. Similarly, canned ham and frozen, boxed strawberries are substitutes for bulk hams and raw strawberries. Consumption of more canned ham and frozen strawberries can increase greatly the demand for cans and freezing facilities, but increase the demand for hams and strawberries by very little. And this is the main prospect in the realm of improved product quality and service for the bulk of current agriculture. Small gains can be made by the farm industry in adapting resources to the quality product. But the shift will not itself absorb large surplus of resources or boost their returns to levels comparable with the food processing levels. The activity needs to be emphasized, particularly in research of agriculture, as one consistent with higher income and changing consumer preferences of Americans, and as one more consistent with increased returns to commercial farm operators than emphasis on quantity alone. It does not, however, promise to absorb excess labor resources or the extreme poverty found in the industry.

Marketing Efficiency

Farm groups have long viewed the spread between retail and farm prices, the marketing margin, as a possible source of income which might be redistributed in their direction. This spread or marketing margin has been increasing in both rate and magnitude as illustrated in Figure 6.2 for all farm commodities and in Table 6.15 for specified products. As the latter shows, the spread has tended to widen for farm commodities even in

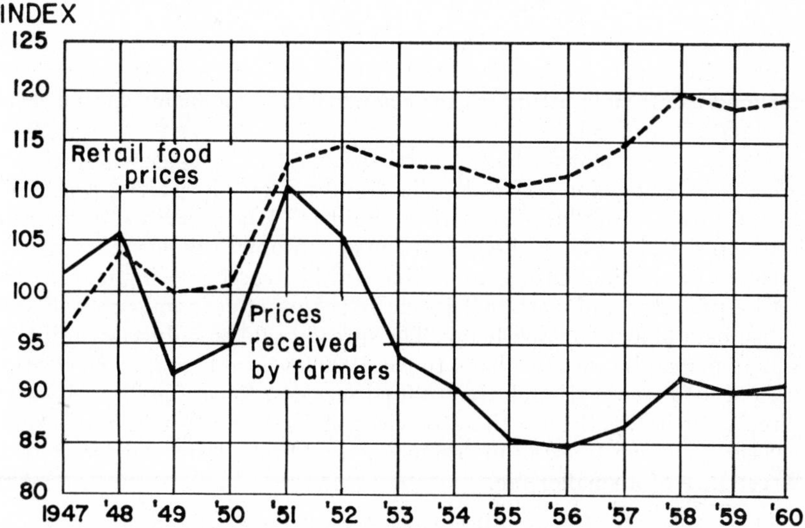

Fig. 6.2. Prices Received by Farmers and Retail Food Prices (1947–49 = 100).

TABLE 6.15
U.S. FARM AND RETAIL PRICES OF DAIRY PRODUCTS, WHEAT, FATS AND OILS AND FRUITS AND VEGETABLES, 1947–58 (1947–49=100)

	Farm Prices				Retail Prices			
Year	Dairy products	Wheat	Fats and oils	Fruits and vegetables	Dairy products	Wheat products	Fats and oils	Fruits and vegetables
1947	99	112	119	101	96	94	108	98
1948	110	97	118	99	106	103	108	100
1949	92	92	62	100	98	103	84	102
1950	91	98	75	92	97	105	81	97
1951	104	103	97	97	108	114	94	105
1952	110	102	67	116	113	117	79	117
1953	97	100	76	102	111	119	80	114
1954	90	103	81	101	107	122	85	113
1955	90	97	67	101	107	124	82	114
1956	93	96	73	109	110	126	83	119
1957	94	95	73	102	112	130	87	118
1958	92	84	62	110	114	133	86	120

Source: USDA Agr. Marketing Service.

cases where (1) farm prices have gone down and retail prices have gone up (2) farm prices and retail prices have both gone up and (3) both sets of prices have declined.

How can it be explained? Does it represent monopolistic and monopsonistic elements of the food processing and marketing sector of the economy? Statistics and analysis are not available to answer this question fully. However, an important portion of this growing spread is itself economic development phenomena. With growth in income and level of consumption, expenditures turn in the direction of quality and services of food as explained above. The income elasticity of demand for marketing services has been estimated to be five times as large as the elasticity for food itself. Daly estimates the elasticity to be .7 for marketing services and .15 for food.[52]

Hence, as the market basket carried home by the housewife includes an increasing portion of frozen, sliced and packaged services, preconditioned forms of products and other "built-in" labor services, or "exotic characteristics" of food, the proportion of consumer's dollar reaching the farmer's hand will continue to decline. In this sense, growing margin between producer and consumer is one reflection of economic growth and consumer affluence or well-being. The spread could be reduced readily by rolling per capita incomes back to the 1900 level, so that income elasticities of food would rise relative to food services. Farm families who also directly or indirectly use these services of foods, even if in crates purchased for home freezing of products, would not desire this road to a larger slice of a smaller pie.

[52] R. F. Daly, "The Long-Run Demand for Farm Products," *Agr. Econ. Res.*, Vol. 8; and *Demand for Farm Products at Retail and Farm Level*, Mimeo., Oct. 1957.

To the extent that growing spread is due to resource inefficiencies in processing and marketing firms, gain might be reflected back to farmers through creation of experiment stations and extension services which would show these nonfarm units how to use their resources more effectively. This was one general concentration and hope of the Agricultural Marketing Act of 1947. A portion of these research funds were allocated to marketing efficiency studies, in expectation of some gain at the farmer level. It is not likely, however, that the food industry is highly lacking in research or efficiency. It has been nearly as dynamic as any sector of the economy since 1930. Relatively, this sector is quite primitive in less developed countries of Asia and Africa. Further economic growth in these countries will require further public and private encouragement of improvement in processing and marketing industries. Yet inefficiency is not likely to be great enough in these sectors of the U.S. economy to guarantee that improvement will erase the widespread problems of farm surpluses and low incomes.

Industrial Utilization of Farm Products

Industrial processes represent a production function requiring raw materials as resources, as well as requiring labor and capital in the form of machinery, equipment and buildings. Each of these classes of resources has substitutes, both within the class and between the particular class and other classes. Labor of one class is a substitute for labor of another class, or labor and machinery are substitutes. Similarly raw materials from farm sources and those from other sources of nature are substitutes in producing alcohol, motor fuels, plastics, cellulose and other organic quantities. In the complete industrial process, the optimum combination of resources, ranging from human effort to raw materials, depends on the quantities discussed and illustrated in Chapter 4; namely, the prices of the resources and their marginal rates of substitution. The hope of increased demand for farm products through industrial use depends on the magnitude of these quantities, rather than on new technical discoveries alone. It is likely that materials from farm sources have a near-constant marginal rate of substitution for materials from other sources in fabrication of a given chemical or industrial substance, the product isoquant being linear. Under these conditions, the industrial firm will use only material from farm source, or only that from alternative source. The source selected will depend on the supply price of the material to the industrial plant.

Except during war periods and restricted raw material supplies, farm products have not had large demand in industrial utilization. The reason is that their marginal rate of substitution for substitute materials is too low or the price is too high. Either is a sufficient reason. Thus activity which would expand industrial demand for farm product must either establish a higher rate of substitution of farm products for other chemical compounds or lower the relative supply price of farm products. But the latter does not give positive promise of solving the farm price problem.

Calculation at 1960 price levels indicates that corn and wheat would find demand in industrial production of alcohol only at prices of around 40 cents per bushel for the grains. Prices of grain at this level would drive even the most efficient farmers bankrupt.

Thus, under current market and demand structure for resources and products, the other prospect is in research which increases the marginal rate of substitution as spelled out above. But chemists provide no great hope here. They point out that agricultural production involves complex chemical processes in converting simple elements and compounds of nature into much more complex organic compounds. Utilization of the latter in industrial production requires that the complex molecules be reduced back to more simple form. This process is more costly than starting with molecules of less complex form from nature's direct sources, and converting them into the desired product. As long as this is true, in the sense that simple-form compounds and molecules from nature's direct sources come at lower supply price than those developed through agriculture's biological process, the marginal rates of substitution and pricing of chemical compounds will favor the former source. Currently industrial utilization to result in large expansion in industrial utilization of farm products is one of the less positive hopes in demand expansion.

The avenue needs further exploring, just as do all other alternatives relating to the exploration of the nation's basic resources supplies and their opportunity in product transformation. Yet until stocks of compounds directly from nature dwindle to a point where their supply price rises sharply against materials from farm sources, the opportunity for substitution will remain small. An industry such as the chemical sector wishes a stable supply of raw material. It is not, therefore, well adapted to utilization of periodic farm surpluses. If farm surpluses were readily solved through industrial utilization, the supply of material would dry up as the "higher level" consumer demand had higher price priority on food products. Hence, chemical plants would need to switch periodically from farm to nature's sources of raw materials, or close down intermittingly, if they were to serve as the salvation in solving periodic farm surpluses.

Whereas chemurgy may promise slight increases in demand for farm products, the expansion is most likely to be for minor products representing a small proportion of farm resources. Those used may be mostly derivatives representing by-products from other farm enterprises and commodities. For the major or "bulk" uses and products of chemurgy, the substitute supplies of materials more directly from nature, particularly with opening up of supplies through development of less advanced countries, may cause these sources to decline in real supply price, as against those from farm origin. It is even possible that chemurgy will sooner develop materials which substitute for farm products as foods, than develop efficient means of substituting farm products for other raw materials in synthesizing nonfood consumer commodities. This has been true in textiles and it is not impossible in proteins, carbohydrates and other materials used for food. While the chemical industry converts grain into starch for industrial use, cotton and wood into cellulose for nonfood fabrication, soybeans into drying oil and corn into butyl alcohol, it also has developed latex-based paints which reduce the demand for vegetable and animal oils. Industrial improvements in fractionation of vegetable oils enhanced the substitution of margarine for butter. It is possible that the chemical and agricultural industries will shift increasingly fron complementary relation to competitive role.

New Crops and Production Possibilities

Standing at level of industrial uses in hope for demand expansion is development of new crops with alternatives to food use. This is the "new look" in hopes for increased nonfood demands of farm products. In the 1930's, the public established four regional laboratories to do research on new uses of existing farm products. Public Law 540 was passed by the 84th Congress (1958) to invest further in development of new crops. This is a useful direction in emphasis, somewhat in conflict with the core of research in agricultural colleges wherein emphasis has been on increasing yield and output of existing crops; supposing demand to be elastic enough to absorb augmentation of supply at positive revenue increment to farmers. Through new crops which have nonfood uses, the former emphasis would use biological research on the farm production process to extend the magnitude and elasticity of demand for farm output.

The direction is worthy in the sense that it at least reflects refreshing and renewed thought in gearing research to economic development. The obstacles are mainly those discussed above in industrial utilization of existing farm products. New products which use nature to convert simple molecules into compound molecules, with the chemical industry transforming them back to simple form, encounters the same price, cost and substitution processes already discussed. Yet this research and emphasis is relevant for more of research resources in experiment stations, unless they can be allocated more to conventional style research for overcoming problems in underdeveloped nations. Certainly some of these resources would have greater marginal social productivity if they were devoted to improved quality and forms of farm products. Development of the soybean industry and the demand for its products in paints and lubricants is a classic example in the direction of positive-sum outcome among producers and consumers.

There likely are other unexploited opportunities in this direction if research is to come abreast of stage of economic development. Demands which have greater income elasticities than food are those for pulp and paper, gum materials for textile printing, waxes and pharmaceuticals. Even new characteristics of existing crops might be created, or changed, to increase demand outside of the U.S. food market. Consumers in the Middle East prefer poultry with dark color, produced partly through grain of high pigmentation. While this is only an example, social gain might be greater if some of the plant breeding resources were so adapted, in contrast to concentration on higher yield varieties of the same domestic grain complex.

We should not be overly optimistic in this direction, however. The hope to develop coffee, substituting for that of South America, cannot be successful if it cuts uneconomically into the balance of foreign exchange; or if coffee cannot be mechanized, and labor used in producing it in home plant must compete with labor of lower price in South American countries. Also, in terms of national goals in defense and external economic development, an important question is: are our research resources more effectively deployed in this direction, or in developing products and resources to sell in exchange for coffee, bamboo and mangoes?

Foreign Market Opportunity

The man from Mars would never understand why two problems exist side-by-side on earth: one of hungry people and one of people with surplus food. Why can the one problem not be solved through elimination of the other? The number of persons in the world who still desire some more food is still larger than the number who worry about overweight, even though the opposite exists in the United States. Physically, one problem effectively could be used to solve the other problem. But economically and politically, the solution is not so simple.

Political and economic mechanisms are the creation of man. They should be his servant and not his master, certainly in those societies where the state exists to serve man. If the world were composed of a single society with economic and political mechanisms created as man's servant, an optimum allocation of resources over the globe would allow resources with high productivity in food at one location to be used in betterment of consumer welfare on other continents. But given the reality of the moment, distinct societies existing with their own particular value and goal orientations, opportunities are not this fluid. International economic goals and purposes of one nation must thus conform to a pattern consistent with those of nations which complement its long-run objectives and goals. This framework prevents unleashing the full productive capacity of U.S. food resources and surplus stocks in alleviating hunger and misery in less developed nations. It is not convenient and practical to substitute U.S. food products for those serving as the market outlet of nations serving in complementary economic and political capacity.

Worldwide, a growing public conscience and concern is developing, placing high value on the freedom from hunger and misery and self determination by all people. This public or social purpose is being given quantitative reflection in liquidation of colonies, and investment in developmental aids even by small nations. While they may be restrained and sometimes set back by international political forces, the broad and long sweep of history is in the direction of minimum well-being and freedom of all nations. Over a shorter period of time, ability to use productive capacity of U.S. food resources for these purposes will need to be restricted, but the pace may grow.

These are crucial factors: the changing economic and political structure in less developed countries, and the mechanisms and institutions which man can create to cause growth and alleviate hunger through use of surpluses. Hence, the computation, presentation and analysis of demand elasticities and structural demand functions for underdeveloped nations is largely meaningless and obsolete. The large humanitarian and economic opportunities and strides for filling developmental voids will come not from inverting matrices and exacting derivatives in respect to these quantities, but from simple logical analysis of needs and possibilities and refined education of administrators, politicians and publics at large to accomplish these ends.

Physically, it is easy to define ways in which surplus food stocks of particular nations might be used to promote economic development in other countries. Examples abound on all sides: give students free food, the main cost of subsistence, while they obtain education; provide food for workers who build roads, schools and factories—with their time freed from the retarded task of squeezing food for subsistence from paltry resources. Yet there are major economic and political hurdles to be overcome, within and between both recipient and extending nations as outlined in Chapter 17.

The extremely basic question before American society is not how farm products can be shipped to food deficit countries to rid the United States of its surpluses and maintain manpower on farms. It is one of optimum procedures and allocation of investment to speed economic development and true freedom of peoples, with use of farm commodities and productive power to conform to this end—large or small as the outlet may be. This framework promises to develop. But until it is more nearly clarified, the utilization of services from U.S. farms will follow the model: particular commodities in surplus will be used, to the extent allowed by U.S. public appropriations and political expediency within receiving countries, for shipment as gifts or low-priced contributions in alleviating food shortages where supply is small relative to population. Perhaps it can even be argued that surplus farm production has been beneficial to promotion of humanitarian goals by U.S. society. With surpluses on hand, and with investment already committed to them, the public has cast about looking for physical disposal alternatives—those which would not bother the public's value or creed of "waste avoidance." It has thus been possible to contribute modestly to elimination of hunger and economic development in more tardy world regions through foreign food disposal. Without surpluses and the pressure to eliminate their cumulative costs, persuasion of the public to invest in food shipments of equal magnitude might have been difficult, if not impossible.

One cannot say that world demand, in the "effective economic sense" of the term, for U.S. food has been growing rapidly. However, shipment of food under the framework mentioned above, has been growing at quite rapid rate. Exports of wheat now approximate U.S. food uses of this commodity, with nearly three-fourths of exports attributable to special governmental disposal programs. The pattern for other commodities is included in Table 6.16. Johnson's projections to 1965, assuming extention of current structures of U.S. foreign and farm policy and world economic growth, also are included for comparison.[53] Foreign demand growth under current policy structure cannot absorb current productive power, or even current wheat stocks, at prospective growth rate. Johnson's estimates of production potential also provide negative expectation that export growth at this rate can absorb excess plant capacity in feed grains. His projections, consistent with those discussed previously, estimate feed

TABLE 6.16

U.S. FARM PRODUCT EXPORTS, 1955–59 AND 1959

Item	Unit	1955–59	1959	Projected 1965	Change 1959 to 1965
					(Percent)
Wheat, including flour	Mil. bu.	418	443	475	7
Commercial exports	Mil. bu.	131	123		
Special govt. programs	Mil. bu.	287	320		
Rice	1,000 MT	695	698	750	7
Commercial exports	1,000 MT	264	316		
Special govt. programs	1,000 MT	431	382		
Feed grains	1,000 MT	8,043	11,261	11,750	4
Commercial exports	1,000 MT	5,010	8,703		
Special govt. programs	1,000 MT	3,033	2,558		
Cotton	1,000 bales	4,468	3,678	6,500	77
Commercial exports	1,000 bales	2,560	2,229		
Special govt. programs	1,000 bales	1,908	1,449		
Fats and oils	1,000 MT	2,020	2,242	2,900	29
Commercial exports	1,000 MT	1,405	1,769		
Special govt. programs	1,000 MT	615	473		
Total agricultural exports	Bil. dol.	3.9	3.9	4.7	21

grain production potential at 176 million tons in 1965—against 128 million tons needed for livestock (1954–58 feed-livestock conversion rates of .83 ton) at the same point in time. Excesses this large are not great when diets of the masses of consumers the world over are examined. But opportunities and needs for U.S. agricultural production, in the context of optimum rate and extent of world development, need to be appraised in a larger economic framework.

[53] S. E. Johnson, *Agricultural Outlook in the 1960's*, 38th Annual USDA National Outlook Conference, November, 1960 (Mimeo). The changes shown are percent of 1959 exports, and not of production.

Other nations also have supply potential which is large relative to effective demand.[54] Disposal of U.S. surplus does not take place in a market vacuum, but must be evaluated against an interrelated network of supply and demand functions. Increased shipment of food to one nation decreases the demand and price for food from others where farm production potential is increasing at rates equal to or faster than those in the United States. It is not yet established that less developed nations can use food with greater marginal benefit than capital for industrial development, with the latter providing remunerative opportunity for masses now underemployed in agriculture. As a purely dumping activity, the impact of supplies from the United States which restrain internal market prices (a condition which, however, does not prevail in countries where food shortages are extreme and prices are controlled at ceiling level) also must be appraised. The shortage in some countries is not caloric, a low cost component of diet and nutrition, but of particular nutrients and variety which are not largely supplied in U.S. excesses. Finally, a surplus disposal program which itself creates uncertainty of supply source—to the extent that it is effective in removing surplus stocks, is not conducive to systematic planning by other nations; nor is it always consistent with the nation's broader foreign policy. Economic analysis in a broader developmental framework may even specify that export of fertilizer, or the machinery to produce fertilizer, is more desirable than export of food.

The elements within the matrix outlined above cause foreign disposal to be less a simple physical and economic alternative in space than first appears true. Hence, we need to postpone more complete analysis of this alternative in demand until a later point.

SOLUTIONS IN SUPPLY AND RESOURCE STRUCTURE

Even were foreign disposal or exports to provide the means for enlarging demands, thus lifting commodity prices and resource returns of U.S. agriculture, the internal pull of economic development on resource reallocation would not be obviated. Modern technology which has boosted the marginal productivity of capital and land to the individual farmer would still press for firms of larger scale and for industry labor input of smaller magnitude. Increase in demand would not erase the conditions of technical and economic development giving rise to scale economies and factor prices favoring the substitution of capital for labor. Its immediate effect would be to allow farm prices to be maintained at government supported levels, without such large investment of the public in nonrecourse loans for commodity acquisition, in storage of public stocks and payments for sterilizing the productivity of resources.

Our analysis of demand has been significant in one respect: it illustrates

---

[54] Colin Clark, *et al.*, *United Kingdom Projected Level of Demand and Supply of Farm Products*, ERS-F-19, USDA, 1962.

clearly that problems of price and resource return in agriculture must be solved on the side of commodity and resource supply structures of the industry. This would appear a negative perspective if fixation were in historic farm values and policy. In a broader context of economic development and human opportunity, the inability to push domestic demand functions to the speed of supply functions connotes attainments. Greater containment of human aspiration exists when the opposite prevails. Our conclusion in this chapter is that we can neither "export" nor "eat up" our food surplus and production capacity problems in present regime of international market, U.S. foreign policy and national population increase. The attack must be more fundamental and broader. Exports, and largely those subsidized under public policy, have represented the large, nonsecular demand increment of the 1950's. Whether this opportunity grows, maintains or declines will be determined by the nation's and world's political and humanitarian choices during the 1960's.

7

Structure of Agriculture

DATA OF CHAPTERS 4, 5 and 6 lead us to the proposition that major imbalance of agriculture can be lessened but little from the direction of domestic demand, by, increasing consumption sufficiently that excess resources do not exist and returns to factors are comparable with those in other economic sectors. Hence, major adjustment apparently must come from the direction of supply and quantity of inputs committed to particular commodities, lessening of inputs and outputs so that returns are increased. The latter can be accomplished through the market, or through policies which restrict inputs and outputs. Farm groups would harmonize if demand could be increased to erase the problem of low incomes and resource returns. But when balance must be restored through the side of supply, agreement on method is not so universal. To understand what is implied in structure of agriculture under economic growth, if major structural variables are to be changed, we need to review prospective directions of agriculture under further national development.

PRESSURE OF DEVELOPMENT ON STRUCTURE

The employment of resources and the mix of products of an economic system change under development in the manner outlined in previous chapters. The changes in structure of agriculture partly reflect those of the national economy, but more so on the side of resource mix than in product mix. This is true since the same developments in factor markets and prices which cause nonfarm sectors to employ a richer mix of capital relative to labor function similarly for agriculture. On the side of product mix, however, the relative shift under rapid or continuous development is much more away from food products and other biological necessities to commodities and services which have greater appeal and marginal utility in convenience and psychological orientation. Of course, the structure of agriculture is caught up somewhat in the same shift in consumption as consumers grow wealthier. As the income elasticities of Chapter 6 illustrate, the makeup of the food product mix, even aside from incorporated processing and marketing services, shifts from inferior goods with income elasticities smaller than zero but representing low cost in calories and appeasement of hunger, to foods of higher per unit cost but containing greater proportion of protein, calcium and other nutritional components. But, because of biological restraints, satiation per capita in food is approached and the over-all mix cannot change continuously over time to the extent of the national product.

There is a fundamental requirement in farm and food policy, if it is to provide a reasonable or workable combination of income stability, compensation for progress sacrifices, opportunity in growth, market power and other goals desired or attained by major social groups. This requirement is that the basic trend in resource allocation and product mix, which stems from economic development, must be recognized. Unless it is, mammoth surpluses and large public costs in storing them arise, as has been the case since 1930, and void exists in opportunity or facilities to provide it for youth and other persons who have greater opportunity in real income and self-expression in growing nonfarm sectors.

Self-administered and legislated powers in other groups may have provided greater market power and income stability than in agriculture generally. However, even with these opportunities and mechanisms, nonfarm sectors have not caused or have been unable to cause the historic mix of products to be so tightly maintained over time as held true in agriculture during the 1950's and early 1960's. Perhaps this difference has grown partly out of ability of particular sectors to manage supply and schedule prices according to marginal urgency of consumer preferences. But more than that, it has been the change in pattern of consumer preferences, the slope of the indifference map, as per capita income has increased, and the broad pull of competition over firms and sectors in a large and complex economy which have caused nonfarm resources to change in pattern of allocation under economic growth. As we have mentioned in previous chapters, nonprice competition and short-run stability have not obviated long-run competition on a nonprice basis—including creation of new products. Ability of oligopolistic industries to administer production and price policy in buggies, kerosene lanterns and wooden matches could not have caused their supply to be maintained and consumers to use historic quantities of them, even at some modest subsidy.

We need, then, to examine the structure of agriculture as it might develop further under the pull of economic change and inter-industry competition for resources. It is not necessary, in terms of portion of nation's resources represented by agriculture and over-all public purposes, that this structure be attained immediately. It could be attained in a relatively short-time span by simple public policy, namely, that of completely free markets and prices. The need or ability of agriculture and national economy to absorb change of this rate and abruptness, as reflected in policy, has been questioned by American society. The questioning undoubtedly rests on the concepts of equity in distribution of gains and costs of progress outlined in following chapters.

This is not to say that farm policy has completely blocked change in agricultural structure. It has not. It has only slowed down the rate of change in technology and resource structure, perhaps only modestly relative to that which would have occurred in the absence of price policy and public compensation. Still, the structural possibility of the agricultural sector under continued economic growth needs to remain in sight of policy formulation. There are several reasons for this. One in conventional economic logic is, of course, that given the technology and consumer preferences of the time, some best or optimum allocation of resources will prevail for the particular economic regime. Increasingly with time, this argument has less significance, although no less logically than for other sectors, as agriculture declines to a minor portion of the economy in terms of portion of resources used and national income generated. But just as it falls to minority magnitudes in this sense, agriculture also becomes too small to ward off the complete pressures of the market under economic change.

To take U.S. agriculture in one direction in 1800 was almost to take the national economy with it. But to take agriculture in a direction differing from the national economy today is quite a different thing. Only discrete legislation prescribing exactly the size and resource makeup of farms could pretend to do so; and even then it would have difficulty as labor responded to off-farm employment and price opportunity, or as capital is substituted for labor in response to relative prices favoring this shift. Simple policy measures, as lower prices for resources such as credit and knowledge, cannot check the stronger pulls of the market in a dominant nonfarm economy.

Finally, there is no evidence that values of society, and those of farm people in particular, prefer perpetuation of an historic agricultural structure, to a point several decades into the future. There is not evidence to indicate that child-bearing farm families wish to have opportunities for their off-spring restricted to agriculture, or to have a structure of agriculture maintained to fit their grandchildren as it fitted themselves or their ancestors. There is empirical evidence that farm persons generally have desired better opportunities for their children than was their own lot. They have not preferred this necessarily to be in agriculture. The empirical evidence is given in the high value and priority given to education and training by each new wave of pioneers which moved westward.[1] Whether

[1] Cf. Douglas C. North, *The Economic Growth of the United States, 1790–1860*, Prentice-Hall, New York, 1960, p. 155.

the resources were logs or sod, schoolhouses arose about as rapidly as farm domiciles. But even more now than previously, young farm couples predominantly wish for education and training which prepare their sons to be engineers, doctors and business executives. While it is common to find hopes that one child may take over farm operations, if they grow successfully, this is not the dominant wish forced on farm children. It never has been, as migration figures and early investment in education illustrate. It is misleading for economists and farm leaders to expound this wish as that of agriculture. Delve into it deeply and one finds it to be not so, this supposition that the farm population wishes an "Indian reservation policy"—one which would maintain the structure, culture and philosophical role in society only as it has been in the past. Farm people of this generation do want policy which gives them promising economic opportunity, and which puts them on equal footing with other industries in respect to market power, income stability and preservation of equity. But they do not look to a cluster of policies which holds agriculture to resource and price structure of the past and present as a foundation of life and living for their young children or grandchildren.

Distinction needs to be made between values of society and farm people for policy of the present generation, over-lapping as it does with the next, and that for future generations. They generally point to two different poles.

Prices, Knowledge and Powers of Markets

Hence, given the pressures of the factor markets and development of technology favoring change in structure, it is useful that image of future industry and firm mold of agriculture be viewed. Projections of its structure can aid in education and action programs in the sense of providing an intellectual environment for decision of individuals, in respect to commitment of their own resources or as voters making choices regarding public policy. It provides a basis also for decision concerning whether a particular trend direction should be diverted or slowed down. But, largely, projection of future potential in agricultural structure serves best to indicate policy consistent with current goals but allowing progress towards longer-run national goals and economic development possibilities. This is not to say that structure as it develops more or less automatically under economic growth is God-given and transcendental, or that it should be man's master rather than his slave. Public policy is needed mainly because of growth and change, and to guarantee positive-sum utility gains from progress, in aggregation of welfare over all major strata of society.

It is the function of policy to assess the impact of this change, modifying the effects where community welfare promises to be lessened materially through sacrifice of particular groups, or speeding it up where it gives rise to potential welfare increase to aggregate society. The structure implied under true economic growth, in contrast to social change where population grows against supplies of capital and commodities, provides basis for increase along the social welfare function. The day is still so far away when the marginal utility of all goods and services for all members of the U.S. population approaches limit zero that further economic progress can be abandoned. As long as this is true and as long as change in structure of agriculture can add to social welfare, anthropological retrogression to primitive or animal cultures aside, markets in the private sector and policy in the public sector will compose a matrix with elements encouraging change.

Given the degree of "under-development" in even the most developed nations of the world, the crucial policy question is not one of how change in agricultural structure can be brought to a dead stop. Instead, it is one of how policy can adapt rate of change to that which is consistent with values of this generation of farm people and society, or to that which is consistent with ability of the remainder of the economy to absorb. Further, it is one of encouraging change but guaranteeing equity in income distribution and in the distribution of the fruits of progress among various strata of society. Policy which tempers progress to conform with these two conditions will have general public basis or acceptance, although not necessarily approval by groups who would benefit more at the expense of others under more revolutionary change.

American farm policy since 1930 has not "zeroed" structural change or technical progress of agriculture. Alone, it has had insignificant effect. We can even hypothesize that the greater certainty it has provided in price and income has effectively speeded the rate of technical change, both in causing farmers to make resource substitutions otherwise consistent with extended planning horizons and in reducing the discounts and restraints of uncertainty. At most, compensation policy has been a method of "buying time" and checking slightly or somewhat the rate at which certain changes in structure have taken place. Quantities cited earlier, on rate of migration, increase in farm size, capital investment, labor productivity and other items of change, indicate clearly that even the retarding elements are difficult to isolate. It has not been an absolute and outright limit to change. Neither will future farm policy be so, as it takes place in a market of national economy so large relative to agriculture that it completely over-rides this sector.

In the sense of buying time, the positive and beneficial aspects of previous policy have probably been in giving farm people added time to gain in knowledge and understanding of the national economy, economic development and the relation of agriculture to both. Regardless of the fact that the farm sector has been blessed with public machinery for adult education not provided other strata of society, this mechanism was used hardly at all in early or previous decades to inform farm people of the phenomena most basic to their economic welfare and decisions, namely, the interrelationships of agriculture and the national economy under economic growth.

Only a minority of farmers had rough knowledge of the nature of demand elasticities. Accordingly, they hoped for the impossible, such as relieving farm income depression through greater output and efficiency improvements in the marketing system. Subsidies and price supports made it possible for some farmers to maintain a living level which kept them in agriculture, particularly older persons without income and progress aspirations drawing them to other industries. For many, it gave time for learning more clearly of the role and prospects of agriculture under economic growth. Farmers beyond middle age at 1950 associated, from their experience in two inflations and depressions, agricultural prosperity with general prosperity in the economy. Farmers beyond middle age at 1960 no longer made this direct association and many even knew, some with the help of their state extension services, the general magnitude of demand elasticities, the prospects in capital and managerial requirements for the developing agriculture and even the relative prospects for growth-oriented employment for their sons and daughters in nonfarm industries.

Policies of the 1950's purchased time in the sense that they provided income supplements so that more farm families had time to learn these things without driving themselves and their children into blind allies; in allowing debate and consolidation of beliefs in respect to value orientations for policy; perhaps in providing surpluses of such magnitude that pressures led to their use in international humanitarianism, when the opportunity likely would otherwise have been absent; and so that an excess of labor was not driven into labor ranks in brief periods of unemployment. Aside from these positive elements, policy of the decade did little to correct the structural imbalances of agriculture, and accomplished certain of the above at public costs higher than necessary for the same level of accomplishment.

At this point in time it cannot yet be proven that certain developments in the knowledge of nature of science have made a positive contribution to man. Atomic fission falls in this category to date. Although its promise of benefit is great and some small peaceful contributions have been realized from it, man is largely its slave. Contemporary societies divert large sums from consumption and human betterment because of it, and cower in fear because of possible consequences of its use. Farm technology is not so awesome, and its potential and very real contribution to human welfare is closer at hand and is not a weapon for mutual extermination by competing nations. But U.S. society cannot yet prove that net benefit, in the sense of gain and loss distributions which guarantee positive-sum utility outcome, has resulted entirely from the rapid output progress of the years 1950–60. It has given rise to frustration within agriculture and by the general public in trying to assess its results and the relative merits of the alternative structure to which it might draw agriculture. It has, on the one hand, caused depressed farm income because of the rate at which it has, along with compensation policies, shifted the commodity supply function against factor supplies and commodity demand of relatively low elasticities. Society, in general, has had to provide large sums and, through taxation, has had to divert expenditures from alternative lines of consumption because of its income-depressing effects.

Because of the rapid entry of farm technology, and inability of farm groups to agree more nearly on policy means and objective, large investments have had to be made in storage facilities for large surplus stocks which accumulated and added nothing to net social welfare. Man was somewhat the slave of technical advance and some of his own farm policy configurations during the 1950's, not only in the sense outlined above, but also in the manner of the competitive model outlined earlier.

Ideally, man would be the master of technology, as well as of the market, adapting its rate and uses to his own benefit. Largely this has been true, but not necessarily for the phases of technology and the time period mentioned. Man can be the master of technology, but he must incorporate it into appropriate policy and economic and social bounds and institutions. It is not God-given that man must adjust himself to rates of technological change and their impacts which are brought about by the undirected play of markets—in India where the market regime may cause the rate to be too slow, or in the United States where it may cause the rate to be too fast. American society did not, in fact, accept the rate of the market, but assumed the function of research in, and communication of, technical knowledge for agriculture. It is not an inalienable law of nature, over which man does not or should not have control, that technology developed must be allowed unchecked momentum in reducing the number of farms by 90 percent in Iowa or Kansas, and the particular distribution of gains and social costs of this transformation.

Variables in Structure

Technical advance, cultural change, economic organization and political mechanism have together promoted economic development and have even lifted man from the status of primate. Technical advance has been the necessary condition, the social structure, the sufficient condition. Man's innate ability to organize would have been for naught without mastery of nature and technological advance. But technical advance in the absence of organization would not even have carried man to the economic status of the Middle Ages. This emphasis is made to indicate that we do not believe economic structure which evolves in various stages of economic growth must be taken as given, without ability to adapt it or turn it in preferred directions. We do, however, believe that a systematic set of variables, with ordered coefficients attached to them, evolve under economic development, whether the social system is one of a completely managed economy or its opposite, a pure market economy. The environment lending force or magnitude to these variables and their parameters will persist as long as development takes place in the sense of increase of ends relative to means; as long as technology and capital accumulation leads to prices of these resources which are low relative to labor; and as long as all possible preferences of consumers are not satiated and differential ability in biological and psychological absorption of commodities and services prevails.

Economic growth is a systematic process in the sense that its different stages and phases in the continuum encourages, through relative differences in factor supplies or scarcities and in factor prices, different technology and resource structure to prevail where alternative technologies are known, or causes premium to attach to uncovering of particular technologies where they are unknown. As development progresses and capital becomes more abundant relative to labor, technologies which encompass greater scale economies to capital and cause higher marginal rates of substitution of capital for labor are encouraged, just as is research to discover and develop them.

We discussed this "natural order" in Chapter 3, illustrating how, at low stages of development with largeness of labor supply relative to capital and smallness of labor price relative to capital, labor technologies with limited scale economies tend to be optimum; but with high rate of economic development and the opposite of factor supply and pricing, technology emphasizing capital and extended scale economies becomes more consistent with economic structure. (See discussion of Figure 3.1 and Chapter 15). Within the continuum of economic development, the direction of American agriculture still is towards the latter pole. If all technology had been known at the outset but capital and labor supplies existed as they did two centuries back, the trend in structure of American agriculture would still have been highly similar to its past. In early decades, with elastic supply and small price of labor relative to capital, technique of production would have favored a large proportion of labor in total inputs. Under labor technology, or technologies using a large proportion of labor, scale economies or cost advantage for large units is not great. Hence, a larger number of small farms exist, with a greater proportion of the inputs furnished directly by the households in agriculture. But with economic growth and shift in price relative between capital and labor, substitution of the former for the latter is encouraged and technologies which increase the substitution rate are especially of mechanical nature, wherein cost advantages more clearly lead to large output per firm.

With greater capital per worker, output per worker is greater, requiring a smaller labor force and farm population with larger and fewer farms. While not quite so restrained, the trend in farm technology would still have been largely over man and hoe, man and animal, man and small power unit and man and larger power unit, had all technology been known over the centuries but with capital supply increasing and its price decreasing relative to labor with economic growth and time. Roughly, the pattern of technology outlined above extends over national boundaries of today's world.

Labor technology and small units exist in less developed nations, not necessarily because of "backwardness" and complete lack of technical knowledge, but because of abundance of labor relative to capital and stage of economic development providing less industrial opportunity for drawing labor from farms. It is not purely a mark of differential efficiency that 75 percent of national labor force is employed in agriculture in India, or that 40 percent is required in Russia and less than 10 percent in the United States. Mixes in these directions are, or have been, consistent with the level of economic development and the relative supplies and prices of capital and labor in all three countries.

Long-run trends in relative prices of labor and capital items used by U.S. agriculture are summarized in Table 7.1. The effect of the growing cost of labor relative to capital, or a declining real cost of capital relative to labor, is that expected under economic growth wherein capital supply becomes large and labor becomes relatively more scarce and expensive to the total economy. Agriculture has changed its structure against these shifts in relative factor prices about as theory would lead us to propose, namely, capital has been substituted for labor with each man who reremains handling a greater aggregate of nonhuman resources. The process will continue, not only because of the direct substitution of capital for labor, but indirectly as nonfarm wage rates act as a magnet drawing labor from agriculture. Farm policies of recent structure can do, or have done, little to retard the latter. Even the cost of transportation and communication has declined relatively to labor price, requiring farm people less real investment in obtaining knowledge about nonfarm employment opportunity or about the technology of capital/labor substitution.

These forces will continue to pull American agriculture in the direction of larger and more specialized farms, resting more on machine capital and less on labor, and more on biological capital and less on land. Change will not be discrete and revolutionary, but gradual and continuous as it has been in recent decades. Whether this trend over the longer run is considered "good" or "bad" depends on the values of the individual, or the goals and values of the nation. Reduction of commercial farms to a million or of total farms by 60 percent, a physical opportunity which already exists when it is noted that 39 percent of farms produced 87 percent of output in 1959, would indeed diminish the effect and power of agricul-

TABLE 7.1

INDICES OF PRICES FOR CAPITAL ITEMS FOR U.S. AGRICULTURE, 1910–59
(1910–14=100)

Resource	1910–19	1920–29	1930–39	1940–49	1950–59
Short-term interest rate	95.4	94.0	88.0	78.3	77.1
Farm wage rates	123.7	182.8	121.4	309.4	521.7
Farm machinery	114.9	154.2	149.0	189.0	321.2
Fertilizer	122.1	137.8	104.6	121.0	153.2
Seed	125.2	145.3	106.9	179.5	259.2
All capital items	118.4	119.5	117.9	183.7	259.2

Source: *Economic Report of the President*, 1960 and USDA.

ture in national culture and politics. But whether farm population constitutes 5 or 8 percent of total in 1980 is not highly significant—either magnitude being too small for dominance of the industry over the affairs of the nation. The shape of economic development has already largely accomplished this diminution for the industry as a whole, given wide variance in interests of commodity, regional and income groups of agriculture (although dominance by agriculture still prevails in selected state economies and legislatures). To the contrary, national society has had sympathy with agriculture and has extended policies to it in compensation for sacrifices growing out of progress and to provide it with income security and market power paralleling that possessed by other sectors in the national economy.

GROWING INTERDEPENDENCE WITH NATIONAL ECONOMY

Growing interdependence of agriculture with the national economy is itself a function of economic development. This fact and the relationships expressing it could be measured in time-series sense over the history of the United States, or in cross-sectional manner over the boundaries of nations at varying levels of economic development. Subsistence agriculture and dominance of inputs supplied by farm households characterizes the industry at low stages of development. Labor is the major resource, with land being important to capital generated either within or outside the industry.

Consumption of farm households similarly rests on physical product of the industry and few of the services incorporated with the food flow from outside industry. But with economic progress and relative increase of labor price relative to capital, technology favoring supply of capital from outside develops or is encouraged, giving rise to an agricultural product composed less of labor and land furnished from within the industry and more on capital furnished from outside the sector.

Too, as income increases, the preferences of farm consumers develop not unlike those of nonfarm consumers with rising incomes. Communication in developed societies is too great to allow long-term dispersion in values between farm and nonfarm persons. With media such as television, radio, newspapers and magazines, automobiles and expansion of scale economies to the re-districting of schools, the trend will continue. Hence, development of the national economy impinges on agriculture from the side of production with a growing proportion of nonfarm inputs. It finds agriculture leashed more tightly to factor prices and technology of national markets, with income increase or decline more directly related to the allocation of resources in line with preferences of consumers, and from the side of consumption with families depending less on farm produced foods, using more of the nonfarm services mixed with foods and preferring an "affluence mix" of commodities not unlike middle income groups of other sectors.

Figure 7.1 illustrates the increase in proportion of inputs purchased by agriculture and the decline in inputs supplied directly from farm

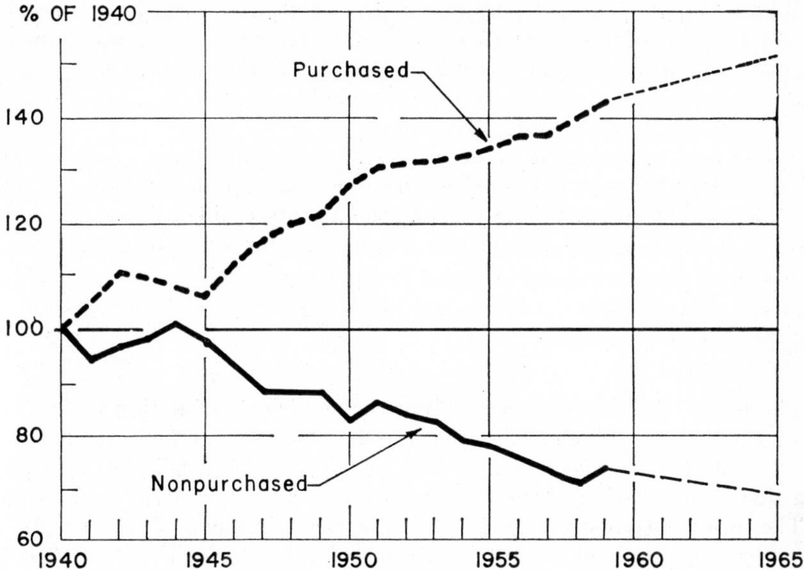

Fig. 7.1. Trends in Purchased and Nonpurchased Inputs of U.S. Farms. (Source: USDA Neg. 60 (10)—9020.)

households. This trend can only continue because of the limited area of land, and because of further substitution of capital in new technology for land, and because of capital and labor prices which extend the degree of mechanization. This increase in proportion of "outside" inputs causes income and structure of agriculture to become increasingly sensitive to prices of the nonfarm economy. It places greater pressure on agriculture to adjust resource structure and output with consumer preferences as expressed in commodity and factor markets.

Regional and Commodity Interdependence

Interdependence of agriculture with the nonfarm economy varies among regions and commodities, depending on the products of advantage and the general nature of the production function. This degree and variation in interdependence can be illustrated partially, and imperfectly, by review of coefficients derived in input-output models emphasizing agriculture. The models presented have the implications and limitations outlined in the following summary of the models. Open models of the economy were used. The basis or descriptive phase of the models can be written in the notation of (7.1).

$$
\begin{array}{l}
X_1 - x_{11} - x_{12} - \cdots - x_{1n} = Y_1 \\
X_2 - x_{21} - x_{22} - \cdots - x_{2n} = Y_2 \\
\vdots \qquad\qquad\qquad\qquad\qquad\qquad \vdots \\
X_n - x_{n1} - x_{n2} - \cdots - x_{nn} = Y_n
\end{array}
\tag{7.1}
$$

Where $X_1, X_2, \cdots, X_n$ represent gross output of specific economic sectors of the economy, x_{ij} $(i, j=1, \cdots, n)$ represents the actual flow of goods and services from sector i to sector j; and Y_i $(i=1, \cdots, n)$ are the flows to final demand sectors (household consumption, investment, government, foreign trade, inventory).

The basic assumption made in the input-output analysis pertains to the relation between purchases of an endogenous sector (i.e., the x_{ij}) and the level of output of this sector (i.e., the X_j). Assuming a linear relationship (the appropriateness of this assumption for agriculture sectors is discussed elsewhere[2]), we obtain the equation in (7.2)

$$x_{ij} = a_{ij}X_j + c_{ij} \tag{7.2}$$

$$a_{ij} = x_{ij}X_j^{-1} \tag{7.3}$$

where a_{ij} and c_{ij} are parameters. For the empirical estimation which follows, the assumption is made that $c_{ij}=0$. The a_{ij} (commonly referred to as an input-output coefficient or technological coefficient) is derived from a single observation of the ratio between x_{ij} and X_j written as in (7.3). The input-output coefficient is the direct requirement of sector j upon sector i, per unit of output in sector j. For example, if industry purchased 25 billion dollars' worth of agricultural goods and total output for industry is 500 billion dollars, the corresponding input-output coefficient is 25/500, or .05, meaning that industry directly requires 5 cents worth of goods and services from agriculture per dollar of output in industry. Assuming $c_{ij}=0$, substituting (7.2) into (7.1) yields (7.4) in equation form, or (7.5) in matrix notation, where X is a vector of outputs from all sectors, A is a matrix of input-output coefficients and Y is a vector of final demand quantities.

$$\begin{aligned} X_1 - a_{11}X_1 - a_{12}X_2 - \cdots - a_{1n}X_n &= Y_1 \\ X_2 - a_{21}X_1 - a_{22}X_2 - \cdots - a_{2n}X_n &= Y_2 \\ \vdots \qquad\qquad\qquad\qquad &\quad \vdots \\ X_n - a_{n1}X_1 - a_{n2}X_2 - \cdots - a_{nn}X_n &= Y_n \end{aligned} \tag{7.4}$$

$$X - AX = Y \tag{7.5}$$

Hence, with specified final demands $Y_1, Y_2, \cdots, Y_n$ and constant input-output coefficients, equations (7.1) can be solved for the outputs $X_1, X_2, \cdots, X_n$. The resulting equations are given in (7.6). The A_{ij}'s (commonly referred to as interdependence coefficients) are elements of the inverse matrix $(I-A)^{-1}$ with the value of X expressed in the matrix notation of (7.7).

---

[2] See Earl O. Heady and H. O. Carter, "Input-Output Models as Techniques of Analysis for Interregional Competition," *Jour. Farm Econ.*, Vol. 41; H. O. Carter and Earl O. Heady, *An Input-Output Analysis Emphasizing Regional and Commodity Groups of Agriculture*, Iowa Agr. Exp. Sta. Bul. 469; Earl O. Heady and John A. Schnittker, "Application of Input-Output Models to Agriculture," *Jour. Farm Econ.*, Vol. 39.

$$
(7.6) \quad \begin{aligned}
X_1 &= A_{11}Y_1 + A_{12}Y_2 + \cdots + A_{1n}Y_n \\
X_2 &= A_{21}Y_1 + A_{22}Y_2 + \cdots + A_{2n}Y_n \\
&\vdots \\
X_n &= A_{n1}Y_1 + A_{n2}Y_2 + \cdots + A_{nn}Y_n
\end{aligned}
$$

$$
(7.7) \quad X = (1 - A)^{-1}Y
$$

The interdependence coefficients (A_{ij}'s) represent the direct and indirect requirements upon sector i for a one-unit change in the amount of goods delivered to final demand by industry j. This characteristic makes the method pertinent to relationships among regional and industrial sectors, since both the indirect and direct effects of change are reflected among both sectors. Equations (7.1) through (7.4) represent the descriptive component, while equations (7.5) through (7.6) represent the analytical quantities of the input-output model. A simple model within the above general framework suggests the growth manner of interdependence of agriculture in aggregate with nonfarm sectors.[3]

We now turn to an input-output model from 1949 data emphasizing regional stratification of agriculture. It emphasizes the small extent to which the nonfarm sector now depends on agriculture and the fairly elaborate extent to which certain farm sectors depend on the former.[4] This model includes 12 agricultural sectors, a crop or primary sector (sectors 1 to 6) and a livestock or secondary sector (sectors 7 to 12) for each of the six geographic regions shown in Table 7.2. It includes 8 industrial or nonfarm sectors, with aggregation to emphasize sectors that furnish inputs for, or process products from, agriculture. The objectives of the study include describing relationships between agriculture and certain components of the nonagricultural economy. Industry aggregation

TABLE 7.2

Composition of Agricultural Regions by States

Region 1	Region 2	Region 3	Region 4	Region 5	Region 6
Maine	Ohio	Va.	N.Dak.	Mont.	Ariz.
N.H.	Ind.	W.Va.	S.Dak.	Idaho	Wash.
Vt.	Ill.	N.C.	Nebr.	Wyo.	Oreg.
Mass.	Wis.	S.C.	Kans.	Colo.	Calif.
R.I.	Mich.	Ga.	Okla.	N.Mex.	
Conn.	Minn.	Fla.	Tex.	Utah	
N.Y.	Iowa	Tenn.		Nev.	
N.J.	Mo.	Ala.			
Pa..	Ky.	Miss.			
Del.		Ark.			
Md.		La.			

[3] G. A. Peterson and Earl O. Heady, *Application of an Input-Output Analysis to a Simple Model Emphasizing Agriculture,* Iowa Agr. Exp. Sta. Bul. 427.

[4] See Heady and Schnittker, *op. cit.*, and Schnittker and Heady, *Application of Input-Output Analysis to a Regional Model Stressing Agriculture,* Iowa Agr. Exp. Sta. Bul. 454.

is based mostly on a detailed study of the United States economy made by the Bureau of Labor Statistics for 1947.[5] The industry sectors are:

Sector 13. Industries processing the products of primary agriculture, chiefly for food use, but including livestock feeds as by-products.

Sector 14. Industries processing the products of primary agriculture, chiefly for nonfood use.

Sector 15. Industries processing the food products of secondary agriculture.

Sector 16. Industries providing machinery, machine services, fuel and oil to all sectors of the economy.

Sector 17. Industries furnishing fertilizers, seeds and other supplies to agriculture, as well as many products to other sectors.

Sector 18. All other industries, including most services and transportation and merchandising.

Sector 19. Foreign trade.

Sector 20. Government.

In the simple model, intersector flows for agricultural regions were computed only for primary crops. Data on feeder stock were inadequate; all secondary livestock products were treated as if they went directly to sector 15. Although there were blanks in the table of input-output coefficients, there are none in the table of interdependence coefficients, however, because interrelationships are expressed both directly to a sector and indirectly back through other sectors.

Interdependence Coefficients

The interdependence coefficients computed for the model outlined above are included in Table 7.2. These quantities are equivalent to the A_{ij} values shown in the inverse matrix of (7.7) and the equations of (7.6). If put in matrix form and multiplied by the 1949 direct consumption of each of the 20 sectors, the product provides the output of the producing sectors. In the conventions of input-output literature, these coefficients might be interpreted as indicating the change in output of one producing sector associated with a *dollar's worth* of change in final demand (direct consumption) for the output of any other sector. However, we prefer to interpret the quantities shown as the average amount of product in a particular sector associated, in 1949, with each *dollar's worth* of product consumed directly from each other producing sector. In this vein, we do not suppose that the "fixed-mix" representing output of one sector will be projected into the future as national income increases. Neither do we suppose that the technical coefficients will remain constant as demand for the product of any one sector increases. Although

[5] See U.S. Dept. of Labor, *Industry Classification Manual for the 1947 Interindustry Relations Study*, Washington, D.C., 1953, (Mimeo.); and *Interindustry Flow of Goods and Services of Origin and Destination*, 1947, Washington, D.C., 1952.

TABLE 7.3

Interdependence Coefficients Between the Final Bill of Goods and Net Outputs for 1949

	1	2	3	4	5	6	7	8	9	10	11	12	13	14	15	16	17	18	19	20
	Primary (Crop) Agriculture Sectors						Secondary (Livestock) Agriculture Sectors						Industry Sectors							
Sector No.	Reg. 1	Reg. 2	Reg. 3	Reg. 4	Reg. 5	Reg. 6	Reg. 1	Reg. 2	Reg. 3	Reg. 4	Reg. 5	Reg. 6	Crop-food products	Nonfood crop products	Livestock products	Machinery and fuel	Miscellaneous supplies	All other products	Foreign trade	Government
1	1.024	.002	.002	.001	.001	.002	.301	.003	.006	.003	.002	.005	.021	.007	.032	.001	.009	.002	.006	.003
2	.010	1.037	.007	.006	.007	.007	.034	.401	.017	.010	.012	.023	.068	.068	.137	.008	.023	.011	.040	.016
3	.008	.006	1.020	.005	.006	.006	.018	.009	.424	.009	.008	.015	.058	.108	.040	.009	.013	.010	.073	.016
4	.008	.006	.006	1.032	.007	.006	.018	.009	.014	.485	.020	.026	.058	.057	.067	.008	.017	.009	.046	.021
5	.002	.002	.002	.001	1.038	.002	.006	.003	.004	.003	.041	.005	.021	.007	.020	.002	.006	.002	.006	.005
6	.004	.003	.003	.002	.003	1.013	.018	.006	.013	.007	.006	.317	.066	.020	.023	.003	.009	.004	.017	.007
7	.076	.001	.001	.001	.001	.001	1.024	.001	.002	.001	.001	.002	.007	.005	.101	.001	.003	.002	.005	.003
8	.005	.081	.004	.003	.004	.004	.009	1.034	.006	.005	.004	.007	.022	.020	.331	.005	.008	.008	.019	.010
9	.001	.001	.037	.001	.001	.009	.002	.001	1.016	.001	.001	.002	.006	.007	.076	.001	.002	.002	.006	.003
10	.002	.002	.002	.060	.002	.002	.004	.002	.003	.030	.003	.004	.010	.002	.123	.002	.003	.003	.009	.004
11	.001	.001	.001	.001	.082	.001	.001	.001	.001	.001	1.037	.001	.004	.005	.040	.001	.001	.001	.003	.002
12	.001	.001	.001	.001	.001	.035	.002	.001	.001	.001	.001	1.012	.005	.004	.053	.008	.001	.001	.003	.002
13	.031	.016	.018	.014	.015	.016	.256	.082	.177	.092	.068	.195	1.020	.034	.103	.013	.020	.021	.061	.022
14	.027	.025	.023	.021	.025	.023	.039	.025	.033	.025	.024	.032	.081	1.024	.026	.046	.037	.049	.119	.031
15	.012	.011	.010	.009	.011	.010	.020	.011	.016	.002	.011	.017	.052	.044	1.012	.014	.019	.021	.050	.026
16	.164	.170	.136	.146	.185	.161	.113	.110	.109	.113	.126	.108	.091	.073	.089	1.042	.062	.067	.292	.066
17	.145	.087	.106	.048	.052	.082	.062	.044	.058	.033	.034	.041	.044	.043	.036	.033	1.018	.024	.097	.021
18	.467	.466	.408	.399	.477	.424	.462	.393	.431	.396	.409	.414	.449	.406	.368	.648	.546	1.157	1.022	.482
19	.028	.025	.021	.021	.025	.023	.045	.026	.035	.026	.025	.036	.112	.070	.034	.033	.042	.043	1.052	.089
20	.165	.155	.114	.125	.154	.146	.135	.114	.113	.113	.121	.120	.143	.163	.109	.165	.165	.188	.236	1.088

the "fixed-mix" restriction is not always a serious limitation when emphasis is on industry, the problem is more difficult for agricultural sectors specializing in products with definite inter-regional differences in income elasticities of demand.

Given the model employed, the important elements affecting farm sectors are magnitudes of final demand for the products of industries processing the products of agricultural sectors. The figures presented represent inter-industry relationships for a given point in time, 1949. The coefficients in the table show the amount of output in the row sector per dollar's worth of final demand for the products of the column sector. (The table is the matrix of interdependence coefficients such as the matrix of A_{ij}'s in (7.6). The column headings indicate the Y_i elements in the Y matrix and the row-stub headings represent the X_i values of the X matrix.) Thus a dollar's worth of final demand for crop-food products, sector 13, is associated with an output of only $.0211 in sector 1 (the Northeast), and $.0655 in sector 6 (the Pacific Coast), where a large proportion of fruits and vegetables move into sector 13, processing, and then to final demand. The interdependence coefficient of sector 13 with sector 5 (crop production in the Mountain states) is only $.0207. The bulk of crop production there consists of forage crops, which move to livestock in the same region.

The sum of the first six rows in column 13 is only .291, pointing up, in numerical terms, the existing situation in respect to the farmer's share of the consumer's dollar spent for crop-food products. Each dollar of final demand or household consumption of products in sector 13 requires only a 29-cent output by all agricultural crop sectors. The large interdependence coefficient, 45 cents (column 13, row 18), indicates that each dollar's worth of consumption of products in sector 13 is associated with a large output by sector 18, which includes mainly transportation and merchandising services.

A dollar of final demand for sector 15 or livestock products is associated with a *total mix value* of 72 cents (the sum of rows 7 to 12 in column 15) for the six secondary agricultural sectors. The fact that this figure is much greater for livestock than for crops indicates that a much larger proportion of the consumer's dollar, for livestock products, reaches the farmer. More than 33 cents of the 72-cent total is drawn from the Cornbelt where the main farm product, livestock, provides the major part of the pork, beef and milk consumed by the nation. The next largest interdependence coefficient is for sector 10, the western portion of the hog-raising and beef-feeding area, which provides a considerable amount of beef processed directly from the range. Although livestock is the important product of sector 11, most of this is range beef and sheep, which moves to the feedlots of sectors 8 and 10, rather than directly to processing, sector 15.

The interdependence coefficients of sector 15 on regional crop-producing sectors show the largest coefficient again to be for the Cornbelt (sector 8). A dollar's worth of final demand for the product of livestock processing in sector 15 was associated in 1949 with a 14-cent output of crops in sector 8; since most of the Cornbelt crop product (sector 2) moved to livestock in the same region (sector 8), and then into the livestock-processing industry (sector 15). A dollar's worth of final demand for products in sector 15 (livestock at retail) required a Cornbelt crop output greater than the livestock output in any other region.

Based on the model, final demand for the product of industrial sector 18 has little relationship to the output of agricultural sectors. The coefficients range from .0011 for secondary output in the Intermountain states (sector 11) to .0160 for primary output in the Cornbelt. In contrast, however, final demand for products of agricultural sectors required a much greater output from sector 18. These quantities (row 18, columns 1 to 12) range from .3928 for secondary products in the Cornbelt to .4768 for primary products in the Intermountain states. Similarly, while sector 16 (machinery and fuel) final demand bears only a trivial relationship to output of agricultural sectors (column 16, rows 1 to 12), the opposite is not true. One dollar of final demand for crop or primary agricultural products in sector 5 (the Intermountain states) was associated with an 18-cent output in the machinery and fuel sector. The figure was 14 cents for the Southeast (sector 3), where more of the work is done by man and horsepower and machine inputs per dollar of crop output are generally lower than for other regions (row 18, columns 1 to 6).

Interindustry Dependence

We now summarize a second regional input-output model where 1954 agriculture has been divided into the 10 regional sectors indicated in Table 7.4, for comparison against three nonfarm sectors—namely, industries processing farm products, industries furnishing inputs to agriculture and all other industries.[6] The agricultural processing industry is, of course, highly dependent on agriculture. In Table 7.4, a one dollar increase in demand for the product of this sector (I) is associated with a 59.1 output (the sum of the first 10 rows under column I) in all 10 agricultural sectors, with 25 percent or 15.3 cents of this from the Cornbelt and only 4 percent, or 2.3 cents, from the Delta states.

But the more significant figures in interdependence are those of agricultural furnishing (II) and other sectors (III) with agriculture. All agricultural sectors have demand on sector II greater than 31 cents for each dollar of output in the regional farm sectors—the largest being 55.2 cents for the Northeast and the smallest being 31.2 cents for the Pacific states. The interdependence, per dollar of output, is even greater of farm sectors on the "other" (III) sector, amounting to more than 42 cents for all farm sectors and ranging from 56.2 cents in the Northeast to 44.4 cents in the Pacific states. In contrast, for each dollar of output, the agricultural furnishing sector draws no more than 3 cents from any farm sector, with the predominant magnitude being less than a single cent. Each dollar of

[6] See Heady and Carter, *op. cit.* and Carter and Heady, *op. cit.*

TABLE 7.4

INTERDEPENDENCE COEFFICIENTS, UNITED STATES ECONOMY, 1954,* AGGREGATION OF REGIONS AND SUBDIVISIONS OF INDUSTRY

	Agricultural Regions										Industry		
	1 North-east	2 Corn-belt	3 Lake States	4 Appal. States	5 South-east	6 Delta States	7 S. Plains	8 N. Plains	9 Mount. States	10 Pacific States	I Agr. processing	II Agr. furnishing	III All other
1	1.295	.002	.002	002	.002	.002	.002	.002	.002	.002	.063	.005	.003
2	.019	1.419	.010	.023	.009	.049	.014	.010	.009	.008	.153	.030	.009
3	.006	.004	1.436	.003	.003	.003	.003	.003	.003	.003	.068	.009	.004
4	.006	.002	.002	1.306	.002	.002	.002	.002	.002	.002	.053	.006	.003
5	.002	.002	.002	.002	1.259	.001	.002	.002	.002	.001	.038	.005	.002
6	.002	.001	.002	.001	.001	1.193	.001	.002	.001	.001	.023	.005	.001
7	.003	.010	.002	.007	.005	.002	1.211	.012	.002	.013	.040	.007	.002
8	.011	.039	.013	.003	.003	.004	.019	1.447	.006	.015	.060	.009	.003
9	.003	.012	.007	.002	.002	.002	.038	.059	1.410	.035	.043	.005	.002
10	.003	.002	.002	.002	.002	.002	.002	.003	.002	1.186	.063	.005	.003
I	.040	.032	.033	.029	.027	.026	.030	.037	.031	.028	1.199	.071	.060
II	.552	.335	.373	.370	.365	.329	.358	.369	.326	.312	.234	1.372	.088
III	.562	.549	.502	.454	.431	.422	.477	.610	.486	.444	.461	.801	1.610

* Each entry shows the amount that the gross output of the sector named at the left would change, given a change of one dollar in the final demand for products of the sector named at the top.

final demand for product of sector III requires less than a cent of output from any farm sector.

Quite obviously, even under the limitations of mathematical form in the model, the "influence of agriculture per se on general economy" is minor but the interdependence of agriculture with national economy is major. The proportions are so clear that agricultural policy to serve as backfire against the rolling flame of national economic development at the stage of United States growth cannot be effective in the long run.

REGIONAL ADJUSTMENT NEEDS AND POTENTIAL

Agriculture of all regions is caught up in the pressures of factor prices, technological change, alternative employment opportunity and preferences and aspirations of consumers which will change farming structure. Economic development will, in the decades of 1960 through the 1980's, cause greater adjustment in labor input, relative capital employment and farm size in some regions than in others, depending on the extent to which market imperfections and institutional restrictions have impeded balance in use of, and returns to, agricultural resources as compared to those of nonfarm sectors. Some sectors of agriculture have long had returns to human resources which were mere pittance of factor returns in other sectors and of income against the American standard of living. As illustration of this point, we select 1950 for basic income comparisons of farm production regions in the United States. At this point in time, U.S. agriculture had just emerged from the most profitable period in history, important nonfarm recessions had been unimportant and nonfarm employment opportunity had been great. Existing prices mainly reflected consumer preferences apart from price supports and surplus build-up.

Figure 7.2 indicates geographic average return to operator's labor of commercial farms in 1949, after returns were imputed at market rates to other resources.[7] Over the major expanse of space and population, return for operator labor was less than $1,500 as compared to labor income (excluding all capital return) of $2,544 per employed nonfarm person in 1949. In large areas of the South and East, operator labor income was less than $500, being negative on the computational basis, in the mountain areas stretching from Tennessee through Pennsylvania. By 1960, the relative position of agriculture, labor income of farms compared with nonfarm sectors, had deteriorated even more over the nation, but the relative rank of regions largely still paralleled that of Figure 7.2.

Variance in income among regions is related closely, but not entirely, to capital and total inputs used per farm and per unit of labor. This fact

[7] From Earl O. Heady and E. G. Strand, "Efficiency Within American Agriculture," *Jour. Farm Econ.*, Vol. 37; and E. G. Strand, Earl O. Heady and J. A. Seagraves, *Productivity and Resources Used on Commercial Farms*, USDA Tech. Bul. 1128. Farms included were the 3.7 million commercial farms (out of 5.4 million total farms) with 97.5 percent of total value of farm products sold in 1949. Included are farms with sales of $1,200 or more and excluding part-time, residential and abnormal farms.

is illustrated by comparison of Figure 7.2 with 7.3, the latter indicating regional averages of annual inputs per farm, with capital expressed on a service rather than on an investment basis. Input per farm is greatest in areas of highly specialized agriculture such as dairy and fruit production in the Southwest and specialized poultry production on the Eastern Seaboard. It is lowest in cotton and mountain areas where institutional and related factors have caused the elasticity of capital and labor supply to individual farms and regional aggregates to be low. Highly specialized farming areas are those already geared most closely with factor and commodity markets of the nonfarm economy. Regions with low capital per farm, and large use of labor relative to capital, are those where the factor markets for agriculture have been highly apart from those of the nonfarm economy.

With increased public investment in education and vocational guidance, rural development and depressed area legislation, connection between factor markets of farms and nonfarm sectors will be greater in those areas of lowest farm and operator incomes. Industrial development, complemented with increased communication and knowledge, as pointed out in Chapter 4, also will pull in this direction. As it occurs, and input of labor declines still further, interdependence of agriculture with national economy will grow even tighter. Without these price and communication links between factor markets, however, great disparity can still exist between returns of farm and nonfarm resources.

This point is well illustrated in two broad regions of Figure 7.2. In the Southwest, largely California, where industrialization has been at a rapid rate, and labor and capital markets for agriculture are closely related to those of other sectors, a highly commercialized agriculture with favorable factor returns has developed. In the Southeast, where industrialization also has been at a fairly high rate, certainly as compared to the Plains and western Cornbelt, similar development in commercialization of farming has been highly absent. Farming in much of the old cotton and sharecropping areas is but little advanced beyond that of India in technology, and differs by only a small margin in the proportion of labor in the input mix. Capital supply to these farmers is of low elasticity, causing it to be high in price and rationed closely against tangible equity; labor is lacking in nonfarm connection and is of low supply elasticity to agriculture, thus being priced at low levels. As much as any, this is the blighted area of American society. But the rate of adjustment can and will be high. Given the practical elements that cause labor markets to work efficiently—education, employment services, job communication and transport foods—this segment of agriculture can become much more closely attached to the national economy and its growth rewards.

Sample Marginal Resource Productivities

Differentials in resource productivities for scattered segments of U.S. agriculture at about the same time can be illustrated from estimation of resource productivities from farm samples. Samples drawn from the

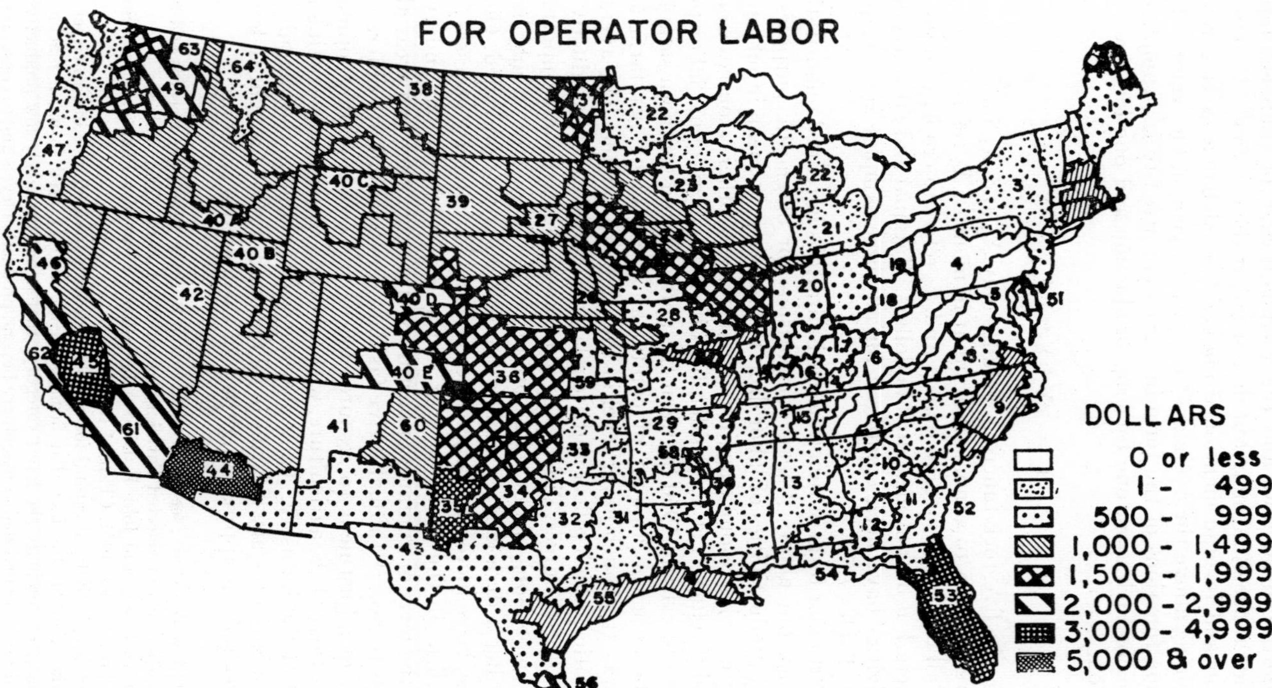

Fig. 7.2. Residual Operator Labor Income by Productivity Region, 1949. Commercial Farms Only.

commercial wheat area of Montana, the productive Clarion-Webster soil area of north central Iowa and the Piedmont area of Alabama represent a wide range of farming but do not fall at the extremes of commercialization and income mentioned above. The Alabama sample represents farming above the average of the general geographic region.[8] Two production functions of the form in (7.8) were fitted to the sample observations of each area, one for crop production and one for livestock production.

$$Y = aX_1^{b_1}X_2^{b_2}X_3^{b_3} \tag{7.8}$$

However, the livestock function includes only X_1 and X_2 input categories where X_1 refers to annual labor input in months, X_2 refers to annual input of all capital services in dollars and X_3 refers to cropland input in acres where Y is output measured in dollars. Marginal and gross average productivities have been computed for all three samples and are presented in Tables 7.5.

The particular form of function has limitations in refined quantitative predictions, but allows "mean comparisons for diagnostic purposes."[9] Marginal productivities of labor drop to low levels at mean input, since greater use of this resource against zero increase of other resources would add small product. Yet a considerable difference in marginal labor productivity did exist in 1950 between the northern and southern samples, largely because the amount of capital and technology per farm and worker was at a much lower level in the Alabama sample. The average productivities, which reflect and are related to the marginal productivity of all units of resources, differ even more and likely are more important for the comparisons. While value productivities in all areas would have been smaller a decade later, similar relative difference prevailed. Quite obviously, large increase in inputs per farm and laborer are necessary to bring returns in the Alabama area to the level of Montana, and even more to the level of nonfarm opportunity since the other two areas also lag in this respect.[10] In qualitative fashion, the data indicate differences in extent of adjustment to resource prices and economic development which exist over U.S. agriculture, with an even greater range existing for the total of the industry. They also suggest the differential magnitude of adjustment necessary if farms in all regions are to be brought to levels of resource returns approaching those of the nonfarm economy.

---

[8] For details of this study, see Earl O. Heady and R. Shaw, "Resource Returns and Productivity Coefficients in Selected Farming Areas," *Jour. Farm Econ.*, Vol. 36.

[9] Cf. Earl O. Heady and John F. Dillon, *Agricultural Production Functions*, Iowa State University Press, Ames, 1961. Chaps. 1 to 4.

[10] The low productivity of capital for crops in northern Iowa may be due to either (1) sample variance or (2) the fact that farmers on the average used so much machinery (machine services dominate the input category) that it had extremely low productivity. Farms in the area had invested in machinery beyond production levels and to consumption levels for matters of convenience and avoidance of drudgery, etc.

VALUE OF TOTAL INPUT

Per Commercial Farm, by Productivity Regions, 1949

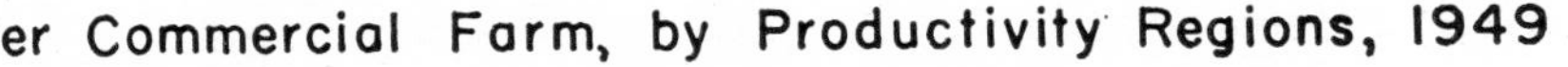

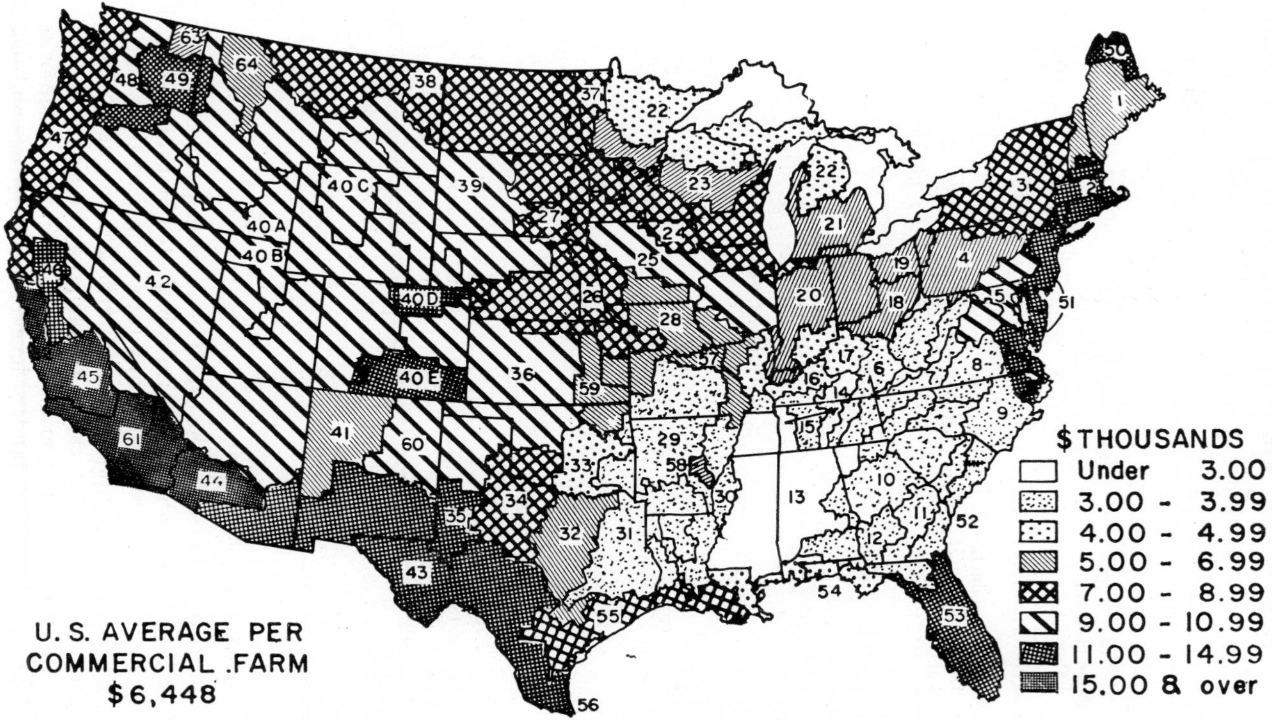

Fig. 7.3. Value of Total Inputs for Commercial Farms, 1949. Annual Services of Land, Labor and Capital.

TABLE 7.5

PRODUCTION ELASTICITIES AND MARGINAL AND AVERAGE PRODUCTIVITIES FOR FARM SAMPLES, 1950

Item	Montana	N. Iowa	Alabama
Crop Function			
Value of a (log)	.595	1.273	.979
Value of b_i			
Labor	.039	.088	.319
Land	.503	.912	.385
Capital	.580	.165	.463
Marginal products			
Labor ($/acre)	11	47	21
Land ($/mo.)	62	68	40
Capital ($/$)	2.39	.65	1.15
Gross average elasticities			
Labor ($/acre)	22	51	56
Land ($/mo.)	1,559	905	127
Capital ($/$)	4.11	3.94	2.39
Livestock Function			
Value of a (log)	.276	.359	.737
Value of b_i			
Labor	.084	.077	.233
Capital	.937	.907	.743
Marginal products			
Labor ($/mo.)	114	131	89
Capital ($/$)	1.27	1.06	.97
Gross average productivity			
Labor ($/mo.)	1,351	1,694	378
Capital ($/$)	1.36	1.11	1.31
Mean input ($)	30,634	22,718	2,734
Mean output ($)	14,741	16,710	1,694
Labor (mo.)	20.3	17.5	13.9

Classes of Farms

Further indication of the extent of adjustment in structure of agriculture by region and class of farm is indicated in Table 7.6. It shows the percentage of commercial farms (excluding part-time and residential farms) in each geographic region with gross value of sales less than $5,000. Given the per capita income and the high standard of living spread widely over the society, a farm with gross value of sales under $5,000 provides a substandard level of family income and returns to resources. From the gross value of sales must be subtracted annual ex-

TABLE 7.6
PERCENT OF FARMS BY REGIONS WITH VALUE OF SALES LESS THAN $5,000 IN 1954

Region	Percent of All Farms in Region	Percent of U.S. Farms With Sales Less Than $5,000
New England	39.5	1.0
Mid Atlantic	43.4	3.8
E. N. Central	49.3	16.1
W. N. Central	44.7	19.1
S. Atlantic	76.0	19.6
E. S. Central	87.4	21.5
W. S. Central	65.2	13.4
Mountain	33.9	2.9
Pacific	33.3	2.6
U.S.	58.4	100.0

penses, leaving a net for family living and resource returns much smaller than the $4,732 annual wage of labor in all manufacturing industries in 1954.

Adjustments for prices of consumption items need to be made, of course, to indicate relative differences in real income. However, it also must be remembered that gross sales of $5,000 not only requires deduction of annual expenses but also the remainder represents return to capital as well as labor. Somewhat more than 87 percent of all farms in the East South Central region had value of sales less than $5,000 in 1954, while 76.0 percent in the South Atlantic fell in this category. In contrast, the Mountain and Pacific regions had only 33.9 and 33.3 respectively. The number of farms in the Pacific region with value of sales less than $5,000 was only 2.6 percent of the U.S. total. The corresponding figure for the East South Central region was 21.5 percent.

The magnitude of $5,000 gross sales might seem high at first glance. But certainly it is not when we are reminded that it is gross income and that the median per family net income of the nation was $5,600 in 1960 while mean family income was $6,900; or that net income of skilled wage workers, with adjustment for price level, exceeds even this gross quantity. But even in 1959 over 25 percent of all commercial farms in the U.S. had gross value of sales less than $5,000. Over 63 percent of all farms in the East South Central region and 46 percent in the South Atlantic had value of sales less than $2,500 in 1954. In contrast, the percentage was only 20 percent in the West North Central, 17 percent in the Mountain and 13 percent in the Pacific regions.

These data suggest magnitudes of adjustment in farm number, size and resource structure required if farm family income is to be brought to levels consistent with the magnitude of general living standards and national income of the United States. A "simple" goal (lacking refinement in economic definition and marginal quantities) of commercial farms which produce more than $5,000 in gross sales per annum is hardly an unrealistic and fantastic goal, given the degree of economic development and mean per capita income for the nation.[11] Attainment of this goal will not be attained by price and production policy which restrains supply to match demand growth. Too many of the farms in the above categories have such small volume and so few resources that a policy boosting prices by a fourth would still leave them with incomes far below our simple standard. To an important extent, major income improvement for these classes of farms must come from farm enlargement and increased proportion of capital with labor for those that remain. Over the longer run, for younger and flexible persons, many will need off-farm employment opportunity if they are to find full expression of their abilities and opportunity for living standard and consumption consistent with the U.S. norm.

The problem of adjustment is most complex in the regions where need is greatest, not only because of the number of small farms with inadequate resources but also because institutional forces and factor markets are more restraining than in areas where the proportion of farms with low volume is smallest. Too, it is in these same areas that social overhead capital is too low to allow production of human resources most adaptable to employment opportunities under growth. In any case, price policy and supply management cannot solve this problem of low volume and inadequate resources for all families falling in this category. It is misleading for farm spokesmen to lead farm families in believing so. Even more, it turns the hope of people in misleading directions, with longer-run impact on lives and well-being of farm children and younger persons. Needed more, or simultaneously, is improved education, training and employment services and job opportunities which allow those who cannot acquire adequate resources, if even because of restraints in land area and space as farms are enlarged, fuller opportunity for expression of their abilities and living standard consistent with the developing status of the American economy.

REGIONAL ADJUSTMENT IN STRUCTURE

The income figures cited above indicate one reason why adjustment of agriculture to a structure more consistent with the wealth and economic development of the nation would cause differential change among regions. Aside from these phenomena, changes in the structure of agriculture to conform with economic growth would be of equal nature and

---

[11] Part-time farms, on the basis of census definition, have been excluded from the classifications in Table 7.6. However, some commercial farms in these groups have family members receiving income from off-farm sources while other units have low income because they are operated by beginning farmers, older people in semi-retirement and a normal number of persons of poor health. Hence, not all farms with gross value of sales of $5,000 would need elimination if we were to move towards the "simple" goal mentioned in the paragraph.

magnitude only under certain conditions. Changes in production and price functions, and any other quantities relating to supply of factors and commodities, would have to be of the same relative magnitude in all regions. Degree of economic development, providing employment opportunities and factor returns in nonfarm uses, would have to be of similar magnitude for each region. Finally, rate of growth in population and consumer demand would have to be the same at all locations so that relative advantage from the side of commodity prices and space would be the same. Under this condition, supply functions, production possibilities and comparative advantage would remain relatively the same for all agricultural regions. Adjustment in resource inputs and product outputs then would be of similar nature for all regions. With supply increase exceeding demand increase, the same proportion of resources would need to leave agriculture in each region, and similar pattern of change in farm size and numbers would occur. The commodity mix of the nation would contain about the same proportions of product from the various spatial and commodity components of agriculture as in the past. But the latter would be possible only if consumers desired all food in "fixed-mix" proportions, meaning that they would not shift among commodities as their incomes increased as reflected by the demand elasticities in Chapter 6.

This uniformity in economic development of agriculture and industry would ease and simplify social adjustment. Each community would have relatively the same increase in investment and industry, tax source and public services, employment and occupational shift. However, development has never been characterized by this spatial "evenness." Even in days of an agricultural nation and westward movement, it was not true. Not all communities can expect equal rates of growth, and therefore equal pleasure or pain in economic adjustment. In the first place, growth of the industrial and consumer sectors does not take place evenly over space, due to differential opportunity of different locations as they are reflected in supply price of commodities and resources such as raw materials, climatic elements, transportation and others. With orientation of industry to locations with lowest supply price for such elements of production, population and consumer growth is oriented similarly, thus causing the relative demands for food and other commodities to shift in similar fashion in respect to space. Demand for labor resources and job opportunities thus grows differentially among communities, drawing surplus resources more readily from farms or other "oversupplied" industries in some localities. Even without this shift of industrial and consumer pattern over space, differential demand growth between general commodity groups, and within the food category itself, comes about as per capita income increases.

Since agricultural regions differ in their endowment of soil, climate and other resources of nature, they respond differentially to increased resource inputs. They also respond differentially with new forms of capital representing technological advance. Supply functions of greater differentials in elasticity arise, even in the absence of new technology, as inputs are extended and ranges of the production function with greater or lesser elasticity, depending on nature's endowment, are reached. Hence, comparative advantage among regions changes, and change in the spatial and commodity mix of farm products occurs, with resources in some regions rewarded more or less handsomely than those of others.

This shift also would occur even in the absence of technical change in agriculture. The latter, along with growth in per capita income and shift in consumer preferences for foods, provides the major force in causing the relative advantage and structure of agriculture to differ under economic development. New technology does not affect, or result in, the same increase in marginal resource productivities in all regions. Again this is true because different regions are endowed variously with natural resources. A new seed variety has great productivity in an area of warm climate and long growing season, but not where the magnitude of these natural resources is small. Fertilizer, perhaps in interaction with the new seed variety, has greater productivity where nature's input of moisture or a complementary element is large. Large-scale machinery is better adapted for plains than for mountainous regions. But further, economic development and alteration of factor prices may cause mechanization to become more profitable in the one region, thus causing the region to grow in supply function and comparative advantage relative to another. With labor low in price relative to capital in another region, labor technology may be more economical than machine technology, with crops such as coffee remaining on the mountainsides and away from the plains. But if labor rises sufficiently in relation to capital, machine technology may prevail, with the crop moving from the mountains to the plains. This complex of forces has not been unimportant in causing cotton to shift from the Southeast to the Southwest.

Implication in Policy

We have mentioned a second reason why policy, particularly that designed to make income compensation to current farmers, needs to orient itself to change in structure of agriculture implied by economic development. Policy which attempts to fit all regions into the same mold may prevail momentarily. But over the decades, pressure will increase it to break out of the mold. If policy is designed to provide market power, income stability and similar elements possessed by other sectors, it needs to consider variables and forces leading to change in supply structure and comparative advantage among regions. It needs to recognize that these policy elements in the hands of other economic sectors do not eliminate change, or competition among sectors, in the long-run. Even where other sectors have been given opportunity in the market or through legislation to attain certain economic goals, the mechanisms have not generally been to contain economic growth or employment opportunity to particular spatial pattern.

Space is, of course, more nearly a factor of production in agriculture. However, to the extent that farm policy is aimed mainly at putting agriculture on the same footing as other sectors in respect to market control and stability, opportunity for the industry to change its spatial concentration and configuration would not only be consistent with general policy but would allow greater rate of economic development. Where farm policy is mainly to provide temporary compensation for sacrifices growing out of progress and development, such as more food at lower expenditure for consumers but smaller revenue to producers, elements of policy which even allow step-by-step transition to new spatial pattern would be consistent with developmental opportunities and goals. This is in line with our earlier proposition—namely, that while farmers of this generation may believe compensation to be due them while they remain in farming, they do not hold equally that a structure of agriculture should be maintained to restrain and subsidize their children and grandchildren in agriculture, holding them apart from opportunity in other sectors of a growing economy. Finally, policy which tries to maintain an historic structure of agriculture is certain to be confronted with strong forces of the market tending to pull it apart, and, for the same reason, with inability of competing regional and commodity groups to obtain agreement on policy.

Regional Structure

With the progress of time and under upcoming national goals, the pricing system should be given greater opportunity to serve as a guide in resource allocation than has held true in the past decade. If for no other reasons, this should be accomplished to avoid tremendous build-up of surpluses with their heavy treasury costs and the image and stigma which served to embarrass agriculture as an industry. This does not mean that agriculture must be turned to the caprices of a stampeding market of pure competition and great short-run instability of income while other major segments of the economy are not so characterized. But while other sectors have self-administered and legislated mechanisms for assuring degree of stability and short-run destiny over their prices, they have not been able to circumvent the draw of the pricing mechanism as it represents consumer's desires, relative supplies of factors, technical change and the general shift of resources among commodity and factor mixes.

The extreme control over supply and price exercised by unions and railroads did not prevent a rapid substitution of air and auto travel for train transportation. The structure of the steel industry and the ability to manage supply and specify price did not prevent a relative substitution of aluminum produced by a competing industry. Neither did the motion picture industry, one not characterized by pure competition, have power to prevent consumers from substituting television for movies, thus bringing about a re-allocation of resources. At most, industries with monopolistic and oligopolistic market powers provide short-run stability to price, but do not and cannot prevent broader change and re-allocations of resources from occurring as the structure of consumer demand

and factor supply changes under development. Perhaps price policy of agriculture should be viewed in the same light, namely, to provide short-run stability but to allow and facilitate long-run adaptation of resources to broad changes in consumer demand, technology and factor supplies.

In this light, the spatial pattern of agriculture will be modified to correspond with differential change among regions in economic development and population, employment opportunities, technology and factor prices. Elements of both gradual and rapid change already have shown up in U.S. agriculture, causing its products to become more specialized to particular regions. From the *gradual pole* we have the Northeast and parts of the Middle Atlantic Coast where decline of land in farms has been relatively great, but over several decades. Land has shifted not only to industrial and urban uses, but also, and more important in terms of acreage, into forestry. A similar but somewhat less rapid shift has taken place in the Southeast. From the *rapid pole*, broiler production shifted quickly to specialized areas of the East and Southeast. Under economic development, it appears that shifts of this type will continue. Feed grains and wheat could become more centrally concentrated in those regions which now specialize in them. Feed-grain production could recede from east to west, leaving the central Cornbelt relatively more important than previously in total output. Wheat could recede back from the more arid regions of the Plains to the hubs of spring and winter wheat areas of greater comparative advantage in this crop. Cotton would shift, particularly with time and change in resource structure from pull of nonfarm wage rates, to the West and areas most adapted to yield and mechanization.

These points can be illustrated with a model designed to examine the regional concentration of production, if production were to be brought into line with demand, and comparative advantage were to reign by regions. The first model presented applies to 1954 conditions in terms of technology and demand level. Brought to 1965 level, it specifies a somewhat larger acreage to be withdrawn from production, but the general configuration is somewhat the same. We deal only with feed grains and wheat in three models, and with these plus soybeans and cotton in a fourth. A later model is being developed to include technology and demand extended to a more future point in time.[12] We use a linear programming model since it suits the purposes at hand, namely, approximation of the acreage and location of land which would be removed from production to balance output against "requirements." Ideally, the analysis would include a system of demand curves and supply functions, related over regions to indicate equilibrium of price and quantities. However, the model employed serves for the "diagnostic purposes" at hand, although it has obvious limits for particular regions.

---

[12] For further details of the model, see Earl O. Heady and Alvin C. Egbert, "Programming Regional Adjustments in Grain Production to Eliminate Surpluses," *Jour. Farm Econ.*, Vol. 41; and Alvin C. Egbert and Earl O. Heady, *Regional Adjustments in Grain Production: A Linear Programming Analysis*. USDA Tech. Bul. 1241.

Downward adjustments in production to meet demand entail two types of input changes: (1) withdrawal of land and complementary inputs from grain production in extensive regions so that the geographic pattern of production would be consistent with restricted comparative advantages of various regions, and (2) maintenance of land in production but a lessening of other inputs or reduction of farming intensity in areas remaining in production of current crops. While we analyze only the first of these, we believe that this is the major adjustment involved and that the second would alter results only slightly.

Our concern in the first models is mainly with production of wheat and of feed grains (corn, oats, barley and grain sorghums), commodities of greatest burden in surplus storage. Because of the size of the empirical task, we attempt to determine which regions should continue to produce these grains and which should shift to other products to make annual output approximate annual "requirements" or disappearance of these products. The year 1954 serves, for the data presented, as the basis for relating output to requirements because the research was initiated soon after this date. Requirements are considered to be a "discrete" quantity. They represent disappearance of grain in 1954 adjusted for normal exports, livestock populations, and food requirements. We suppose, because we could only thus make the computational burden manageable, that requirements coefficients are constant within each region.

Three programming models (A, B and C), given first, represent, without inclusion of disposal activities or slack variables, coefficient matrices of 106×310 order. The United States was broken down into 104 producing regions, each with the three activities: feed grains, wheat for food and wheat for feed. Restrictions included land or acreage constraints for these crop activities in the 104 regions, plus two restrictions for total U.S. feed grain and food wheat demand. A fourth model reviewed (D), included more activities than 310 since soybeans and cotton also were included as competing crops. The procedure used considers the comparative advantage of different regions in producing food and feed grains. Our objective function in two models is that for minimizing the cost of meeting demand requirements. In two models, maximizing profits is the objective.

Model A. The objective function for this model is (7.9) where C_k is a subvector of per unit costs, containing n elements to represent costs of producing feed grains and wheat in the kth region; and X_k is a subvector of crop outputs, with n elements representing production levels in the kth region. In this case, c_{jk}, the unit cost of producing the jth crop in the kth region includes only the labor, power, machine, seed, fertilizer and related inputs for each grain. In other words, land rent is not included as a cost. Neither are farm overhead or fixed costs included.

$$\text{(7.9)} \qquad \text{Min.}\, f(X) = C_1X_1 + \cdots + C_kX_k + \cdots + C_rX_r$$

$$\text{(7.10)} \qquad x_{1k}p_{1k} + x_{2k}p_{2k} + x_{3k}p_{3k} \leq S_k$$

We have $r = 104$ regions and minimize (7.9) subject to the restraints in (7.10) where x_{1k}, x_{2k} and x_{3k} refer respectively to outputs of feed grains (corn, barley, oats and grain sorghums), feed wheat, and food wheat in the kth region and p_{1k}, p_{2k} and p_{3k} stand for the per unit land inputs for these activities in the kth region, while S_k is a vector of acreage restrictions in this same region. The total programming matrices include 104 inequalities such as those in (7.10). The restrictions in S_k are set equal to the largest acreages devoted to feed grains and wheat in the previous 8 years when production control was not in effect.

In addition, to these 104 inequalities to represent acreage restraints, there are two *discrete* demand restrictions,

$$(7.11) \quad x_{11} + x_{21} + x_{12} + x_{22} + \cdots + x_{1k} + x_{2k} + \cdots + x_{1r} + x_{2r} = d_1$$

$$(7.12) \quad x_{31} + x_{32} + \cdots + x_{3k} + \cdots + x_{3r} = d_2.$$

In (7.11), a national "demand" restriction for feed grains, the coefficient of all x_{jk} is 1 because units of output are in terms of a feed equivalent expressed in corn. The feed grain demand restriction is measured in this same unit, with total units representing the 1954 level of feed grain disappearance adjusted for normal livestock production. Coefficients in (7.12), a national demand restriction for food wheat, are also 1, since no distinction is made between types and classes of wheat (a detail corrected in later analysis). For requirements restrictions in both (7.11) and (7.12) an equality is used to indicate that annual production must equal annual requirements. Requirements are at 1954 level adjusted to normal livestock production, exports, population and food uses.

Feed grains other than wheat are combined into a single activity, with acreage in each region proportionate to the acreages in the period 1950–53 in this model. This procedure takes into account the fact that crops such as corn and small grains are grown in fixed rotational proportions in regions such as the Cornbelt. Computations were made with another model, not presented, in which each grain crop was considered to be independent. However, since it does not consider current rotational requirements, it probably over-estimates the magnitude and nature of regional adjustments needed in grain production, but is probably more realistic in predicting a greater acreage to be withdrawn.

Model B. This model is the same as A, except that land rent is included in the c_{jk}, the per unit cost of producing the jth crop in the kth region. The modification of B was used because only grain crops are included as competitive alternatives in programming. Inclusion of land rent as a cost in B gives recognition to alternative crops. However, since grains are the major crops in the regions programmed, market rents are largely based on feed grains and wheat. For this reason the estimates arising under Models A and C are believed to be more appropriate than those of B. Neither Model A nor Model B takes into account the magnitude of demand in each region.

Model C. This model is the same as A in nature and number of activities and restrictions and production costs. However, it gives recognition to transportation costs to regions of demand and also gives partial recognition to demand requirements in different regions. (If transport costs between regions of production and regions of demand, as well as demand magnitudes in each region, were readily available, the pattern of production which minimizes costs, including transport costs, to meet the "fixed" demand of each region, could be determined.) Instead of minimizing costs as in (7.9) we now maximize profit; X_k is as before but C_k is now a vector of net prices for the kth region. We assume that net prices in each region account for transportation costs to consuming regions. Using historic price differentials between these regions to reflect transport costs as they would be expressed in a purely competitive market, we use an equation similar to (7.9) to indicate the pattern of feed grain and wheat production which maximizes profit. This is equivalent to a minimum-cost solution under the above assumptions and assuming that the geographic markets absorb programmed quantities at implied prices. In an interregional competition manner, however, it is assumed that crops not included in X_k are lower alternatives than those which are included.

At 1954 levels of technology and consumption, a point in time where the large surpluses of the 1950's were only beginning to mount up, the models specified up to 35 million acres which could be withdrawn from production of wheat and feed grains (soybeans and cotton excluded), with annual output equated to annual disappearance of the crops mentioned. With progress of time, and technology increasing at a faster rate than population, the surplus acreage grew even more. However, the figures cited above refer to actual cropped land in the grains mentioned, and do not include derelict land of the character of much which went into the 1956 soil bank. Neither does it include land surplus to cotton production. But our interest here is more in the spatial reorganization of the nation's agriculture as it might be allowed to shift pattern with the developmental variables unleashed with time.

Regional Patterns of Withdrawal and Production

There is an important similarity in the regional production patterns resulting from the first three models. Figures 7.4, 7.5 and 7.6 indicate the regions in which production of feed grains and wheat would be located if average annual production were to equal requirements under the conditions assumed and if the geographic pattern of production were consistent with certain restricted comparative advantages of various regions. Figure 7.7 indicates the extent of agreement in number of times a particular region is specified for a particular use by the three models. The nonshaded areas include feed grain and wheat production at the same levels as in the base year. We assume that the small portion of grains produced in these nonshaded areas (8 percent of the total United States tonnage)

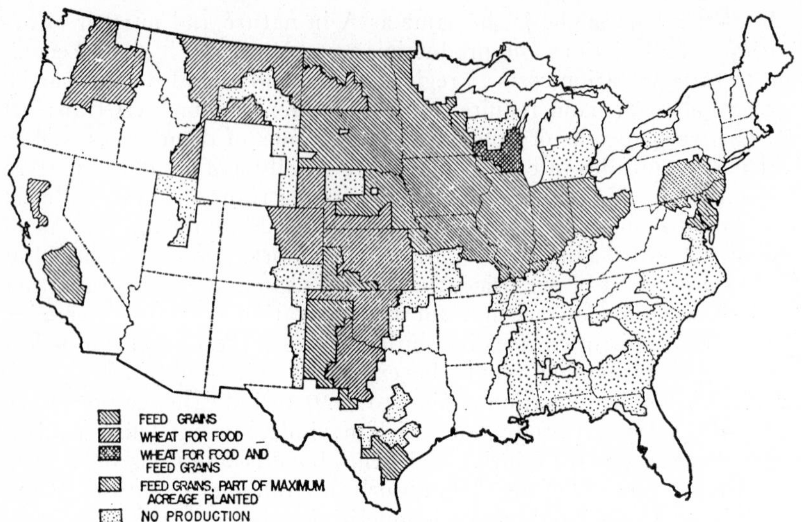

Fig. 7.4. Production Pattern Specified by Model A.

is grown for complementary and supplementary reasons and would largely continue even under competitive markets and prices. These regions were not included in the programming model.

Under the assumptions of Model A, regions would be withdrawn from production of all grains in southeastern Colorado, eastern New Mexico, northern Utah and eastern Wyoming and Montana. Regions scattered among Texas, Nebraska, Wisconsin, Michigan, Oklahoma, Missouri, Kansas and New York also would be withdrawn. In the Southeast, regions representing a large acreage would be withdrawn from production of grains. The *major* wheat and feed grain areas would remain entirely in production under the construction and assumptions of the models. Southwestern Kansas and western Texas would shift to sorghums for feed. Model B (Figure 7.5) provides a spatial production pattern differing somewhat from both A and C. The main differences under B are: All of Montana would be devoted to wheat for food, the Oklahoma panhandle and Pennsylvania would be shifted out of grains, and the region in southwest Missouri would be used for food wheat. Also, a large portion of Kansas would be used for both wheat and feed grain.

Under Model C, as compared to Model A, large parts of Montana, Washington, Oregon, Idaho and Nebraska would be devoted to wheat for feed only. In parts of Nebraska and Colorado wheat would be grown for both feed and food. In the upper Plains, North Dakota and South Dakota, along with parts of Minnesota and Wisconsin, would be devoted to wheat for food. Also, slightly more feed grain would be produced along the Atlantic Seaboard and the Gulf of Mexico. Under this profit-maximizing model, it is the relatively high wheat prices, because of location near larger milling and consuming centers and because of prices paid for hard red spring and durum wheats, which cause wheat for food to be specified in Minnesota and Wisconsin, as well as the Dakotas.

While there is considerable difference in the food wheat and feed grain patterns specified by Models A and C, they largely agree regarding regions specified to remain in grain production. Only five regions specified for production of some grain by Model C are not specified by Model A. Conversely, only one region specified to remain in grain production by Model A is not specified by Model C. Hence, only four more of the 104 regions would be needed to meet feed grain and food wheat requirements in Model C than in A. The five additional regions for fulfilling feed or food requirements under C include regions in eastern Virginia, northeast Ohio, western Kansas, southern Alabama and northern Utah. The region specified by Model A, but not by C, is in northeast South Dakota. Thirty-five entire regions and part of a small region in western Kentucky would not be required for grain production in Model C. These 36 regions represent the acreage which could be shifted to nongrain uses. The pattern is the same, except for the six regions noted above, for Model A.

Consistency or lack of consistency in the three models, as indicated by Figure 7.7, shows the major corn and winter and spring wheat areas to be specified to remain in production of grain in all three models. In a similar manner, all three models specify withdrawal from grain production of eastern Colorado and New Mexico, parts of Kansas, Oklahoma, Texas, Michigan and New York and practically all of the Southeast—from Arkansas, Tennessee and southeastern Virginia to the coasts. Only one model (B) specified grain production in eastern Wyoming, southeast

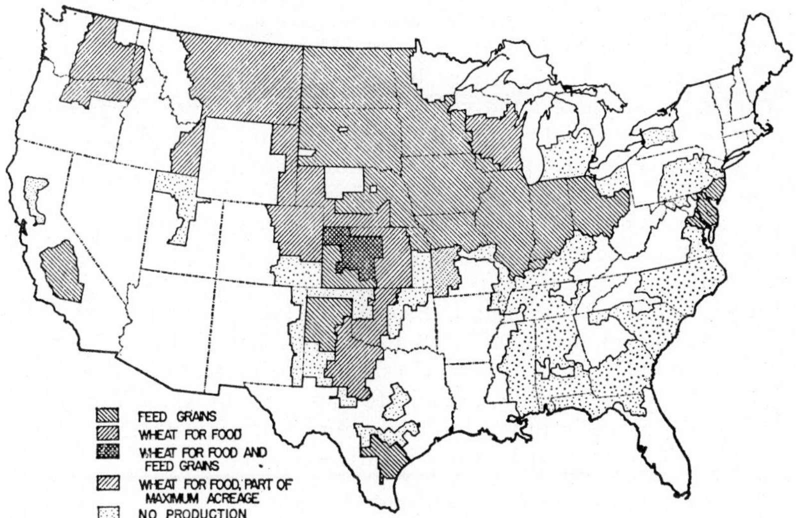

Fig. 7.5. Production Pattern Specified by Model B.

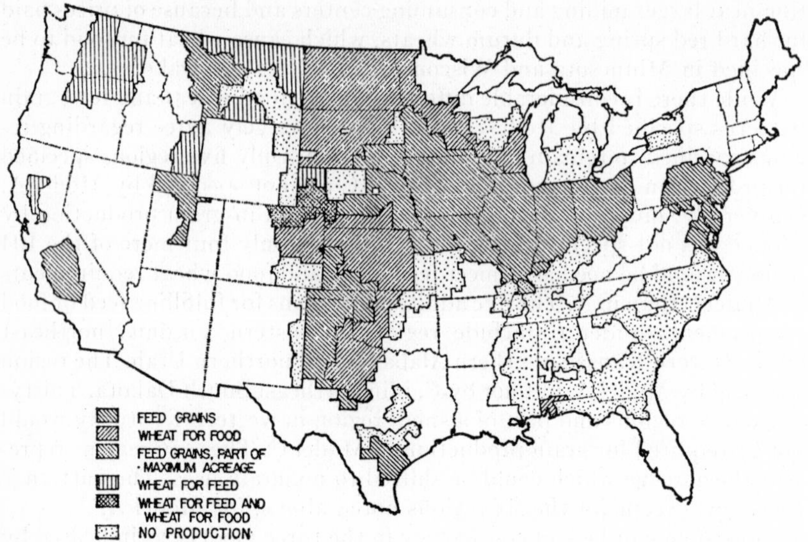

Fig. 7.6. Production Pattern Specified by Model C.

Montana, western Missouri and a few other scattered areas.

All three models are consistent for 88 of the 104 regions in the sense that they specify 88 regions (those indicated in Figure 7.7 as "all agree") that should remain in grain production or shift completely out of grains. Hence, disagreement among the three models existed for 16 regions. However, disagreement between Models A and C, the two models deemed most appropriate by the research workers, existed for only six regions in specification of feed grains apart from soybeans.

The fourth set of computations, based on Model D paralleling Model C but including soybeans and cotton, and computed for "1965 point in time," provides spatial results indicated in Figure 7.8. It assumes technology in fertilizer use projected to "profitable" levels at the present. Again the pattern largely is one of withdrawal of acreage over the low moisture areas of the Great Plains and the lower-yielding grain areas of the Southeast. Some regions of the Southeast would have increased comparative advantage in feed grain. The main wheat and corn areas remain devoted to these crops but some shift take place in cotton.[13] The market would not make "discrete distinction" between wheat for feed and that for food, since the two prices would be interrelated. Distinction on the map is made mainly to indicate those regions which would have relative advantage in producing wheat for feed, against other alternatives, even if food wheat had no advantage in price.

[13] The region in central Texas would be partly required for cotton production; the upper region of Minnesota and Wisconsin would be partly required for wheat and feed.

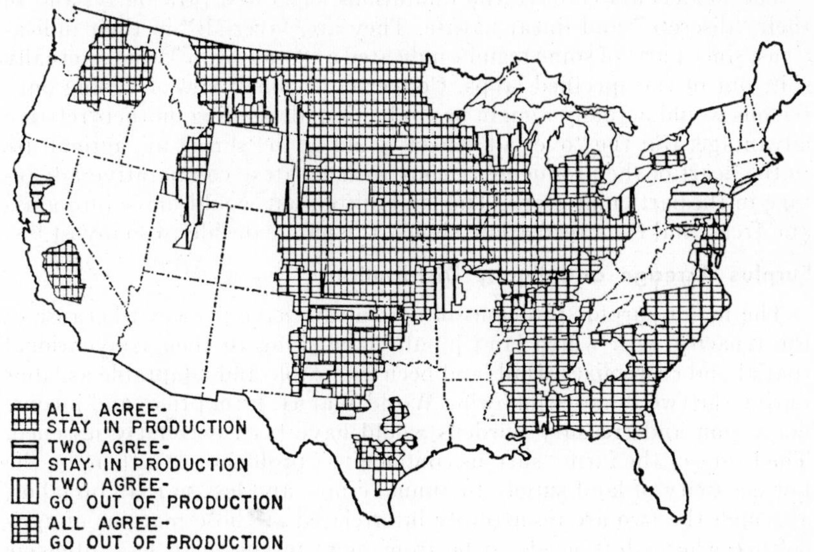

Fig. 7.7. Consistency of Three Models.

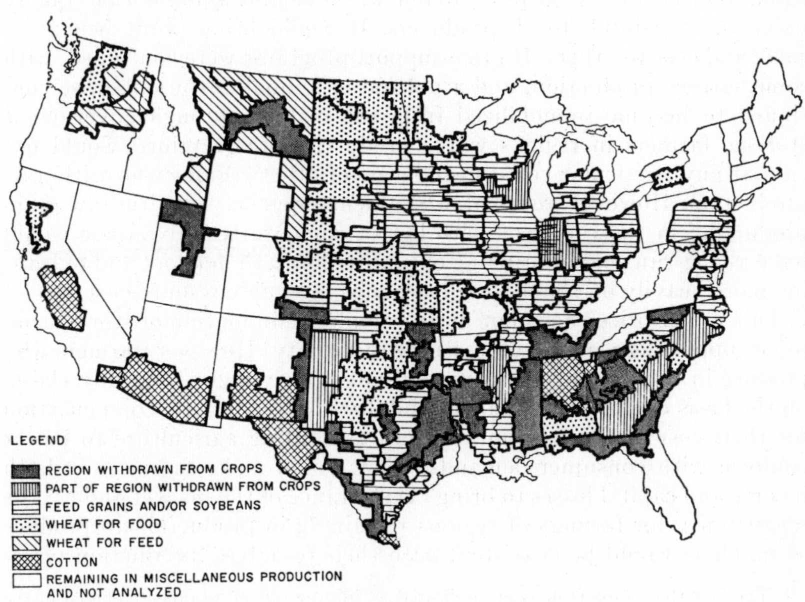

Fig. 7.8. Spatial Production Pattern With Soybeans and Cotton Included in the Model With Feed Grains and Wheat.

The models above have the limitations suggested previously, and in their "discrete" and linear nature. They are "over-all" in their indications, since parts of some regions indicated as "staying in" would actually shift out of the specified crops. Conversely, some parts of "going out" regions would actually remain in production, depending on their relative advantage. But the "over-all" effect would be to "shrink in" agriculture to the heart of the producing regions with greatest comparative advantage in the particular crops. The land shifted out would move into grass and trees, and even recreation, should the public decide to so invest.[14]

Surplus Acreage and Equity Distributions

The major surplus problems of agriculture have persisted because of the tenacity with which land inputs have clung to their conventional spatial and crop mixes. Had land been as flexible and adaptable as labor during the two decades following World War II, farm prices and income depression and treasury burdens would have been extremely lessened. The brunt of the farm "surplus commodity" problem rests, then, on the low elasticity of land supply to annual crops; and less so than on labor, although the two are inseparably interrelated at those margins of agriculture where shift needs to be from more intensive to less intensive crops.

Regional adjustment of production in directions of changing equilibrium, to bring annual output into line with demand would not be equally painless, or painful, to all producers. It would bring profit benefit to some and cost to others. If price-support programs were continued, with some surplus production, and a portion of annual output likewise continued to become immobilized from the market through government storage, farmers in regions where production was retained would not gain at any particular cost to producers of other regions who withdraw production. However, regional adjustment programs to withdraw grain production in those regions with lowest comparative advantage would have a long-run goal of bringing output in line with demand and of leaning more heavily on the pricing mechanism to guide resource use.

This use of prices need not mean complete elimination of storage and price support as a means of lessening instability. However, farmers who produce in regions of comparative disadvantage might rightfully claim, on the basis of welfare economics and distributive justice, compensation for their costs and contribution towards shifting agriculture to better conform with consumer demands. They would make sacrifices in both income and capital losses to bring (1) clearance of the market and (2) the opportunity for farmers of regions remaining in production to produce as much as would be consistent with their resources, production possi-

[14] The fact that some regions are indicated as shifting out of all crops included in the models need not preclude future technological innovations which might restore production. Because of computational burden, and not because of linearity restraints, the question of intensity of production was not examined. Also, while the techniques considered were those of 1954, and the magnitude of surplus capacity had grown by 1960, analysis assuming technology of later periods indicated the spatial pattern of farm re-alignment generally to coincide with the shifts indicated.

bilities and prices. Yet regions of high comparative advantage remaining in production could "produce to their heart's content." And many farmers with highest comparative advantage, being free to use new techniques and to feed more livestock, could earn even more at slightly lower grain prices. The burden of bringing production into equilibrium through this means would fall on those farmers who must drop out of annual crops and resort to the next closest alternative. This is a long drop in some wheat and cotton areas. Farmers in these concentrated areas could ask why they should stand the social costs involved in solving a surplus problem with earlier origin and perpetuated by programs designed to supplement incomes of farmers in areas of comparative advantage, as well as those in areas of disadvantage. This problem of gains to some against costs to others could be solved by various compensation schemes. (See Chapter 11 also.)

Means Available

Several means are available specifically to aid land-use shifts on a regional basis. One is direct purchase of land by the government. This approach may not be entirely consistent with U.S. value systems in times of general prosperity. There is need, however, for purchase of some land as national economic development and income growth continue.

One land product with a high income elasticity of demand and for which the nation is short is recreation. Other "higher-use alternatives" under economic growth, as outlined in Chapter 14, are forest products and grazing. Purchase of land might best serve in re-allocation from annual crops to forestry. But other systems of compensation need to be explored, especially for shifting to such uses as grazing. Systems of compensation other than direct land purchase may have greater public acceptance for major land-use adjustments. One method is Federal Government rental of land withdrawn from surplus crops, with investment in the seeding and other costs for shifting to grass and other specified uses. An alternative with simpler administrative and managerial requirements is purchase of farmers' rights to produce any crops but those specified over a relevant time period. Farmers could still handle the land, and most of the administrative and managerial problems in getting the shifts accomplished would fall into their hands. But for many farmers a sizeable increment in capital investment would be required for seeding and/or stocking land. Hence, a special credit program should be included in the "action bundle" to provide farmers with the assets for making the shift.

Abrupt adjustment of the regional pattern of production to the forces of economic development without any mode of compensation would have this supposition: The distribution of gains and losses from change are of positive-sum nature, with individuals who gain having greater change in utility than those who lose. Propositions in economics suggest that this knowledge is not given *a priori*. In this case, compensation is required as a guarantee of net community betterment. These propositions are examined further in Chapter 8.

INTENSITY OF AGRICULTURE

Shift of annual crops back to the heartland of the producing regions where advantage is greatest and away from the margins in terms of moisture and soil productivity would represent a decrease in intensity in use of resource. Less capital and labor would be used for land shifted from annual crops to grazing and forestry. But what about land remaining in conventional crops, and becoming relatively more specialized in them? With production as a continuous function of known inputs and known productivities as in (7.13), following equation (4.18), farmers could maximize profits in the sense of equating the derivative of product with respect to the *i*th resource against factor/product price ratios, as reflected in equation (7.14).

$$Y = f(X_1, X_2, \cdots X_i, \cdots X_g) \tag{7.13}$$

$$\frac{\partial Y}{\partial X_i} = \frac{P_i}{P} \tag{7.14}$$

A decline in product price, P with factor price, P_i, remaining constant would call for a larger partial derivative or marginal product. This could be attained only by decreasing the magnitude of X_i. Hence, if all farmers maximized profits in the static sense of perfect knowledge, an increase in the factor/product price ratio, brought about by freeing commodity price to be more effective in resource allocation, would lessen the magnitude of all inputs, the rate and degree of lag depending on the fixity of the resource and the rate at which its resources are given off over time.

The extent to which a given reduction in commodity price will reduce input and output, even under perfect knowledge, would depend on the elasticity of the production function. Under conditions of profit maximization, the elasticity for each factor, and as a sum for all factors, must be less than 1.0. Hence, a given percentage reduction in input will be accompanied by a smaller percentage decline in output.

Responsiveness in input and output will be by different proportions as can be illustrated by the simple production function represented in (7.15), with its accompanying marginal product and elasticity equations in (7.16) and (7.17) respectively. With a price ratio of 1.0, per unit price

$$Y = 5X - .2X^2 \tag{7.15}$$

$$\frac{dY}{dX} = 5 - .4X \tag{7.16}$$

$$E = (5X - .4X^2)Y^{-1} \tag{7.17}$$

of factor and product being equal, profit is maximized in the static manner of (7.14), with X equal to 10 and the corresponding output being 30. The elasticity for this combination is .333, indicating that reduction of input will be accompanied by a smaller percentage decline in output. In this case, a 1 percent decrease in input will decrease output by only .33

percent. If the factor/product price ratio now increases to 1.4, with price of resource constant and commodity price declining, the optimum input is now 9 and corresponding output is 28.8. Input has declined by $100(1 \div 10) = 10$ percent while output has declined by only $100(1.2 \div 30) = 4$ percent. The price ratio has increased by $100(.4 \div 1) = 40$ percent.

The facts are, then that the factor/product price ratio must increase by a greater percentage than input declines—which, in turn, is greater than the percentage decline in output. Or, in other terms: a decline of the price ratio by (say) 10 percent will be accompanied by a smaller percentage decrease in input and an even smaller percentage decline in output. (The elasticity of supply in respect to commodity price will be less than the elasticity of factor demand in respect to commodity price.)

Increase in factor/product price ratios, through absolute decline in commodity price are always expected to have their most immediate effect in checking input of resources such as fertilizer with short transformation periods, and greater lagged effect in checking input of longer-lived resources. (See Chapter 4.) Also, we know that uncertainty, capital limitations and other restraints on decision making prevent farmers from maximizing profits in the static sense of (7.14). But in these cases we expect the percentage decline in price ratio to exceed the percentage decline in input and output by an even greater proportion than where (7.14) does prevail.

However, it is worthwhile to review the production elasticity of such resources as fertilizer, to ascertain how a restructuring of prices for agriculture might be expected to reduce the intensity of production in specialized and other regions. To do so, we examine static supply elasticities derived from statistically derived production functions. The production functions, based on experimental data, have been used over the steps illustrated in previous chapters, namely, in computing marginal cost and then static supply and elasticity functions.[15] (The data also have been used to compute static factor demand functions and their elasticities. As pointed out above, the elasticity of static supply is generally less than elasticity of static demand.)

Figure 7.9 includes static corn supply elasticity curves derived for selected locations of the country. (Letters on curves indicate locations.)[16] The capital letters indicate the nutrient or nutrients (nitrogen, phosphate or potash) which are considered to be variable. At a price of \$1 for corn (with per pound prices of N, P_2O_5 and K_2O of 13, 8 and 5 cents respectively), static price elasticity is less than .3 for all functions and locations, meaning that a 10 percent decline in corn price would cause output per acre to recede by 3 percent or less, depending on the year and location,

[15] See Earl O. Heady and Luther G. Tweeten, *Corn Supply and Fertilizer Demand Functions Derived from Experimental Data; A Static Analysis*, Iowa Agr. Exp. Sta. Bul., forthcoming.

[16] The locations and soils are: (a) Clarion silt loam in Iowa with three nutrients variable, (b) same with *N* and *K* variable, (c) same with *P* and *K* variable, (d) Ida silt loam in Iowa, (e) Carrington silt loam in Iowa, (f) North Carolina coastal plain, (g) Kansas Verdigis soil, (h) Tennessee Lintonia soil, and (i) North Carolina Norfolk soils. Elasticities are computed on per acre basis of production functions.

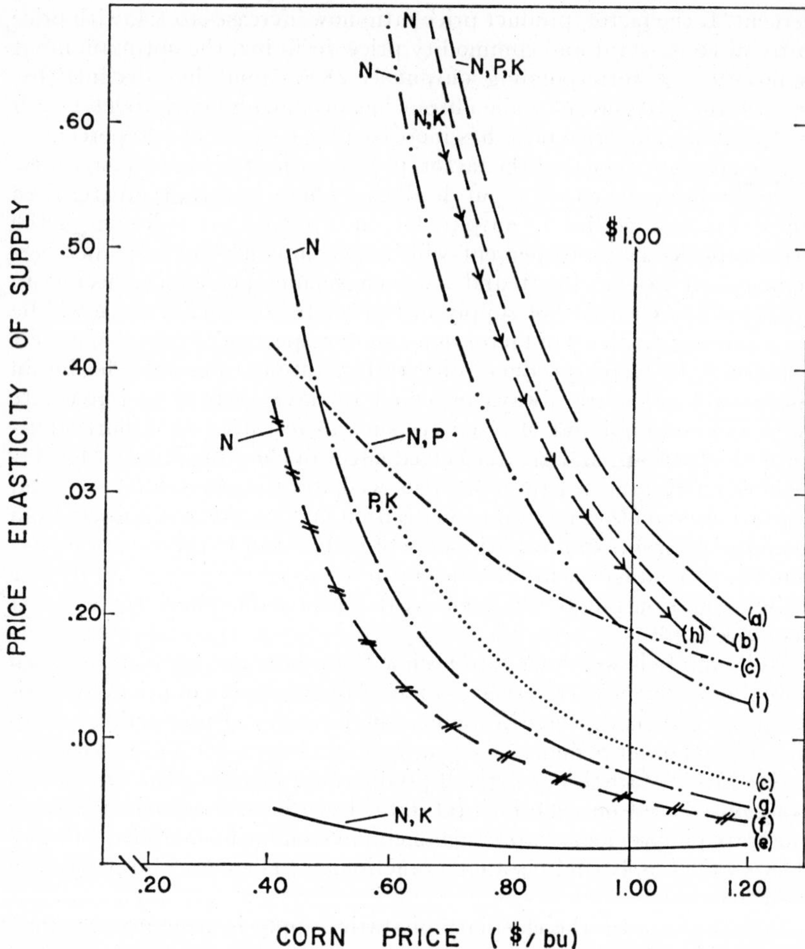

Fig. 7.9. Corn Supply Elasticities Derived From Static Supply Functions and Experimental Production Functions.

were farmers able to maximize profit and respond accordingly. Some of the functions indicate, at $1 price for corn, a decline of less than 1 percent for a 10 percent decline in corn price. At higher corn prices, the elasticity is even lower, just as it is higher for lower fertilizer prices. Elasticity of product supply so computed, as also is true of elasticity of factor demands, is low in regions of small rainfall because the corresponding elasticity of production is low.

While the illustration is for fertilizer and corn, the same general pattern is expected for other crops—along with annual inputs such as seed, irrigation water, insecticides and similar resources—if farmers used inputs to levels which maximized profits under price relationships of the

1950's. Typically, individual farmers do not drive the marginal productivity of all such factors to the level of the price ratio because of lack of knowledge, capital shortage, uncertainty and related phenomena. However, since the marginal product is then greater than price ratio, the latter can increase through commodity price decline without causing the magnitude of input to become uneconomic (except as it lowers the marginal value productivity of the resource and calls for a different allocation of scarce capital).

Both phenomena, low elasticity of commodity supply and factor demand based on low ultra-short-run production eleasticity and on inputs which do not drive marginal products to levels of price ratios in an individual farm context, probably mean that a re-gearing of U.S. agriculture to market and consumer preference would have but little effect on lowering intensity of production in the regions which remain specialized in particular crops. (Tobacco, and similar crops, might be an exception since fertilization rates are high, but elasticity of production is low accordingly.) Hence, it is proposed that the main readjustment to a different price schedule, output decreasing to demand levels, would be more the receding of production into the heartland of regions with comparative advantage in particular crops, with marginal areas shifting to other crops in the long run, and much less a reduction in intensity of biological capital resources in the specialized areas. Increase in farm size and reduction of labor force over these specialized areas is itself a reduction in intensity (especially of labor and mechanical capital), and magnitude of aggregate resource input, but not necessarily one to decrease output in the short run as noted earlier.

For particular crops, such as summer-fallow wheat, inputs are used in near-limitational manner. Where fertilizer is not used, seed bed preparation, planting and harvesting use a highly "fixed" collection of biological inputs per acre, with elasticity of production low or near zero. Regions remaining in production likely would use about the same quantity per acre of these physical and biological inputs, the major reduction in output coming largely from acres shifted to other crops.

It has been indicated that farmers do respond, even in the short run, to prices in use of particular resources. For example, equation (5.58) illustrates, year-to-year change in use of fertilizer in response to crop prices. However, this contraction does not come about only directly and causitively through a reduction of the right member of (7.14) but through that of the left member (in inability to buy inputs), due more nearly or equally to the effect on income and investment funds, degree of uncertainty and similar considerations. In post-war years, as the fertilizer/crop price ratio gradually declined, fertilizer use continued to go up, except in years of sharp break in farm prices. The increase came about as more farmers learned about fertilizer, as capital was accumulated, allowing them to drive marginal product of fertilizer to lower levels, and as capital-short farmers left the industry and their units were taken over by operators longer on capital supply. This trend can continue for some time before the condition of (7.14) holds true generally for fertilizer in U.S. agriculture.

RELATIVE IMPORTANCE OF FACTORS

The following conditions have caused the relative mix of inputs in agriculture to change: Constancy of land supply and the continuous development of substitutes for it, changes in the relative prices of labor and capital and technical development of capital items with increased marginal rates of substitution. This trend, with output embodying many fewer labor services and much more capital, will continue with national economic development.

As Table 7.7 indicates, labor input requirements represented nearly 75 percent of all inputs in 1910, but had fallen to less than a third of inputs by 1960. In contrast, inputs of capital had risen from less than a quarter to nearly two-thirds of all inputs. (If we include land as a "financial" or capital input, total capital increased from 25 percent in 1910 to 70 percent in 1959.) Land, as a proportion of all inputs, apparently has remained about constant, but perhaps has decreased since 1940. Constancy in relative importance of land is itself significant. In the absence of technical development and with declining long-run elasticity of production and supply functions for food, food price would have risen. Land, a factor of lowest supply elasticity, would thus have grown in relative value importance and contribution. As it is, capital substitutes have caused a near-fixed supply of land to remain relatively constant in its input value contribution to agriculture's output. The figures in Table 7.7 include land producing surplus crops in the period 1930–60. Estimates state that surplus cropland was as much as 10 percent of the total for the 1950's. With this amount of land services subtracted out, the data of Table 7.7 would show a decline for land. (We present data in Chapter 14 suggesting more clearly a decline in "value productivity importance of land."[17]) But at the maximum, land has not grown in relative contribution to farm output, as would be true under growth of population and food demand and constancy of agricultural technology.

The data of Table 7.7 also are significant in their reflection of the growing relative importance of capital. In 1910, with major inputs being those of labor, the beginning or other farmer could make his living largely with the resources representing his human endowment. Pressure of economic development through factor markets touched him but little, because his own person represented the major input. In 1960, however, this situation was reversed, with capital representing over 70 percent of total inputs if land is included. Hence, in later periods, capital and its investment in large scale becomes a necessary condition for success and income. Too, farm income is much more the direct functon of the factor

[17] For earlier propositions to this effect, and explaining the nature of land-substituting and land-using innovations, see Earl O. Heady, "Changes in Income Distribution in Agriculture With Special Reference to Technological Change," *Jour. Farm Econ.*, Vol. 24.

TABLE 7.7

PERCENT OF TOTAL ANNUAL INPUTS OF AGRICULTURE REPRESENTED BY LABOR, LAND AND CAPITAL (1910–60, SELECTED YEARS)[a]

Year	Labor	Land	Capital	All Inputs	All Inputs as Percent of 1910[a]
1910	74.6	8.7	16.7	100.0	100.0
1915	72.6	8.4	19.0	100.0	105.9
1920	70.1	8.3	21.6	100.0	113.1
1925	69.3	8.0	22.7	100.0	113.6
1930	65.8	8.3	25.9	100.0	115.2
1935	66.7	9.6	23.8	100.0	104.4
1940	58.6	9.1	32.3	100.0	115.6
1945	52.5	8.9	38.7	100.0	118.7
1950	41.8	8.9	49.3	100.0	119.8
1955	35.0	8.6	56.5	100.0	120.5
1959	30.1	8.5	61.4	100.0	121.3

Source: Basic Data from Agricultural Research Service, USDA. See page 232 of *Economic Report of the President, 1960* and USDA Tech. Bul. 1238 for the basic series. Proportions are values of annual inputs with deflation to a 1947–49 dollar basis. Capital includes interest on investment plus depreciation (cost for annual inputs). Land includes rental and interest value of annual input. Labor is physical requirement times wage rate.

[a] Based on all inputs but taxes excluded. Without taxes included as an input, the index differs slightly from that used in earlier chapters.

market, since capital and investment comes almost entirely from the market and not directly from the household.

Output in Relation to Input

Examination of Table 7.7 again emphasizes an important characteristic of U.S. agriculture under economic growth, namely, the tendency for output to increase with a highly "constant" aggregate input, with a consequent large growth in the output-input ratio. The input aggregation is made for the data of the table by computing annual inputs on the basis of depreciation of durable capital, price of mono-period resources, interest on durable capital and land, and wage rate for labor, all converted to a constant value of the dollar. If all inputs have been accurately measured in this aggregation, with the prices for input of resources of nonfarm origin incorporating services used in these resource-furnishing industries, society is indeed fortunate in having a larger food output produced, in fact, with less aggregate resource per unit of aggregate product. Important weighting problems are involved, but even with some error due to this, it appears certain that the output/input ratio has declined remarkably and aggregate input has remained highly stable, with labor decline offset by capital increase, or increased remarkably little with a much greater output.

We now inquire how these changes might be possible, supposing that important inputs have not been neglected in the data of Table 7.7. The production process is not adequately represented by a production function in which there are only three factors of production, capital, labor and land. It is better represented by a production function such as (4.18), where n may be equal to several thousand, with many possible categories of specific inputs. Some of these resources are known. If their price is not too high relative to productivity, they are used in positive quantities. Some are unknown, and their input is zero. Input of others, zero for centuries because they or their productivity coefficients were not known, increased rapidly as innovation identified them. The role of technical innovation is to identify these hundreds of individual resources and their productivity coefficients so that they can be used in nonzero quantities if prices are favorable. Granulated ammonium nitrate 2-4D, Pioneer 907 hybrid seed corn, row crop tractors and irrigation water in Indiana are resources distinctly different from rock phosphate, pig weeds, open-pollinated or best 206 hybrid seed corn, mules and winter snow in Indiana. The production process is not adequately represented if we aggregate these many different resources into a single resource category, capital or value of inputs, and try to explain changes in the physical production function. These distinctly different resources, some known and some yet unknown, serve as substitutes for each other. Input of some has increased by extremely large magnitudes over the past several decades, with a consequent decrease or disappearance in others.

Innovations generally would not be adopted if they failed to lessen the value of inputs (the measure conventionally used for aggregate input) required to produce a given output. This is an obvious reason why continuous innovation would lead to a decline in capital value of inputs relative to output. For an individual farmer, and in aggregate for the agricultural industry, the situation is like that represented in Figure 7.10.

We could examine the case in which both an individual form of resource (technique or capital form) and its productivity coefficient are unknown or the material or resource (hybrid corn) is known but its productivity coefficient is not. For simplicity purposes, we use the second example, although the logic is the same in both. Suppose that one particular resource (such as open-pollinated corn or horsepower) in the *total* production function is known and is X_g. Another particular resource (hybrid corn or tractors) newly discovered or identified is X_h. However,

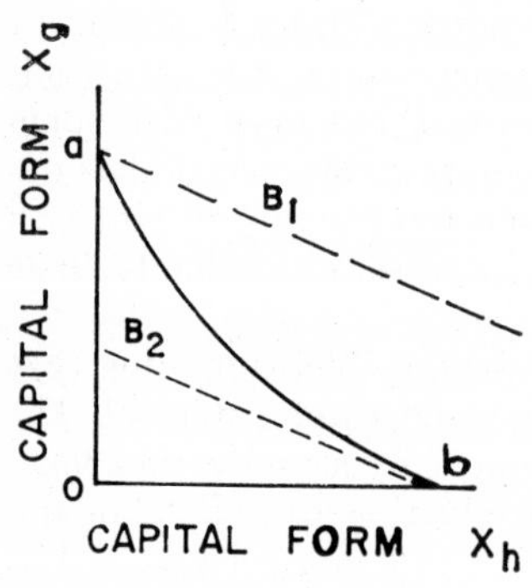

Fig. 7.10. Effect of Innovation on Value of Input Per Unit of Output.

nothing is known about its productivity coefficient. Therefore, the product isoquant in Figure 7.9, denoting substitution rates between the two distinct resources or materials, is unknown. Hence, the amount of X_g used to produce the given quantity should be a, if profits are maximized in the situation. Although both materials may have a price, with the price ratio represented by the slope of B_1, only resource X_g is used because the effects of resource X_h are unknown. Now suppose that research uncovers the productivity coefficient and establishes the isoquant ab. Given the price ratio indicated, costs can be lowered (the amount of capital or value quantity of all inputs can be decreased) and profits increased by substituting resource X_h (hybrid corn or ammonium nitrate) for X_g (open-pollinated corn or ammonium sulfate), to the extent of b. In doing so, capital resources measured in dollar value decline from the level B_1 to B_q. Farmers figure this out for themselves and lower "capital value inputs" for any given output. They would be foolish indeed to substitute one physical resource for another which increased "value inputs" for any given output. For this reason, the one physical resource is substituted for another in producing a given output, and the basis is laid for producing more output without a similar increase in "dollar-aggregated" input.

But in addition to a substitution effect, a price effect, in respect to quantity of output and resources used after the innovation, is expected. In this case, output can expand with a smaller "dollar capital input" as long as the equilibrium production is less than that denoted by an isoquant tangent to B_1. Given the particular geometry, output could be more than doubled, while inputs valued on a dollar basis would show a decline.

That which would hold true for an individual farm could also hold true for the agricultural industry. Or, if a curved iso-revenue line is assumed, the figure would apply equally to the industry. Of course, if price elasticity of demand for the product were sufficiently great, the price effect of the innovation (discovery of the new resource form) could cause a sufficient increase in output to also cause dollar value (capital as conventionally measured) of inputs to increase, but the latter would not increase by the same proportion. If demand were sufficiently inelastic, the increase in output would be produced with a proportionately smaller increase in input. Agriculture is notably "low" in respect to demand elasticity coefficients.

To better illustrate conditions under which output might increase at a greater rate than input, given the situation of demand elasticity and technical advance of agriculture, a very simple algebraic example is now used. It illustrates that the phenomenon might be explained by conventional concepts in economics without need to resort to a yet undeveloped growth theory. A simple model with some numerical coefficients is used for simplicity and ease of following by the reader, but other algebraic forms and coefficients would give similar results under the elasticity and technical conditions which characterize agriculture.

First, we suppose a demand function of a form indicated earlier and repeated in (7.18), with quantity expressed as a function of price and a price elasticity of $-.4$ exceeding that at farm level for food products in aggregate. (We might consider the demand and production functions to relate to a particular product or to products in aggregate. The results, in respect to magnitude of output relative to input, are the same in either case for elasticities and changes such as those used for illustration.) For illustrative and simplicity purposes, the variables in the demand function are those enumerated earlier, namely Q_d, the amount purchased at any particular price, P, and c, a constant to reflect the effects of income, population magnitudes and related variables at a particular point in time.

(7.18) $$Q_d = cP^{-.4}$$

(7.19) $$Q_p = \pi X_g^{.8}$$

The production function used for illustrative purposes follows that of equation (2.3) and is that of (7.19), where X_g is factor input and π is, as outlined earlier, a coefficient to reflect the effects of a quantity of fixed resources and technical conditions at one point in time. The g subscript indicates that resource input is in a form representing an early stage of innovation (open-pollinated corn, horses, oats without ceresan treatment, etc.). Obviously, as the state of the arts increases (π becomes larger), a smaller quantity of resources, X_g, will be required to produce a given amount of product. The variable X_g refers to resources used in the form of particular techniques at one point in time. It could be a quantity measured by some standard such as mass (tons) or value (constant dollars). The elasticity of .8 is arbitrary, taken to illustrate a fixed plant in acreage for a given state of arts.[18] Hence, at a given point in time, an increase in quantity of inputs representing given techniques would result in an increase in output by a smaller proportion.

Expressing input requirements as a function of output, computing total cost, equating its derivative to commodity price and solving for Q, we obtain the supply function in (7.20). Equating (7.20) to demand in (7.18) and solving for P, we obtain the equilibrium price in (7.21) where P_x is price of the resource:

(7.20) $$Q_s = .4096\pi^5 P^4 P_x^{-4}$$

(7.21) $$P = 1.22496c^{.2273}\pi^{-1.1365}P_x^{.9092}$$

Substituting the equilibrium price into demand and supply functions, the equilibrium output is (7.22). From the production function (7.19), the equilibrium resource input is thus (7.23).

---

[18] By using an elasticity of production smaller than 1.0, we do not assume diminishing returns over (to) time. As illustrated later, innovations can (as actually experienced in agriculture) allow output to increase by a greater proportion than inputs.

(7.22) $$Q = .9223c^{.9092}\pi^{.4540}P_x^{-.3632}$$

(7.23) $$X_g = .9037c^{1.1365}\pi^{-.6825}P_x^{-.4540}$$

The equilibrium output/input ratio is that in (7.24) which represents an index of 100 for this period.

(7.24) $$QX_g^{-1} = 1.0204c^{-.2273}\pi^{1.1365}P_x^{.0908}$$

(7.25) $$Q_p = \Gamma\pi X_h^{.8}$$

Now suppose demand growth takes place with increase in population in the manner that (7.18) is multiplied by λ (or $\lambda = 1.0$ in the original function but $\lambda > 1.0$ after the increase). Further, technical advance changes the production function by the ratio Γ, more product being obtained from a given tonnage, value (constant dollar) or other physical measure of input as in (7.25) where the subscript h now refers to the new form of resource in the same unit of measurement as X_g. The proportionate increase in equilibrium output, r_q, resulting from the increase in demand and technology, is that in (7.26). The proportionate increase in equilibrium input, r_x, is that in (7.27).

(7.26) $$r_q = \lambda^{.9092}\Gamma^{.4540}$$

(7.27) $$r_x = \lambda^{1.1365}\Gamma^{-.6825}$$

These two proportions (i.e. rates of increase in input and output) are the same only under the conditions of (7.28), indicating that the rate of increase in resource productivity, resulting from technical improvement, must be much smaller than the rate of demand increase if the rate by which equilibrium input increases is the same as the rate at which equilibrium output increases.

(7.28) $$\Gamma = \lambda^{.2}$$

(7.29) $$Q = 1.6728c^{.9092}\pi^{.4540}P_x^{-.3632}$$

Thus, if the proportionate increase in demand were 1.5 (i.e., the demand function in (7.18) were increased by 1.5) as a result of increases in population and income, the production function could increase only by the much smaller fraction or by 1.08; the production function in (7.19) could be multiplied by only 1.08 if ratios of increase were to remain the same.

As a further example, suppose the λ is 1.5 while Γ in (7.25) is 1.65, indicating that demand and resource productivity have increased by these proportions. The output and input quantities will now be those in (7.29) and (7.30) respectively, as compared to those in (7.22) and (7.23) before the improvement in demand and technology.

(7.30) $$X_h = 1.0170c^{1.1365}\pi^{-.6825}P_x^{-.4540}$$

In other words, equilibrium output is 1.82 times (82 percent) greater than before the improvement and technology, while equilibrium input is only 1.13 times (13 percent) greater. Obviously, the relative demand and physical resource productivity depends on the elasticity coefficients. The output/input ratio has increased from that in (7.24) to that in (7.31), or by 37 percent. (The index now stands at 137 as compared to the base period.)

$$(7.31) \qquad QX_h^{-1} = 1.6448c^{-.2273}\pi^{1.1365}P_x^{.0908}$$

The magnitudes of the elasticity coefficients and the demand and production multipliers concerned have caused inputs to increase by a smaller proportion than output. It is obvious that the relative rate at which inputs and outputs change, with given change in demand and techniques, will depend on the production and elasticity coefficients. Or, with given elasticity coefficients, the relative rate of increase between output and input will depend on the rate of growth in demand and technical advance. The change in ratio of output to input will be greater as the price elasticity of demand is lower or as the elasticity of production is greater. If the elasticity of production is sufficiently great relative to λ, input can even decline while output is increasing. Or, if the price elasticity of demand is sufficiently low, an improvement in techniques which results in a higher transformation rate of resources (measured in some standard unit such as dollars, tons, etc.) and a greater elasticity of production, output can increase while input (measured in the standard units) is decreasing.[19] For simplicity purposes in our example, demand and technical change are reflected through the two multipliers, with the elasticity coefficients remaining constant. Actually, the tendency is for price elasticity of demand to decline with growth in income and perhaps for the agricultural production elasticity to increase with technical innovation. Incorporation of these changing elasticity coefficients into the example would cause the growth in input to be restricted even more relative to growth in output.[20]

There are two general cases under which the output/input ratio would remain constant (i.e., the index of output divided by the index of input would remain at unity) over time. One is the case of constant resource productivity (an elasticity of coefficient of 1.0) and no improvement in

[19] For example, if we start with the original demand and production functions and increase the demand function by the ratio $\lambda=1.3$ and the production function by the ratio $\Gamma=2.0$, equilibrium output will increase by the ratio $r_q=1.7388$ or by 73.9 percent while equilibrium input will decrease to the ratio $r_x=.8333$ or by 16.7 percent. This is true, for the elasticity coefficients used, because $\Gamma>\lambda^{.2}$. In other words, equilibrium input can decline absolutely while output increases if the elasticity of production and Γ, the change in technology, are sufficiently great relative to the demand elasticity and λ, the demand multiplier.

[20] We determined equilibrium output and input in the classical example which did not allow for discounting due to uncertainty and other causes. However, even if a discount coefficient were attached to the supply functions before and after innovation, the result would be the same for equal discounts. Even with a growth in the discount coefficient, output could still increase more than input, if the rate of technical improvement and the elasticity of production are sufficiently large.

techniques as demand increases. The other parallels that above where production elasticity is not unity and the improvement in technology must bear some particular relationship to the increase in demand, given the elasticity coefficients. But in neither of these cases, with the ratio of output to input remaining constant, or the ratio of increases remaining at unity, would society in general gain, as compared to the case in which the output/input ratio increases with time.

For example, starting with the first case, if the original demand is that in equation (7.18), while the production function is $Q_p = \pi X_g$, an elasticity coefficient of unity, the equilibrium output/input ratio then is π. Now if demand increases by the proportion λ, while technical improvement does not take place, the equilibrium output will increase but the equilibrium output/input ratio will remain constant at the original value of π. Society would gain more if technical change also could occur at the rate of $\Gamma > 1.0$, so that the output/input ratio could increase to $\Gamma\pi$, rather than to remain constant. Then for a given agricultural output for consumers, an amount of resources equal to $\Gamma^{-1} X_g$ could be transferred to production of other goods and services. However, farmers in aggregate would not gain in revenue because of the low price elasticity.

As a second case, with the elasticity of production not at unity, suppose that demand and production functions are originally those in (7.18) and (7.19). Now suppose that through demand increases λ becomes 1.5 and, through technological improvement, Γ becomes 1.0845. Under this very small improvement in technology, equilibrium output will be that in (7.32) while the equilibrium input will be that in (7.33).

$$Q = 1.3825 c^{.9092} \pi^{.4540} P_x^{-.3632} \tag{7.32}$$

$$X_h = 1.3548 c^{1.1365} \pi^{-.6825} P_x^{-.4540} \tag{7.33}$$

The new equilibrium output/input ratio will thus remain constant at the level in (7.24) and the index ratio, output index over input index, will remain at unity. This condition, attained by holding technical improvement at a very low level, is not desirable from a consumer welfare standpoint. The same output could be attained by a saving of resources if we caused the output/input ratio to increase through a more rapid pace in technical improvement. In fact, the output in (7.32) could be attained by an amount of resources equal to (7.34) if we allowed Γ to be 1.65 rather than to restrict it to 1.0845.[21] In other words, we could save the proportion,

$$1 - \frac{.8017}{1.3548} \quad \text{or} \quad 44.9 \text{ percent,}$$

of the resources used in producing (7.32), if we allowed the output/input

[21] Computed by setting $1.65 \pi X_h^{.8} = 1.3825 c^{.9092} \pi^{.4540} P_x^{-.3632}$ and solving for X_h where the left-hand quantity is from (7.25) with $\Gamma = 1.65$ while the right-hand quantity is Q in (7.32) the equilibrium output where we hold technical change to $\Gamma = 1.0845$.

ratio to increase to the level consistent with $\Gamma = 1.65$, rather than to hold it constant at the level of $\Gamma = 1.0845$.

$$X_h = .8017c^{1.1365}\pi^{-.6825}P_x^{-.4540} \tag{7.34}$$

Obviously, it is economically more desirable to consumer welfare to have the index ratio, index of output divided by index of input, increase with time (i.e., depart from unity) because it is then possible to get a given percentage increase in output, to meet increased demands, with a smaller percentage increase in inputs. This statement is in terms of overall economic development and long-run consumer welfare. But, again, and in the short run as a particular sector of society, the revenue to farm producers can decline because of low price elasticity of demand for food in aggregate. It is this problem of gain to consumer sector but sacrifice to producer sector which is the crux of policy where the general level of income per capita is high and all groups wish further gain in income, both as members of a wealthy society and of a group contributing to economic progress.

TECHNOLOGY AND STRUCTURE OF AGRICULTURE

We have already indicated that had all technical knowledge—the resources entering into agricultural production functions with positive productivities—been known from the outset, structural development of the industry would have followed a pattern quite similar to that of the last two centuries, perhaps the main difference being the speed and timing of change in resource mix and supply structure.

Large and elastic supplies of labor and land at low relative prices, with the opposite true for capital, early would have favored labor types of agriculture with low capital intensity, small units and a large farm population. But with resources shifting relative position in supply and price, emphasis is on large units, a smaller labor force and rural population and a more intensive use of capital or technology with given plant in land acres. We should expect this pattern of structural modification to continue under the continuous change in relative supply and price of resources under further economic development.

Since the endowment of resources by nature to agriculture was not equal over space, differential advantage will occur by regions as encouraged by changing resource prices and as allowed by technical knowledge. Agricultural policy per se can do little to stop these forces of national factor markets which reach over into agriculture and alter the resource and supply structure of the industry, unless it goes so far as to check national economic growth. But this is a Herculean and likely impossible accomplishment on the part of agricultural policy. The variables found in agriculture, per se, now have too little influence on the total economy, given the decline in proportion represented by agriculture.

Farm policy can only attempt to manipulate variables in agriculture which have an effect contrary to those variables reaching into the industry from outside factor markets. Even in the realm of technical change, farm policy can do much less than in the past. This is true because nonfarm or purchased inputs are coming to dominate agricultural production and supply. Under this condition, nonfarm sectors invest more heavily in uncovering and communicating the productivity of new resources to farmers. Even if the public were to cease investment in research and communication of technological change, the activity would continue at rapid tempo, financed by outside firms with even greater emphasis on resources and capital items produced external to agriculture. (Major resources such as machinery, tractors, hybrid corn, stilbestrol and others were discovered or developed outside of public research institutions.)

But how far can substitute resources go, in effectively replacing land and labor by capital? Relative prices are only one set of data determining factor combinations. Relative productivities and marginal rates of substitution are quantities of equal importance. Are we approaching the mathematical limit of zero-rate in substitution of capital for labor and land in agriculture? This proposition is not infrequently put forth, just as it was by Malthus and Ricardo. Thus far, diminishing marginal productivity of conventional capital items has always been offset by development of new capital items or technologies with greater marginal rates of productivity and substitution (a jump from curve representing one production function to one representing a new function, rather than movement along the first).

An important portion of the increment in yield per acre has come from fertilizer and improved varieties. Agronomists estimate that of the 17.5 bushel increase in corn yield per acre between 1940 and 1958, about 47 percent came from fertilizer and 40 percent from improved seed.[22] Fertilizer is an input which has spread rapidly over the U.S. since 1940. Its use increased several-fold in the two decades, 1940–60. (See Chapter 5.) It has served as a tremendous substitute for both land and labor. It is still used in relatively small quantities by many farmers who could, from an individual rather than aggregative basis, profitably employ it. Fertilizer still has considerable slack, in the sense of being spread to many farms at relatively low level of input. But after this has been accomplished, the next opportunity is in using it at higher level of input on farms already using it. While much more fertilizer can be used following the second route, it will have a much lower marginal rate of substitution for land. Table 7.8 illustrates the declining marginal rate of substitution of fertilizer for land when input is of particular magnitudes. These computations, following equations (2.22) to (2.26), would also indicate a decline in marginal rates of substitution of fertilizer for labor as the former is used more widely and intensively. The data are for particular soils (those indicated for Figure 7.9), climatic conditions

[22] L. M. Thompson *et al.*, *Causes of Recent High Yields in Feed Grains*, Iowa Center for Agricultural and Economic Adjustment, Iowa State University, Feed-Livestock Workshop, Ames, 1959, pp. 15–39.

TABLE 7.8

Marginal Rates of Substitution of Fertilizer Nutrients (Lbs.) for Land (Acre) in Corn Production Based on Production Functions at Particular Locations*

Rate of Application (Lbs. Per Acre)	North Carolina (*f*)	Kansas (*g*)	Miss. (*j*)	Iowa (*a*)	Iowa (*e*)
25	.0247	.0035	.0089	.0394	.0027
50	.0181	.0025	.0018	.0014	.0021
75	.0121	.0014	—	—	.0016
100	.0074	.0004	—	—	.0013
125	.0034	—	—	—	.0010
150	.0018	—	—	—	.0007
175	.0002	—	—	—	.0005

* Refer to Figure 7.7 for sources and soil type. (*j*) indicates Mississippi experimental data for corn. The marginal rates of substitution are computed as in equation (2.23) where $Y=f(X)$ is the original experimental production function with Y yield per acre, X fertilizer per acre and A land acres. The original function is computed on a per acre basis, and is multiplied by A to indicate production from varying acreage at the various input levels. Hence, the substitution rate is of fertilizer for the particular soil. Rate would be greater if we compared fertilizer on central Iowa soil with the number of acres which could be thus replaced in the northern Ozarks. Too, the substitution rates are "gross physical rates," since they do not account for other inputs such as labor.

and other variables. Hence, they do not serve as a predictive base for U.S. agriculture as a universe. They do indicate, however, that as average rate of fertilization moves up a scale of 25, 50 and 75 pounds per acre, the rate of replacement of land by fertilizer capital declines. Given constancy of other techniques, the opportunity for substitution of fertilizer for land is not as great for the future as for the past.

However, the restraint of "constancy in other techniques" has not been operative in past decades, and mathematical limit of zero productivity for input extensions has been lifted by development of new techniques or capital forms which complement certain of the old. Previous data presented indicated that the supply function of food will have sufficient elasticity over the next decade, or perhaps two, that farm surplus problems are more probable than deficit and high real price of food. The extent to which food has high or real cost beyond that time depends on the success and magnitude of investment in research in biology related to agriculture, but it also may depend on chemistry as it is practical in synthesizing foods outside of agriculture.

For the next decade, however, capital can continue to substitute for land and labor. At 1960 point of time, various estimates predicted that from 40 to 80 million acres (10 to 20 percent with the amount depending on the method of withdrawal) of U.S. cropland could be withdrawn from production without material effect on retail price of food.[23] (See Chapter 14.) Christensen, Johnson and Baumann predict this surplus acreage will grow over the next half dozen years.[24] The supply of land, in relation

[23] See Heady and Egbert, *op. cit.;* Earl O. Heady and Arnold Paulson, *U.S. News and World Report*, May 30, 1960, pp. 104–6; and J. Carroll Bottum, *Increase the Conservation Reserve,* Iowa Center for Economic and Agricultural Adjustment, Feed-Livestock Workshop, pp. 141–49; R. P. Christensen, S. E. Johnson and R. V. Baumann, *Production Prospects for Wheat, Feed and Livestock,* 1960–65.

[24] *Ibid.*, pp. 43–115.

to food demand and productivity and not in physical extent, was greater in 1960 than at any time in the previous half century. The effect of capital substitution on supply was equivalent to discovery of a new land area the size of Iowa or Kansas. Nations concerned with stepping up rate of economic development and alleviating problems of population pressure would rejoice in this equivalent of discovery. It provides assurance and certainty for U.S. consumers, plus perhaps others of the world, and is an important product of economic development. Yet its net benefits will not be reflected fully to society until a later time when supply of land is made more elastic to grains and other products of agriculture for which surpluses are prone to develop, and until policy guarantees distribution of gains with positive-sum utility outcome over all major groups of producers and consumers.

8

Criteria for Policy

Public policy requires some framework or set of criteria serving as a foundation on which both ends and means are based and can be judged. Generally, too, policy requires some concept of community or national goals to which policy can be directed and in which it can be evaluated. Without some scaffolding in framework and goals, there could be no order within and among policies for different groups and communities. Each conflicting group or sector could pressure for any end or means, without regard for those of other groups, and there would be no machinery for gauging the importance of these competitive interests, goals and means. Some concept of community whose interests transcend the individual must exist unless political and economic chaos is to reign.

Society is characterized by groups with divergent and conflicting ends and values, just as it also has interests which transcend those of groups. The existence of groups with different values and ends (i.e., indifference curves with different slopes along a scale line) does not preclude the development of policy consistent with maximization of the social welfare function. Society in democratic organization exists, in fact, not apart from persons attaching different values and weights to various goals, but largely because of these contrasts and the fact that it provides the mechanism for resolving extreme differences while still allowing others to exist. If the goals and values of all individuals were identical, with exactly homogeneous consumption functions and indifference maps, organized society would hardly be needed, aside from direction of traffic.

CRITERIA OF WELFARE ECONOMICS

One analytical framework providing a set of concepts for suggesting and evaluating policy in an over-all societal or community context is that of welfare economics. We need, then, to review its propositions and determine the rough extent which they can serve as guides in evaluating policy to cope with economic problems of agriculture under development. We will do so briefly, since the main elements of welfare economics are detailed elsewhere. Here we are concerned with the "new" welfare economics principles, now quite old, which do not require cardinal characteristics in utility measurement and recognize inability in making exact interpersonal utility comparisons. Issues in farm policy stem directly from this complex, namely, of change which distributes gains to some and losses to others, but with inability to measure directly these positive and negative outcomes.

Our first concern is in defining a social optimum or economic reorganization which will increase aggregate or community welfare and lead in the direction of a social optimum. We employ a social optimum in the sense of Pareto, namely, organization or position wherein no one individual can move to a position which he prefers without moving another individual to a position which is less preferred and without the requirement that utility be measurable.[1] Or, stated conversely, economic reorganization of resources in production and commodities (or income) in consumption should take place if any individual can be made better off, in goods or services which he prefers, without making other individuals "worse off."

Quite obviously, much government policy takes place outside of this framework, more nearly under the assumption that differentials among individuals in utility or welfare are apparent or measurable, and that distribution of gains and losses is such that community welfare is increased in the sense of a positive-sum game. Still other governmental policy adheres roughly to this general skeleton, especially if we include the principle of compensation—a foundation block of agricultural policy since 1930.

In general, Paretoan welfare economics only tells us which reorganizations increase or decrease the social welfare function, without specifying the exact organization which maximizes it. Or, put in different words, it only specifies conditions under which aggregate welfare will be increased without specifying unique organizations which will optimize it. In an over-all or aggregative sense, Pareto welfare economics explains how resources should be organized and allocated among products and industries and how income should be distributed among individuals and over time, but in the restricted sense mentioned above. We could employ conditions of economic organization and particular "offshoots" of welfare economics

---

[1] While the concept of indifference curves were developed by Pareto, much of the basis for welfare economics must be attributed to F. Y. Edgeworth, *Mathematical Physics*, London, 1881.

which suppose measurement of all relevant quantities is possible and that a unique optimizing (mathematical maximum in community welfare) organization of resources and distribution of income can be specified. It is not, however, necessary to go this far in useful application of welfare economics to policy problems.

Pareto Optimum and Contract Curve

We begin our discussion of a bargaining framework, since it appears appropriate in terms of such policy problems as conflict among farm organizations in means of attaining ends (e.g., free market prices and managed supply) or bargaining among farm and nonfarm groups in the extent of compensation to be awarded agriculture for its contribution to abundant and low-priced food. For purposes of generality, we simply suppose two classes of assets, goods or services which are to be allocated among two individuals or groups. Starting from a historic or current distribution, how can the quantity of these be reallocated with certainty of increased total welfare, or with guarantee that while some gain, others do not sacrifice and positive-sum outcome in aggregate utility is given.

To illustrate these opportunities, we resort to the Edgeworth opportunity box in Figure 8.1, where we suppose two individuals (or groups, if we

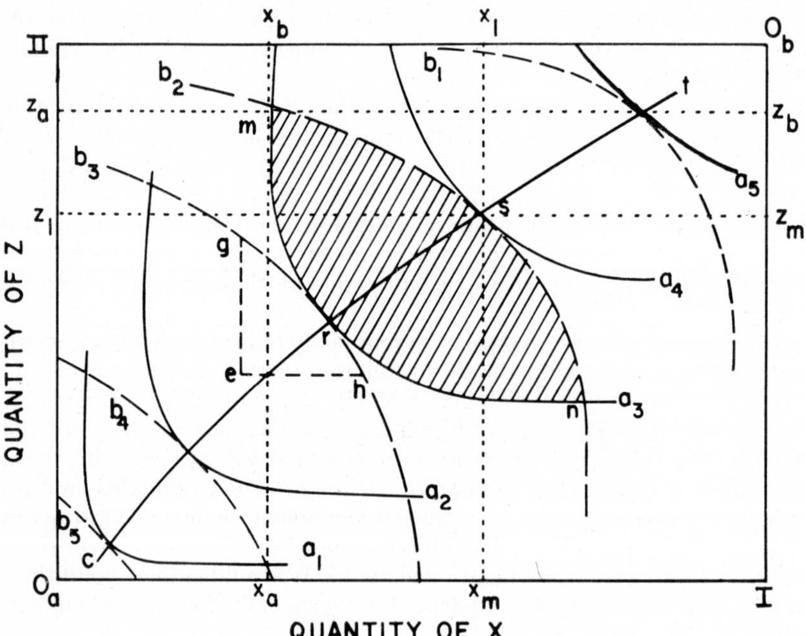

Fig. 8.1. Opportunity Box for Pareto Optimum in Allocation.

could suppose that internal indifference maps are sufficiently similar) denoted as A and B and two commodities, services or assets denoted as X and Z. The box represents the total quantities of the two goods to be distributed between A and B. Quantities are O_aI (equals O_bII) of X and O_aII (equals O_bI) of Z. The indifference map denoted by solid indifference curves is for A; that indicated by dashed curves is for B. The map for A is in the usual position; that for B is "upside down" with origin at O_b and with level of utility characterized by $b_1 < b_2 < \cdots b_i < \cdots b_n$. Hence movement along any vector originating at O_a causes A to have greater welfare; along any one orginating at O_b allows B to increase welfare. Obviously conflict can arise, one being made better off and one worse off, from a large number of reorganizations. Any point in the opportunity box represents an allocation of products between the two individuals. Point m is one such allocation with products allocated as follows: O_ax_a of X and O_az_a of Z to A, O_bx_b of X and O_bz_b of Z to B. But this allocation is one allowing reorganization and policy to increase welfare of one or both individuals, thus guaranteeing that total or community welfare is increased.

Since an indifference curve is an isoquant indicating all combinations of the two products which provides the same utility, movement along it, representing change in the mix of products to the individual, denotes changes which make him neither better nor worse off, compared to the initial quantities of products allocated to it. Thus, starting at point m, we can move rightward along indifference curve b_2 for individual B. Any point along b_2 to the right of m thus intersects an indifference curve of greater utility than a_3 for A, up to the point where b_2 intersects a_3 on the lower side. Hence, we can find many new proportions or allocations, starting from m, which provide A with more utility but which do not subtract from B's utility. Any one of these is, therefore, an allocation preferred over m. It guarantees positive-sum utility outcomes to the community represented by summation of A and B. Each of these new alternatives in allocation will take some of X away from B and give it to A, but will transfer some of Z from A to B. In other words, the two individuals can make a trade of products, leaving B as well off as previously but increasing welfare of A. One such reorganization allows maximization of A's utility, with utility of B remaining constant at original level as denoted by curve b_2. It is that at point s, denoted by tangency of b_2, B's constant utility curve, with a_4, the latter representing the highest indifference curve of A which can be attained without worsening B's position. If we select a point in allocation allowing a higher level of utility than a_4 for A, we would necessarily lower utility of B below the level indicated by b_2. We would make A better off at the expense of B. Being unable to compare utility quantities between A and B (i.e. we can only assume $a_4 - a_3 \neq b_3 - b_2$), we cannot say whether this utility sum is greater or smaller than that represented at point m. We have no certainty that $(a_4 - a_3) + (b_3 - b_2) \geq 0$. Or, if we assume that we have n individuals involved in such re-organization and if Δ_i represents the utility change, either positive or negative, of the ith individual, we have no certainty that:

$$\sum_{i=1}^{n} \Delta_i > 0 \tag{8.1}$$

Hence, for our two-person case, a indicates the highest position, with reallocation of products, to which we can lift A without reducing B's welfare. At this point we have an allocation: $O_a x_m$ of X and $O_a z_1$ of Z to A; $O_b x_1$ of X and $O_b z_m$ of Z to B.

Similarly, starting at point m, we could move downward along a_3, denoting reallocations which hold A's utility constant while increasing that for B. In this Paretoan sense, the extreme allocation would be at point r, allowing a maximum gain in utility for B without sacrifice for A. But any point within the cigar-shaped boundaries enclosed within intersection of a_3 and b_2 is one which guarantees an increase in total or community welfare. Points on the boundary, away from the intersections of the curves, allow one individual to be made better off, with utility of the other constant. All points within these boundaries represent allocations which make both individuals better off, and thus increase community welfare over points m and n. We cannot say which point within or on the boundary of this Paretoan area is best, since this statement would require cardinal representation of utility for the two individuals. We can only say that any of these allocations is better than that at point m or n. But in general for changes which lead to points within the "cigar," we can be certain that the inequality of (8.1) prevails and positive-sum utility outcome is guaranteed because Δ_i is positive for all individuals. Thus, in economic progress such as characterizes agriculture, we guarantee community welfare gain where change in income and consumer's surplus is positive for all farmers and consumers because it falls within our bounds, but not if the new distribution falls outside the bounds.

Given the level of utility of one individual, distribution which maximizes the utility of the other individual is denoted by tangency of the indifference curves, indicating that the marginal rate of substitution between the two products is equal for all individuals. The latter, then, is a necessary condition in economic organization if welfare of the society is to be maximized. It is similarly true, as indicated below, that marginal quantities must be equal for other inter-unit allocative opportunities if utility is to be maximized. It is not a necessary condition, however, when we search only for changes and reorganizations which simply guarantee positive-sum outcomes, without the restraint that they define an optimum in the sense of maximization.

The line *ct* is a contract curve, a locus of points of tangency, defining equal marginal rates of substitution for the two sets of indifference curves. Welfare is never maximized, even given inability of interpersonal utility comparisons, for any distribution not located on the contract curve. For other points, we can always move to the contract curve, moving at least one or both individuals to a preferred position. But once on this curve, it is impossible to move to any point not on it without making one individual worse off than previously. The curve *ct* then traces out allocations which are consistent with maximum welfare. Any allocation from which it would be impossible to improve position of one without lessening position of the other is an economically efficient allocation. Any policy leading to such a position is a change increasing economic efficiency. We cannot, however, say which point on *ct* represents a social or community optimum, since movement along it will always increase utility of one while decreasing that of the other individual.

Various points in the opportunity box represent areas of bargaining which may lead to trades and agreement or to pure conflict. Points not on the contract curves are those where trades are possible between groups, such as between agriculture and taxpayers in general or between two competing farm organizations. Starting at point m, movement down a_3 makes B better off and A no worse off; movement down b_2 makes A worse off with B's position maintained. Recognizing this, the two can bargain and make trades, each giving up some of one product or activity and gaining some of the other, which leads to improved position of both.

In agricultural policy, farm organization groups might try the Paretoan game in respect to level of support prices and degree of production control (supply management) or freedom and ascertain whether aggregate welfare might still be increased. Once, however, the contract curve is attained, bargaining and trades can no longer be made which increase welfare of one without causing sacrifice of the other. As a special case, an important question in this respect is: Can abundance be increased and real price of food be lowered further with benefit to consumer and without sacrifice, or with some gain, to farmers? During one realm of demand and price elasticities, farmers could increase food output at net gain to both mass groups, with the public gaining more control over knowledge creation and its distribution to agriculture and farmers losing more control over knowledge creation and the market development of technology. Under the present demand and price elasticity realm, this appears no longer to be possible in the free market, although the "free market" may be modified by policy mechanisms to still guarantee these positive-sum outcomes. It is no longer possible in the sense that rush of output against inelastic demand and lower prices allows positive outcome for consumers but negative outcome for producers as a group. The positions on *ct* define only those of conflict, where further bargaining and rearrangement of position cannot lead to gain by both unless compensation is possible through a third variable or "outside good," to offset the loss of utility represented in the two-variable or product case.

Other Marginal Conditions for Welfare Maximization

Figure 8.1, as well as explaining reallocations which lead to *increased group welfare,* illustrates conditions necessary for *maximum community welfare:* The marginal rate of substitution among goods must be equal for all consumers as reflected in tangency of sets of indifference curves. This condition applies in allocation of the same goods among different time periods, as well as among different goods in the same time period. Certain other marginal conditions must also hold true for maximization of the social welfare function. Hence, policy also can be judged in respect to the sense that it leads in the direction or attainment of the complete set of marginal conditions, as well as in terms of simple guarantee of welfare increase. We review the additional marginal conditions but briefly since their implications and importance are apparent.[2]

For allocation of resource among two producers of the same product, the marginal rate of transformation of resource into product must be the same for both. If not, total product to be distributed among members of society can be increased by transfering resource from one to the other producer.

For proportion of resources used in producing a given product, the marginal rate of substitution between two resources used in producing a given product must be the same for all producers. Otherwise resources can be exchanged, allowing a greater output of one or both producers as in the manner of Figure 8.1 where we now suppose X and Z are factors used by two producers. The total product to society can be enhanced if X and Z are distributed so that isoquants are tangent.

For proportions of resources used for different products by different firms and industries, the marginal rates of substitution among factors must be the same for all producers and industries using them. Otherwise, as suggested by Figure 8.1, where A and B are different products and X and Z are different factors, output of one or both products can be increased, allowing larger aggregate income to be allocated among consumers.

For proportions of products produced with given resources, the marginal rate of transformation among the same commodities must be the same for all producers. If this condition is not represented by appropriate tangency of production possibility curves, it is possible to increase the combined outputs of products of all producers without increasing inputs of factors. In other words, considering b_i and a_i to be production possibility curves, an optimum is indicated only by a tangent pair.

For transformation of factors into product or substitution of resources and products over time, the above marginal conditions must exist, with modification to allow discount of future quantities for time, otherwise inter-

[2] For further detail on these conditions, see the following: H. Myint, *Theories of Welfare Economics*, Harvard University Press, Cambridge, 1948; M. R. Reder, Columbia University Press, New York, 1947; I. M. D. Little, *A Critique of Welfare Economics*, Oxford University Press, Oxford, 1950; J. M. Buchanan and G. Tullock, *The Calculus of Consent*, Michigan State University Press, East Lansing, 1961; T. Scitovsky, *Welfare and Competition*, Richard D. Irwin, New York, 1951; A. P. Lerner, *The Economics of Control*, Macmillan, New York, 1944; Earl O. Heady, *The Economics of Agricultural Production and Resource Use*, Prentice-Hall, New York, 1952, Chap. 21; F. Bator, "The Simple Analytics of Welfare Maximization," *Amer. Econ. Rev.*, Vol. 47; and N. Georgescue-Roegen, "Choice Expectations and Measurability," *Quar. Jour. Econ.*, 1954.

temporal reallocations could be made to increase total product of one time period without reducing that of the other, or with product of both periods increased.

For joint allocation of resources to production and consumption, the marginal rate of substitution between two commodities in production must equal the marginal rate of substitution of the two commodities in consumption. In other words, the production possibility curve of the producing unit must be tangent to the indifference curve of the consuming unit. If the b_i in Figure 8.1 are production possibility curves and the a_i are indifference curves, movement from the product mix at point *m* to that at point *s* allows utility to be raised from the level indicated by a_3 to that indicated by a_4.[3]

For allocation of time to production and consumption or leisure, the marginal rate of substitution between commodities purchased with income, X, and leisure, Z, must be the same for all persons. (We simply transform production into money income and the commodities which can be purchased with money income for this comparison.) If it is not, Pareto movements can be made within an opportunity box to attain the contract line *ct* in Figure 8.1.

In modification of the above points to allow for consumer preference, location of resources and the effect of transportation costs on factor prices, to account for disutility of work and to allow discounting for time, we might aggregate these conditions as follows: The marginal value productivity of resources used by one firm, in one industry, at one location and in one time period must be equal to that of another firm, industry, location and time period. It is, of course, the marginal value productivity, rather than marginal physical productivity or the value of the marginal product: to allow the consumer to express the relative weight which he attaches to a particular product, produced in varying quantity, or the relative values attached to alternative products forthcoming in various proportions, against the supplies of factors used in producing them. Alternatively, it can be stated that the marginal cost of product must equal price of product for all commodities, firms, industries and locations. In general, too, the equilibrium or stability conditions of the competitive firm, meaning marginal transformation and substitution rates equal to price ratios, must hold true and the consumer must equate slopes of budget lines and indifference curves. For the above summary conditions, we refer to resources and products of given quality. Those of differential quality can be considered as different resources and commodities, with exactly the same conditions applying to them.

Maximization of the social welfare function would generally suppose pure competition of firms (although pure competition does not have to

[3] The framework proposed in this condition is generally static. However, in a broad sense and more difficult in actual measurement, the same marginal conditions generally must prevail against all dimensions, whether these be in products, space, and time or over products such as uncertainty and income, time preference and saving, etc.

be postulated in using propositions of welfare economics in specifying agricultural policy leading in positive-sum outcomes as between alternative groups such as farmers and consumers or two groups of farmers). Under pure competition, attainment of all the stability conditions, defined by equation marginal rates of transformation and substitution with price ratios, would automatically result in attainment of the above conditions. This would suppose, of course, that markets are sufficiently perfect to reflect accurately the marginal value productivity of resource and the relative preferences of consumers. Quite obviously, these conditions cannot be attained where mixed organization exists, with some firms and industries equating marginal costs with marginal revenue of commodity and competitive firms equating marginal costs with average revenue of price, or, with monopoly firms in equilibrium of price exceeding average total costs and competitive firms with average variable costs exceeding price in the short run. (Existence of a single-firm industry with pricing to equate value of product with average and marginal costs does not obviate the maximum, however.) Here, then, we have one question of agriculture against nonagriculture. Should the latter be converted to pure competition to allow attainment of maximum welfare conditions, or should the former be converted to provide it with monopoly pricing power, to make marginal costs proportional to price for all sectors?

In the exposition above, we explained two types of changes: (1) those which guarantee an increase in aggregate welfare without particular concern with mathematical maximization and (2) those which lead to conditions necessary in maximization of community welfare. The latter is possible only under the condition that marginal quantities be equated in the vein of pure competition. But it is not necessary to impose all marginal conditions necessary for maximization, and hence the framework of pure competition, to cause principles of welfare economics to be useful in the analysis of policy. Rather than follow this approach, which is unrealistic in an economy where pure competition is not the general standard, we can simply follow the first approach, namely, the pursuit of reorganizations which guarantee positive-sum outcomes in the sense that change leaves all persons better off, or improves the position of one without deterioration in position of the other. We also can concentrate on policy issues which revolve around changes where some have been made better off at the expense of others; and inquire how these conditions can be alleviated to best insure positive-sum outcomes over all major groups. It is, we believe, the absence of this simple condition to guarantee welfare increase that gives rise to the major commercial farm policy problems under rapid development of agriculture.

Magnitude of Labor Return and Welfare Gains

If the organizational propositions underlying economics, specifying the marginal conditions for an optimum, were followed strictly, we would need only to compute the marginal value productivities of labor in various occupations and locations, diverting human resources from points where it is low to points where it is higher.

In absence of refined computations for these purposes the average returns to labor in various facets of agriculture might serve as the gauge in directing it to sectors where wages for unskilled, skilled and other categories of labor and management are higher. This would be a simple solution if we could be certain that the comparative value returns were true reflection of net gains from economic reorganization and progress. It would be a simple solution if, as mentioned elsewhere, people were inanimate resources detached from households and communities like bricks, so that trucks could be backed up to the industry and labor resources could be carted to other occupations and locations where they have greater value returns. Bricks have no internal mechanisms which generate or reflect utility. But comparative value returns to labor in various occupations are not an expression of net gains from progress. This is true because people and families are attached to labor, and value return in the market—while reflecting roughly the relative gain to other consumers in the economy as it is diverted among industries—does not reflect the magnitude of utility gains or losses to the particular family.

This is a basic reason why farm labor, while importantly mobile, has not migrated rapidly enough to solve the problems of commodity supply and resource returns in agriculture. Labor return of our 48-year-old Kansas wheat farmer in Chapter 5 may be only half the wage of a skilled electronics worker in Minneapolis. The market suggests that consumers in general would gain if the Kansan shifted from wheat to electronics. But the figures are gross in their comparison. As is true for the majority of farm migrants of middle age or older, his main opportunity is in unskilled employment of industry. Even though the Kansas farmer's real income might have declined and is low, his real income often would be lower in nonfarm industry. An element of his real income gain or loss is represented in different cultural mooring as he moves from the community to which he has attachment and related values, to the urban complex where this is much less true. Part of his loss may stem from liquidation of his physical assets and reduction in their capital value. This type of loss attaches especially to machinery and buildings which have one supply price when furnished new from outside the industry, and another as used equipment from within the industry. Frequently, the loss stemming from the resource is less when retained in production than when sold in the market. Finally, to this, must be added the costs of liquidation and transfer to a new location and occupation. Gross market comparisons of labor returns in different industries do not account for differences of this kind. Too, to be fully effective as gauges, they have to be made in a market where all industries operate under conditions of pure competition, a condition which does not prevail entirely in the U.S. economy. If market mechanisms are used to serve as the guide in resource allocation and if certainty of net welfare gains from progress is to exist, then compensation for transfer indeed is logical, just as it is for certain reorganizations which lead to income reduction without transfer.

Relative labor returns are a better gauge of net welfare gain from economic progress in reflection to farm youth first entering the labor force or to younger persons who are still flexible. Perhaps typically for farm youth with values oriented to urban life, the value surplus of nonfarm return over farm labor return is a fairly true reflection of net social gain, the individual having no capital loss in transfer and some preferences leading him to nonfarm employment. An important explanation in differential migration rate rests on this difference in net welfare gain or less to younger as compared to older people.

Compensation Principle

Since direct measurement of satisfaction (i.e. interpersonal utility measurements) are deemed impossible, modern welfare economics says that reorganizations which improve the position of one person or group at sacrifice to another person or group cannot guarantee increase in total welfare except under one condition. The condition required is that the sacrificing individual or group be given compensation so that it is left no worse off than previously. In general, this use of the compensation principle would suppose that slack exists (nonoptimum conditions prevail) in an added dimension of resource use so that, through harnessing it, product and income can be increased to compensate some who must move away from a Pareto optimum in respect to given or established dimensions.

Society has made and does make direct use of the compensation principle. For example, when the public wishes land for a dam or highway to benefit fishermen and travelers, it recognizes that while the first group will gain, the landowner will sacrifice in income, home or both. Hence, it provides compensation in the form of monetary payment. If he were left no worse off, the payment would allow him to cover the costs of moving and investment in resources which will provide him as much real income as formerly.[4] In a rough way, we might also interpret farm policies leading to extra market returns to farmers over recent decades as being application of the compensation principle. Through its investment in technological improvement and rapid supply increase for food, the public has brought forth gain to consumers in certainty and abundance of food and in lower budget cost for it alone, considering its low price elasticity. But farm families in aggregate have sacrificed, because of greater output against inelastic demand, in less revenue and capital losses. In rough, albeit imperfect fashion, society has tried to compensate farmers so that they are made no worse off, while total welfare increase is guaranteed through consumer gain.

---

[4] We use real income to allow for the fact that the person with condemned property might also attach value to life in a particular community. Here, monetary compensation would need to exceed that to give investment returning money income equal to that of the previous property.

APPLICATION IN AGRICULTURAL POLICY

Welfare economics propositions provide one framework for gauging and recommending policy. Farm policy has its best basis, its claim for compensation because of the market distribution of gains and losses under technical progress, in some propositions of the general theory. The complete set of welfare principles stated above provides a set of logical conditions for economic reorganization and policy where the single-valued goal is that of maximizing the social welfare function. Selected propositions of welfare propositions applied alone to an industry such as agriculture have, however, less applicability and do not guarantee aggregate welfare increase. Not infrequently we find an attempt to apply to agriculture, alone and out of economy-wide context, the marginal conditions of resource allocation outlined above. Application of this particular subset of principles to (1) agriculture alone when certain conditions do not prevail elsewhere in the economy or (2) farming without accompaniment by the subset dealing with consumption and compensation, need not lead to aggregate welfare increase or guarantee positive-sum outcome from change in use of resources.

Certain questions are left unanswered by welfare economic principles. They do not answer questions of equity or distributive justice, starting from position of Pareto optima along a contract curve. They do not answer questions of politics and political power as these relate to economic policy and the gain of some at sacrifice of others. Many public decisions are made in a realm where the overriding interest is not group welfare but that of individual interest groups. For certain allocations or public decisions, particular groups are willing to conform with the notion of maximum community welfare,[5] but for other decisions, prefer to improve their own position at the expense of others.

There are few major changes which can be brought about in complex societies where sacrifice for some individuals or groups is lacking. Many public choices and decisions thus refer to conflict along a contract curve, rather than to bargaining in movement to it. Further difficulty arises over the fact that not all sectors of firms and industries are organized under pure competition to allow attainment of the necessary marginal conditions and maximization of the social welfare function, nor are they about to let themselves be so organized. This is a condition applying as well to the elite planners under socialism as to firms in favorable position in enterprise economies.

Some thread of societal interest and optimizing does transcend the special interests of particular economic groups. If this is less true for the immediate period within society, it is more true for long periods where the pressing interests and conflicts of the moment carry less weight.

---

[5] They conform with group interests in the sense that they do not withdraw if they are on the "losing side." Still, group choice or selection may provide them with positive utility, if not maximum utility gain.

For this reason it is easier for the numerous publics which make up a society to agree on more distant goals than on those immediately ahead. If it were not true that some over-all concept of optimizing or societal maximum prevails, social organization would retrogress and break down, with eventual dictatorial control by the "strong men" who rise over their adversaries in pursuit of maximum individual welfare at the expense of those with conflicting preferences. To abandon all concepts, elements and notions of possible betterment in welfare or collective position of community is thus inappropriate and inconsistent with the activities, efforts and aspirations of a society which obviously does have some subset of common public purposes. Welfare economics propositions dealing with community utility maximization do, therefore, have applicability in over-all societal sense. To belittle and entirely neglect all propositions of welfare economics would itself be inconsistent with the being of a society which maintains its organization, especially by democratic procedures and under wide range of individual freedom.

But just as it would be foolish to abandon all concepts of welfare economics and possibility of increasing the social welfare function, it would be equally foolish to suppose that society can be pushed with certainty to great heights on utility surfaces by an attempt to impose subsets of welfare economic propositions and the conditions of pure competition only on agriculture, an industry which uses a minor fraction of the nation's resources and has an inherent structure which violates these propositions and conditions less than other major industries and sectors. In fact, rapid effort and progress in imposing and extending the particular subsets of welfare economics propositions and pure competition on agriculture, while at least a larger proportion of resources (as compared to those of agriculture's) are employed under monopoly and related conditions, with the remainder and majority of resource employment falling somewhere in between these two extremes, has no certainty of increasing community welfare. This would not be true if equal progress and intensity were applied to imposing the same subset of conditions on all other sectors of the economy, or in applying the full set of propositions to agriculture, rather than just the subset dealing with resource allocation.

The resources of agriculture are no longer large enough to "save" the society, even if they were used twice as efficiently. Those of the remainder of the economy are. To reorganize agriculture, improving its productivity and releasing more of its resources to the general economy without making general welfare improvements in the other sectors, and without exercising the compensation principle, need not guarantee a community welfare increase. A positive-sum game is not guaranteed because the sacrifice of persons crowded out of agriculture is not guaranteed to be less than the gain by consumers in the nonfarm sector, or by farmers remaining in agriculture. This statement applies where some loss of money or real income occurs in the transfer and interpersonal utility comparisons remain elusive.

Those who wish to make economics apart from reality, too simple and ruled purely by mechanics and arithmetic quantities, will discard welfare economics on this very point, by discarding its proposition of inability in interpersonal utility measurement because these propositions overrule recommendations based on arithmetic quantities and implicit assumptions of cardinal utility. But here is where welfare economics perhaps has its greatest relevance. In the sense of resource reorganization, the concept of a Pareto optimum, or simply a Pareto-better position, gives rise to suggestions of change which benefits different groups and the application of the compensation principle does provide a framework for getting greater utility under distributions which otherwise include both gains and losses.

Our argument is not with the general applicability of welfare economic propositions. Instead, it is with the attempt to apply only part of these rigidly to agriculture when they are equally, and sometimes more widely, violated by industries employing more resources. Is it an inefficient allocation of the economist's time, where he purports to be concerned with the broadest and most urgent policy problems of society, to dote on the figures of agriculture, showing how inefficiently resources are organized and how many of them could be transferred out of agriculture to increase the social welfare function, but does not do similarly for the major portion of the economy outside of agriculture? The marginal productivity of his time would be much greater if applied with equal intensity to that broader expanse of human and capital resources which lie outside of agriculture. The waste of resources, and the potential for reorganizing them to increase national product, indeed are greater over other sectors of the economy.

It is perhaps unfortunate, in the allocation of scarce societal research resources, that the public has several thousands of economists and other scientists assigned to the agricultural industry, computing quantities to determine its efficiency, increase its productivity and extend the transfer of resources out of it, with hardly a handful directly assigned (as in the manner of public research institutions) to other sectors of the economy where the majority of human and capital resources are invested. Certainly the same resources would allow closer attainment of the social optimum if more of them were allocated to lowering the cost of housing and medicine to the relative level of food; in extending research and facilities for the large number of persons whose psychiatric moorings retard their output and utility level; in increasing the quantity and quality of education and other means for a fuller expression of human capabilities; in improving the abilities and allocation of a large body of unskilled labor; in improving the effectiveness of industrial plants and layouts; in tackling the problems of monopoly; and in lessening inputs for purely neutralizing advertisement in industries of imperfect competition.

The gauge of welfare economics, although lacking a lead for measurements where certain quantities are crucial for public decision and being unable to specify which of certain optima provide greatest social utility or equitable allocations, provides some useful concepts and guides when applied to the entire economy or when the complete set of conditions is applied to a particular sector. The concept of inability in interpersonal utility measurement and the compensation principle, an important foundation in welfare economics, must accompany the subset of marginal conditions dealing with resource allocation if a particular industry is to be singled out for concentration, suboptimum conditions being allowed to prevail over a wider body of the economy. But once the complete set is applied, the general concepts have applicability and usefulness.

Without compensation, we cannot say that the social welfare function is increased by policy which increases food supply and lowers its cost to consumers at the reduction of income to agriculture, or that transfer of a farmer of older age into manufacture of zippers for cigarette packages, for benefit of consumers in total, will do so if the former has a conflicting set of values and lower real income in his urban setting. But with application of the compensation principle, this enigma can be lifted. The fuller set of welfare economics propositions has been applied by the public in farm policy of recent decades, more than by economists in agricultural policy analyses obsessed with the marginal or stability conditions relating to nonfarm consumer welfare. Application in policy of the complete set on a broader scale perhaps would have done even more in permanent solution of the basic problems of agriculture, and at less long-run cost to the general public. Rather than continuous annual payments as compensation to farmers for income reduction from augmented supply and as costs of carrying surpluses, lump-sum compensation to purchase land, cover capital losses and pay transfer and relocation costs could have more readily restrained the agricultural supply function.

Such alternatives need not be forced upon people against their values and in lowering their utility position. They could be put in the realm of individual choice and welfare betterment in the manner of discussion for Figure 8.1, the bargaining concept being used with bids to allow acceptance by those farmers who could see their utility position so improved. Or, under a range of policy alternatives, choices might have been offered, with the individual family better able to exercise its preferences in utility improvement. For example, rather than attempt to impose a single policy formulation on all producers and regions, such as withdrawal of a historic land proportion at a specific relative price, farmers might better be given a range of choices. (Chapters 12 and 14 discuss policy alternatives which provide choice to farm people and allow them to select alternatives which they appraise to increase their utility position, thus allowing positive-sum reorganizations to be favored.) Individual freedom and movement from the contract curve would not be violated since the family could make its own appraisal and choice. The choices to allow greater certainty of utility improvement for all concerned could simultaneously include public offer to purchase and retire land at a schedule of prices, public rental of land for specified periods, government purchase of rights to produce certain crops, eligibility for loans and price supports at different levels for varying levels of acreage reduction and opportunity for complete nonparticipation by those attaching most value to complete freedom.

Under such a range of choices, and one needed to conform with differential regional change of agriculture and economic development, a particular point within the opportunity box of Figure 8.1 would be forced on no person. He would be allowed to make his own choice, and specify which shift pushed him towards the contract curve. The U.S. public has not been unwilling to appropriate funds in exercise of the compensation principle for agriculture. Its main impatience has been in the fact that money appropriated has not been used in a general manner to solve basic structural problems of the industry. A more complete usage of welfare economics propositions in the manner outlined above could have done so from the magnitude of public funds invested in some broad attempts to impose single molds on all persons and regions.

It is consistent with democracy and continuance of social organization that individuals have different values and indifference maps. It also is consistent that choice for the individual be allowed even in policy. Policy need not be maintained at a conflict position when opportunity for choice and movement to Pareto optima exists. The sharp farm policy conflicts of the 1950's have not given proper recognition to this opportunity.

In recapitulation, we propose that the portion of modern welfare economics, that dealing simply with Pareto-better movements within the "cigar" of Figure 8.1, which stresses change to guarantee utility gain by all individuals or groups, is a useful basis for analysis of the problems of commercial agriculture. The problem specifically is that of a rate of development in the industry which distributes gains of progress to consumers but distributes the main costs of progress to agriculture in aggregate. We wish to specify change and policy which allows simultaneous gain to contrasting groups such as these, causing some to be made no worse off while others are made better off or which generally insures positive-sum utility outcomes from progress over all major groups. Thus we do not search here for the "very best" organization and social structure; we are satisfied with the second, third or "*n*th best," as long as it represents a higher community welfare level than that now existing and does not cause major sacrifice to fall on some in order that others may gain. This is a "workable" concept of welfare economics for policy purposes and does not require us to force a rigid application of marginal conditions and pure competition. A concept of optimizing and the "first best" economic organization is useful as a long-range goal, but it is more difficult to apply in the short run when many of its basic assumptions in respect to industry organization and equilibrium structure do not prevail.

Distribution of Gains Under Fluctuating Output

We have been talking about progress changes which distribute gains to some and losses to other persons, thus calling for policy and compensation. But there also are other economic phenomena which do not provide a symmetrical distribution of gains and positive-sum outcomes within agriculture. Cycles in output and price of farm commodities fall in a realm of benefit and sacrifice which do not guarantee aggregate welfare gains. They represent phenomena not unlike that of the wider-spread business cycle. For the latter, society has decided that gains and losses are not spread in a manner to guarantee positive-sum welfare increase from a market devoid of monetary and fiscal policy. It also is true that some producers gain as feed and livestock decline in one phase, and shoot to heights in another phase, of the farm commodity cycle. However, it is easily possible to find farmers who sacrifice under general progress and decline of relative price for farm prices and who clamor for compensation or other policy to eliminate these losses; but who gain from farm commodity cycles and who resist policy to eliminate them.

In welfare economics propositions there is no basic difference between these two cases. If net community gain cannot be guaranteed in the first case, absence of net welfare loss cannot be guaranteed in the second, as losses of some under commodity cycles provide the basis for gain by others. Policy is logically possible in either case to guarantee that losses do not outweigh gains in contribution to aggregate welfare. In this sense they are similar. In adapted policy sense, however, they are dissimilar. The first, stemming from progress, requires that change be continued but that compensation be provided for losses inherent in it; the second, stemming from particular configurations of supply function and producer response, requires elimination of instability and the losses to particular individuals which accompany it.

Similarly income fluctuations from weather provide distribution of gains and losses which do not guarantee positive-sum utility effect and provide logical basis for policy. With inelastic demand for farm commodities, gains to producers in aggregate are forthcoming from unfavorable weather and small crops. But again, yield losses are seldom distributed proportionately, and producers with full yields gain as those with no yields lose. Even favorable weather, which leads to bumper crops and reduced aggregate revenue under inelastic demand, brings gain to some as it brings loss to others. Those who further process the product as a factor, store it or otherwise engage in it through the market, may gain. But diminution of aggregate welfare is always a likelihood when it cannot be guaranteed that gain in utility to this group exceeds loss to farmers with diminished output. Hence, policy resting on storage to even aggregate interyear supply and crop insurance to provide equivalent of stable individual output becomes a means of preventing losses to some individuals when there is no assurance that gain to others is of sufficient magnitude to guarantee increase in aggregate welfare. Again, policy in this area for agriculture has its counterpart in national policy aimed at preventing fluctuations of the business cycle.

COMPLEMENTARY ALLOCATIONS

Conceptually, not all adjustments which provide potential increase in the social welfare function require a redistribution of products, services or opportunities in the manner of Figure 8.1. Choices are not wholly competitive, with one individual directly sacrificing so that another individual can increase quantity of a commodity. Prevailing allocations and technologies of production, including the use of basic human capacities, need not always fall at the boundary of the production possibility curve. If, for example, we view b_3 in Figure 8.1 as a production possibility curve attainable with potential technology of given resources (or capacity of a human), point *e* is a nonoptimum and inefficient use of factors where it represents the same quantity of resources as b_3. We can move production over any vector between *eh* and *eg*, with a gain in both. It is not necessary to reduce the quantity of one product in order that more of another be attained. We also can think of the horizontal axis as representing the amount of utility or income distributed to one person and the vertical axis as representing the amount to another person. If, by different technology or skills, the same resources can be used to extend production to the boundary of b_3, then reorganization is possible which need not lower the utility of one individual so that another may gain. Any position on the boundary of b_3, defined within the range opposite the angle at *e*, or over the segment *gh*, provides opportunity for more of income or utility to one individual without sacrifice to the other, or more to both. We need not know that utility surface of either individual or group to know that certain "movements" from *e* allow change of positive-sum utility outcomes for the community. Any position off from *e*, and over the quadrant *egh* extending from it, allows attainment of a higher level of utility for both, or a higher level for one without sacrifice by the other.[6]

Opportunity in Agriculture

There are many opportunities for adjustment of resources in agriculture which are similar to movement from *e* to a boundary position on b_3. A large number of these do not involve gain of one individual at direct expense of another, even in the sense of trade in commodities (although some have this effect indirectly through the market). Policy aimed at market standards and qualities of food products sometimes has been of this general character, allowing a more specific and certain price for the producer and greater quality and pricing for the consumer. But the important area of opportunity approaching our example of nonboundary position and mutual gain of individual and consumer sector is in appli-

[6] If b_3 were a production possibility curve for two physical products or services and we could construct a community indifference map, the isoquant which intersects *e* is lower than any one which intersects b_3 between *g* and *h*, maximum utility level being defined by tangency of b_3 with an indifference curve between points *g* and *h*.

cation to human resources of agriculture. To leave them, divert them by subsidy inverted towards agriculture, blindly counsel them in this direction alone and educate them for farming only, is to lessen the level of attainment for many. Aided and compensated in training and moved to growth industries, not only could a larger number of farm persons have greater income and rewards for their skills, but also consuming society could be provided with more commodities and services which it values as income grows. This would be accomplished without sacrifice in supply and price of food where remaining farmers are capable. This condition and opportunity exists over a wide range of human resource in agriculture, especially children and younger persons. Here, the adjustment of agricultural resources in the sense of a social optimum need not require sacrifice on the part of the individual and hence does not require compensation. In general the quantity of educational and guidance resources now in use could be diverted to a much greater extent to accomplish this shift.

There are, of course, alternative uses of these resources which would benefit the general consumer and the individual going out of agriculture, but which conflict with the interest of other labor or economic groups. It is not currently possible to invest in medical education, to transfer youth from agriculture into medicine, in quantity which brings reward of human effort in the two fields together, without some trespass on the interests of the medical profession and some confrontation with obstacles to entry by the latter. Neither is it possible for labor from agriculture to transfer to all areas of labor union jurisdiction without encountering conflict of interest and restraints on entry. Still, there are sufficient realms of employment opportunity where conflict is absent or small and a redirection of educational resources could transfer a person from agriculture to an area where his long-run rewards would be extremely greater. In selected growth industries which provide increasing factor rewards, the transfer process is gradual and the growth and gain for consumer enhancement is rapid enough that existing labor is not squeezed out. The opportunities for such general complementarity between reward to agricultural labor resource and consumer gain are great enough that it is unnecessary to invoke the principle of compensation at every turn, or to focus on policy which is negative in the sense of failure to recognize the broader opportunities in economic growth, and turn only to policy of supply control and resource containment.

As we have mentioned previously, it is likely that early developmental policies for agriculture fell in a realm of "unanimous consent" or general complementarity, such as movement from e to a point between g and h on b_3 as a production possibility curve in Figure 8.1. Public action in land settlement and at the initiation of public agricultural institutions could likely increase supply of farm products with positive gain in real income and utility to aggregate agriculture and consumers at the same time. The rapid growth in market for food and higher demand elasticities provided a realm allowing or approaching this condition. In more recent decades, however, this market and demand realm no longer exists and rapid output development of agriculture can cause gain to consumers but sacrifice to farmers in aggregate. Developmental policy is still desirable and needed to bring national welfare increase, but it needs to be mixed with policy to allow both consumers and farmers to derive positive gain from progress in agriculture; or where this is impossible through the market or market improvements to do so, it needs to provide compensation which guarantees against costs of progress falling heavily on agriculture.

Choices in Conflict

Welfare economics makes no attempt to say which of the reorganizations along the contract line are preferable. It doesn't even attempt to state which of two Pareto optimum positions are best, except as bargaining range is defined for individuals and groups. Neither does it say whether a given allocation or distribution is equitable or optimum.

In starting out from point *m* in Figure 8.1, for example, we can move to point *s*, with certainty of greater aggregate welfare. But is *s* an equitable distribution? Would point *r* be more so, supposing that the bargaining power of *A* is sufficiently great to move the position from *m* to *s* rather than *r*? Or, is the tangency point between b_4 and a_2 even more so? Principles of welfare economics as they now exist can only indicate changes which will lead to movements up the total utility surface, without indicating whether the surface is an ant hill whereas mountains might exist for ascension. But society does have to make decisions between ant hills and mountains of utility. It has to do so even where competition and conflict exist. Within some realms, it can use the compensation principle to override utility loss in certain groups. In other cases it cannot, or does not, because it would end up holding its own hand. These cases must be decided largely in the political process, but not necessarily in complete domination of one group by another. Fortunately, many such issues have not always arisen for agriculture. And where they have, they have more nearly been among the competing commodity, regional and organization groups within agriculture. Society, having made certain choices about the altitude of ant hills as compared to mountains, has quite readily invoked the compensation principle on behalf of agriculture.

LONG-RUN AND WELFARE PROPOSITIONS

Our statement in the last chapter was: Policy designed for agriculture should view the long-run structure implied in economic growth and allow and encourage at least gradual progress in this direction. In fact, progress ought to be as rapid as possible within the restraints of change as fast as culture and value structure allow it, and as rapid as is consistent with general welfare gain and the ability of policy to guarantee the same.

There are several reasons for encouraging this progress in agriculture.

The force of prices, even in the factor markets if shut off in farm commodity markets, provide a strength which cannot be offset by policy aimed at an industry employing less than 10 percent of the nation's capital and labor resources. Farm people increasingly do not want to be blocked off from the values and consumer patterns of other society, but increasingly wish to meld with them. Finally, the nation does have over-all public purposes which call for and require progress.

The process of progress is not blocked, perhaps only slowed slightly if at all, even in industries which have some monopoly power or other control over their commodity prices. Some of the more monopolistic industries have displayed great progress, not only in technical discovery but also in factor combinations which are consistent with resource prices under economic growth. The electrical equipment industry has been highly progressive, as compared to agriculture or other competitive sectors, even though it was convicted of monopoly practice and price-rigging in 1961. But even though it, like many other industries which are not pure competition, did not compete on the basis of commodity prices, firms did compete for resources in developing new products and in furthering technology used in producing given commodities.

Similarly, the agricultural industry needs to progress more than in the sense of adopting new biological practices. It needs to shift firm size and capital-labor structure in line with factor pricing. It will do so regardless of farm price policy, even if only as a result of farm youth who are attracted to industry because of higher labor earnings. This will be true increasingly as the nation invests more vigorously in education, with more reaching rural areas where it has been scantiest and as it promotes national economic growth, with the latter favoring the relative expansion of nonfarm sectors. The farm youth so inclined—and the data indicate that the extreme majority has been so inclined since 1940—will continue to turn a muted ear to the professional and industry spokesmen of agriculture who extoll the virtues of the industry and its need for price supports at levels to hold the structure of agriculture to the past. An "Indian reservation policy," one attempting to maintain agriculture as a "national muesum" with its image drawn from history, is impossible for these reasons. This does not rule out the very real need for compensation policy and other policy aimed at price instability and the desirability of putting agriculture on the same footing as other industries in respect to market power and capture of an equitable share of economic progress for themselves. It only means that any attempt of policy to retain an obsolescent craft structure of agriculture is impossible under the level of growth already attained and rates in prospect for the U.S. economy.

Our view in application of the propositions of welfare economics is similar. Emphasis does need to be on a "larger pie" to be allocated among consumers. Gain in community welfare is certain if the absolute size of the piece going to each consumer is larger, even if it is *relatively* smaller. Modern welfare economics, as we apply it, only tries to tell how to increase the size of the national product, with each person getting a larger income, even if it is a declining percentage. The several marginal conditions spelled out above are more general guides in the direction of a social optimum organization for movement in the long run. In the short run, greatest urgency for agriculture is simple movement from a point such as *m* to one within the Pareto-better area, rather than to one outside of this area. The proposition is not that distributions be changed from *t* to *r* or vice versa. The Marxists rested their case on the supposition of measurable utility and the redistribution of a pie of given size. Economic growth has itself been rapid and awarding enough in the United States that it allows possibility of equitable sharing of a larger pie. Modern issue, and especially that in the farm economy, needs to be more with the continuance and the equitable sharing of economic progress rather than concentration on a given product and its redistribution.

The profound recommendations of modern welfare economics, translated slightly, are the following: Economic growth and a larger aggregate product should be promoted with vigor. No individual should end up with a smaller absolute share if increase in the social welfare function is to be guaranteed. Individuals may have smaller relative shares, but no one should have smaller absolute share. This, especially, is where farm policy becomes laced to welfare economics and general policy. The fundamental claim of agriculture to compensation policies falls in this realm and itself arises from progress. But if the compensation method is made too binding and apart from progress and change, it can prevent (in a small way, since the industry uses relatively few resources) rearrangements which lead to progress and a larger national pie to divide.

We are supposing here, of course, that the same conditions will hold true for other industries—that monopolistic and general feather-bedding policies of other groups will not be allowed in sufficient strength to stop growth in product, or to invert it. And generally this has been true. Progress, although its rate has not been at maximum feasible level, has been quite rapid, even with some degree of monopoly in particular sectors, and the spread of the fruits of progress over the population has been wide. So true is this that social reform concentration in the United States hinges less on income redistribution and more on the promotion and continuance of economic growth. Under growth, and development of countervailing power, the bargaining process, labor and industrial sectors guarantee themselves each a larger absolute amount of an augmented product. Most groups are generally so absorbed in the success of this process that political interest in socialistic movements to appropriate the capital of industries or distribute its return equally to the populace are approaching the mathematical limit of zero. In the context of economic progress and a growing absolute share to both capital and labor groups, the general propositions of modern welfare economics have been broadly used in American society. Social legislation to create some equality of bargaining power has helped to assure these mutual or Pareto-better gains.

Principles of welfare economics that suppose compensation to redress sacrifice, and guarantee that individuals be left no worse off from change, do not require permanent farm subsidy for this purpose, or that new entrants in the industry, who have not experienced sacrifice from previous change, be compensated equally with those who have. Agricultural policy would have been much more efficient, supposing funds of the magnitude appropriated in the past and used for this general purpose, had it made these distinctions in compensation. It would have been more efficient in better compensating those actually making income and welfare sacrifices and in pulling agriculture to new structure consistent with economic growth. Neither do the propositions state that when compensation is made to agriculture, compensation should be made to related industries and groups which have made no sacrifice.

Certainly, then, compensation funds of the 1950's could have been used more efficiently if structured into programs which channeled more of public appropriations to farmers and less to grain storage sectors which were given call for investment and return far beyond that required in the normal food market. But in the same vein, the propositions would say that all persons making sacrifices in economic reorganization and progress should be compensated if increase in community welfare is to be guaranteed, and not just part of them. This was not entirely recognized in the massive farm policies of the 1950's. For example, town, trade and public service families in rural areas are tied nearly as close, and suffer income reduction almost as readily as farmers when revenue of agriculture declines. They are no less important than farm people. As productive agents and consumers in the next generation, their sons and daughters are equally as important as farm youth. Oversight of this group, and the fact that welfare increase cannot be guaranteed unless compensation is awarded all who sacrifice materially, has led to resistance, and likely prohibition, of policy forms which could have been more effective than those used in the 1950's and 1960's, in solving the supply and storage problem of agriculture. In general, townspeople in rural areas resisted and lobbied against regional concentration of the soil bank and conservation reserve because, while it compensated farm people and drew them from agriculture, it lowered income of rural businesses.

The propositions of welfare economics would suppose that under allocations differing from the compensation policies of the 1950's, either (1) fewer funds would have been necessary for complete compensation, with savings available for better educating farm youth and thus generally extending national welfare, or (2) more complete compensation would have been possible from given funds. Townspeople with losses in income, rather than owners of storage facilities (who not only obtain volumes of grain much greater than normal, but also made tremendous return on investment), would have been awarded compensation. Similarly, older farmers who sacrificed income and capital values would have had greater proportion of public funds so allocated while beginning farmers not previously realizing sacrifice, or without large indirect sacrifice from parents and with flexible opportunity of nonfarm employment, would not have been compensated through eligibility as new farmers. Neither would nonfarm individuals have been allowed to buy up land and divert compensation to themselves when it was originally directed to farm families. These are general constructs in farm policy formulation to best allow gains and compensation which guarantee utility gain and guarantee against costs of progress.

Compensation, Poverty and Equity in Income Distribution

Modern welfare economics disavows ability to measure utility, and, hence, to specify redistributions of personal incomes which will optimize the social welfare function. Accordingly it has emphasized change and reorganization which allow more to all individuals concerned or, minimally, with no loss to some and gain to others, and with compensation to those who should actually incur loss. These propositions are axiomatic. In the sense that they specify conditions guaranteeing community welfare increase where utility of individuals is not measurable, they cannot be refuted. They have much applicability for the commercial farm problem which falls in this general category. But they have less applicability for low-income farms which are on the fringe of commercial agriculture, those sharecroppers, mountain farmers and others of the poverty class whose resources are so few that they produce little income. This stratum of agriculture is little affected by major economic reorganization which shifts economic positions between individuals and groups because it produces little for the market. Its problem is not that the absolute position of families in it is lowered by reorganization and change improving the position of others, but only that their income is extremely low and inconsistent with the U.S. standard in any case, and especially under rapid postwar growth in per capita income for the nation.

The two problems are quite different, not only in their case but also in their relevant role in policy formulation. For policy that is compensation-oriented, to redress potential loss from economic change and reorganization, it is consistent that individuals be compensated in line with magnitude of their sacrifice. For this element of policy, it is consistent that a California cotton farmer, with income sacrificed being 100 times that of a Mississippi tenant, should expect to receive compensation of this relative magnitude as compared to the southern farmer. It does not call for limit on magnitude of payment, restricting the California farmer to less than sacrifice and awarding the Mississippian more than his original return. This is not a problem and concern in the optimum distribution of a given income but rather in organization to guarantee that no one is made "worse off." Modern welfare economics offers little specific recommendation on the distribution of a given income, since it does not recognize measurability of utility.

But society has something to say in this respect . A value of American society has never been that income should be distributed equally. To do so would assume identical utility function for all individuals, supposing that exactly an *i*th dollar of income has equal marginal utility for all persons. To do so, too, would result in awards of fixed magnitude to all persons, without incentive in effort and productivity so that marginal outputs are drawn forth to approach the marginal social value of this output, or to match the marginal disutility of effort. Even Russian planners soon found this to be true and scheduled awards to human effort somewhat in the manner of the market. U.S. society has said, at least in its actions, that while it has been willing to embrace the general concept of modern welfare economics in the realm of reorganization and the compensation principle in respect to agricultural policy, it has found negative or pure passiveness interest in respect to equality in income distribution. It has not guaranteed wealth to those who sing while others store the grain, but in general it has held a concept of rough minimum in income and services to which all persons should have some right. It has not made judgment about the exact algebraic nature and magnitude of parameters describing the consumption functions of all individuals, but it has said that the marginal utility of income for persons who have very little must be greater than that of individuals who have very much income. To this extent, it has made quantitative judgment about relative utility of income among individuals. This judgment is reflected in progressive income tax rates, exemption of food from sales taxes in some states, relief food allotments and certain other public legislation.

Income has always been low for a large number of farmers such as those in the Appalachian and Cumberland mountains, and it would have been almost equally low even without progress in the rest of the economy. This problem of equity in income distribution need not be viewed entirely as one apart from possible gains in progress, however. It has been too greatly separated in the past. Consequently, society has not aided sufficiently in development of a large pool of human resources which might otherwise have been possible. Education and other training and guidance facilities in most of the true poverty areas of agriculture have had small investment. This, along with some malnutrition stemming from poverty, has prevented development of human resources which might have added greatly to economic progress. Over the longer run, a higher minimum restraint for educational investment and for personal income, to improve health and human aspiration, can benefit not only individuals falling in the poverty class, but also the consuming society in general. Gain can be mutual, as in moving from m to a point within the Pareto-better area of Figure 8.1, through opening of greater economic opportunity for the former and through expanded supply of skilled and professional manpower to growth products and industries for the latter. One set of policies needs to be directed towards this problem of poverty and potential productivity of human resources, another towards those problems of welfare gains and losses stemming more directly from conscious public policy of economic progress. There are, of course, subsets of policy elements which can be the same, or similar, for the two major segments of agriculture involved.

Poverty in particular sectors of agriculture has existed so long that its initial causes are largely forgotten and unimportant. Some did stem from social change nearly a century back, either as capital assets were wiped out or as individuals had their own labor freed in a restrained market. Others—those in the more mountainous areas—had resources which were comparably adequate in an immature subsistence economy, but entirely inadequate in a mature, growing economy. Smallness of resources and detachment from markets have largely extended incomes into the present which were comparatively adequate decades back. These conditions have prevailed through several generations, and persons suffering first incidence of loss, where change was the cause, are largely gone and can no longer be compensated in any systematic manner. Hence, the current problem is hardly one of recent or ongoing distributions of gains and losses, but largely one of poverty and equity in income distribution.

One question is: Can income be transferred to this group from other sectors to increase total welfare? In earlier days when cardinal utility was supposed, the conscience of welfare economists would have been bothered little in answering this question—had someone made the utility measurements for them. But this problem can be thrown into a context of welfare economics and social policy which is not based on cardinal utility. Given the human resources that are involved and the current product produced by them, can reorganizations be made which provide this group of individuals with gain while maintaining or improving the position of other consumers? It appears that this question can be answered positively. As mentioned previously, here exists a pool of human resources which has had little opportunity, in the markets of previous decades and generations, to contribute to the product of general society. In a similar vein, it has had little opportunity to develop talents and sell them at prices increasing its own income. Research in psychology indicates that the potential of rocket scientists, engineers, biologists, managers and doctors is generally as great for children from this stratum as for those from other strata of society. Investment in education particularly can allow gain to children of this group, while also allowing more product and gain to other groups in an expanding economy.

GENERAL CONCEPTS OF PROGRESS IN RELATION TO NET WELFARE GAINS

Agriculture is not the only industry which has been uprooted in technology and factor employment. A general characteristic of a mature and growing society is shift in its makeup. Under economic progress, some industries expand positively in output and employment. Others decline, either relatively and absolutely. New industries and even new firms arise continuously while others disappear. Managers, investors and labor in new industries frequently realize large windfall profits as well as the high capital gains expected for participation in uncertain adventures. Investors in declining industries see their capital values melt away and laborers see their skills and group status developed in a particular occupation become inapplicable in another. Does net welfare gain always result from these continuous and simultaneous processes of blossoming and withering in labor and investment returns?

If society were certain that the welfare gains to recipients of expected and windfall gains from progress exceeded the losses of those who sacrifice from it, economic expansion could take place with certainty of increased social welfare function, without public policy to provide compensation to the latter group. In a quantitative sense, increased group welfare under chance distribution of gains and losses would hold only under these conditions: The utility function of all individuals is linear and of equal slope or it is known with certainty that those with gain have little income and high utility of money while those with loss have high income and low utility.

Early traditions in societies of market economies either supposed these conditions to prevail, or that the direction and extent of economic change were so differential, infrequent, unpredictable, or uncontrollable that attendant gains or losses might best have incidence as they happen to fall. Thus those with loss from change were expected to bear the incidence. This was never wholly true in U.S. society, since compensation was provided for such minor changes as condemnation of private property for use in public purposes. But for major changes and eruptions, such as those growing out of business fluctuations and economic growth, it was true. The large group of persons who sacrificed from major depressions bore the incidence without compensation from the smaller group that was in a position to invest and gain or to benefit in real income from reduction in price level. Those whose skills and plants were made obsolete by new technical developments or factor market changes were not compensated. But in one of these realms, that of business cycles, societal reflection has changed under the supposition that gains to those in favored position during depression do not outweigh losses to others in unfavorable position. Hence, policy to provide economic stability in this respect is a widely held public goal, just as is emphasis on economic growth to prevent recession and unemployment.

The stability goal itself provides but little controversial base, although agreement on how best to achieve it, as in debate over means of attaining selected farm policy goals, and on some technical problems in economic prediction, is not complete. Unemployment compensation, available during periods of full employment as well as during recession, also can be looked upon as a societal shift to provide redress to those with unpredicted loss from economic change. It is available in short periods to persons thrown out of work by changing technology, as well as those unemployed during recession. Tax write-offs, allowed for capital in certain cases, also fall in this category. Yet the largest public outlay which might best be interpreted as compensation to those suffering losses from economic change has been the funds channeled to agriculture. Evidently society has said that the gains to consumers from greater output and lower price of food are not measurable against the losses to farmers in reduced revenue.

Thus, compensation occurs under a policy wherein the public has a designed program to invest in technology and expand food supply.[7] In other realms where change is induced and implemented through the market, the tradition still calls for gains and losses to fall as they may, except as unemployment compensation and control of the business cycle are provided. If economic change were purely random in its outcome and if welfare gains and losses were strewn randomly over the population, with change of sufficient frequency, compensation to redress losses would be unnecessary to guarantee net community welfare gain in each generation. Under sample of this size or frequency and of random nature, and supposing that the effect of economic change is net welfare gain where business cycles are controlled, all persons would experience loss and gain, but the latter more often or to a greater extent than the former. Hence, net gain would accrue to each person during his life.

But this expanse and randomness of gains and losses of progress do not prevail. Some individuals absorb losses in respect to productive assets and abilities which are not offset through their gains as consumers, or even as producers at later times. While the gains of progress are spread, on the side of asset, to all consumers, they are not always as great, on the liability side, as losses on the side of resources.

Society that values progress for its own sake, or as a means of political and military equality, requires that marginal effort of resources be encouraged in accordance with their endowed ability, and against any disutility accompanying this effort. Against both of these bases, productivity and progress are best encouraged if gains from change do accrue in sufficient magnitude to those who allocate resources and invest capital and effort in a quantity bringing forth change in sufficient magnitude. If gain is the award to those shifting resources and loss is the penalty for those who do not, incentive is great for re-allocations of resources which facilitate change and progress. There are, of course, exceptions to this general condition, mainly those in uncertainty where the prospect of major loss may dampen willingness to select change. Undoubtedly this general framework has added greatly to mobility and migration of resources. Capital and labor made obsolete in some locations and occupations, and bearing the incident of loss, have lessened further potential sacrifice by moving to other alternatives. Where uncertainty has not been too great, resources have been invested in new techniques and commodities leading to progress in order to capture gains forthcoming from these ventures. Dictatorial economies have used less humane means of penalty and less flexible methods of award for change and marginal effort. But they have used them even with loss being the literal magnitude of the individual's head. The necessity of a system in relative awards has not yet found substitute in promoting progress in any type of social organization.

---

[7] For an early discussion of the distribution of gains and losses from technical development of agriculture, see Earl O. Heady, "Basic Welfare Considerations in Farm Technological Advance" *Jour. Farm Econ.* 1947

Yet what are the purposes of progress? For progress itself as an intrinsic end? Progress is not an ultimate end. It is only a means to other ends. As a means, it is expected to lead to greater utility and welfare through growth in income and consumption possibilities. Even if progress were pursued alone for purposes of world military and political comparability, it would still serve as a means. But we have greater eventual hope for humanity than progress alone as a means of world comparability. Supposing it to serve as a means for income growth and welfare betterment, it is important that a system of awards for resource re-allocations and commitments leading to progress and change be retained.

The system of distribution of welfare gains and losses in whatever manner they fall, more so in history than at present, but even greatly so now, has led to progress. Few persons would question that it has contributed to net or community welfare gain, especially if we ignore inter-generation comparisons. Yet it cannot be proven that this distribution of gains and losses leads to maximum community welfare. Net or larger community welfare gain could be better guaranteed and incentive to progress still assured under policy which allows shift of resources to new areas of demand but still provides compensation to individuals with loss incidence. It is not necessary that compensation be either passive or of a nature tying resources to their present employment. To the contrary, if it gives sufficient attention to value orientations and cultural moorings and is of appropriate magnitude, it can still redress all losses and more readily bring resources into employments meshing with consumer preferences.

The number, location, nature and effect of changes and progress elements in the American economy are so varied that gains and losses are not easily identified and measured. Some changes, especially those of smaller impact, do have a "balancing out" effect to nearly all members of the population (on the side of resource returns or as gains on the consumer side balancing losses on the producer and resource side). For other changes, where some individuals are left with small losses, the judgement is made that these are too small to be measurable and any force assigned to numerical expression of them would be too costly.

But there are major changes where this clearly is not the case. For these situations, too, it is obvious that those bearing the burden of loss cannot simply wait until a change brings gain, with the latter more than offsetting the former. Some localities have experienced mostly loss from change and they remain as decaying economic and social communities. The pain has not been sudden, soon to be over, killed with a blast of gains from development. It has persisted, both with important misery to people of these communities and potential gain sacrificed by other segments of society. Mammoth illustrations of sacrificing communities and their attendant welfare losses exist. Some have persisted since the Civil War. Others are more recent in change giving rise to their origin but are rapidly becoming chronic. The depressed areas of former mining and textile centers are examples. So are many rural communities which are dependent on agriculture, and more will thus develop as technology progresses and adjustment of people is sluggish. While change need bear no loss to youth and but little loss to young persons of flexibility in capacities and skills, it does provide burden to older persons in farm communities whose skills and values have become extremely rigid.

Few elements of change and progress can occur in a market economy without bringing losses to some persons as they bring gains to others. Some of the losses, as indicated above, are small and spread thinly so that they are acceptable and conventional (the assumption of positive-sum game) and can be borne by those upon whom they fall from the market. Others can be large and persistent, hanging to people and communities for decades.

As uneven distributions of gains and loss from economic growth have occurred in the past, they will be so distributed by the market and somewhat unpredictable nature of economic growth over the future. The uneven first distribution is not, however, a basis for doing away with the market as a mechanism for expression of consumer preference and as a force pulling relative factor supplies in the direction of change. It is yet to be proved that any other allocating method is as efficient as the market in promoting growth in a highly mature and complex economy where the consumer is given major autonomy, even given the imperfections and lags that exist and the ability of some groups to transfer a disproportionate share of the gains in their direction.

But just as the market provides flexibility and guidance in this sense, it is known to have imperfections in guaranteeing attainment of welfare goals and maximization. As mentioned previously, society need not take the market as its master or as transcendental in character. It has not done so, adapting institutions and mechanisms to modify its effects, as illustrated in the early socialization of agricultural research, public investment in schools, monetary and fiscal policy to arrest depressions, unemployment compensation, progressive income taxation, public roads and others. As the economy grows and becomes capable of even greater strength in progress, policy to spread the gains of progress equitably comes to have increased importance. The commercial farm problem itself is not one of hungry people unable to pay taxes. It is not even one of low living standard. It is one of relative rate of progress in income.

When we speak of the market as an allocative mechanism, we refer to the private sector and allocation in the choice realm of the individual consumer. When consumers are miserable with cold, hunger and sickness, any planner who alleviates these almost certainly can cause resources to be used in a manner preferable to the mass of consumers. But when consumers have abundance in these areas, plus many others which were considered luxuries a quarter century earlier, the choice and allocating mechanism needs to be flexible, as perhaps it can only be through the pricing system. Still, there remains the essential function of social policy causing appropriate quantities of resources to be allocated to the public sector in a manner aiding the maximization of community welfare where it is certain that the distribution of gains and losses is not otherwise positive-sum, or that the allocations so attained still allow further movement to Pareto optimality.

Even with ironclad rules enforcing pure competition in all industries, it is yet to be proven that the pricing system would have provided adequate facilities for education, defense, public roads, agricultural research and other services produced in the public sector. The social decision in obtaining an optimum balance of resources between the public and private sectors is of no less importance than that of utility-maximizing allocations within the private sector. The maxims of "the least government the better" or "the most public planning the better" provide no logical basis for allocations directed at social welfare maximization, or in assuring distribution of gains of progress with some benefit to all individuals.

BASIS FOR AGRICULTURAL POLICY

Agriculture does not have a basis for policy unique from all other sectors of society. More nearly, the problem is broad policy to encompass agriculture as well as other sectors which have similar types of problems and are faced with welfare loss from the same category of variables in change and progress. In some cases, as in market power, the challenge is not one of finding a distinct policy for agriculture but more nearly to give it the same basis as other sectors, if this is to be looked upon as a problem in equity, or as a method of assuring Pareto optimality in the sense that all groups realize gain from change or that one does not gain at the expense of the other.

Policies for commercial agriculture have appeal and basis in compensation to redress losses stemming from change which brings gain to other groups. The major "other group" includes all consumers. In the manner explained previously, the nation has a positive development policy to augment the supply and lower the real price of food. Farm families in aggregate have less income than would prevail with smaller supply. Yet the problem is basically the same as that of depressed communities once important in fabrication of fuel and textiles but now passed over as a result of substitutes which augment total supply. The latter groups, no less than agriculture, merit compensation if net community welfare gain is to be guaranteed.

But what form should this take? Should substitute locations and materials be neutralized so that change is not invoked in the original community? Should the public provide a market for New England textiles and West Virginia coal, investing in immense warehouse facilities with never-ending restraint on surplus stocks? Is it a basic social value that compensation can be provided these depressed areas only through policy which keeps resources directed to textiles and coal? Few economists or industry leaders would answer positively to these questions. But some would if the term agriculture were substituted. Still, are there not more efficient means for compensation of welfare losses to these particular groups? Can sacrifices be offset by means which guarantee that the first recipients are made no worse off, or with positive opportunity for gain for them in other segments of the economy which are characterized by growth?

Other Policy Bases

The above analysis provides the major basis for agricultural policy, just as it does for economic policy in general. If we examine these foundations, we find the case of agriculture to be not generally unique, but to parallel that of the total economy where the same problems exist with wider spread. Where a particular policy element is needed for the subset of farm problems, within the matrix of general economic problems, it generally has its counterpart in national policy. It might be claimed that policy is needed for agriculture for purposes apart from those mentioned above. What about economic development? Economic development policy is itself the process of reorganization to allow greater product and welfare. It is accepted policy for agriculture, the claims of the farm industry to compensation being based on its distribution of gains and losses.

What about market and bargaining power? These are mechanisms of policy, placed in the hands of groups to help guarantee that equitable shares of progress flow to each, in attempt to be certain that no group is made worse off as change and reorganization are brought about. Bargaining and market power is somewhat the antithesis of pure competition, a condition necessary if community welfare is to be lifted to the very maximum. But since Pareto welfare economics propositions do not attempt to state exactly which distribution and organization provides a unique maximum, but only those changes which will certainly increase the community level of utility, it is not required (even if scale economies were lacking) that the organization of industries be revamped, converting the structure of steel, petroleum, electrical equipment and farm machinery to the pure competition structure of agriculture. Industry structure is a problem of national policy, and not of farm policy. It is doubted whether farm policy is the pole from which attack on this problem should be launched. As mentioned previously, the political power of agriculture is now too small to bowl over the established position of major industry and labor groups in their acquired market power.

Supposing the structure of industry and labor groups to be given, as it certainly is considering their political strength, and serving as means where one group averts loss from gain to another or a sharing of fruits of progress so that each has positive gain, a policy question becomes that of whether agriculture should also permanently abandon the pure competition model—as an industry of completely ineffective individuals taking price and particular sharing of progress as given. Certainly there is no economic or other logic which says that agriculture must be a "pure price taker," if aggregate welfare increase is to be guaranteed under economic growth and technical change.

In other words, if we take as given that industry organization is mixed, with market power in the hands of one group so that they can bargain and alter price but pure competition and lack of control over price is the lot of a second group, organization of the second group to give it bargaining power to guarantee either (1) that it does not sacrifice from change or (2) that it gains along with the other group, is entirely consistent with welfare propositions and attainment of either Pareto optimality or Pareto-better welfare conditions.

The development of bargaining power is a policy implicitly approved in welfare economics where lack of bargaining power of one group must be taken as given and conditions of the market, such as price elasticity of demand less than unity, cause agriculture to sacrifice at the gain of other groups which have market power. And it is true, as pointed out previously, that agriculture must take the structure of certain other sectors as given. It does not have the political force to convert them back to a pure competition structure.

It is the presence of some monopoly in the economy (or industry structure which leads to market power, price control and sheltered advantage in short-run resource productivity) which causes the marginal conditions for maximum social welfare to be somewhat obviated. Given some extent of monopoly power or its near relative in nonprice competition, relative factor returns are not a clear short-run indication for resource allocation. And as Galbraith points out, losses from a suboptimal allocation of resources stemming from a degree of monopoly may not have great social significance in the private and consumer oriented sector with a level of income and degree of affluence which leads it to ask what its marginal preferences are.

Of course, we can always argue that imposition of pure competition structure on all industries provides a logical basis for welfare greater than that possible under the best organization in a mixed economy. So that this is true, of course, we would have to be certain that while industries are matched to the competition mold, they did not have other imperfections attached to them. Galbraith has emphasized that the competitive nature of the bituminous coal industry did not lead to progress in this sector, but the petroleum industry, characterized by oligopoly rather than pure competition, has been progressive and efficient.[8] Not only must the mixed structure of the economy be taken as given by an industry such as agriculture, but also the expectation that economic change or progress would be much faster or as great under a complete economy of pure competition, as represented by breaking the steel and electrical equipment industry into more small firms, is perhaps misleading.

The existence of mixed organization and some sectors with short-run control over commodity prices does not obviate the major pulls of the price system and competition under economic growth. One industry, such as the electrical equipment industry which cannot be characterized by

---

[8] J. K. Galbraith, *American Capitalism, The Concept of Countervailing Power*, Houghton-Mifflin Co., Boston, 1952, p. 92.

pure competition, can serve to bid scientists and materials away from another such as the oil industry, and spur both on to progress. Perhaps the main essential in progress is maintenance of "workable competition" and prevention of monopoly excesses.[9] Pure competition, in attachment with certain market imperfections, has not led to progress-oriented utilization of the human resources found on farms in the Appalachian Mountain area, or even in efficient farming thereon.

It could be argued, of course, that if pure competition prevailed, greater factor price flexibility would exist, thus obviating many of the losses stemming from economic change and the need for policy applying the compensation principle. Change might bring short, sharp pains, but flexibility of factor prices would cause resources immediately to be re-employed so that prolonged maladies of losses could be avoided. The short-term losses might then be insignificant as compared to the long-term gains of all individuals. A small-scale model of this type exists in agriculture. It is the commodity cycle touching on such products as feed and hogs. True, prices are flexible and as change or large outputs occur, price plummets and resources respond. As feeds are low, they become employed in animal production. Employment of these resources does follow prices and there is never lack of a market for them. Yet this degree of pure competition, price flexibility and factor employment does not eliminate short-run loss of important magnitude to many individuals.

Economic and technical development of a long-term nature also is accompanied by great adaptation in prices and employment of resources in agriculture. Witness how technical improvement has increased feed output, with the latter responding in price and employment in livestock production (except to the extent of supply restrained by government storage). Wage rates of family labor also have been flexible, people remaining employed in agriculture almost at whatever price they could earn. While competition and flexibility have led to heavy resource employment, it has not obviated losses and frustration to many people, not alone because of inflexibilities elsewhere in the economy but also because of the general market imperfections which typically attach to industries of pure competition.

SOCIAL EVALUATION AND CHOICE

Society can and does make choice and distributions which involve judgment of interpersonal utility quantities. Some of these are ethical judgments made in the realm of the political and democratic process. In some cases, the choice is sharp and clear and a great deal of economic analysis is not needed or desired, the height of the two utility surfaces between which choice is made being apparent, and refined calculations and detailed logic to provide proof would only slow down the process. In other cases, elevation is attained on a particular surface, with a plateau

[9] See J. M. Clark, "Toward a Concept of Workable Competition," *Amer. Econ. Rev.*, June, 1940.

approached so that loss is small when alternative decisions are tried, with policies frequently reversing themselves. Measurement of gains and losses thus have empirical expression as one policy is tried, its satisfaction or solutions weighed, then another is tried with perhaps eventual swing back to the first.[10]

This is the political process. The process takes this apparent lumbering and meandering course, not necessarily because it is inefficient or inapplicable, but because it is the only means which a democratic society has for rough quantitative assessment of gains and losses. One policy may represent two steps up the utility surface, its replacement a step down. This is the political process which eventually allows expression of greater attainment in community welfare.

Much of agricultural policy has necessarily fallen in this process of trial and error, try and retry, because relevant quantities are not given *a priori* and in errorless estimates. It is possible and frequently true that one policy can be chosen through the political process, with later discovery that an alternative voted down, or a former policy voted out, is socially estimated to provide greater community utility. If, under majority rule, the gain to some individuals was always equal absolutely to the loss of others, this experimentation in policy to maintain or increase public welfare would be unnecessary, and an optimum policy could be adopted at the first try. However, where different persons have varying intensity in their preference for alternatives, an alternative can be selected by vote which does not maximize group utility, because the loss per person for the minority group is greater than the gain per person for the majority group.

[10] A first choice, specified by majority at the polls, need not necessarily be the one leading to higher, or highest, utility. For an explanation of such situations, see K. A. Arrow, *Social Choice and Individual Values*, Wiley & Sons, New York, 1951.

9

Games, Goals and Political Processes

Few industries have been as blessed as agriculture in willingness of society to develop and invest in special policy for it. As explained in Chapter 1, U.S. society first acquired and distributed land resources to farmers at favorable prices, without similar action for capital plant of other industries. At restraint of land resources, it invested further in developmental policy for agriculture, turning to socialization of research and adult educational facilities as a means of extending agricultural supply. With initial high return and great extended success of these efforts, supply has pushed hard on demand, with consumers benefiting greatly in food prices and resources freed to other sectors. Society then turned to compensation policies, with price supports and direct payments, to redress losses to farmers arising from the smaller revenue of extended supply. Evidently it supposed positive-sum effects in utility to be possible in development of agriculture, but that the initial distribution of gains and losses did not guarantee aggregate welfare increase unless development was accompanied by compensation. Some general conditions of modern welfare economics have indeed been enacted with vigor and willingness by American society. Compensation payments have been large in both time and monetary quantity. Still, however, farm problems of important magnitude exist. Why is this so?

Structural imbalances underlying agriculture are not lacking in physical and economic means of solution. A large number of persons can suggest several means by which these problems might be erased, either temporarily or permanently. The difficulty has not been in possible solutions but in agreement on policy means for solution. Conflict arises because of differences in goals and values of individuals and groups in respect to farm policy. General society has been less directly involved in this conflict than have groups within and around agriculture. Society, kind in magnitude of funds appropriated for solution, has questioned less whether they should be provided, but more why they have not been used better in eliminating the problem.

Agriculture is not a subsociety made up of individuals and groups with identical indifference maps and values. Apparently, too, from previous disagreement within the industry, on policy means and ends, not all possible exchanges in policy alternatives are predicted directly to bring mutual gains, as in movement from point *m* in Figure 8.1 to a point on the contract curve within the shaded area. The sharpness of conflict over the type of policy suggests a point on the contract curve, movement from which would improve the position of one group and lessen that of another. The alternatives in policy choice often involve issues such as more or less price support as against less or more of freedom from supply restraints, or of more or fewer farms as against more or less control over the market. In this sense, they are alternatives which can be exchanged, as for X and Z in Figure 8.1.

Perhaps the alternatives are too often viewed in two dimensions, such as free markets versus price supports without consideration of "third dimension of trade" and compensation which would allow exchanges making all groups better off. It is likely that policy choices have been placed too much in a "black and white" context, without enough alternatives allowed so that negative-sum utility outcomes are averted. Or, is it possible that all policy possibilities must have negative-sum or zero-sum outcomes? The farm policy debate of the 1950's would lead to this appearance; that inability exists for trades which allow mutual gain, or that gain to one which causes loss to another cannot be offset even by compensation from "outside society." But trades, the equivalent of the side payments mentioned later, are typical in much of agricultural policy. These trades perhaps are more apparent within the different groups which make up a single farm organization than between major farm organizations. For example, there is little homogeneity between farm organization members in the Cotton South, irrigated areas of the West and wheat areas of the Great Plains. But they are willing to belong to the same organization and often support, through their congressmen, votes for each other's interests and "live together" in harmony through trades among public appropriations for water and support prices, or protection of sugar quotas. Trades as the equivalent of side payments are not inconsistent with welfare maximization, the movement to successive Pareto-better positions improving welfare level for the several groups involved, and democratic process in the extent that they allow better indication of intensity of preferences by particular groups.

HETEROGENEITY IN INTEREST AND VALUES

Differences in values or indifference maps do not themselves preclude policy and other organization which leaves all better off or in preferred position. In Figure 8.1, for example, it is unnecessary for indifference maps to have the same slopes along vectors originating from the origin of the plane. If a nonoptimal point such as *m* exists, one farm group which prefers more freedom might obtain such by transfer of more price support or direct subsidy money to a second group which accepts less freedom or vice versa. If movement from *m* to points within the shaded area is attained, both groups gain and greater community utility is assured. In effect, this method has been explored in soil bank policy wherein some producers gave up part or all of their ability to produce farm products while others were not given payments and were allowed complete freedom in production. Many alternatives such as this do exist and perhaps need to be explored or applied more widely for attaining progress in farm policy. It is not only possible, in policy stalemate, for opposing groups to be at points on the contract curve, but also choices may not be of the continuous nature of Figure 8.1. In the latter case, the choices are of "either or" and "fork in the road" nature, being mutually exclusive. If one is chosen, the other must be rejected in entirety. Choices in this category more nearly fall in the ideological realm and outside continuous opportunity in degree of substitution and combination. Examples are the institution of slavery, and concept or not of a particular god. Some of the extreme statements on free or supported price for agriculture might appear to fall in this realm.

Conflicting Groups for Policy

General conflict in policy is perhaps less that of ideological nature, however, and more that of position along a contract curve so that economic gain to one group means loss to another in the particular ends pursued. A maze of conflicting groups exists. Some have made trades in policy elements, as between regional commodity groups allowing different types of control restraints or shifts among crops. Often, too, these trades have allowed mutual gain in price supports and ability to produce other crops, but with the effect that the policy goal of restrained output has been violated. In other cases, position on the contract curve apparently would not allow this type of bargaining, and the situation has been more or less stalemated.

Conflicting groups within and surrounding agriculture are many. They do not necessarily have opposing value systems in respect to preference for more income, religion, the virtues of farm and city life in general or relative preference among items of family consumption. More frequently, it is likely that conflict arises because policy which increases income of one group decreases that of another. Milk producers in New England may sacrifice as support prices provide gain to grain producers in the Midwest. The established farmer with ample capital and large-scale livestock production may lose as the beginning farmer emphasizing cash grain production gains under price supports and public storage. Conversely, the livestock producer may gain and the grain farmer may lose from developmental events leading to growing yields and output accompanied by lower feed prices. Conflict over income effects of policy also exists between farm groups such as: cotton producers in the Southwest against those in the Southeast; cattle producers in the intermountain states against farmers in the Cornbelt who may shift from grain to grass; wheat producers, in respect to two-price plans, against corn farmers; large farmers against small farmers; those who would be squeezed out by free market prices against those who would remain and expand; and others.

Similarly, sectors which sell inputs to or buy outputs from farms conflict in interest with farmers, or each other, in respect to income effects of different policies. A policy of high support prices for feed grains with unrestricted acreage and public purchase of excess production is favorable to the fertilizer industries. The same policy is favorable to the grain storage sector, although it may conflict with the interests of the exporting industry. Policies which retire land in whole farms in concentrated blocks are against the economic interests of merchants in rural areas. Programs to reduce grain acreage conflict with interest of seed corn producers; those retiring land permanently, as against rotation fashion, conflict with interests of grass seed producers. Lime producers and earth movers favor programs of direct subsidy for farm practices, while some farm groups vigorously resist direct payments. Other conflicts could be cited. Not all of the groups represented in these conflicts stand idly by as policy is being formulated, but exert extreme effort to push it in the direction of their interest.

Conflicts also can and do exist between farm policy and national policy, or between the consumer's willingness to contribute tax money for farm subsidies and the desire of agricultural segments for it. In national conflict, the practice of camouflaging surplus disposal under international development programs may slow the speed at which the nation is able to aid in promoting growth in less-developed countries. In more recent years, farm policy has come into sharper conflict with other national policies because of magnitude of drain on the public treasury. Policy means may be altered accordingly for farming.

It is within this framework of conflicting interests that agricultural policy must be formulated. Interests of the various agricultural groups are more heterogeneous than for other major industry groups which join forces in uniform front to obtain legislation favorable to their particular economic interest. It is not at all certain that the various agricultural groups look upon themselves as a total community, nor that they have the common interest of devising a policy to increase the aggregate welfare of the community of subgroups. Apparently some would be willing to accept negative-sum outcomes for the community if goals of their own groups were attained in sufficient magnitude.[1]

[1] Numerous analyses have been undertaken which deal with problems of utility measurement and outcome under various voting and public choice mechanisms. These emphasize the problems of preference summation and selection of public actions which do or do not guarantee an increase in community welfare: Duncan Black, *The Theory of Committees and Elections*, Cambridge University Press, Cambridge, 1958; K. J. Arrow, *Social Choice and Individual Values*, Wiley and Sons, New York, 1951; Corrine Hoexter, *Does the Majority Ever Rule?* Portfolio and Art News Annual, 1961; Wm. Vickery, "Utility, Strategy and Social Decision Rules," *Quar. Jour. Econ.*, Vol. 74; R. D. Luce, *Individual*

Goal Conflicts and Equity Versus Compensation

Some conflict among farm organizations is over the goals of policy elements. One such conflict is over the magnitudes of payment or price subsidy which should be allowed individual farmers. One organization has argued that size of payments should not be limited but should be in proportion to size of operations. Another organization has argued that absolute ceilings should be placed on payments, with a greater proportion of the income transfers from general society going to small and low income farmers. This conflict arises because of failure to distinguish sufficiently between the policy goals of (1) compensation to assure that aggregate welfare outcome, resulting from the distribution of gains and losses under economic change, is not zero sum and (2) equity in the distribution of income and in providing greater equality of opportunity for persons in highly disadvantageous position. Policy elements for the two should not be confused. Public funds allocated for purposes of compensation should not be restrained to absolute limit, but should be in proportion to sacrifice in income from change (a magnitude highly synonomous with scale of operations). Funds for equity purposes should indeed be retrogressive with income and scale of operations. The two policy goals might best have clear distinction in the form of payment used, payments for both being relevant in a sense of maximizing society welfare.

Conflict in Means and Merging With Ends

Farm policy conflict is perhaps less over ultimate ends and more over means to attain particular ends. Most groups agree that farm surplus buildup should be eliminated or prevented. But the method of attaining this intermediate end itself gives rise to policy conflict. The conflict may grow out of true differences in values, or because income of various groups will be affected differentially. The buildup and costs of stocks during the 1950's, for example, could have been eliminated through either strict marketing quotas or free market prices. Incomes could be supplemented by either direct payments or support prices and public storage. Income per farm can be increased by the alternative means of (1) fewer people in agriculture, (2) public supply control or (3) subsidies of direct, or price support nature. Conflict and debate over means such as these often has been sharp, more so than over the ends or objectives to which they lead. The means themselves become intermediate ends, over which there is disagreement because of difference in values or economic interests.

This is a general development in social policy and organization: Once established, means have a tendency to become ends. Or the means and ends become intertwined and it is difficult for the public to distinguish between them. In general, ends and means of policy are not discrete. Neither do they, at various levels in the means-ends hierarchy, serve en-

---

Choice Behavior, Wiley and Sons, New York, 1959; Murray Kemp and A. Asimakopolos, "A Note on Social Welfare Functions and Cardinal Utility," *Canad. Jour. Econ. and Polit. Sci.*, Vol. 18; and Leo Goodman and Harry Markowitz, "Social Welfare Functions Based on Individual Rankings," *Amer. Jour. Soc.*, Vol. 58.

tirely at the extremes of discrete alternatives with zero substitution rates, or as continuous opportunities with constant substitution rates.

Even for an individual or group with a particular indifference map or set of values, the problem is not one of determining which discrete goal or end should be selected over another or all others. Instead, it is a problem of determining, at the various levels in the means-ends hierarchy, what mix or combination of goals is optimum, desirable or acceptable. This is true since the value system of an individual, community or society is not represented by an indifference map wherein the individual indifference curve is linear, denoting that each unit gain towards one goal causes an equal sacrifice in satisfaction for all units of other goals foregone. Instead the indifference lines serving as the counterpart of social values in respect to goals for public policy are curved, denoting that a combination of competing goals or ends is necessary for maximizing quantities which are relevant both for the individual and the community. Under these conditions, except for purely ideological or "black and white" alternatives, one goal is seldom selected to the exclusion of all others. Instead there exists some combination of competing goals, with some of one being sacrificed to gain part of another, with decision of the optimum mix to be decided by society.

The public, however, often has no particularly systematic method for articulating goals and values or means and ends so that they stand out apart from each other or in form for clear choice. Frequently it does not know that one mean or end conflicts with another. Just as often, it has no clear prediction or knowledge of consequence in using a particular policy element as a means towards a particular goal. Sometimes it has not had prior knowledge that a particular action program would intensify the problem it was attempting to solve, as in the cases of surpluses relative to support prices and unlimited corn acreage. Accordingly, major conflicts exist in the means used and the ends pursued. Sometimes public administrators are not even aware of conflicts which exist between two policies or ends. The developmental and compensation policies since the 1930's are examples. On the one hand, society has invested heavily in agricultural development and output increase through partial payments for inputs under the label of conservation practices, through land reclamation and through research and education. On the other hand, it has paid farmers directly for reducing land input and restraining supply. Education and information, or a third policy construct, can eliminate these inconsistencies in policy accomplishments, but much less so the conflicts growing out of values and interest positions along a contract curve.

Conflicts in Beliefs

Conflicts do grow out of lack of knowledge and could be partially alleviated with greater education and information. This is true in the area of beliefs, where particular conditions are thought to be true. Some sectors of agriculture believe competition to be the dominant organization of American economy; some believe monopoly and market power through collective action to be the dominant structure. One belief evidently held is that economies of scale are limited in agriculture, and that free market prices would not lead to elimination of family farms through growth of large-scale units operated by hired labor. Another belief supposes scale economies to be great and claims that policy is necessary to protect survival of the family farm. Somewhat widely it is believed that democracy in society can be best safeguarded by maintaining a family farm and large portion of the population in agriculture. Other people have pointed to European and Asiatic evidence suggesting the opposite. (Democracy is the prevailing form of society in the labor-industrial complex of Great Britain, but has not persisted in the agrarian complexes of Eastern Europe.) Empirical evidence needs to be extended and established in order that such conflicting beliefs can be reconciled, with selection of those which square with facts.

Facts, where they can be readily established, and education can be extremely useful in clearing up those policy conflicts based on (1) lack of articulation among means and ends, (2) ranges over which means and ends are inconsistent and competitive, (3) the consequences of particular means, in quantitative result in particular ends, or in undesired side effects and (4) inconsistent beliefs about particular states of facts or relationships. Research and education, and particularly the latter, have too often failed to provide the public with sufficient knowledge in these areas. Empirical and logical knowledge can provide a basis for solutions of differences which grow out of different beliefs and misinformation. It cannot, however, do so for those that stem from basic value conflicts relating in an ethical sense to states which "ought to exist."

True Value Conflicts and Policy Structures

Conflict prevails even if all persons and groups have the same values represented by identical indifference maps, as long as some prefer increase in their income and collection of goods at the expense of others. As mentioned previously, if the two sets of indifference curves in Figure 8.1 are identical, conflict still prevails along the contract line. However, conflicts also grow out of differences in values per se, where the choices are not continuous substitution opportunities but represent distinct "either or" choices. Policy takes on configuration accordingly. Some arguments in agricultural policy over free market prices versus support prices and bargaining power may fall near this pole, although they may still involve income conflicts along the contract line. (Free market prices are more favorable to income increase for one group of farmers while support and bargained prices are more favorable for another group.)

While true value conflicts may give rise to policy stalemates, value orientations also may lead to particular policy constructs. There are many examples. The orientation of policy to family farms, excluding large-scale operations based on hired labor, rests partly on a foundation in early values. The large treasury costs of storing surpluses from previous years could have been eliminated simply by touching a match to grain stocks, or dumping them in the ocean. Yet farmer and society abhorrence of waste prevented this solution of costly surplus stocks. Conservation has such great public appeal in "goodness" that numerous policy elements have borne this label, even though some had no important relationship to extending the time services of resource and others shifted production from the future to the present. These value orientations highly favoring policy elements which lead to "efficiency," and firmly opposing those which lead to "waste," perhaps all fall under Brewster's work ethic.[2] The value-based expression that man should be compensated for his contribution to society perhaps causes subsidies to become cloaked under farm improvement practices rather than as direct payments. The value judgements implied in Brewster's democratic creed "(1) all men are of equal worth and dignity and (2) none, however wise or good, is wise enough to have dictatorial power over another,"[3] perhaps serve to restrain one group related to farming from being able to impose completely its values and wishes on others, although this may result mainly from checks and blocks in the political process.

GENERALIZED GOALS

The goals of American society were largely those of agriculture a century back. The population was mainly on farms. Rapidly, however, the value structure of agriculture is becoming that of society. This trend will continue. Farm people, while retaining some values dissimilar to those of society in total, now have the same general desires, goals and aspirations as the rest of society. This condition holds true, especially for commercial agriculture because (1) communication media are widespread and effective, providing a greater common denominator of knowledge and preferences, (2) the income, at least of commercial farmers, has risen to levels which cause relevant goals no longer to be oriented directly towards overcoming the arduousness of farm life, isolation, and inadequate shelter and nutrition in the hinterlands and (3) agriculture now has such a small proportion of the total population.

Farm youth generally have the same preferences as urban youth, this force causing younger persons to have large mobility to industry and urban centers. The appeal associated with urban-centered conveniences and related goods and services binds the values and aspirations of farm people closer to those of the city. For this reason, stemming from economic growth and its reshaping of preferences and population, policy of agriculture needs to become less unique to the specific industry and more in general conformance to the economic and social structure which faces families and firms in the farm industry.

Policy of the 1950's focused too much on industry structure and value differences which existed in the past. To make farm policy consistent with more general economic and value structure would mean, for example, that the industry be provided with powers of the market in the

---

[2] J. M. Brewster, "The Impact of Technical Advance and Migration on Agricultural Society and Policy," *Jour. Farm Econ.*, Vol. 41.

[3] Brewster, *ibid.*

hands of other major economic groups, but that income supplementation conform more to current consumer preferences, production technology and factor prices. Policy since 1930 has been bent to a structure of agriculture existing at the turn of the century and to a set of problems characterized by the major depression of the 1930's. (Depression has not prevailed in most of the years, during which policy borrowed from the 1930's has been the focus.) It is time that policy be brought abreast of the times in farm value orientation, and in economic structure and growth. There should be greater separation of elements aimed at (1) equity in income distribution and human opportunity (2) compensation to guarantee welfare increase under the pattern of gains and losses growing out of economic progress and (3) general economic fluctuations. (But this clarification of policy is possible only under a clarification of goals.)

Steps in Generality of Goals

Goals can be identified which conform with generalized values of society and have high acceptance throughout the population. Some of the more generalized goals of American society and other societies, where states are selected to represent the individual, include these: (1) progress in the availability of goods and services or real income with increased effectiveness of resources and rate at which product can be transformed from them, (2) equity in the distribution of income and economic opportunity, (3) equity in sharing the fruits of economic progress, (4) security and stability of a national economic enterprise in the sense of freedom from fluctuations growing out of major depression and weather instability, (5) maintenance of an internally and democratically selected social system and protection of it from competing systems, (6) freedom of choice in the degree consistent with health, level of desired progress, equity and stability and (7) opportunity for upcoming generations consistent with progress and individual abilities.

These diverse generalized goals have wide acceptance by U.S. society. But taken together, each does not have equal intensity of preference at all levels of attainment. As they are attained in varying degree, the marginal utility of further increment in some declines relative to others. Hence, at a point in time, one particular goal takes on particular urgency but, as it is attained in greater positive level, another takes on greater marginal urgency for increase. They do, however, serve as relevant criteria for over-all and specific policy. But goodness of policy cannot be measured entirely in the extent to which it furthers any one of these specific goals. This is true since the generalized goals are themselves competitive beyond some level of attainment. Complete freedom can interfere with progress for the system as a whole, where the community appraisal of goals to be attained is not the aggregation of individual preferences when all individuals operate separately. Progress itself can be at rates which conflict with freedom. The individual is not allowed the freedom of robbery, or even of driving up the wrong side of the highway, because the equity of others, either in capital possessions or life, would be violated.

In a broad manner, the several generalized goals above can be summarized into a single one of even greater generality in the sense of aggregation but of more particular sense in its reference to the individual. The above goals are held by democratic society, largely to protect the dignity of the individual and to provide him with fullest opportunity in line with his abilities. If U.S. society had unique character in its creation by the constitution and in subsequent public decisions, it has been in this emphasis on individuals. Progress itself is an instrumental goal or end, as a means to other ends which relate to all individuals. Progress, or its common synonym of efficiency, in the physical context of more factories, more commercial airlines or more corn per acre, has no intrinsic value. It has value only as it creates opportunity for the individual, allows expression of his consumer characteristics and does not lessen his dignity and outlook. Freedom, in the sense of behavior of institutions, markets and individuals, which closes opportunities and reduces dignity of other persons, or does not provide them with education for expression of their abilities, lacks positive contribution to this one generalized goal or purpose.

The several generalized goals mentioned above often are involved in specific policy, but seldom provide the "working data" used or required in coming to grips with a particular economic problem of the smaller scale found in agriculture. They do serve as general criteria on which policy can be evaluated and directed. But they are too broad and general to have great content in formulating specific policy elements. Even at this level of generalization, however, agreement could not be obtained by all sectors on farm policy.

While all farm groups undoubtedly agree on liberty for society, as freedom for the nation to govern without interference by an outside country, they do not agree similarly on complete liberty in production and marketing decisions. On the one hand, some organized groups strongly insist that more freedom of decision be retained or returned in the farm industry. But just as vigorously, other groups campaign for more control over production and marketing. Selected farm groups have democratically voted production controls, marketing orders and other degree of sacrifice in liberty of decisions. Farm commodity groups which serve as examples are milk, wheat, tobacco and fruits and vegetables. But even farmers who are homogeneous in the sense of deriving income from cattle do not agree in respect to degree of decision liberty. Cattle ranchers stump strongly for freedom while dairy farmers in major milk sheds willingly accept quotas and marketing orders.

At a somewhat lower level in generalization are the more mechanical goals of economics. Two general goals, directed toward maximization of utility or satisfaction by society, are efficiency in production and efficiency in consumption—the optimum allocation of resources and income respectively among persons, commodities, time periods and locations. Criteria exist, in the marginal terms outlined earlier, as a means of specifying sub-goals or conditions which must exist if these two general economic goals are to be attained. At another step down the ladder of generalization, we have the goals of economic progress, equity and stability, as held by society. They are "less strenuous" than the goals for optimum economic organization in the sense that they do not require the "tight" marginal conditions associated with the over-all rules for economic organization. Society may simply define the degree to which these goals are desirable, or failure to attain them is undesirable. The maximum level may not be spelled out and only minimum restraints are exercised accordingly through social policy.

Evidently most individual publics or groups which make up U.S. society desire economic progress. Yet we have no evidence that the maximum rate of economic growth is desired. Most economists could mention a dozen ways in which obstacles to progress would be lessened and the rate of economic growth accelerated. Greater public investment in education, improved counseling and employment services, aid to underdeveloped communities, elimination of feather-bedding and particular monopoly restraints in use of technologies and longer work weeks are examples. Still we accept a less-than-maximum rate of growth, even though economic progress is an obvious national purpose, because it is not an ultimate goal and is not valued discretely at a higher level than all other goals. Too, while American society has reflected a goal of some equity in income distribution, it has not tried to maximize this goal. Rather it more nearly has tried to provide a minimum in level and availability of consumption opportunities.

Another step down the ladder of goal generality is represented by goals rooted in economics, political structure and sociology and tied directly to farming. These include preservation of the family farm and the Jeffersonian doctrine of a large rural population to insure democracy. But again, while society may have accepted such specific goals for agriculture, it has not attempted to maximize them, because they fail to serve as discrete goals substituting at a sufficiently high and constant marginal rate for all other goals.

Need for re-examination of goals and values for agricultural organization and policy arises because the physical and economic structure of the industry has been changing rapidly, due largely to continued national economic growth, affecting both the relative rewards of resources used in different industries and the consumption opportunities open to people. Agricultural production is oriented increasingly towards, and highly integrated with, the dominant commercial-industrial interests and social systems of our total society. Modern agriculture must be analyzed and explained in terms of the major developments in U.S. society. Its value systems, goal patterns, social organization, technical development, and its recurring social, political and economic crises are becoming inseparable from those of total society.

In origin, U.S. society was rural with values and policy constructs oriented towards an arduous and isolated country enterprise. With beginning of industrialization, a set of unique values continued to prevail, with a somewhat different set emerging in the urban sector. But with attainment of rapid economic progress and high levels of per capita income, values peculiar to agriculture have rapidly been disappearing, just as agriculture as a majority in population and political strength has been disappearing. Evidently, and to an extent which can reasonably be expected, the main policy goals of commercial agriculture are the same as those for the rest of society. Too, society evidently has no major policy goals for agriculture which are distinguishable from those for society as a whole. Nonfarm sectors of society have concerned themselves particularly with positive policy in respect to growth in employment, investment and income opportunities. At even less general level and in more specific meaning, industry and business prefer emphasis on monetary and fiscal policies to promote economic growth, rather than on those which combat recession. Labor prefers policies which provide growth and greater employment opportunities, rather than unemployment compensation during depression. It is unlikely that commercial farmers longer are in search of relief policies aimed at protecting income during depression, but likewise seek economic policy leading to production and price environments allowing successful ventures for those efficient in business.

Near Goals for Agriculture

The goals of freedom, equity, progress (efficiency) and security desired by total society are equally desired by farm society. There is not societal obligation to provide any of these in quantities greater for agriculture than for the total population. Neither is there basis for providing them in smaller quantities. To an extent, these goals have to be looked upon as competing ends to be attained with limited means or resources. Not all, therefore, can be attained in unlimited extent. A proper balance or mix must be attained, partly in the sense of allocations in Figure 8.1 and in an equity sense, but in a manner consistent with social organization itself. Security cannot be absolute and final, with no one ever faced with penalties of price in failure to respond to change, otherwise there can be no progress. Freedom, a cornerstone of U.S. society, must be restrained to the extent that the amount enjoyed by one person does not encroach unduly on that of another person, to the extent that its exercise by one is the denial of it to another, or to the extent that equity is violated. Equity cannot be pushed to the extent of equality and complete restraint on progress incentive and freedom. However, as we have suggested previously, not all goals to which values attach represent transformation of limited but divisible means among a collection of ends, all of which are desired in positive quantity. Resource quantities per se are not involved in certain questions of the goals mentioned above. Whether resource quantities are large or small have no bearing on such freedom and human right questions as those dealing with existence or lack of slavery. Neither are quantities of resources involved in equity of life itself, with one individual taking that of another. Fortunately, farm policy issues seldom touch upon such "resourceless" decisions as these, unless in some of the more extreme ideological discussions of market free prices.

The socially preferred mix or precedent for these generalized goals will be provided by over-all society to agriculture, or by agriculture along with other occupational and cultural elements of society. Urban society, being largest in population and seeing inability of agriculture to arrive at its own goals, may even specify and write the farm policy legislation of the future. Hence, it is useful to discuss farm policy goals which are more closely related to agriculture's contribution to the general community, in attaining the minimum restraints in equity and opportunity held by the urban sector and in erasing some of the more chronic conditions which have existed in agriculture. Within this framework, some immediate and practical goals for agriculture are these: (1) Excess productive capacity of agriculture needs to be immobilized to prevent accumulation of unused surpluses and to be shifted to uses which are more consistent with demand under economic growth; (2) stocks larger than magnitudes to cover pipeline supplies in domestic and international requirements and to meet fluctuations in weather and yields, should be prevented, along with treasury costs of carrying them; (3) food should be produced in degree of abundance and efficiency that keeps its real price low to consumers but which allows resource returns in agriculture comparable with factors of equal quality in other broad sectors; (4) progress by agriculture in rate of transformation of resources into products should parallel that of the urban economy, but agriculture should reap an equitable share of the gain from this process; (5) mechanisms should be provided for general society to share the social costs of adjusting structure and supply of agriculture to a pattern conforming with current and prospective demand for food; (6) living standards and conveniences in agriculture, including housing for all strata of the farm population, should be at levels of minimum decency prescribed for society at large; (7) poverty and underemployment embracing a large number of farm families should be wiped out; (8) farm-born children and labor should be given opportunities for gainful employment and useful citizenship equal to those of general society, through appropriate public investment in education, training, guidance and employment services; (9) mechanisms for compensation should be provided to guarantee that the distribution of gains and losses from economic progress sponsored by the public has positive-sum outcome for people in agriculture, and especially for the older and less mobile portion of the population; (10) mechanisms should exist to lessen and prevent the economic cycles peculiar to agriculture and to guarantee that their effects are not negative-sum in distribution of gains and losses over time and among farms and processing firms; (11) the pricing system, as an expression of consumer preferences and particular national needs, but not to force farming into sacrificing through an unstable competitive system or as the sole means of attaining pressing national purposes, should have greater play in resource allocation than reflected in surplus buildup and storage investment in the 1950's; and (12) the subset of national policy with focus on agriculture should be geared to the same quantitative target as general social policy in respect to rate of economic growth and rise in per capita incomes, minimum level of income, security and stability of income, market and price power and efficacy of pricing mechanism in drawing resources into sectors of growth and demand expansion. These can be looked upon as minimum restraints to be attained, rather than as goals to be optimized in a tight mathematical sense.

In broad outline, this policy subset is one of minimum restraint in respect to income, stability and opportunity—the main elements of farm problems. It allows recognition that the promising opportunity for the major portion of farm youth is in growth opportunity outside the industry. It also allows recognition that while older farm persons have little flexibility, the policy goals held for themselves are not necessarily those held for their children and grandchildren. It recognizes that degree of difference exists between (1) the instability and compensation problems of commercial agriculture and (2) the poverty and underemployment problems of farms with extremely low income. In attainment of such goals, however, it should be recognized that all persons in the rural complex, including those of farm oriented businesses and services, are equally important as individuals and members of society. The fortunes of this latter group generally fluctuate with those of agriculture. Therefore, it has the same claims on social policy as agriculture. And just as citizens of agriculture are no less important than those of general society, in respect to community welfare maximization, individual opportunity and national aspirations, those of the service complex in rural areas are no less important than those of agriculture. Finally, the subset directs farm policy towards an environment favorable to success for farmers who are efficient in their business, rather than focusing on relief measures oriented to major depressions of the past and a structure of agriculture that has long been gone and can't possibly return.

COMPETITION AMONG AGRICULTURAL POLICY GOALS

There are ranges over which different goals of farm policy are complementary, with increased attainment of one also bringing increased attainment of the other. Both should then be increased together, regardless of the values or weights attached to either. More policy elements could be made complementary, as illustrated in Chapter 16 in respect to research and development with contribution to general progress under mechanisms reserving a share of gains to farmers. But greatest policy issue is over competitive goals.

Few farm policy goals are discrete and mutually exclusive, but are best represented by a production possibility curve as b_3 in Figure 8.1 where we take X as indicative of attainment for one goal and Z as that for another. Substitution thus is possible and the task is one of obtaining the correct mix, given the heterogeneity of values and interests surrounding agriculture. Policies of agriculture have long been directed to competing goals, partly because this is as it should be and partly because the public and administrators have not realized that certain policies are opposite in their effect. Goals of agricultural policy over time have dealt with development and efficiency, to uncover new technologies for farmers and to help them reorganize their resources in order to increase factor/product transformation rates. But in the short run and for a particular stock of resources in agriculture, this progress goal requires smaller attainment in farm income under inelastic demand. It also conflicts with larger numbers of farms, and even family farms under certain circumstances. On the other hand, greater income has been the goal of recent policy, but the means sometimes used to attain it, immobilization of particular inputs, have led to lower efficiency. Goals dealing with compensation and income have sometimes included means which make both positive and negative contribution to this end. For example, ACP payments put money in the hands of farmers but the practices to which they are attached increase output and, under the conditions of inelastic demand, are expected to serve as income reducers. Even within agriculture, positive attainment of goal for one geographic or commodity sector has often meant smaller attainment for another. Higher prices for corn as a commodity on cash grain farms increases its price as a resource on livestock farms. High support prices representing positive income gain for some commodities have resulted in smaller sales in world markets for such commodities as cotton. In the area of foreign policy, restraint of international aid to conform with disposal of farm surpluses and use of domestic shipping facilities has caused U.S. investment in international economic development to be restrained.

Many of the direct goals of policy are not themselves ends, but are only means in a complex means-ends chain. This is true of parity prices, although concentration on them for so many decades has caused them to become viewed somewhat as an end. As a means, however, the intermediate goal of price level may come to interfere with attainment of other ends, as illustrated above. Considered as a means relative to the end of higher income, price support level through commodity loans has substitutes in attaining the particular goal. A relevant question, then, is whether means other than price supports with nonrecourse loans can be used to bolster and stabilize farm income and provide progress equity without causing some of the negative side effects in respect to still other goals. Obviously, in respect to parity prices or price supports as a means to higher income and equity in the sharing of progress, substitute means are possible, to the extent that they are not excluded by ideological differences or by the economic interests of particular groups which furnish inputs and process and store the products of agriculture.

Conflicts in goals and interests do not, of course, arise purely from economic policies aired in the public. Some arise similarly from policies in the control of private firms and sectors. Income goals of the medical profession are not entirely compatible with maximum health goals of the public, in respect to spread and price of medical services. Neither are the pricing and production policies of industries which use informal price agreements and market sharing consistent with the marginal conditions of efficiency and consumer welfare outlined in Chapter 8. These self-administered policies which give rise to favorable prices in nonfarm industries are much less evident to the public than those of agriculture because their price is paid through the market, rather than through taxation.

THE POLITICAL PROCESS

Farm policy has often been deeply imbedded in and restrained by politics. The "patchwork" nature of policy sometimes appears to be a compromise or mixed strategy of the nature obtained in a minimax solution of zero-sum games. The political struggle over farm policy sometimes also seems to suggest that payoff must be zero-sum, with gain to one group being a balancing loss to another. In other views, however, the miscellaneous character may be selection of mixed policy elements to allow Pareto optima as suggested in later chapters. Compromise through the political process itself perhaps is reflection of the value-based creed that "all men are of equal worth and dignity and none . . . is wise enough to have dictatorial power over another."[4]

A common plea is that "farm policy be removed from politics." But this would be unfortunate. The political process provides a forum to which policy issues can be brought for public debate and evaluation. It is the means by which the distribution of gains and losses from policy and change can be evaluated and estimated. Economists have disavowed any ability to make interpersonal or intergroup utility comparisons. As subjective, clumsy and imperfect as it may be, the political process is the means by which this measurement is made. Aided by information available to guide it, a quantity often too meager, the political mechanism is a means for predicting gains to be had and losses to be realized, and the nature of their distribution, as policy is enacted towards particular goals. Judgement is made, outside the realm of Pareto optimality, whether the gains to particular sectors outweigh sacrifices to others, or whether the national interests and purposes are furthered by enactment of particular policy.

The "fuss and struggle" which accompanies political debate, both at the level of special interest groups and legislative bodies, is one method of reflecting possible gains and losses from particular legislation, and in suggesting intensity of desire by groups whose wishes may be submerged by majority vote. Notwithstanding the fact that the process is sometimes accompanied by pure chicanery and log-rolling, the latter not always un-

[4] Brewster, *ibid.*

like a scheme of compensation or side payments allowing expression of varying intensity of preference among goals and policies, its pull over the long run undoubtedly is towards social policy following the thread of public interest and increasing aggregate or community welfare.[5]

If farm policy were removed from politics, there would be no public forum for weighing distribution of gains and losses over the population to provide mechanisms which redress sacrifices not foreseen in previous legislation and for legislating new policy which promises to increase aggregate welfare. No opportunity would exist for minority groups to express the magnitude of losses they believe to prevail from particular enactments. Farm policy formulation has appeared a complex and time-consuming process in recent decades. Agreement on means of solving some obvious problems has been difficult, and resulting policy appears to be anything but systematic.

But permanent long-run policies seldom are developed and accepted quickly. As Benedict indicates, reform movements often must persist for a century before they obtain results.[6] It took a good half century for formulation of a generally agreeable land policy after independence. Even the emergency legislation of the 1930's rested on nearly two decades of debate, and some experimentation, which led up to it. However, knowledge and learning can, as outlined later, aid the political process and speed its policy decisions under democracy. Too, when we consider the many groups involved in coalitions representing different policy goals, the conflicting groups over alternative policy elements, the intensity of interests of even minority groups and the consequent need for "side payments in policy allowances," the system and pattern of legislation which arises is not entirely unsystematic.

Model of Competition and Power

Freedom surrounding agriculture will best persist as long as there is more than one organization or interest group which is able to carry on policy debate and to have its concepts, philosophy and recommendations brought to the public. The possibility or tendency towards elimination of opposition in farm views and effects evidently led McConnell to title his book "The Decline in Agrarian Democracy."[7] Even should it stump greatly for freedom, the existence of a single farm organization or interest group with monopoly power over farm legislation would be inconsistent

---

[5] For indication of log-rolling as a method for expression of intensity of desire, see R. D. Luce and H. Raiffa, *Games and Decisions, Introduction and Critical Survey,* Wiley and Sons, New York, 1957, p. 361. The condition that individual preferences are equal or symmetrical is more nearly assumed where methods for expressing intensity are considered to be inappproprite. For discussion of political equality and equal weights for preferences, see R. A. Dahl, *A Preface to Democratic Theory,* University of Chicago Press, Chicago, 1956, pp. 35–40.

[6] M. R. Benedict, *Farm Policies of the United States, 1790–1950,* Twentieth Century Fund, New York, 1953, p. xii.

[7] Grant McConnell, *The Decline of Agrarian Democracy,* University of California Press, Berkeley, 1953.

with the very concept of competition. It would be the equivalent of national politics and policy with only a single political party.

Progress is safeguarded and promoted by more than one political party, under democracy such as that of the United States, even though the political process gives rise to "much noise" and, sometimes, roundabout movement to policy goals. Further, given the existence of various groups with unlike opportunity and production possibilities in agriculture, existence of more than one farm organization or pressure group with effect on farm legislation helps to insure a mix of policy elements providing positive-sum outcome in utility increase for the industry and society. Some modern political theory proposes group and social choice based on the end of power maximization by the individual or particular group.[8] Maximum power and control over others rather than utility maximization per se—although the two need not be separate—is sought. In this sense, the activity is the same as a zero-sum, two-person game: what one gains the other must lose. One wishes to increase its power and utility at the expense of the other, without concern over the aggregate outcome. This concept of attempted power maximization may characterize the power struggle of farm groups over agricultural policy, a conflict relating not to mutual gains in welfare or Pareto-better opportunities of such but in terms of "who shall have the political strength," with policy adapted towards this end more than others. The point is suggested in the following statement by Schultz:

> Underneath all of this is a concealed issue that burns all our minds, which is not brought to the surface and analyzed and treated. . . . In our day, we are more concerned with who has power and what we have done to power relationships and the whole political aspect than with the thing that is accomplished. What we are worried about most is what we have done to ourselves in the political structure and relationships.[9]

The struggle for power per se, or the power maximization model may go a long way in explaining major splits over farm policy, especially among major farm organizations. Is it the attempt of organization to create policies and administrative frameworks which maximize their political power and control over others which dominates conflict over policy? Or is it straight competition in economic interest and difference in basic values? Some recent maneuvering might lead conclusion towards the power maximizing model, rather than any definite attempt of all farm organizations to maximize economic welfare of all agriculture, or even to wrest greatest economic advantage for interests of farmers who make up membership of major farm organizations.[10]

---

[8] For discussion, see W. H. Riker, "A Test of Adequacy of the Power Index," *Behavioral Science*, Vol. 4; and R. A. Dahl, "The Concept of Power," *Behavioral Science*, Vol. 2.

[9] T. W. Schultz in J. D. Black, *Federal State Relations in Agriculture*, National Planning Association, Agricultural Committee, Mimeo, 1949. Also, see Grant McConnell, *The Decline of Agrarian Democracy*, University of California Press, Berkeley, 1953, Chap. 17, p. 134.

[10] For similar discussion of related issues, see McConnell, *op. cit.* and R. E. Dahl and C. E. Lindbloom, *Politics, Economics and Welfare*, Harper and Brothers, New York, 1953, Chap. 17.

GROUP AND INDIVIDUAL INTERESTS

U.S. society is not now composed of millions of persons with identical tastes, preferences and values, nor was this ever so.[11] Accordingly, it is necessary that balance in goal attainment be decided in the political process, with appropriate consideration for the values and preferences of the many groups which make up the society. In few cases is one group allowed to impose or dictate its goals entirely over another. Examples where differences have been so conflicting and discrete that one sector of society attempted absolutely and completely to impose its values and preferences over other sectors, were in slavery and prohibition. But most value and goal differences are not this extreme. Hence, methods of resolving conflicts are possible over time and through less violent political means and mechanisms. Groups with conflicting interests have, in U.S. society, been able to use time and the bargaining process better to understand each other's positions and finally to agree on policy which is mutually acceptable.

Democratic societies seldom articulate a single valued long-run policy and immediately adopt it. Instead, they formulate a broad general concept of long-run goals and move in their direction, away from structures existing at the moment, through a succession of short-run improvisions upon which agreement can be obtained. While this process is less spectacular and revolutionary than those political mechanisms which allow or force sudden and discrete breaks from the present or past, or which force a violent break between alternative sets of values, it is more consistent (1) with social mechanisms which recognize the acquired values of individuals and groups and (2) with the democratic process.

Brewster's creed of *self integrity*, the central judgement that in case of conflict both the individual and group are responsible for seeking a new mode of thought to unify conflicting views, does reflect itself through the political process in the long run.[12] However, while certain basic and original values or creeds harmonized well with the premachine economy of agriculture, they are less consistently held with respect to the current capacity and structure of agriculture and with respect to the economic social and power structures of other industry and resource groups. Political debate and conflict in respect to farm policy during the 1950's are indicative of the metamorphosis now taking place within agriculture, in respect to its economic role in an industrial society and in one where pure types of neither competition nor monopoly are predominant.

The United States was never motivated by an inspirational conviction of a single goal and purpose. Initial differences have always existed and they have been resolved by time and the political process. Our society has made progress because certain national interests do transcend special interests and because competing individual groups do exist. The purpose

---

[11] For different concepts and difficulties in defining the public interest, see G. Shubert, *The Public Interest*, The Free Press, Glencoe, Ill., 1960.

[12] Brewster, *op. cit.*

of public policy is precisely to reconcile conflicting interests and points of view and to establish some harmony of purpose "amidst a welter of interests." This process is possible in a democratic society to the extent that government officials who formulate policy and the individuals comprising the competing interest groups are capable of being influenced by some conceptions of national interest transcending their particular interests. Demeter, goddess of agriculture, cannot wave her wand over the countryside, providing immediate insight and agreement on areas where national interest transcends group interests for agriculture. No single "round package of farm legislation as a once and for all cure-all" for farm problems will ever be in sight. Or is this necessary. As we outline in later chapters, policy with numerous elements is necessary to guarantee aggregate welfare increase.

Differences in farm policy are no sharper than those for other national policy problems which are resolved outside the framework of discrete ideological choices and violent subordination of one set of interests and values by another. In these cases where group values and interests have led to conflict in choice of means or goal mixes, but have eventually been transcended by national interests, the process has not been accomplished in a lightning flash. Instead, some broad and general national goals have first been articulated, even if nebulous and distant in character. Then starting from where it was, society composed of various groups has, through the process of bargaining and re-examining positions, taken gradual steps from the prevailing conditions in the direction of broader and more ultimate goals. And while, in the long sweep of history, the general movement has almost always been in the direction of national purposes which could be articulated, not every step was so, a few being sideways and occasionally one backwards, as time and the bargaining opportunity of the political process were exercised in resolving special interests with national interests, or in bringing distributions of gains and losses to better assure increase in aggregate welfare. Compared with most other nations and social institutions over the past 200 years, the process has been extremely successful as evidenced by the stability of the bargaining institution itself, and by the stability and continuance of both a democratic form of government and the political process.

Debate and Discussion in Inventory of Ends and Prediction of Means Consequences

Goals below the generalized level of life, liberty and happiness are so numerous that all cannot be selected in equal quantities or pursued until their marginal utility is driven to zero. Hence, "measurement" by the public is necessary for guidance in the level and mix to be selected. Political debate and "give and take" is a method of discussion, for a more ample inventory of goals and sub-goals and their effects as they are known in fact or held in belief. Discussion is the most ancient and universal process for reasoned calculation in social policy, whether this be through the house organs or officers of farm organizations, the P.T.A., the politburo or the legislative committee. In a manner, it is an analysis or history of experience; it is a prediction, albeit imperfectly at times, of expected outcomes where payoff matrices have not been and cannot be, constructed empirically. Misunderstandings and previous biased or accidental distortion of facts can be uncovered. Seldom can voting be conducted successfully without discussion, whether this be at the program committee of the 4-H Club or in presidential elections.

Discussion and explanation, the exchange of information, also is used in that other major mechanism of decision, the pricing mechanism, except that it often is less public, involves fewer people and leads to more rapid acceptance or rejection of a particular alternative. Decision making through either the voting or pricing mechanisms would generally be inefficient without discussion and information. Discussion and examination of alternatives for social choice are typically minimized where one body wants its particular choice to be forced, as in "ramrodding" an alternative through an organization's executive committee or in the sham of democracy under a dictatorship. The strategy here is to hide the facts and distort the extent of knowledge (even to extent of stifling education and scientific fact). In the same vein, removal of farm policy from politics would generally remove the advantages of discussion in public decision making, and bring the imposition of alternatives by those in the position to dictate particular actions. The larger the group over which the discussion must occur, of course, the longer and more difficult is the process of weighing and choice among alternatives. It is understandable, then, that time is required to obtain policy with an important degree of unanimity over the complex and large industry identified as agriculture.

Trial and error is required in social policy because knowledge often is only subjective and consequences cannot be articulated accurately. The public, group representatives and legislators often have little knowledge of economic principles, and but meager information of useful research even where it is available. Often, or almost typically, the broad range of choices to be made and the many means of attaining them extend over phenomena far outside the realm of aid from theoretical economics. However, the general logic of economics is still applicable and itself explains, in rough manner, why equilibrium in policy changes and shifts back and forth between program elements as progress in goal attainment takes place.

As one goal is selected and approached through relevant policy, its marginal urgency or utility declines and others are increased in marginal value. These values at the margin are constantly changing, as has been true between equity in income distribution and economic progress. At lower levels of economic progress, income equity, even to the extent of redistribution, had great apparent marginal attraction to the masses. But with economic growth and attainment of high per capita incomes in such nations as the United States, income redistribution comes to take on less marginal value, while economic progress, and an equitable share in its fruits, takes on greater marginal preference among laboring groups, as well as industrialists. The emphasis in national policy thus shifts accordingly. Finally, re-examination of policies and switchback among them is necessary because man cannot always tell which ones he prefers until he tries them. To remove farm policy from politics and the political process would destroy this opportunity in information collection, weighing of preferences and flexibility in the decision-making process.

If we look upon political debate as trial and error measurement of alternatives, as a method of listing alternative goals and their degree of competition and as a tool for predicting the consequences of different policies, there are obvious ways in which the process can be facilitated and improved. An obvious method is the provision of more research, facts and information for these exact purposes. We have more to say about the opportunities in this respect in Chapter 16. However, at this point, one relationship is worthy of mention: As societies grow and expand, and simple biological desires become fulfilled, with spread of preference into the broader realm of complex services resting in psychological and sociological phenomena, the process of decision also becomes more complex. However, as society becomes this rich it also has the resources for investment in greater research and education to aid the public decision-making process. Too little of research, and particularly of education, has been made available and used in public decision on farm policy, although the void here is no greater than in other phases of national policy, such as that dealing with foreign and fiscal affairs.

APPROACHES IN GAME THEORY

We have seen that policy goals themselves are competitive for both individuals and the nation. Also, competition exists between different individuals in respect to the gain they derive from different goals. To specify an over-all policy, in respect to level of attainment of various goals, which will maximize national or group welfare is one thing. To specify how over-all policy is developed is quite a different thing. Hence, it is worthy of time to pause and illustrate the types of policy strategies that may arise under particular conditions of special group interests, coalitions of various groups interested in policy and by voting procedures. We illustrate only two, but they are useful examples with real life counterparts.[13] Our examples are with two-person, zero-sum and *n*-person, nonzero-sum games. Some conflicts in policy fall in the zero-sum category —what one group gains, the other loses. The conflict over free market versus production control falls best in this category with (1) one group gaining more money income from a free market and another group gaining more from production control and price supports or (2) one group with values which give it greater utility under "pure competition" free-

[13] Other approaches and phases of game theory would be relevant, such as those of "fair division," bilateral monopoly, nonstrictly competitive, side payments and uncertainty. For discussion of these see M. Shubek, *Strategy and Market Structure*, Wiley and Sons, New York, 1959; Luce and Raiffa, *op. cit.*

dom and the other group gaining greater utility from more money income and less freedom. Other conflicts in policy are clearly of positive-sum construct. For example, farmers in different regions, producers of different commodities, firms selling fertilizer or machinery to agriculture or sectors storing surpluses all may push legislative elements which helps to syphon more of public appropriations, or their indirect effects, in the direction of the particular group.

Over the longer run and on broad party basis farm policy is decided in elections. If the population has strong feelings for or against a particular policy structure, it can vote it out or maintain it, although in the short run and through mechanism of congressional committees, particular policy arrangements come into being which are not direct reflection of choices of the majority of the voting population. Typically, farm policy does not arise from alternatives posed to the voting populace for decision. Instead, it arises in congressional committees where vote is representative of different commodity, geographic or other interests. Only later does it have opportunity for evaluation by the voting public. Knowledge or estimates of gains and losses ordinarily is initially greater in the committees and the groups they represent than over the public at large. Hence, if the coalitions which gave it initiation persist, a given policy also may tend to persist for some time.

In the theory of political decision making, it can be shown that there are conditions under which majority selection, through committee or other precedure representing individuals or groups, need be that which is estimated to be "equitable," or which will give gain to all members of the group.[14] Coalitions may be formed which allow gain to some of the group but not to others. This condition arises where each separate individual or group wishes to maximize its own gain or utility. The individual or group does not concern itself with optimal conditions necessary for maximization of gain or utility to the aggregation of individuals or the community, considering interpersonal differences, or even to Pareto-better positions which better guarantee positive-sum utility outcome over all groups. The effort, in a game theoretic framework, is for the individual or group to select the strategy which promises to maximize its own gain, considering strategies of others who also are involved in the game and the fact that gain to some may be kept at zero, or even may be negative. In this sense, the individual or group doesn't "give a hang" about welfare per se of others; its indifference map is fixed and does not change configuration depending on the level of utility of competing individuals or groups.

Rules in modern welfare economics can only specify changes under which the total product will increase and patterns of distribution which will increase total utility in the sense that some are better off and none are worse off, or that all are better off. It can specify only solutions of unanimous consent, or where there is basis for agreement among all

[14] For example, see Arrow, *op. cit.*, and J. M. Buchanan and G. Tullock, *The Calculus of Consent*, Michigan State University Press, East Lansing, 1961.

individuals or groups concerned. It cannot specify a change which involves conflict in the sense that gain by one means loss for the other. This point is emphasized in Figure 8.1 where, starting from point m, two individuals can agree, have unanimous consent, in step-by-step movement to selected points within the shaded area where other indifference curves intersect, until tangency of two curves is attained along the contract line. But at this point, conflict arises and consent can no longer be unanimous, each gain in position of one individual being loss by the other. This also is true starting at point e and supposing X to represent the utility of one person and Z the utility of another with b_3 as an opportunity curve. Any change between e and the boundary of b_3 as a set of possibilities, within the right angle, causes increase of utility by one or both and allows possibility of unanimous consent. But any change which gives a combination outside of the quadrant *egh* increases utility of one at the expense of the other. Consent can still be attained in a Paretoan optimum sense for movements along the contract line if gain to one is accompanied by compensation to the other individual in amount equal to or greater than the latter's direct loss, supposing that there is exterior source for the necessary side payments. Assumed, obviously, is the equivalent of positive-sum reorganizations; otherwise the status quo would be maintained. But we must also examine game theoretic situations where this is not true and positive-sum outcomes are not guaranteed in the short run, although national interests and the political process will tend to direct them back to this condition in the long run.

Two-Person, Zero-Sum Games and Pressure Group Strategy

To illustrate these possibilities, we examine some simple political decisions which may be put in a game theoretic framework and which represent choice between competitors which need not, or do not, imply maximization of community or aggregate utility. On the one hand, we have political activity which parallels decision under two-person, constant-sum games with solutions in the minimax manner. Others perhaps are in the manner of Savage's minimization of regret or in the terms of the Hurwicz optimism-pessimism principle.

We select a problem subjected to the more conservative minimax principle as an illustration of mixed policy strategies and structures which may arise under these conditions.[15] Here the strategy is put in the context of a "game against nature" where the opposition is malevolent, always using its most devastating strategy. We suppose two special interest groups, each having resources (money, time of staff, vote trading ability, influence on congress or legislative committees, etc.) which can be

---

[15] For detailed discussion of the various approaches, see Earl O. Heady and W. V. Candler, *Linear Programming Methods*, Iowa State University Press, Ames, 1959, Chap. 17; L. J. Savage, *The Foundations of Statistics*, Wiley, New York, 1954, Chap. 2; L. Hurwicz, "Some Specification Problems and Applications to Econometric Models," *Econometrica*, Vol. 19; R. D. Luce and H. Raiffa, *op. cit.*, Chaps. 4 and 5; Martin Shubik (ed), *Readings in Game Theory and Political Behavior*, Doubleday, Garden City, 1954. (Doubleday Short Studies in Political Science.)

allocated to different strategies bringing gain to it, or allowing it to avert loss. Its problem is to determine the manner of allocating these resources (i.e. the proportion to use for each strategy—the frequency) to best meet its individual goals of gain. We suppose the resources are used to influence opinion and votes of the public, or in lobbying to influence Congressmen who vote on actual legislation.

We believe that many farm policy conflicts do approach a zero-sum game in nature. Some farms which can expand, under certain policies, gain at the expense of those who must give up farming. Greater output and less revenue in aggregate may bring greater income to more progressive farmers who increase output by more than the average, but loss to those who increase output at a lower rate. Similarly, higher feed prices under quotas may cause grain producers to gain at the expense of livestock farmers. Hence, groups (coalitions) may congregate around a particular policy possibility, trying to set up different strategies in order to bring policy elements, considering the strategies of their opponents, which will "maximize the minimum of gains" or will "minimize the maximum of losses" considering the strategies of their opponents. The result logically need not be a pure strategy, or a single policy element, but a collection of policy elements resulting from the "game" as reflected through political bargaining and trades.

Represented as a two-person zero-sum game, we can suppose two coalitions, or groups A and B. That represented by A has the set of strategies of finite number represented in (9.1), where a_1 may represent trade with an outside group to receive a particular price support level (or lack of it), a_2 represents a land withdrawal scheme, a_3 represents provision to maintain particular limits on farm size, and so forth.

$$A = [a_1, a_2, \cdots a_m] \tag{9.1}$$

$$B = [b_1, b_2, \cdots, b_n] \tag{9.2}$$

Similarly, B has strategies represented in (9.2) where the elements, b_i, have similar meaning. Arranging the two sets of strategies as in (9.3), we have elements of the payoff matrix, C, where c_{ij} represents the gain to A and the loss to B if the former uses the strategy a_i and the latter uses the strategy b_j.

$$\begin{array}{c} \\ a_1 \\ a_2 \\ a_i \\ a_m \end{array} \begin{array}{c} \begin{matrix} b_1 & b_2 & \cdots & b_j & \cdots & b_n \end{matrix} \\ \begin{pmatrix} c_{11} & c_{12} & \cdots & c_{1j} & \cdots & c_{1n} \\ c_{21} & c_{22} & \cdots & c_{2j} & \cdots & c_{2n} \\ c_{i1} & c_{i2} & \cdots & c_{ij} & \cdots & c_{in} \\ c_{m1} & c_{m2} & \cdots & c_{mj} & \cdots & c_{mn} \end{pmatrix} \end{array} \tag{9.3}$$

Policy outcomes may mean income or utility gains to some but not to others, as in the case of large farms versus small farms and extended output versus revenue change, or the value attached to price supports or their opposite among grain buyers and sellers.

However, payoff elements need not always represent loss to one and gain to another, but may represent differential magnitudes of gains or losses (i.e. we may add constants to the elements of a zero-sum game). Now, if A wishes to guarantee a minimum loss (maximum gain) regardless of the strategy employed by B, he must determine "frequencies" $p_1, p_2, \cdots, p_m$ to attach to his various strategies. Similarly, if B wishes to guarantee maximum gain (minimum loss) regardless of A's strategy, he must specify "frequencies" $q_1, q_2, \cdots, q_n$ to attach to his strategies where we have the restraints:

$$\sum_{i=1}^{m} p_i = \sum_{j=1}^{n} q_j = 1, \tag{9.4}$$

$$0 \leq p_i \leq 1 \tag{9.5}$$

$$0 \leq q_j \leq 1 \tag{9.6}$$

and A wishes to guarantee a given gain (loss) or value v, regardless of the strategy used by B. Thus the problem in matrix notation is to solve the set of relationships in (9.7) for B and (9.8) for A where V is vector with all elements equal to v, with v being the maximum of minimum gain to be attained by B, considering the strategies available to A (the minimum of the maximum losses which can be attained by A considering the strategies open to B).

$$CQ \leq V \tag{9.7}$$

$$C'P \geq V \tag{9.8}$$

Q and P are the vectors of frequencies respectively for B and A. The solutions will indicate the mixture of strategies, frequencies of such, that A should employ if it wishes to minimize its loss and that B should employ if gain is maximized, depending on the strategies open to each, and the player considered to be the minimizer.

In terms of a pressure group, the solution (of the p_i and the q_j) can be considered to indicate the proportion (p_i and q_j) of outlay (money or effort) to be allocated to each of its possible strategies. Hence, within this conservative framework wherein the first player assumes that the second will use the strategy most devastating to the first and selects a collection or mix of moves to guarantee a given level of gain (or loss), a collection of policy elements may be selected by each.[16] The resulting policy thus may be looked upon as a "compromise."

The above framework is more nearly one where we assume zero-sum outcomes, with one gaining what the other loses and with unwillingness to "put all eggs in one basket." It would seem, however, that competing

---

[16] A single strategy will be selected only in case the minimum element of a row in C is identical with the maximum element of a column of (9.3), the existence of a single element defining a saddle point.

groups might better examine the possibility of trades such as those outlined in Figure 8.1 and guaranteeing positive-sum rather than zero-sum, or even the possibility of negative-sum, outcomes for the aggregate of groups. But as we outline later, a policy including a mixed strategy, rather than a "pure" approach, has basis in equitable and positive distribution of gains to all groups, and need not arise purely from opposition and conservative strategies.

Compromise and miscellaneous policies of this same general mixed nature, but not necessarily determined in the degree of empirical sophistication or in the inflexible formulation above, quite typically arise in appeal of major policies to miscellaneous interest groups. In a large and complex society such as that of the United States, decisive majority is not frequently provided by any single sector of voters. Hence, policy in respect to particular over-all problems or goals often has elements with some appeal in gains to numerous sectors. Farm policy in the late 1950's was so composed, with support prices for those who could so gain, unrestricted plantings of corn for those who preferred more freedom, land withdrawal on dispersed basis to help restrain production but to meet criticism of rural businessmen who feared concentrated withdrawal, storage of grains favored by those who store it and foreign disposed purported to aid in international political and developmental obligations.

Even though numerous of these elements were in conflict in respect to attainment of particular ends, "mixed strategy" was used to invite voting majority of persons with interests surrounding agriculture, even if policies with more distinct contribution to group ends and national welfare maximization might have been specified. Or the policies which arise may be likened to games and decisions with side payments, thus breaking out of the tight zero-sum construct above. The side payment does not take the form of money transfer but is a particular program allowance to one group so that it will "go along" with a major policy proposal. Producers in one region may be allowed a particular provision if they will "go along" with a major legislative proposal. For example, if the policy involves production control and support prices, one regional group may be allowed to shift its "withdrawn land" into other crops. Or it may be given an amendment to legislation, providing it with a somewhat different support level. Side payments are not inconsistent with community welfare maximization, even though they give rise to policy constructs which appear heterogeneous and unsystematic. They do, as pointed out later, allow recognition of intensity of desire by minority groups.

The above framework illustrates procedure by which miscellaneous policy structure may arise. We go further in the game theoretic framework below, illustrating how choice of policy can be made under democratic procedure and voting majority where concentration is on individual or group rather than aggregate-society gain. Even though the situation we now illustrate is known to have its "everyday" counterpart in political decision, no one has yet come up with a substitute for majority voting which allows better attainment of certain desired conditions in group decision making.[17]

n-Person, Constant-Sum Games and Voting Majority

The diversity of groups within agriculture and those surrounding agriculture, some with consistent and some with conflicting interests in particular policy programs, perhaps provides for decisions falling more nearly in the framework of an n-person, constant-sum game wherein coalitions can be formed, in effect through either general elections or congressional committee memberships. It is here that interests of the particular group in maximization of its own gain prevail without regard to aggregate or community welfare, if we assume lack of side payments. In other words, a particular group or individual is not concerned with the smallness of gain to another, whether this be zero, small or even negative.

The general outcome can be illustrated by a simple example, although it has application with greater numbers and certain greater complexities in alternatives and decisions.[18] For illustrative purposes, assume a public program which results in m dollars which will find allocation as benefits to three groups or individuals, the latter being different geographic or commodity groups in agriculture—agriculture as compared to groups outside of agriculture which handle farm inputs and products, etc. Or, m may be the magnitude of a market return which can be distributed differently among large or small farms, feed producers or livestock farmers, or over other various commodity and geographic groups, depending on the type of farm policy selected. Selection of policy in this case will be determined by majority vote, with different policies bringing different fractions of m to each group or individual.

Normalizing the game, expressing it in functional form and letting 1, 2 and 3 refer to the respective individuals or groups, we have the following characteristic function or values of different groupings or coalitions of individuals or groups where v indicates the value or payoff to the coalition indicated in the parentheses:

$$v(1) = v(2) = v(3) = 0 \tag{9.9}$$

$$v(1, 2) = v(1, 3) = v(2, 3) = m \tag{9.10}$$

$$v(1, 2, 3) = m \tag{9.11}$$

---

[17] *Cf.*, K. O. May, "A Set of Independent Necessary and Sufficient Conditions for Simple Majority Decisions," *Econometrica*, Vol. 20. He points out that simple majority rule alone is the only rule resulting in the properties of (1) decisiveness, (2) anonymity, (3) neutrality and (4) positive responsiveness.

[18] For other application or discussion of game theory in political decision, see: K. W. Deutsch, "Game Theory and Politics," *Canad. Jour. Econ. and Polit. Sci.*, Vol. 20; Luce and Raiffa, *op. cit.*, Chap. 14; A. Downs, *An Economic Theory of Democracy*, Harper and Brothers, New York, 1957, Chap. 10; M. Shubek (ed.), *Readings in Game Theory and Political Behavior*, Doubleday, New York, 1954; and Buchanan and Tullock, *op. cit.*, Chap. 11.

If each stands alone—no coalition as in (9.9)—the coalition value is zero for all groups. If coalition is formed to give a majority, any pair as (9.10) in this case, the value of coalition is the total benefits, *m*, to be allocated under the policy, as also is true in (9.11), or for any coalition including more than a majority of individuals. An "equitable" sharing of policy gains, through selection of a particular structure of government program, is the distribution or imputation of *m* indicated in the set of (9.12), with equal portions of *m* going to all three "players" as indicated by the proportions of *m* representing, from left to right, the respective shares to groups 1, 2 and 3.

(9.12) $$(\tfrac{1}{3}m, \tfrac{1}{3}m, \tfrac{1}{3}m)$$

However, this imputation is not stable and does not provide a "solution" to the game. The requirement for a stable solution is that the set of alternative imputations—e.g. the proportions in (9.12)—from which it is selected (1) dominates any imputation not included in the set and (2) must include imputations all of which dominate others or are dominated by others in the same set. A set of imputations satisfying these requirements is included in all three sets of (9.13).

(9.13) $$(\tfrac{1}{2}m, 0, \tfrac{1}{2}m) \quad (\tfrac{1}{2}m, \tfrac{1}{2}m, 0) \quad (0, \tfrac{1}{2}m, \tfrac{1}{2}m)$$

The imputation in (9.12) is not stable because 1 and 3 can form the coalition (1, 3) in (9.13), both gaining over (9.12) at the expense of 2. Hence, with each trying to maximize individual gain, (9.12) is not a solution for any one. However, if the coalition (1, 3) is formed to give the imputation $(\frac{1}{2}m, 0, \frac{1}{2}m)$, individual 2 can propose the alternative coalition (2, 3) with gain from an imputation such as $(0, \frac{2}{5}m, \frac{3}{5}m)$, 2 now having payoff of $\frac{2}{5}m$ rather than zero as under the first imputation in (9.13).

In terms of maximizing individual gain, this coalition and imputation also is preferable to individual 3 over the coalition (1, 3) and equal sharing of *m*. But the (2, 3) coalition, and its imputation above, now can be changed to better the position of both 1 and 2 if they form the coalition (1, 2) and vote for policy elements which result in the imputation $(\frac{1}{2}m, \frac{1}{2}m, 0)$. Either 1 or 2 now might "forsake his friend," and form a coalition with 3 at his own personal gain. But obviously, unless the game were to go on endlessly without stopping for gain of any individual, either 1 or 2 might end up outside the coalition and with zero gain. Hence, in terms of their own interest, 1 and 2 may simply call a halt to the "juggling," each having a greater gain than under the "equitable" sharing. They also have equal gains.

There are, of course, many imputations that could be retained in this manner. However, the set of imputations in (9.13) are considered to be more stable than any of those not in it, and particularly that in (9.12). The "equitable" imputation is considered to be the least stable of all imputations. Any coalition can upset it, while particular coalitions are needed to upset others. With the imputation $(\frac{2}{5}m, 0, \frac{3}{5}m)$ only two other coalitions are possible to bring down that existing. Under the proposition of maximizing individual gain, independence of utility functions and the absence of side payments, it is expected that coalitions will arise which leave no gain to some (or even loss if we suppose different types of games).

The analysis can be extended to any number of groups or individuals, with the solution set always containing a symmetrical distribution of gains to the smallest possible number forming the majority coalition. However, as the number of participants increases, the individual becomes less important in position, thus perhaps more inclined to depart from particular imputations. Coalitions formed will be less stable and permanent with greater number of individuals or groups, a phenomena not without example in agricultural policy. In the example above, we generally assumed symmetrical gain to the individuals of coalitions. However, where this is untrue, with the gain being differential and where all enter equally into voting, but side payments are allowed, imputations may result which are more stable than those outlined above but which do not result in the "equitable" sharing of the policy gains among those who form the coalition.[19]

The *n*-person positive-sum game illustrated above shows how coalitions may be formed to distribute the gains of particular policy or income conditions to particular groups. The gain or quantity to be distributed may, in agricultural policy, be a given public appropriation or it might be the amount of money generated from food expenditures in the market. The groups involved can be different commodity, regional or income groups of agriculture. They also can and do include groups outside of agriculture which have possible payoffs to themselves as alternative policies are selected. In the latter groups are producers of lime, fertilizer and machinery, the sectors and industries which process farm products, provide storage facilities, supply credit or perform numerous other functions relating to agriculture. They do group around agriculture as coalitions with specific interests. While formal games are not played, coalitions are more nearly represented in direction of emphasis in lobbying, public relations and similar activities.[20] During periods such as the 1930's, farm organizations joined efforts in what might be, in game terminology, termed an "equitable imputation." In later decades, however, they have been less able to arrive at "fair exchanges" and "unanimous consent." The result has been that opposing coalitions in interests have been formed among competing organizations in their attempt to affect farm policy legislation, rather than all forming a single coalition as in the early 1930's.

As we have mentioned before, exchanges do take place in policy formulation. These trades, which differ from the example above in the sense

[19] For discussion of these and relative situations, see Buchanan and Tullock, *op. cit.*, Chap. 11.

[20] For one person's presentation and interpretation of the groups interested in farm policy and the methods they employ see: Wesley McCune, *Who's Behind Our Farm Policy?* Praeger, New York, 1957.

that they need not leave some groups with zero gain, certainly give rise to policy with miscellaneous elements as an attempt to impute utility to various competing groups. In game terminology, the miscellaneous elements serve as "logrolling" effects wherein groups make trades. A particular group supports a policy element favored by a second group, if the latter will support a provision desired by the former. In a purely economics context, one cannot say that a mix of policy elements so arising, although they appear highly heterogeneous, are inconsistent with welfare or utility improvement. These trades are comparable to movements within the shaded area of Figure 8.1. Farm organizations are themselves coalitions of interest groups, and include coalitions within their ranks. This point, as well as the manner in which different strata within a farm organization can make trades representing Pareto-optima arrangements among their own ranks and can conduct "logrolling" for mutual benefit is suggested by McConnell in the following:[21]

> The charge sometimes made that the Farm Bureau does not speak for the farmer is not wholly meaningful. "The farmer" is an abstraction. However, the question, for *what farmers* does the Farm Bureau speak, is highly meaningful. The Farm Bureau, in the words of its own publication, is "an organization of superior farmers." Moreover, the record of its action shows that it has served as the spokesman of these "superior farmers." Thus, the narrowed basis of Farm Bureau organization approaches one of *class* within agriculture. . . . Since the basis narrowing the constituency of the Farm Bureau is one of class rather than producer groups, it is clear that local bureaus will show considerable diversity on the latter score. . . . State farm bureaus have seldom opposed the national organization, and the conflict of interests between commodity groups has been minor and transitory. It is a type of controversy readily adapted to settlement by bargaining and logrolling by a few leaders. Thus, support for a labor policy desired by Southern or California interests can quite easily be exchanged for a price policy desired by Middle Western groups. The two policies do not conflict and, while the one side of the bargain may gain nothing from the other's policy which it agrees to support, neither does it suffer any loss. The result is that the national organization adopts both policies. This would appear to be the solution to the seeming paradox that, although the great center of the Farm Bureau is in the Middle West, the Farm Bureau consistently follows a policy on matters of farm labor that benefits plantations and corporation farms in other parts of the country. Any opposition to this policy would have to come on a class basis, and the Farm Bureau organization has been formed in a way which makes this impossible.

The solutions and strategies which arise under coalitions of the type outlined for (9.9) to (9.13) do not guarantee policy which maximizes aggregate or community welfare. Certainly there are many policy proposals and coalitions which are not aimed to do so. If we are to understand the "why" of many policies which apply to individual groups, we must look to frameworks of political decision making which fall in this realm. Fortunately, however, the political process of democracy does provide for debate and reconsideration and the presentation of information and alternatives even by groups left in minority position. Threads of community welfare concept do arise and are given opportunity to transcend gains and interest of particular groups, although the process often is sluggish and open to considerable gain of some at loss to others before it

---

[21] McConnell, *op. cit.*, pp. 170–71.

rectifies a particular policy structure.[22] Hence, while we have outlined some theory explaining the "why" of different policies and decisions, they best refer to the short run, with broader concepts of equity usually coming to prevail in the long run. (However, we can point out some coalitions and strategies in social policy which have indeed prevailed over a *long* short run with equity and opportunity for large population strata excluded accordingly.)

POLITICAL STRENGTH IN ATTAINING FARM POLICY GOALS

Slowly but certainly the political strength of agriculture, of greater proportion than its population or in its contribution to national income, is melting away. The decline in political strength of agriculture is itself a function of economic growth. The process is not exogenous and mysterious, but its variables are endogenous to the economic system as it expands and develops. Primitive societies devote major resources to producing food, clothing and shelter. Since labor is low in price relative to capital, most of the labor force and population is in these extractive industries. But with the eventual conquer of hunger and growth in per capita incomes, the pattern of demand shifts more to nonfarm goods and services in the manner outlined in previous chapters. Directly the demand is for consumer goods, but indirectly it is for resources. With growing scarcity of labor relative to capital and with predominance of labor in service and public enterprises, expansion in size and complexity of the economy draws labor from agriculture to the nonfarm economy in amounts more than proportional to capital. Accompanying labor in the shift to nonfarm sectors are families and voters. Hence, the shift in political power from farms to urban sector is chartered. This process will continue in American society, just as it will in other nations where both the right of decision through the voting mechanism and economic growth prevail. In fact the two sets of decision-making mechanisms—the pricing system and the ballot box—are not separate but closely intertwined as they shift the pattern of demands and powers relatively from agriculture towards nonfarm sectors.

Following the first reapportionment of the U.S. House of Representatives, 101 of the 106 representatives were elected by farmers and planters. It has been suggested that not more than 100 of 435 representatives were directly affected by the farm vote by 1957.[23] Too, it is becoming increasingly easy for the President, and major party policy, to be elected apart from the vote of the farm states. At the national level particularly, this decline in political power will continue as the economy becomes attached in greater proportion to nonfood products. Farm problems will come less

[22] Means which give rise to "voice" by minorities, allowing some expression of intensity of preference by them as against the majority, are devices as logrolling, vote trading and the filibuster. Enactment of "games of fair division" also allows expression of intensity.

[23] For discussion of these quantities, see: A. N. Holcombe, *Our More Perfect Union*, Harvard University Press, Cambridge, 1950; R. B. Talbot, "Trends in Political Positions of American Farmers," from *Goals and Values in Agricultural Policy*, Iowa Agricultural and Economic Adjustment Center, Iowa State University Press, Ames, 1961.

to dominate other programs of the nation, as in the case of foreign policy where aid has too often been tied to disposal of surplus farm products rather than in investment to give greatest marginal productivity of developmental goals.[24] In the terms of population and resources represented by the industry, agriculture long was able to maintain an important degree of "overrepresentation" in decision on economic policy. Overrepresentation has been especially true in state legislatures where major policy decisions are those of taxation, allocation of road funds and certain economic regulations of commodities and labor. However, it continues at the national level where agriculture still has overrepresentation in geographic allocation of the Senate, control over House committees on agriculture, subcommittees on agricultural appropriations and special congressional arrangements in protection of committees.[25]

As time goes by and the House declines in representation from rural districts, various of these powers will decline. However, as urban areas become more important in the initiation and control of farm policy, it is not given that they will lack interest in guarantee of equitable degree of stability and favorable resource returns in agriculture. General society has been extremely kind and patient with agriculture, in magnitude of appropriations to it and in extended time to experiment with policies which have had high treasury costs. It is unlikely that farm or general society would have allowed government purchases and storage of surplus autos, refrigerators and television sets in the magnitude of farm products during the 1950's. Future urban societies are unlikely to withdraw the opportunity of income policies and opportunities from agriculture, but they are likely to ask how their funds are spent.

Constitutional emphasis on securing and guaranteeing basic human rights and civil liberties can be interpreted as a directive towards equality of opportunity, and not equalization of income or similar rewards, except as the latter is attained by the former.[26] U.S. society is likely to continue this emphasis for the agricultural sector, even as political power of the industry declines further, but with opportunity defined in the broad framework of national purposes and with minimum restraints in market power no less than for other major groups.

ROLE OF RESEARCH AND EDUCATION IN POLITICAL DECISIONS

As we mentioned earlier, political discussion fills a useful function in democratic selection of social policy. It serves to express goals relevant to all groups, the possible distribution of gains and losses from different policy subsets, the expected payoff or consequences of different means, and the general complementarity and competition among ends. The longer and more widespread the discussion, the larger the number of

[24] For discussion of orientation of foreign policy into channels of particular advantage to agriculture, see H. N. Carroll, *The House of Representatives and Foreign Affairs*, University of Pittsburg Press, Pittsburg, 1958, pp. 34–65.

[25] For details on such points as these, see C. M. Hardin, "Farm Political Power and the U. S. Government Crises," *Jour. Farm Econ.*, Vol. 40.

[26] See Buchanan and Tullock, *op. cit.*, Chap. 13.

hypotheses, beliefs and facts ordinarily brought to focus on a given set of policy proposals. The discussion step is essential in social choice. There is method, however, for improving the discussion and informational phase of public decision making. Research and education can be used to contribute information of the type needed for evaluation of policy alternatives. Research cannot, of course, say which values ought to prevail, what goal is "good" or "bad." It can, however, add knowledge for the decision-making process in the sense of indicating or predicting (1) which ends are in conflict with each other, (2) which ends are inconsistent with the resources or means available, (3) the consequences or quantitative effect of a particular means, (4) the possible or expected distribution of gains and losses, in monetary or other measurable units, of a particular subset of policies and (5) similar quantities for predictable phenomena. Not all quantities can be forecast or predicted which are useful for public decision making, but many more than are typically used can be.

As societies grow richer, they can invest more in research and education to help in spread of knowledge and efficiency in choice, although this information probably has greatest marginal social value for poor societies where there are few resources and error in choice is relatively more costly. Of course, it also is true that as societies grow richer, the kind and quantity of public choices becomes more complex. They deal less with means to fill man's basic wants and more to development of opportunity in exotic preferences which have greater variance among individuals. For this same reason, the process of research to aid in public discussion and decision also becomes more complex, with ability of useful research perhaps lagging behind the spread in variety of phenomena concerned.

Research and facts for public knowledge and use in social decisions are useful only if they are communicated. Educational machinery thus is necessary. And the facts must not be suppressed if they are to be useful. "Book burning" takes place, of course, under the extremes of dictatorial society where knowledge and opportunity for democratic selection are withdrawn from the populace. But "book burning" is an activity of degree, ranging from literal attempt to destroy inventory of knowledge and facts to mere attempt of a pressure group to discredit research and suppress communication of it through educational channels. "Book burning" in degree is even reflected in actions of research workers and educators where they allow facts of positive agreement with major pressure or interest groups to come to print but withhold facts that are negative in respect to the groups' stand or position. Land-grant universities have not always been exempt from pressures to "burn the books" in various degrees.[27]

Often the facts needed are simple and time-worn, sometimes appearing

---

[27] For detail of the political pressures and special interests used to herd agricultural research and education in directions desired by particular groups, and to suppress work in particular fields, see C. M. Hardin, *Freedom in Agricultural Education*, University of Chicago Press, Chicago, 1955, pp. 1–154; and *The Politics of Agriculture*, The Free Press, Glencoe, Ill., 1952, pp. 20–34.

of pedestrian nature to the technical economist. For example, few farm people know the meaning of concepts such as price and income elasticities of demand, or their empirical magnitudes. Few know the role of agriculture under economic growth, or the relative promise of prosperity for their son on an inadequate farm as compared to prospective growth industry. Young persons often have little knowledge of capital requirements to allow them success in terms of income approaching the U.S. living standard. Given more knowledge of this type, fewer persons would emphasize policy choices aimed at the moment and more would press for those looking to the longer-run structure of the farm industry and its relation to the national economy. Farm people are intelligent if given objective information, as also is true of most voters over the sweep of a generation.

In particular, land-grant universities need to put much more emphasis on public affairs in extension and other educational programs. Only a small minority of state extension services, covering only a small fraction of the nation's voters, have had a full-time person assigned to public affairs education. National policy is not determined by the people of a dozen states, and increased public investment is needed accordingly.

The specific objective of such education is not, of course, to impose values or value judgements on people. Instead, it is to provide objective facts and information and intelligent discussion so that individuals can better identify alternative goals and formulate their values accordingly; so that they can better understand conditions of conflict and complementarity among various goals and ends; so that they can better evaluate the consequences of following different policy means; so that they can more effectively identify the most efficient and effective means for attaining particular policy ends; and so that they can even make improved distinction between ends and means.

Some states have refrained from making this investment in public affairs education because they fear the subjects involved are controversial.[28] But again, experience of those states with broad extension education programs in social sciences indicates that this need not be so, if educators are objective and do not try to impose value judgements onto the public they serve. In fact, the public image of land-grant universities likely is larger, and public financial support is probably broader, where extensive educational programs in public affairs are carried on with the vigor of education in the production technology. The public image of the land-grant universities needs to be broadened substantially beyond that of purveyors of technical skills, if they are to fulfill their role in helping people more adequately to understand the urgency of better defining public goals and purposes and in developing appropriate policy elements, or even if further improvement in technology is to be better understood in terms of contribution to long-run national objectives and broad financial support is to be made available for it.

---

[28] See Hardin, *op. cit.*

10

Modern Need in Development and Policy

IMPORTANTLY THE ROLE of U.S. agriculture in economic development has been reversed. In primitive stages of social progress, infant sectors in industry and services depend literally on agricultural productivity for their food and release from primary production. Productivity of labor in agriculture must progress, in the primitive traditional society, to the point where some can move from farms into industry and commerce, a very first stage in economic development.

As industry becomes established in greater degree but farm employment absorbs major part of the population and labor force, the contribution of agriculture has still been of important magnitude in economic expansion. In this stage of preconditions for take-off, the contribution is not simply in physical quantity of food for sustenance of nonfarm population but in the transfer of capital accumulation from agriculture to industry. In some nations, this transfer took place in majority through direct taxation of surplus income of agriculture and its reinvestment in social overhead capital. This process was, as outlined earlier, of important magnitude in the United States, giving rise to relatively large and rapid investment in public schools, roads and local government facilities. But a more important process in this transfer was the eventual movement of capital to nonfarm sectors with the migration of labor to urban areas, even as labor force of agriculture grew but birth rates exceeded labor demand in agriculture.

Capital was transferred with people in two ways: (1) the capital investment in persons reared in agriculture and (2) the inheritances that finally went with these people. These contributions are extremely important in the buildup to preconditions for true "take-off," if we use Rostow's terms.[1] But as take-off occurs, agriculture still performs a basic and extremely important role. Take-off best occurs as industrial sectors eventually spawn and generate their own capital surplus in an extent and rate to cause forward burst of progress. Dependence on agriculture then is mainly biologically for food, less importantly for capital and basically for labor force to complement the compounding growth of industrial capital.

As rapid growth in nonfarm population and economy provides a larger market for farm production, so does economic advance of agriculture provide an early market for output of infant industrial sectors. Change in agriculture causing more of capital items to be incorporated into its product draws on machinery, chemicals and other products of industry. Not only do these capital inputs lead to greater productivity of agriculture but also they have some multiplier effect in secondary industry and general economic growth, with a portion of this feeding back, in input-output or interdependence fashion, to nonfarm employment opportunity in rural communities and the commerce arteries spreading from them. Also, this development tends to lessen the "social distance" between farm and nonfarm industries, leading more towards amalgamated general society. Growth of agriculture in population and number of consumers under the preconditions of take-off also provides demand and stimulus for products of the industrial sector.

Finally, it can also be speculated that as agriculture develops and commercializes it turns to concepts in and application of economic rationality over a large number of entrepreneurs, this providing a "breeding ground" or source of human talent with entrepreneurial talent. (Some data suggesting this even at higher development level are included in Chapter 12.) The historic race of birth rate in agriculture ahead of replacement rate supplies part of this force. But development in agriculture itself is extremely important; in order that labor productivity of the industry grows not only to allow decline in the portion of labor force employed in agriculture but also to free labor absolutely (or in the sense that productivity increases to allow declining input of labor per unit of food and growth in labor requirements of smaller proportion than food demand). Largely, however, position of wealth and affluence of societies becomes characterized by absolute decline in farm labor force. The excess of births or labor supply in agriculture over demand for the resource in the farm industry also keeps the factor price low to other industries. Hence, the transfer of labor at favorable price itself is economic encouragement to development of secondary and tertiary industry.

---

[1] W. W. Rostow, *The Stages of Economic Growth,* Cambridge University Press, London, 1960. Chaps. 2 to 4.

RELATIONSHIP AT HIGH DEVELOPMENT LEVEL

This is the picture at lower levels of economic development. But it changes greatly at high levels; the direction of dependency largely is reversed, but still with some causal effect in both directions. (See the contrasts in magnitude of interdependence between agriculture and nonagriculture in Chapter 7.)

Food is important and needed to satisfy elementary wants, but beyond this the national economy depends but little on agriculture and agriculture depends much on the functioning and structure of the national economy. This is an obvious fact when development has reached the stage of maturity in the U.S., with net farm income less than 5 percent of disposable consumer income. Presence or lack of relative income depression in agriculture, even with its multiplier effect in communities and sectors which surround it, has minor impact on the national economy.

Empirical expression of this fact existed in the 1920's, with considerable differential in the prosperity of industrial sector against the farm sector. It was even more apparent during the 1950's as national income rose to new levels but income of farm sectors skidded to twenty-year lows. The loose connection also was expressed in the fact that, given the built-in stabilizers of unemployment compensation, farm price supports and monetary-fiscal policies, agriculture sometimes had its better years (as in 1950, 1958 and 1960) when nonagriculture was in short-lived recession. The magnitudes and effect of depressions are themselves laced to the level of economic development, government policies to provide stability lacking.

When, for example, farm population and subsistence agriculture compose 90 percent of national society, business depression has a mild effect in scatter over the entire complex. The characteristic low supply elasticity and the consequent high price flexibility of factors in agriculture result in their continued full employment in agriculture, with unemployment in other sectors of weak influence when averaged over the aggregate economy. But let agriculture shrink to 10 percent of national economy, with depression of same relative magnitude in the industrial sector, and the impact is much heavier and more serious; hence, the extreme of the 1930's depression against those of earlier centuries. With an agricultural-industrial mix of 90:10, the urgent area for public investment is in development of the former. With a 10:90 mix, it is more nearly in policy to provide stability and to avert depression through spur of economic growth.

The severe consequences of recession to agriculture may now be much less that of a sharp decline in food price, as mentioned elsewhere, and more that of lack in employment opportunity for persons migrating because of technical advance of agriculture. During the 1950's recessions, demand of durable consumer's goods took a beating, but farm products did not. Full employment has special importance as agriculture, caught up in the growth process and encouraged by new technology and changed factor prices, extends its productivity and ejects labor from the industry. The large quantity of labor so released has favorable opportunity for employment only under conditions of full employment and economic growth in the national economy. With continued and rapid rate of unleased technology in agriculture, the complex of industrial growth and full employment is essential so that labor displaced from agriculture has employment opportunity.

As mentioned in Chapter 5, unemployment at a level of 5 to 10 percent of the national labor force, and certainly with 5 million unemployed, a particular burden falls on agriculture in inability to maintain sufficient migration and keep labor from damming up and in restraining structural change. With unemployment of only 2 percent, labor migrating from agriculture finds ready employment opportunity.[2] Furthermore, it has less disadvantage against unions and restriction of entry into particular employments. While the monopolistic element of labor unions may not be great enough to constrain employment opportunity of farm migrants under high employment, it is an important force during unemployment when seniority and other devices even comb the ranks of union members. In this broad and basic sense, the state of economic development in the industrial sector, the bulk of the national economy, is more important to agriculture in providing source of employment—than to industrial society in finding labor force. The technical development in agriculture to free and provide labor to growing industry is of great importance when two-thirds of the labor force is in agriculture, as at 1860 level of development or even in 1920 with 12 million in farm and 30 million in nonfarm employment. But the effect is greatly diluted with perhaps 4 million farm and 87 million nonfarm workers approached in 1970.

Fortunately, for an agriculture going through rapid development, its work force is small relative to the total. With farm labor force only at 10 percent of total, reduction by another fourth allows a quantity quite readily absorbed over large national work force. But reverse population proportions, as in India, and the national economy has great difficulty in absorbing a quarter reduction in farm labor force. Slow growth rate and "permanent unemployment" in the U.S. economy would serve about as effectively as major depression in causing a main restraint in employment and transfer to fall on agriculture. As Colm and Wagner[3] have shown, a growth rate of only 2.5 percent during the late 1960's would pile up a large number of unemployed, and the spill-over effect would be most important in agriculture.

---

[2] More recent of our research shows the predicted rate of unemployment, where net migration from farms drops to zero, is slightly less than 10 percent.

[3] Gerhard Colm and Peter Wagner, *Targets for U.S. Growth in the Early 1960's*, National Planning Association, Planning Pamphlet No. 111. Their figures include an estimate of 13.2 unemployed at a 2.5 percent growth rate, and as low as 4.0 million under growth rate touching on 7.5 percent.

Social Overhead Capital

Even at the level of social overhead capital and investment, the proportionate contributions and direction of interdependencies are much reversed. In the early settlement of the rural United States, the farm sector invested in public schools entirely beyond levels needed in return of the work force to agriculture. Investment in training and education had an important productivity expression as it was moved to nonfarm sectors with labor migration. Agriculture made a tremendous investment in human resources for national economic growth through this process—far beyond the return it captured, aside from the utility of having its sons and daughters obtain advantageous employment in other industries. But in more recent decades, the youth group of greatest disadvantage in capturing gains of greater talent expression in exploding national economic sectors has been farm youth.

In a later chapter we detail the fact that development of skills and input of education has been most meager in rural areas, in a general sense and in low-income farm regions particularly. Many sparsely populated farm areas without a large industrial tax base have had insufficient revenue to provide youth with education oriented to development of skills and talents for economic growth. Farm youth have been at a great disadvantage in capture of the high premiums from growth in particular nonfarm activity. So these can be better provided, it is now more necessary for general society to invest in school facilities and education of farm youth, rather than the opposite dependency which prevailed widely only a half century back. Too, in aggregate and interdependency terms, there is little reason why Ozark communities should make the major investment in work force and human skills later to be deployed in California or Michigan.

Agriculture has made a great contribution to the consuming society in supplying food in abundance and at declining real costs. Soth estimates that if consumers were using the same diet as in the 1930's, food would absorb only 16 percent of the U.S. family budget.[4] Even with the modern mix of food, only about 25 percent of consumer budget is required for food. Part of this cost is in preparing meat for barbecue, in homogenizing wheat, threading it and weaving it into tidbits for breakfast foods. These are expenses little attached to sustenance. More than 60 percent of this total outlay or expenditure for food is for services incorporated with food after it leaves the farmer.

The problem is not, as it once was, the ability of agriculture to provide food for society, but more in the ability of society to provide facilities for agriculture which allow similar degree of communication, fulfillment of aspiration and development of abilities by people. In early days, agriculture filled the biological needs of nonfarm people; now, nonfarm industry fills needs beyond the biological requirements of people from agriculture. Providing electricity, roads and schools to conform with the spatially ex-

---

[4] *Report of President's Commission on National Goals*, Prentice-Hall, New York, 1960, p. 207.

tended and sparsely settled characteristics of agriculture is one aspect of this dependency. But even consumer goods—television, travel and other commodities of affluence produced outside of agriculture, but flowing to consumers in it—have greater marginal urgency than does food furnished by the farm sector to the rest of society. This is true because of the level of progress, with food for the sake of hunger satisfaction being taken for granted and thus remote in reflection of marginal urgency.

Farm people have gained no less from productivity increases in other industries, and general abundance and low real cost, than from the opposite direction. Farmers in total have gained more in real income from progress in agriculture, mobility of people and general progress therefrom, than they would had they been able to block progress and hold per capita incomes at 1860 levels where their relative share of national income was large. As indicated in Chapter 16, growth in productivity of resources was at an annual rate of 2.3 in the total U.S. economy over the period 1940–57, as compared to a rate of 1.6 in agriculture. The comparable figures over the period 1889–1957 were 1.7 for the total economy and .8 for agriculture.

NATIONAL DEVELOPMENT GOALS AND RESPONSIBILITIES

As detailed in Chapter 9, economic progress is a fairly ultimate goal. Few advanced persons or societies would ever admit their lack of interest in self improvement and forward march. But most importantly in a practical sense it is an instrumental goal, held widely by contemporary American society. This is true not only for this society at the moment; it has prevailed as a motivating force in all times and all countries of civilized and advanced man. The drive for progress is easily explained and biologically obvious when the primitive miseries of hunger, illness and cold prevail, even in man's lowest tribal state. It is not as easily explained when copious fulfillment of these demands exists, with adequate food and shelter taken for granted. But still it prevails.

Theory proposes an indifference map, with utility magnitude increasing in order of indifference curves attained up the surface. The facts of life correspond with and prove this theory in a general extent—individuals *en masse* and society striving for greater output and higher attainment, even if frustration sometimes does arise in recognition and quantification of this attainment. Businessman, farmer, housewife, young and aged, few have negative preferences for progress. Individuals want greater utility and self improvement. Not only is progress desired for the greater utility attainment it allows, but it has extremely practical importance and purposes in a wealthy mature society such as that of the United States. Because of these purposes, it will continue to be sought, and it will take place. One of the more practical aspects is as a means of averting major business recessions. No one will ever be able to prove that an economy in a pure state of suspension, in respect to growth, can avoid a continued tendency to swing towards the depth of depression—because society will invest in and bring about growth as a means of avoiding depression with its mass misery in unemployment of man and plant.

The second practical aspect is in greater exploitation of the abilities of man. As long as man believes his abilities, whether towards frivolity or sedateness, to lack full exploitation, he will press to this end. Progress in its various and heterogeneous forms will thus result, because lesser degree in transformation of resource into opportunity has been developed for man than for animal and material. The greater investment in biological and physical science as compared to social science, as it should be at low levels of economic development, causes this relative gap in development of human abilities and resources to still exist. If physical opportunities in destroying himself are not exercised, man will cause progress because of dissatisfaction with his own unexploited possibility—itself a major complement to greater physical and biological progress.

Global Desires for Development

These practical purposes alone would give rise to and guarantee further progress. But a more important appeal for continued and rapid economic progress exists in the widespread and global desire of even backward nations to be swept to levels of progress wherein insecurity, hunger and disease are eliminated and allowance of even a few commonplace and lower class comforts and luxuries exists. Two things in progress themselves give rise to or allow this wider based interest in progress for and by less developed nations: (1) Communication itself is now so highly developed and effective that the possibilities of progress, and knowledge of its existence elsewhere in the world now extend to peasants and cultivators generally, and people under conditions of poverty over the world are unhappy with their past and current lot. (2) The world public opinion or society-held purpose, that all people in all places should enjoy freedom from hunger and the right to determine their own destiny, also is an attitude abetted by economic progress. The interest and need for, and return from, colonialism is of diminished importance when the level of economic growth allows high per capita income in mature nations, apart from colonial investment and with lesser need for exploitation of primary resources. Not only does progress result in this change but also it becomes sought for others when general attainment and widespread distribution of the fruits of progress are realized in advanced, democratic nations.

Given the extent of low development over the globe, this world "public purpose" itself is going to require continued exhortation in progress by advanced nations. But even if this bit of "good will towards men" and respect of human aspiration and dignity everywhere were not an impelling reason for progress as a means for aid to the less developed economies, world political competition would still cause it to be true. And even apart from this, there is little probability of complete peace over the globe, with communication at the present stage, as long as hunger and disease are intense at some points and as long as the gap in level of welfare and economic progress is painfully great among nations.

These things all call for progress in the U.S. economy, and are reasons why it will be attained. The nation has no choice. Progress is required as a means, if not an end. It is needed in agriculture, just as it is needed in other industries. It is needed in national economy with greater linkage to agriculture, so that the human resources of agriculture will be better utilized and so that more persons from the poverty sector of this industry have opportunity for greater expression of their abilities.

AGRICULTURE AND LONG-RUN PRODUCTIVITY GOALS

Change in economic and social structures is taking place in forms and at rates which cause nations and sectors of their societies to be uncomfortable. It is taking place rapidly because knowledge and communication have increased so greatly even for societies and society sectors which have been extremely tardy in education, standards of living, and cultural goals. While some nations and sectors of societies have lacked sufficient capital resources for rapid advance, their contact with others and their accumulated knowledge are now sufficiently great that they no longer accept economic adversity. Changes, both within our own society and the world over, have been so rapid that we have not had time to apply our complete intellectual abilities in understanding and solving the problems created by them or in sufficiently anticipating further changes and the adaptations which they will bring forth or require.

As a society, we have had our visions geared too closely to economic structure and a type of world political and economic stability which existed in the past, but which is not in sight for the next two decades and perhaps never again. Given the magnitude, nature and permanence of the world forces underlying change, it is only practical that we look to the future and select courses of action which, on the one hand, allow us to maximize and spread wisely the benefits of predictable and wanted change, or, on the other hand, to minimize the sacrifices which accompany unpredictable or undesired change. These statements apply both to (1) changes over the world which impinge upon national interests and (2) changes in economic and social structures within the nation. Both have important implications to the conditions and structures to be created for, and in, agriculture.

The most important political and economic challenge facing the nation revolves around world developments and international relationships. This is true if we choose to preserve the type of society and economic system which we value and to aid large numbers of other nations in democratic opportunity, choice of social system, and individual freedom. Competition faces the nation in two respects: in political alignment against major portion of the world's manpower and in devoting a significant portion of our resources to aid in economic development of underdeveloped countries. Competition between major world powers in this second area is no less important than in the first. Perhaps the major competition between the United States and Russia will remain that of devoting internal resources to promoting economic growth and progress of other countries. It will enhance the welfare of mankind if this can happen. But in either case, it is important that productivity of the nation's resources, particularly manpower, be increased as this competition or world need intensifies over the long run. It is less the basic stock of natural resources and more the number and productivity of manpower which serve as restraint in meeting this competition or in contributing to world welfare. In this sense, it is not practical or feasible, in the broader focus of preserving democratic society which is valued, to foster agricultural or other industrial policies and programs, over the long run, which dampen productivity of manpower and retard economic growth.

Hence, an important long-run criterion for agricultural policies of the future can be: They should be consistent with economic growth and manpower productivity in the long run. But at the same time they should not cause the sacrifices and indirect costs which attach to growth to fall too heavily upon one sector of society in the short run. If economic growth is selected by the entire society as a basis for promoting and preserving social structure, there is no basis for allowing disproportionate sacrifices to fall on a particular sector such as agriculture. The indirect costs, as well as the direct costs of these advances, should be spread over all sectors of society, just as should be the gains, in a manner which is consistent with modern concepts of equity.

U.S. society has provided investment and inputs to promote technological development of agriculture as one method of increasing the physical productivity of labor and accelerating economic growth. Fortunately, this has been done. The product, in the form of new technologies, has benefited the entire nation because (1) the welfare of consumers in general has been enhanced, and (2) the nation's industrial productivity power far exceeds that of nations which together have much greater populations but which have a major portion or a large fraction of their labor forces employed in producing food for mere subsistence of masses. We are easily able to meet the food needs of a growing population with a declining labor force in agriculture. However, many persons in United States agriculture do bear a relative sacrifice from these advances. They do so because the demand elasticities of farm products are extremely low, because the spatial characteristics of the farm enterprise provide fewer near-at-hand employment opportunities, because their educational facilities are not adequately geared to human adaptation and mobility, and because the markets connecting agriculture and the rest of the economy, particularly those for labor and related resources and products, function imperfectly.

If we accept the above as the long-run challenge and responsibilities facing society, as they certainly are, then we need a refashioning of programs for agriculture over the long run. On the one hand, we need policies directed less at diverting the fruits of economic progress into "nothingness," such as large surplus grain stocks and the capital to store them, and more in integration of these gains into the economic system. On the other hand, we need a consistent system for equitable compensation in the short run of persons in agriculture who contribute to national productivity gains but who sacrifice because of them.

Short-Run Challenge and Goal Framework

The above is the over-all long-run framework of goal and challenge in national progress, in application to all sectors including agriculture. It is the distant goal towards which near-at-hand ones need to be bent. But it is not necessarily the most feasible or relevant one for the immediate future, given the extent to which "slack" exists in use of resources and consumption of products in nonfarm sectors of the society. The cry for policy of agriculture to boost productivity and save the nation and world has a hollow ring against that collection of goods and uses of resources which we find elsewhere in the economy. A century back, progress in agriculture could go far in accomplishing a similar task. But it can no longer do so. Freeing of another two or three million workers from farms will not save the world; greater productivity of a 65 million nonfarm labor force more nearly will do so.

If labor is freed from agriculture, will it become employed in producing hoes for Africa, fertilizer for India, schools to transform scientists from sons of low-income farmers in southern Mississippi or eastern Tennessee, improved housing, greater psychiatric security for individuals and to develop national parks and highways? Or, will it become employed in producing more zippers for cigarette packages, tail fins for automobiles or commodities and services, including the advertising thereof, with appeal in sex, conceit and sublimation? Is the proportion of nation's labor resources involved in producing pure frills of affluence so great that it outweighs the whole surplus in farm labor force? These are questions in values and basic philosophy, but they are extremely important in respect to the vigor and seriousness with which further rapidity in advance of agricultural productivity and out transfer of farm labor force is taken.

To transfer a 55-year-old western Kansas wheat farmer, attached in values to his community and with skill well calcified to agriculture, to Minneapolis to produce the essentials of common-day life is one thing; but to transfer him to a like place for production of commodities in Madison Avenue appeal is another thing in values. If orthodox marginal conditions and long-run goals are selected for agriculture, they should also be selected for other sectors. Is there a good reason why scientists, economists and others should focus extreme effort on specification biases and other extreme intricacies in trying to measure, perfect and exhort one more degree of productivity from agriculture when the same is not done equally for all other industries?

If other sectors were put under the same degree of public and professional scrutiny as has been done for agriculture, larger maladjustments would be found to stem from imperfect labor markets, monopolistic policy, labor entry restraints and featherbedding, tariff concessions, lack of individual knowledge and people in one walk of life when they could be more productive in another. These questions pose the environment within which short-run policy for agriculture must be formulated. Certainly, as far as they can be seen now, there are basic long-run challenges in progress and efficiency for all industries—some moving rapidly closer to hand. But the inspiration and urgency for trying rapid transformation of agriculture loses much of its appeal in the general short-run environment. Obviously, a short-run environment exists in which policy might well have different character than in the long run. The short run can, in fact, be taken to represent a step-by-step approach to a more desirable long-run structure of the industry.

The marginal conditions of economic efficiency and equity do need to serve as the broad gauge for shaping agriculture, and other sectors, towards the long run. Within the framework of short-run exceptions above, levels of resource returns in agriculture do take on importance, but more in terms of utility of farm families and better opportunities for farm youth than entirely in current magnitude of national product with its particular mix of necessities and tail fins. Mechanisms are needed which allow farm persons to realize as much on their labor and capital, over a relevant time period, as do resources of equal quality and quantity in other industries. Incomes and resource use for farm people are needed which are consistent with national living standards and product. But to the extent that conditions must be created to allow this objective, they should be as consistent as possible with economic growth and greater national product over the long run. Short-run policies have attempted mechanisms over three decades which are not "Pareto optimum" in this respect. Others could be used which better serve in simultaneous attainment of the income and market-power goals of agriculture but which also allow greater progress, for both the present and long run. The huge investment going into surplus commodities and the storage to carry them, for example, contributed to neither of these goals. Hence, policies would appear to be possible which are not optimum in the sense of the tight marginal conditions of equilibrium, but which are Pareto-better in the sense of giving: farmers equal or greater goal in attainment of the above, consumers equal or greater goal in savings of resources surrounding agriculture, and society greater progress toward long-run needs and general marginal conditions.

Practically, policy might be best analyzed in this framework, not of what is "precisely marginal optimum" but what is Pareto optimum in moving in the preferred long-run direction while providing as much or more of short-run goals desired. In terms of political process, this is likely the practical means for improving structure of all industries towards long-run normative goals. It is the important method whereby society averts the disaster of contest over a larger share of smaller pie, as represented when policy is continuously and only oriented towards giving each industry the degree of "economic spoils" enjoyed by others.

Goals and Effects in Rate of Progress

Depression of income and overstocking of resources in agriculture for most of three decades poses the problem of optimum rates of progress. Is there an optimum rate which does not cause serious income loss to particular segments of the population and which paces itself to the ability of families to make adaptations and adjustments in the cultural base of life? A somewhat slower rate of improvement in farm technology, one slightly larger than rate of population growth, would have done so from 1940 to 1960. It would have been one with a rate allowing major reduction in farm labor force through exit of youth and restricted number of entrants. To have youth, flexible in skills and attachment to particular living environments, bring major adjustment is less severe than a rate which uproots older persons with fixation to community and occupation. Older persons are likely to, and do, remain in the industry at large income reduction. The losses attending rapid technological progress have greatest impact on this age group in the bringing of gains to widespread consumer society.

Other industries do not, where they are capable of restraint, unleash productivity capacity so rapidly that resource and commodity markets are flooded and firms suffer major capital losses. Extended production capacity accompanying economic expansion is thus managed in petroleum and steel. This procedure has not stymied progress, but has held productive capacity in restraint to the extent of turning some gains of development to the capital and labor forces of these and similar industries. Can policy attain the same end for agriculture, while still allowing progress to push forward with vigor? This would be the desired procedure, rather than to check the rate of progress in technology. With technology, factor markets and economic organization improved but with contributing sectors sharing or being awarded equitably of gain, greater potential exists in meeting uncertainties and unpredicted contingencies of the future. There are many ways in which the imperfections of pure competition structure of agriculture, in causing relative sacrifice of progress to fall heavily on some population strata, can be offset. These range all the way from restraints on supply such as the marketing orders used by California lettuce and milk producers to university scholarships for talented but income-short farm children of eastern Kentucky and southern Iowa.

The pricing mechanism and technological change are powerful forces in redistribution of income. Of the two forces as they affect prices, development of new technology in agriculture has done more to shove prices in one direction than support prices have in shoving them in the other direction in postwar years. Appropriate extent or threat of relative income redistribution through the pricing mechanism is necessary if the push and pull of penalty and premium in innovation and resource adaptation are to conform to progress and consumer preference. It is not, however, God-given that income redistributions must be made through the unrestricted market mechanism, nor that those so made are transcendental and holy. Policy exists to correct excesses so resulting. The two forces in income redistribution, the pricing mechanism in the private sector and institutional means in the public sector, must necessarily be used simultaneously and in proper balance. This is necessary if progress of desired magnitude is to be attained but gains from it are to be distributed in a manner to guarantee increase in aggregate welfare and fullest exploitation of opportunity in movement to new Pareto-optima or Pareto-better positions.

PRICING SYSTEM AND POLICY

Policy cannot and should not serve to substitute for the pricing system in its reflection of consumer preferences and adaptation of resources accordingly. The pricing mechanism will always need to be more effective and more greatly used than in the late 50's and early 60's when commodity stocks and surpluses turned in directions and quantities desired by no one and with no particular purpose. Under democracy where individuals are sovereign, to the extent that each other's sovereignty is safeguarded, there is no other efficient means whereby direction can be given economy and society except through expression of preference of individuals. The two major means of preference expression are the pricing mechanism as it relates to the private sector and the voting mechanism as it relates to the public sector. Proper balance is needed in the two sectors and appropriate proportioning of the two mechanisms is necessary in a nation faced with the challenges of the next half century. Freedom of all individuals, and not selected ones, depends on the extent to which both mechanisms are used, and not whether one is substituted for the other. Each has its advantages and disadvantages in reflection of individual preference and in guarantee of freedom in choice and opportunity to all individuals. For example, intensity of desire has minimum opportunity for expression in voting mechanism but some individuals lack minimum economic means of expressing desire through the pricing mechanism.

Policy is needed to supplement the pricing mechanism where the latter is imperfect in its ability to implement public goals, to attain certain types of scale economies and to prevent the excesses in income fluctuations and poverty where control extends beyond the ability of the individual. Even with major reliance on pricing mechanism to allow consumers sovereignty and freedom in effect on resource allocation, policy is needed to get the productivities of resources more fully unleashed and to increase fluidity of resources in moving to preferred uses. Public school investment is an excellent example of an historic policy element to accomplish these very steps. The pricing mechanism is, however, the only feasible means whereby a complex and individualistic society can shape and implement its diverse consumer preferences to get the type of exchanges illustrated in going from point *m* to the contract curve in Figure 8.1. Agreement must be found with Dahl and Lindbloom that in a large complex consumer society, excess rigidity and inflexibility of public choice works to prevent change rapidly enough to maximize the goal for which the organization exists.[5] (Inflexibility, rigidity and "unwillingness to change position" are no less found in organizations of the private sector created for particular purposes.)

Pricing system is needed as one means of holding hierarchical control within desired limits, just as public policy sometimes is needed for the same development in the private sector. In the consumer sector, there is an important need to retain fluidity and rapidity of change in opportunity for change in reallocation of resources. The pricing system needs to be used to the maximum extent for these purposes, but supplemented by public policy to prevent its excesses in income redistribution, in failure to produce opportunity for individuals, and in extremity of income fluctuations and instability. Policy and public action are needed, of course, to allow attainment of scale economies impossible for individuals. This is true, for example, in army and education, to provide a minimum of common ends to all persons, to prevent inequity in sharing rewards of the market and of progress and of ascertaining that sufficient progress will be attained. Public policies and organizations created to attain such society goals do, of course, give rise to some hierarchy and bureaucracy in implementation. Even though society prefers freedom, however, the pricing system alone gives rise to "unequal freedom."

One cannot claim that the structure of American society, aside from government, rests purely on a multitude of individuals as distinct decision-making units, each free to make and reject choices and to be highly free of the power of others. A large extent of pyramidal control of "many by a few" is true in the private sector even with the existence of a widely used pricing system wherein an individual family can have some effect on the allocation of resources. As Dahl and Lindbloom point out, whereever we turn we find most people dependent on and conforming to the hierarchical and bureaucratic processes of large scale organizations.[6]

Bureaucratic and hierarchical structure is typically adopted in bodies such as corporations, lobbying organizations, the country plant, labor unions, universities, farm organizations, professional associations, some churches and most other large nongovernmental groups. Black states that corporations, labor unions and churches are as effective as government in organizing and guiding people apart from their own individual inclinations.[7] T. V. Smith raises the same point in his statement.[8] "A new feudalism is upon us; in which each becomes . . . a masterless man unless we join something and let our organization try to master other organizations with which we have to bargain for a living—and then, alas, . . . our own organizations end by mastering us."

---

[5] R. A. Dahl and C. E. Lindbloom, *Politics, Economics and Welfare*, Harper and Brothers, New York, 1953, pp. 250 and 266.

[6] *Op. cit.*, p. 23.

[7] Cyril E. Black, "The Politics of Economic Growth," World Politics, July, 1961.

[8] T. V. Smith and R. A. Taft, *Foundations of Democracy*, Alfred A. Knopf, New York, pp. 247–51.

Typically, decisions and choices are not those which originate with the "masses" at the bottom, but are passed down from the top of modern organizations. Bureaucracy becomes valued itself, apart from money income, as an expression of status and power. As society grows and becomes more complex, this tendency of bureaucratic organization, outside of government and public organization and with existence of a pricing system, appears to grow.[9] The desire of status and power over others is evidently an incentive in this process, about as strong as profit developed through the pricing mechanism. (The two are highly related in corporate structure.) Complexity itself perhaps encourages this delegation in power and simplification of agendas. Government policy to strengthen the pricing mechanism and to make it more effective in attaining broadly accepted economic ends cannot, therefore, be looked upon as the only force leading to hierarchical and bureaucratic process and structure. The need in either case is for proper balance to be brought between autonomy of the individual and control by the organization and group.

The penalties, awards and competition which attach to the pricing system are effective in causing resources to shift among alternative uses as consumer preferences change and new public purposes are defined. They also provide incentive for progress. Yet it is easily agreed that the pricing mechanism is not perfect in these respects. Otherwise we would not have the agricultural colleges, the Soil Conservation Service, public schools, public exploration of space, and we would even allow private enterprise to provide us with police force and navy.

The pricing mechanism, with its tendency to become interlocked with particular institutional mechanisms, is not perfect when it leaves people stranded in low income and small productivity during their lifetime over much of agriculture. It is not perfect and is inconsistent with desires of society when it penalizes some greatly for their contribution in widespread progress gains to consumers generally, or where it leads to cycles and income fluctuations which cause large sacrifice to some in order that others may gain.

The challenge in policy is to improve and maximize the effectiveness of the pricing mechanism in its ability to allocate resources and extend progress. There are obvious examples of opportunities in this direction. Public investment in improved education and vocational guidance of children from the low-income families of the Mississippi Delta and Appalachian Mountains, so that they can better understand and take wider advantage of the price offerings in employment, is one.

But a challenge also exists in policy to balance one goal against another, as in rate of progress against equity in its distribution of gains and losses, or in compensation so that one segment does not make extreme sacrifice for gain of another. Particular restraints and institutional mechanisms may lessen somewhat the degree of competition and the viciousness of the pricing mechanism without stifling progress. Some of

[9] For *bureaucracy* as used here, see the technical meaning used by Dahl and Lindbloom, *op. cit.*, pp. 234–36.

the most progressive industries of the United States are not related to pure competition, even by a single generation or two removed. But selected features of competition and the pricing mechanism are preserved for the few firms that make up the automobile, oil, electrical equipment, steel and similar industries so that they are influenced by consumer preferences in resource allocation and are inspired to promote progress. This is a challenge in agricultural policy—to provide sufficient stability and retention of gains of progress in the industry, but to facilitate the continuous resource reallocation and progress needed and desired.

Pareto Optima in Policy

As we detail in Chapter 11, U.S. society has subscribed heavily to some general tenets of modern welfare economics as applied to agriculture, doing so a decade before these theories were set down fully and systematically. The basic tenet employed has been that of compensation to help guarantee that some are not made worse off while others gain from rapid development in agriculture. This is a useful context for policy, and modern welfare economics indeed has applicability in agricultural policies. Its principles can lead to policies which are more widely accepted within a greatly heterogeneous industry and which allow mutual gains for the industry and consumers. They also suggest policy elements which allow exercise of choice of people in selecting alternatives to better guarantee Pareto optimality, without forcing inflexible policy mold on all of agriculture.

Nostalgic Approaches to Policy

While modern welfare economics does have opportunity in important and broad application, it does have obvious limitations in practical policy formulation. It provides no means for specifying what the important values are (but it isn't expected to do so). And society generally has prescribed to full compensation only where the individual has no alternative in public decision, as in condemnation of land for roads and parks. Where opportunity to redress part of decline in income flow is possible through shift of resources to alternative uses, society has generally made the value judgement that this should be done and compensation should be only partial—a fact not entirely inconsistent with welfare economics principles. A greater limitation in welfare economics is this: It only defines an optimum where allocations can be shifted, or compensation exercised, so that each of two individuals or groups are made better off, or none are made worse off. It says nothing about the importance of the two individuals or who they are. "Who they are" is frequently expressed in the political process and this has been a continuous attempt of the various competing groups and organizations around agriculture. But "who they are" also has great importance if we examine possible policy elements against different people and economic goals.

Should policy be aimed only at lacing cash compensation payments to farms which have sacrificed in net income under supply progress and inelastic demand? Should it be in form allowing portion of it to be syphoned to those representing grain storage, input furnishing and similar sectors surrounding agriculture? Or should it be better attached to people, and particularly to farm youth whose abilities are not being fully trained and exploited? As emphasized elsewhere in this text, policy elements which emphasize only the immediate and the nostalgia of farm life, keeping the horizons of too many farm people and their children welded to a struggle with inadequate resources, are misleading and unfortunate. It diverts attention and investment from more productive areas for youth which often possess little of this nostalgia of older farmers, farm leaders, politicians and some agricultural economists.

Solutions in the Market and Resource Prices

The commercial farm problem has come to be defined as one where returns of resources are lower than those in other sectors. An immediate goal of policy becomes one of lifting the level of return to that of comparable quantity and quality of resources throughout the economy. This has tended to become a goal dominant over parity pricing, as well it should in a dynamic economy. The level of resource return can be boosted by numerous means: by withdrawal of resources from agriculture, as illustrated in the discussion of equations (5.1) through (5.19); by effecting monopoly production and pricing policy; and through the market, by letting prices decline for factors with inelastic supply.

In computations to estimate the level of return on farm resources, factor prices used typically are those existing under policy tying compensation and income transfers to these same resources. Too, the prices attached to land have reflected capitalization of some temporary income increment from abnormal postwar demand, in manner supposing it to be more permanent. Hence, a simple arithmetic means of fetching comparable resource returns to agriculture is simply to allow or encourage factor prices to decline. Land at $200 price per acre and $6 annual income has return of 3 percent. At $120 price, it has return of 5 percent. At the lower price and the same income per unit, investment of $100,000 will bring capital income of $5,000, but at $200 price it will fetch only $3,000. Should policy be extended in perpetuity to retain a comparable rate of return at the higher price, when consumers are willing to reward at this rate only if it is priced at $120?

As mentioned in Chapter 5, this restructuring of factor prices would do much to eliminate a farm problem which to an extent is a "paper problem." But to reshape land prices and bring solution to the "returns problem" by this avenue necessitates adjustments in other resources. To obtain the $5,000 capital returns, 833 acres are required with land price of $120, instead of the 500 acres consistent with the same rate of return on $200 land. Obviously, then, solution of the "paper problem" involves real human problems in a smaller population so that there can be fewer farm families and a smaller labor force over a range of scale economies.

The resource pricing and return problem of the above nature can be solved only as farm people in large numbers take a capital loss in land values and some migrate. Solution through the "paper and land values route" is not as painless as the arithmetic would imply. It would be preferable, however, if compensation to account for such losses could be detached from resources in a manner to facilitate these transfers of labor and to allow land per se to take on lower values for new entrants of farming. Numerous mechanisms would lead to these ends, including cash payments to people who move and negotiable marketing quotas which are entirely unrelated to physical resources.

POLICY FOR GENERAL SOCIAL ADJUSTMENT

Policy which gears agriculture to national economic development would be more readily possible if we turned to broader social policy, and less to farm policy per se. This is true because of the growing economic interdependence of agriculture with national economy, and the supplying of a smaller proportion of inputs from within the industry, as illustrated in Chapter 7; and the economic and political interdependence among farm and nonfarm sectors of rural communities explained in Chapter 9. The latter interdependence, and the concentration purely on agricultural policy per se, helps to restrain or prevent actions which would draw the structure of agriculture nearer to the facts and prospects of national economic growth.

Again, soil bank payments in the late '50's and early '60's were means for redressing low farm incomes, moving people from agriculture and allowing concentrated shift of land resources in marginal areas. But while they contributed thus to solution of farm problems, they promised to create the same problems for other persons and institutions of rural communities with fortunes dependent on the magnitude of farm population. The soil bank approach found strong opposition in the political process, and rather than to cause diminution of land input (1) in pattern consistent with long-run regional adjustment needs and (2) to attain given level of output reduction at minimum cost, its implementation was dispersed over the entire nation.

Here again is where the principles of modern welfare economics have highly practical application in policy. Compensation and transfers which redress losses of some sectors but cause sacrifices to impinge on other sectors will generally be resisted. In fact, a concentrated soil bank or land withdrawal program which compensates farm people for loss from development has the effect of transferring this loss to other people of rural communities. Hence, the important tenet of welfare economics, of practical importance in obtaining acceptable policy, is that which gives rise to programs which attempt to "cause no one to be worse off," or which minimize the extent to which losses are distributed to other persons who do not have offsetting gain.

Sensibly, this means that policy to solve the problems of agriculture should be directed to the entire communities of which agriculture is a part. Pareto optimum would be readily realized in the above context, for example, if policy could lead to industrial development in every community. All persons in agriculture realizing loss from economic development then could have greater compensation from industrial employment in the community, with the market and tax base thus retained or expanded for the nonfarm sector of the same community. Some communities have this hope, and the rural development program initiated in 1956 and depressed area legislation in 1961 were public aids in this direction, the former largely as an informational facet, however. (The retraining and subsistence payments for the retraining period in the depressed area legislation are more consistent with the needs of many communities.)

Unfortunately, the shape of national economic progress does not allow this "fair exchange" for all rural areas, and general policy directed to adjustment problems of the entire community must take other forms. Even depressed area legislation cannot extend effectively to some of the secondary structural changes which stem from technical progress and changed factor prices for agriculture and rural businesses. Existing and prospective technology and changing factor prices which cause substitution of capital for labor will continue to drain labor and population from many farm regions. Parts of such broad regions of the Great Plains and Cornbelt simply are not endowed with location or natural resources which can give rise to either take-off or perpetuation of industry. This also is true in numerous regions in the South and Southeast, and at selected locations over the rest of the nation, where shift to forestry and grassland, plus the change in proportion of capital and labor has caused, and will continue to cause, the farm population to thin further.

With thinning of the farm population and great reach to shopping and commercial centers via automobile, local employment opportunities in concentrated farm communities also dwindle for the nonfarm portion of the labor force. As detailed previously, mobility is greatest for youth entering the labor force and other younger and more flexible persons. With melting away of job opportunities and attraction to higher wages and more challenging living conditions elsewhere, depopulation comes mainly through persons in lower age groups. Increasingly, and alarmingly for some communities, the remaining population tends to be concentrated in the higher age groups. The voting majority then is with the stratum of the population which has time horizon and geographical vision in economic growth and public investment at large variance with those of the nation's population at large. Appropriations for investment in local schools and community facilities become restricted in fashion to penalize those who move out into the national stream of employment and growth. Yet there is not necessarily inconsistency of public action and tax appropriations at these local levels with concepts of equity and investment. Should the mountainous area of east Kentucky make the full investment in education to develop youth into productive human resources for the firms and community of Cleveland? Should Washington County, Colorado, do similarly for the youth who will become work force and community in Orange County, California? Agriculture has always made investments of this type, causing a transfer of the surplus from the industry to other sectors. But over past centuries it was relatively much wealthier and had major resources relative to the rest of the economy.

If national goals and inspiration in economic growth are to be realized, the general public will be obliged to invest much more heavily in education and related public facilities of declining rural communities. Education is dismally inadequate in many rural communities. This need in broader investment is only partly a task of "equalization," to be made within states and from state resources. With greater and longer migration among states, it is a task in national investment in education, training and counseling to provide improved human resources and greater employment opportunities for youth who may serve much more productively in work force and plant in distant states. Only then can we be sure that rural state legislators will not write and pass appropriations for institutions of higher learning with the stipulation that the university graduate who takes employment elsewhere must reimburse the state for the cost of his education.

Scale Economies and the Farm Community

Technological revolution in agriculture and the draw of nonfarm wage rates have decreased the farm population and shifted the demand leftward for many of the consumer commodities and services retailed in towns of rural areas. This trend itself has given rise to "distressed areas" of varying degree. But the forces causing the structure of the rural trading community to be obsolete extend beyond the forces of the farm alone. In a manner, they are caught up in the same sinews of economic development as is agriculture.

Technological developments and factor prices give rise to types of producing units differing from those of the past and embodying scale economies and cost advantages relating to volume. Accordingly, fewer organizations, firms and plants are required in the community to provide consumers goods, to furnish farm inputs, to supply credit and even to provide public sector services. Consequently the bounds of an efficient trading and public service community extend much further in space than formerly.

The structure of the rural community has long been obsolete. It is growing progressively so with automation and similar technical development and the relative lowering of capital price, causing machinery and facilities to replace labor. Farm communities are almost as overequipped with towns as they are with farm resources. On the average, income of nonfarm persons in communities lacking industrial activity is little better than that of agriculture.

Technological changes, giving rise to economies of scale in milk assembly and processing, in livestock and grain marketing, and in commodity storage, have enlarged the size of business units efficient for these operations. The "trading community" thus must extend over more space and farms for efficiency in these techniques, just as the firm using them needs to be larger for efficient operation. Also, technology in transportation causes the community to reach out further, with the scale economies of community size calling for fewer towns and communities—just as in the case of scale economies and fewer farms.

The same situation holds true in retailing of consumer goods and distribution of farm inputs such as fertilizer, feed, fuel and farm machinery. Economies of scale and factor prices cause the supermarket, rather than the small general store, to be the efficient mode of retailing over broad farm regions. But because of these scale economies, there is room for fewer retailers and the trade center needs to be larger. The cost curve representing the spatial extent of town and trading center over surrounding farm territory declines over a much greater mileage than in the days of the blacksmith, the wagonload of hogs or wheat and the five gallon can of cream.

Even the credit suppliers in many rural areas are of inadequate scale and institutional structure for the capital needs emerging in agriculture. The trend in custom mix and bulk blending of fertilizers and feeds and towards larger-scale farm machines, with fewer machines to be retailed, extends the size of the community to be serviced if important scale economies are to be realized. In general, however, country towns still have a skeleton developed for the earlier set of techniques in both farming and the provision of services to farm communities. There are too many of them, in farm resource demand, farm population and the economies of scale involved in processing and retailing.

The spatial extent of the rural trading community is typically inadequate in providing services of direct importance in the development and maintenance of abilities and health of people. Modern medicine, dentistry and hospital services require a large volume for low unit costs and adequate return or attraction of the skilled labor used in them. The "scale of operation" needed for efficient public education also has grown greatly with the complexity of requirements in education.

While Conant has suggested a minimum graduating class of around 100 for efficient education, this number of students exceeds total high school enrollment in a very large number of rural communities. The small-sized rural service community is increasingly handicapped in producing efficient education, government services and other public utilities which also have scale economies requiring a larger volume, as its tax base declines with fewer persons, less personal property and lower real estate values in dwindling country towns. At the very time the small town should be upgrading public services and education, with the latter to prepare human resources for transfer to other growth sectors, it has greater constraint in doing so. The rural community is decreasingly able to subsidize the cost of educating youth who will migrate both occupationally and geographically.

The decline in farm population and the attendant dwindle in younger persons also creates other secondary adjustment problems. Expenditures at the local level are not kept apace of national investments for facilities which are part of the consumer complex in attaining the higher utility and living standards of a wealthy society faced with further economic growth. The resource base is too small to allow their financing through property taxes. Relative to the expanse in opportunities for consumption by older population segments for the nation at large, rural communities often are highly restricted. The community, in historical construct of space and resources, is too small to cope with the many changes falling upon it, in provision of reasonable local public facilities and in the most productive development of human resources for national extension. It alone, for example, cannot support facilities appropriately adapted to support vocational and retraining programs making people most useful for outside opportunities. It needs to be broadened in many ways, ranging from consolidation of county governments and facilities in some regions, to merge with national society in selected investments—such as part of those involved in training and development of human resources.

The land-grant colleges and state extension services, those historic means of implementation of economic development in agriculture, could gear their local services to better meet these needs. A simple precedent, where politically acceptable, would be transformation from county offices in extension education to regional offices including four to six counties. One advantage in this change would be in better attaining scale economies and thus being able to provide extended facilities and guidance to communities. For example, specialists are more nearly possible with consolidation of county units, thus allowing greater concentration on solution of community adjustment and investment problems—as well as on the technical advances of agriculture which give rise to adjustment forces. According to time and transportation, a geographic unit of six counties is smaller, with modern automobiles, than was a single county for local government and public facilities in the days of horse transportation.

With the great interdependence of farm and nonfarm sectors, policy needs broadening to general social construct, rather than in concentration on agriculture. Society should have goals which extend to all communities for greater development and utilization of human resources; for giving more individuals maximum opportunity in development and exercise of their capabilities; for raising the level of living and general opportunity for consumption enjoyment, consistent with a large national income, reasonably to all people; for facilitating the speed, minimizing the pain and in making reasonable indirect redress of social costs for adjustments in the over-all structure of rural communities; and, in the sense of the political process, for causing farm policy which is consistent with the long-run variables of economic growth to become more widely acceptable.

As we have stated before, nonfarm people stranded in rural communities, and with income losses resulting from the same variables causing depression of farm income and labor force, are no less important than those on farms. Transfers from these segments of population in rural communities, like those from farms, have served reasonably well in economic development. Many persons making them, even over long distances, have realized important gains in income and living level. However, in some instances the costs are exceedingly high for families and place an important restraint on them. Often these costs must be borne by people with little ability to carry them. This is true not only for transfer costs falling directly on some who migrate, but also for the relatively greater burden which falls on smaller numbers who remain. This burden consists of making greater investment per head in developing and educating other persons who will feed out into the national machine of expansion.

Extreme Assumptions

Two sets of assumptions have been carried in respect to agriculture and the policies needed for it. These assumptions have both been too extreme, and have carried policy proposals in somewhat unrealistic directions, given the actual environment which exists. At the one extreme has been the implicit assumption of one set of proposals that pure competition prevails throughout the economy. Under this set of assumptions, one is led to measure resource value productivities and urgently to press that resources be uprooted and redistributed until productivities are brought quickly together. This set of concepts supposes that long-run conditions of competitive equilibrium can be brought about readily. But it stands to err in recommendations in the sense that it may reduce aggregate or community welfare. It may do so in the sense that it does not recognize the utility and monetary costs which attach to the resources which have to make rapid transfer. It may impose an inequitable cost of change on older people who have low flexibility.

At the other extreme is the set of assumptions which supposes that the nonfarm economy approaches pure monopoly and that the short-run structure of agriculture should be extended forever into the future through policy which converts the structure of agriculture to that of monopoly industry. This set of recommendations promises to prove inequitable or too restraining on many young people of agriculture. With extreme preoccupation on monopoly and perpetuation of current farm structure, this set of concepts tends to overlook economic growth and the potential of individuals to have their lifetime welfare increased by training and educational investment to better their opportunity in nonfarm industry. The first philosophy tries to accordion the long run into the short run; the second tries to prolong the short run into the long run. But the extreme assumptions of both are unrealistic. Nonfarm industry is not characterized by pure competition, or even short-run commodity price competition. But neither is it one which averts commodity price competition in the long run, or averts short-run competition: for resources, in new products, in improved technology and in capturing a larger share of the short-run demand.

As long as they reside in competing political regimes the highly developed nations of the world have no choice but to promote progress within their boundaries and to aid it in other nations. Developed nations have even come to the point where they must promote and maintain high growth rates partly to insure "status." With these strong forces encouraging and requiring economic growth at acceptable rates, its effects will continue to spill over into agriculture. The market and price forces tying U.S. agriculture to the national economy are now so great that retarded progress of technology in agriculture would be extremely difficult if not impossible. The pull of wage rates in drawing labor out of the industry, the relatively favorable prices of capital causing mechanization and technological innovation, and the farm use of large input of capital items encouraging their research and supply by industry outside of agriculture—these are all strong forces to perpetuate economic development in agriculture. And even though agriculture is declining to a small fraction of the economy, there is no reason that it should be left outside the national development complex. At the same time, however, there is no reason why the conventional and orthodox long-run goals in economic marginalism should be applied tightly to agriculture and not to other industries. Given the total mix of the economy, it is now more important that they be applied to the nonfarm economy if growth at higher rates is to be effectively achieved.

Agriculture has been subjected to a high degree of scrutiny and analysis in respect to its manpower productivity and degree of disequilibrium. When problems of measurement and efficiency and gross national product increments are tackled with equal vigor for all industries and labor sectors, and if the common goal of industry organization and resource combinations to attain this goal are equally promoted for all sectors, then a relevant criterion for fashioning farm programs is: They should result in a use of resources which causes their marginal value productivities, farm family values considered, to be comparable between industries and segments of industries. The method of attainment would be in exodus of resources from farming, rather than in supply control of agriculture. But attainment of these technical conditions for agriculture lacks great practical significance as long as equal effort is not invested in removing the imperfections of factor markets, industry organization, and institutions and conditions of other sectors which stand in the way of maximum efficiency and growth in national product, measured in the classical manner. Excitement can be raised for arguments and programs proposed for measurement and refashioning of agriculture, with the goal being that of even more rapid and national benefit, when equal intensity is devoted to measurement and improvement of resource efficiency in all industries.

Since society has placed high priority on advances in economic growth and agricultural productivity and because these advances now benefit directly and greatly the larger consuming population, sometimes at the expense of the farm population, there is no economic basis for letting people in agriculture bear the major costs and sacrifices attending these broad national gains. Policies can be designed which compensate the inflexible members of this generation of farmers, without unduly forcing them into the nonfarm labor stream, but which do not weld their sons and daughters to agriculture. This can be true particularly where talents of the latter stand to be greatly needed in production of nonfarm products and where their incomes and life satisfactions might be enhanced by these transfers.

Policy also can be designed which allows economic and technical progress in agriculture, as contribution to national developmental goals, while allowing agriculture to retain positive gains in the process. (See Chapter 16.) As much as anything, policy developed for direct compensation should be in terms of living levels which a society characterized by relative wealth and advanced economic development considers to be a minimum, not only in terms of human nutrition but also in terms of the U.S. standard of life and the ability to invest greater amounts in development of the human resource represented by farm children. Economic principle indicates two basic conditions for national welfare maximization: those relating to resource efficiency and those relating to equity in income distribution. No logical or mathematical basis exists for putting the focus only on one, such as resource efficiency.

For many of the current generation of farmers the equity criterion may be more relevant than the efficiency criterion as a standard for programs and adaptation of agriculture. But more important for their children and consequent contributions to progress, policy needs to emphasize development of human talents and opportunity consistent with their abilities in future decades. This loss over recent decades may be much greater than the social costs of retaining too many resources in agriculture during the 1950's.

Demand should not be placed on agriculture to accept types and degrees of resource adjustments and pricing policies which are not also requested of other major resource and industry groups. If prices and their levels in agriculture are suggested to serve largely for purposes of channeling resources into uses which will maximize the national product, in the context of marginal economics, then equal force should be diverted to the same functioning of prices for oligopoly industries, labor unions, etc. If important nonfarm industries and resource groups are permitted to use price and quantity as means of diverting desired or larger shares of the national product to themselves, without great concern over effects on the magnitude of the national product, then agriculture should have the same opportunity. In the same vein, programs for agriculture should not be based on appeals and economic reasoning which do not also apply to other sectors of society.

Planners of programs designed for the short run, which can serve as a step toward long-run needs, should recognize that many established farm people are inflexible, both in their professional abilities and values and attachments developed from life in rural communities. Programs should, in light of these values and the nonmonetary and secondary social costs often associated with transfer, provide alternatives which allow older people to select choices which maximize their longer-run welfare. Still they should not be part, even in the sense of lack in positive educational policy, of a general body of programs which forces values onto farm children and causes them to become inflexible in choice of training, location of effort, and ability to become integrated into other types of communities. Rather than require them to stay on undersized and low-income farms to receive income subsidies through support prices, allotment payments and similar mechanisms, farm people should be given choices in compensation method, with some putting large gains in adjustments which facilitate transfer and national economic progress. The choice would be their own, and they would not be forced into a single alternative. The choice could be entirely consistent with their values and attachment to rural or other communities. They could, for example, be given choice between: collecting as a lump sum at the present the amount which would otherwise be forthcoming over a specified future period (say 5 years) under farm programs of types in past years, should they select to forego currently inadequate units and move to other employment alternatives, or remaining in agriculture and collecting annual payments of the levels realized from various policies applied to farming.

Such programs would simply serve as a financial aid to those who prefer to move elsewhere, so that they could increase their level of income and life satisfactions. As we point out in later chapters, choices such as these would allow attainment of Pareto-better-optimality. But these policy elements, more positive than those of the past, can be successful only under national economic growth rates which allow absorption of migrants into the labor force.

However, policies which are positive in the sense that they result in transfer of people who can lift their level of income and utility and contribute to general economic progress cannot solve all of the progress costs which fall on commercial agriculture as a result of technical advance exceeding rate of demand increase. This progress is certainly desirable and necessary, but means are needed so that some fruit of the progress can remain with farm producers. The historic drag of farm incomes behind nonfarm incomes will be solved only by increasing supply elasticity for resources such as labor which have low mobility rate from agriculture and those such as land which shift too tardily to other agricultural uses. Long-run agricultural policy should rest in this direction. However, as long as large numbers of persons of rural communities also are tied to the fortunes and structure of the industry, and as long as great imbalance exists in agriculture, complete structural change cannot be effected in an extremely short period.

The transition period required for U.S. agriculture is a decade, or even two decades if rate of technical advance continues to race far ahead of demand. Efficient policy would use such a time goal, hoping to bring agriculture into rough resource balance by this time but averting regional or area change at rates which are inconsistent with abilities of people and communities to adjust. It would include elements to increase factor supply elasticity in the manner proposed above. But it also would, as long as society judges agriculture to suffer losses in income and welfare for gain of consumers through rapid supply shift, provide for compensation or other mechanisms which allow commercial agriculture to be rewarded positively for its contribution to progress—but still to maintain progress. The challenge for policy is to encourage flexibility of the industry in adoption of new techniques and in shift of resources within and outside the industry in conformance with consumer demand and factor prices, but also to provide income protection and stability for those who remain in the industry both as producers of food and as contributors to economic growth. After examining policies which are alternatives in the latter sense, we will turn back to those aimed primarily at increasing factor flexibility and supply elasticity.

11

Compensation Policy and Supply Control

Society in the United States has conducted a dichotomous search for satisfactory policy to allow progress but to guarantee that the full cost of technical advance does not fall on agriculture. The various public policies since 1930 represent attempts by society, with nonpassive encouragement from agriculture, to compensate the farm industry for projected losses stemming from sharp technical and supply advance in face of inelastic demand. The creation of institutions and policy mechanisms which allow and encourage progress, redress serious losses to particular groups resulting therefrom and prevent scorn in magnitude of outlay and method of use of public funds is the crucial farm issue of the 1960's. Further developmental policy and investment in agriculture will be desired if, and as, the nation meets its international challenges and obvious responsibilities. Yet how can farmers reap an equitable share of the reward from their contribution to progress?

Our purpose in this chapter is, starting as given with the premise that society does wish to provide compensation and invests on large scale to accomplish the end, to examine some of the economic alternatives and implications of these. Not all of the policies discussed are basically of compensation nature. Some relate to price and income stability and market power. However, we discuss them in this chapter so that the various elements of the policy subset can be seen in better perspective relative to each other. (Other comparisons of policy means are included in Chapter 14 and subsequent chapters.)

COMPENSATION METHODS

The major funds transferred from general society to agriculture as price supports, nonrecourse loans, per acre payments, practice payments and other forms can be interpreted as (1) compensation for reduced income resulting from society's investment in increasing supply under inelastic demand (2) equity payments to draw real per capita income of agriculture, with its historic lag, nearer the level of the nonfarm sector or (3) a method whereby a competitive industry acquires gain comparable to that obtained through market power possessed by less competitive groups. The first is the deeper philosophic reason and the one more compatible with the methods employed and the distribution of transfer funds over the last several decades. Transfers based on equity and low income alone would be retrogressive to level of income, with a much greater proportion going to the poverty sector of agriculture. The operational goal in use of the larger funds evidently has been compensation, to assure that the distribution of gains and losses growing out of technical advance and supply increase in agriculture do, in fact, increase aggregate welfare. The direct gains are distributed widely, in abundance and low real price of food to all consumers. The direct losses result to farmers as output increases under inelastic demand, revenue necessarily declining to the industry.

Within the farm industry, there are gains for those operators favorably situated in respect to technical advance, either in buying feed and related resources at lower price or with own yields increasing in greater proportion than for the industry or than in decline of price. But with industry revenue declining, farmers who experience loss in revenue are faced with welfare decline. If the transfers from 1930 to 1960 were not for compensation purposes, then an entirely different structure of programs should have been used.

Income to resources in agriculture could have been pushed nearer the levels specified by the conventional marginal conditions of economic equilibrium, by moving resources out of agriculture to increase their return through (1) increasing their marginal physical product, (2) decreasing output and increasing price, both leading to an increase in marginal value productivity, and (3) decreasing the return of resources in other industries in the manner of a general equilibrium model. This movement has, of course, taken place but the slack has never been "taken up" because the rate of technical advance has freed more labor as rapidly as some has left farming. Had society selected to use the conventional equilibrium model as its goal, rather than compensation to guarantee that the direct distribution of gains and losses assured aggregate gain, it would have better invested the transfer funds in payments to cover moving, housing, relocation and income costs to a greater number of persons who could have migrated but did not, and also in guaranteeing economic growth of magnitude to absorb a greater number of migrants.

Hence, with interpretation of past transfer funds as compensation for the purposes outlined above, it is appropriate that the method of these payments be analyzed. Given compensation of particular magnitude as an instrumental goal, what is the most efficient means of affecting it? We turn to analysis of alternative compensation means, given a particular set of funds to be transferred. We can compare the means in terms of (1) the equity in the compensation method as against the distribution of gains and losses, (2) the least-cost method of putting compensation of particular magnitude into the hands of farm people, or the method which will transform given appropriations by the public into maximum compensation for agriculture and (3) the extent to which the method interferes least with the allocation of resources and leaves maximum specification to the open market and preference of consumers.

Equity in Method of Compensation

Funds transferred to agriculture for purposes of (1) accomplishing compensation and (2) eliminating the problems of low income and poverty are for quite different purposes. They require somewhat different programs in terms of general structure and entirely different ones in terms of the distribution of transfer payments. Accordingly, the two programs should be kept separate, except as they come together in other realms at the level of education and investment in improved nonfarm opportunities for those who can best improve welfare by occupational migration. Transfer payments to accomplish compensations should be ordered in magnitude of loss to each individual. With inability of interpersonal utility comparisons, the only manageable magnitude to reflect loss is income. Therefore, the individual who has experienced greatest income loss, through growing output and inelastic demand, should receive the greatest compensation. Generally this will be the person with the greatest income. And also generally, though not entirely, the person with the greatest income is the one with the greatest output and resources. On this basis, then, payments for compensation purposes should not have ceiling or upper restraint, but should be distributed in approximation of predicted loss. But at the same time, funds appropriated for these purposes should not be allowed to seep out to persons who have had no loss from the developmental variables of relevance, such as nonfarmers purchasing land to claim compensation, beginning farmers who have been detached from previous losses and sectors surrounding agriculture who have suffered no price or income decline on the services and resources which they provide to the farm industry. In division of compensation between tenant or landlord, payments should be in proportion to incidence of loss. In general, this division should be in proportion to income, but if payment includes an element to cover capital loss, it should go to the owner of the resource, rather than to be divided in any manner.

Here the recommendation of no restraint on magnitude of payment is based on supposition of transfer for compensation basis. Structuring of payments for meeting equity or poverty goals would be on an entirely different basis. The recommendation of compensation in proportion to loss is based on the tenets of welfare economics supposing (1) that change causing both gains and losses cannot guarantee aggregate welfare increase unless compensation is used to redress sacrifice and (2) measurement of utility of income, or its comparison among individuals, is impossible and no basis exists for saying that marginal utility of a dollar is greater for one than for another individual.

DIRECT PAYMENTS IN COMPENSATION

The least-cost method for society to place a given amount of compensation from treasury outlay in the hands of farmers is undoubtedly direct payments. Aside from small administrative costs, a quantity less than for any other type of compensation program, nearly all of the money appropriated for compensation purposes can be put in the hands of farmers. The method allows maximum returns to farmers from a given allocation of funds by the public, or allows a given transfer of funds to agriculture at minimum treasury cost. (But it is not guaranteed as the method which minimizes treasury costs in transfer of a given amount of income to farmers.) Unlike price supports above market levels with required storage, none of the funds from direct payments need be siphoned off into commodity storage and similar sectors. Neither does investment need to be made in a large staff to administer and police the program, as in the case of input or output quotas. Finally, under certain conditions to be outlined later, direct payments can give more complete freedom to the market in allocating resources of agriculture among commodities in line with consumer preference.

Under certain structure of transfers, direct payments can even aid the pricing mechanism in adjusting the resource mix of agriculture so that excess resources leave the industry and move into sectors where they have greater long-run opportunity. Direct payments can have greater flexibility than other compensation methods in providing this mix of (1) minimum cost of a given public compensation outlay and (2) maximum effect for the market.

The compensation method used from 1930 to 1960, based on support prices and loans, caused these imbalances: First, the magnitude of farm output was greater than necessary or desired by consumers. The programs caused, in the conventional economic sense, too many resources to be used for food. Second, they encouraged the wrong mix of farm product, with too many being allocated in the direction of grains and cotton. Third, they caused some resources to be diverted to fertilizer production, storage facilities and other inputs and capital investment to produce more surplus and to store it, when the nation had little or no direct use for the increment of product so represented.

Direct payments could allow supply and demand to interact giving levels of prices which would clear the market without continuous accumulation of surpluses. With markets cleared and average annual output held back to consumption levels, excess resources and treasury costs would not need to go into the nonfarm inputs which otherwise are used to produce surpluses, and to store them after they are produced. But not all direct payment methods will accomplish this collection of instrumental goals. To do so, the payment must be a lump-sum quantity, devoid of relation to units of output or inputs used in future periods. (But lump-sum payment can still be based on past or historic base without affecting future output.) Once direct payments become scheduled to inputs or outputs, they promise to draw or hold an "overage" of resources in agriculture and of products onto the market. The effect is similar to that of support prices which jut above market prices. As price declines because supply shifts more rapidly to the right than demand, a compensation or subsidy scheme which represents an addition to per unit price of the market will cause output to "over-shoot" demand, causing both an intensified depression of market price and a larger quantity of subsidy or compensation payments than flat or lump-sum payments. Under direct payments attached to each unit of output, public outlay will be greater than for price supports through government purchase and storage of commodities. With direct payments this excessive quantity can still clear the markets, but under support prices and government storage, it goes into stocks with surplus buildup.

Other means of compensation (or more correctly, price and income restoration or maintenance) exist which require smaller treasury outlays while throwing more of the burden on consumer expenditures through the market. The latter are much less "visible" than direct payments since the income transfer is made entirely or partly through the market.

Let us illustrate the difference in lump-sum compensation and per unit compensation, both provided as direct payments. To do so adequately, we should start from the firm's production function and trace technological change through the cost and supply functions in the manner of Chapters 3 and 4. However, to provide the reader with less manipulation at this point we start at industry supply and demand with an "overly simple" annual model, remembering, of course, that outcome would be modified slightly if we considered changes in factor prices and production coefficients and the magnitude of compensation so specified—although the qualitative outcome would still be the same. Hence, we suppose the original industry demand and supply functions in (11.1) and (11.2). Then in the new situation, demand increases to (11.3) and through technical change and given factor prices, supply changes to (11.4).

$$Q_d = a - 2P \tag{11.1}$$

$$Q_s = .79a + .1P \tag{11.2}$$

$$Q_d' = 1.1a - 2.2P \tag{11.3}$$

$$Q_s' = .948a + .12P \tag{11.4}$$

The equilibrium quantities for these two situations are indicated in Table 11.1. Total revenue declines from $.08a^2$ to $.0626a^2$ due to a price elasticity less than unity and a rate of increase in supply which exceeds that of demand.

TABLE 11.1

EQUILIBRIUM QUANTITIES UNDER ORIGINAL AND NEW SUPPLY AND DEMAND SITUATIONS. MAGNITUDES DETERMINED IN FREE MARKET

Quantity	Original	New
Equilibrium price	$.1a$	$.0655a$
Equilibrium output	$.8a$	$.9559a$
Total revenue	$.08a^2$	$.0626a^2$
Price elasticity (demand)	.25	.15

Now, to simplify calculations as compared to analysis through cost and net return changes, first suppose compensation is made for this loss in revenue. On a flat or lump-sum basis it would total $.08a^2-.063a^2 = .017a^2$. This amount would be divided among farmers according to their individual losses in revenue, perhaps roughly in proportion to their share of output before the change. In effect, a lump-sum payment would be the same as giving the farmer a base on which he would be paid compensation, with no payment on output exceeding the base.

But instead of such lump-sum compensation, now suppose that direct payments are specified to provide the difference between the old ($.1a$) and new ($.0655a$) price levels—a type of "parity pricing" procedure. Hence, farmers are, in effect, guaranteed a price of $.1a$ on all they produce. Under the new technology and supply function (11.4), they will produce $.948a+.12(.1a)=.960a$ output, an amount exceeding the market equilibrium quantity of $.9559a$. But consumers will absorb this quantity, as indicated by (11.3), only at a price of $.5a-.455(.96a)=.0632a$. Total revenue in the market under this per unit price guarantee is $(.960a)(.0632a)=.0607a^2$. As compared to original revenue, market revenue now declines by $.08a^2-.061a^2=.019a^2$, more than the revenue reduction when markets were cleared without a price guarantee.

If compensation is paid as difference between original ($.1a$) and subsidy-inspired ($.0632a$) market price, the difference to be made up in direct subsidy payment is $.0368a$ per unit, the total subsidy amounting to $(.960a)(.0368a)=.036a^2$, an amount more than twice the amount ($.017a^2$) when subsidy is under a lump-sum system of direct payment. Under flat or lump-sum payment and a market price of $.0655a$, consumers would pay a higher proportion of the supply price. This is as it should be where the pricing system is used as over-all allocative mechanism, and other means as public schools and progressive taxation are used to bring equity in income distribution over consumers in general (supplemented by other means to meet particular public purposes, to redress injustices in distribution of gains and losses and place economic groups on comparable market power footing).

In the case of per unit payments, the consumer would pay a smaller proportion of the supply price and the public treasury would have to bear a larger subsidy burden, with some mal-allocation of resources occurring relative to market-expressed wishes of consumers. In both cases, however, the market would be cleared without buildup in stocks as under support prices and public storage.

Our example has been with "full restitution" of price or revenue loss. Where it is only at "some portion of parity" or price, the results would be of the same relative differences, being only smaller in magnitude. The conclusion is clear in any case: If compensation is made, direct payments can be a lower-cost method, in terms of treasury outlay, than price supports, production control and storage, such as used in the 1930's and 1950's. However, price support through supply control to avoid surpluses and storage requires an even smaller treasury cost of compensation, the incidence of compensation being thrown mainly to the consumer through the market. A lump-sum payment, unrelated to marginal costs or revenues through per unit additions to price or outlays, is the most efficient method of direct compensation, in total costs and in freedom of market to allocate resources. The market freedom applies not only to domestic consumers but also allows a better gearing of output to foreign demand, with farm commodity being less priced out of the international market as under nonrecourse loans and public storage.

Direct payments, but on a unit basis, were used in the United States to encourage production of hogs, milk and other commodities under price ceilings during World War II, for wool production during and after the Korean War, for sugar under quotas, and by Canada for certain livestock products in recent years. In general it can be said that experience conforms to theory. Direct payments per unit of output serve positively to increase production whether this be desired as during war in the U.S. or whether it be a method of income compensation as in Canada in the postwar period.

Payment per unit, to avoid output expansion effects, would have to be limited to some historic quantity such as the amount produced in a previous period, or as a quota representing the new equilibrium quantity. Direct payment in pure lump-sum fashion, estimated to cover income loss and paid without regard for production (or paid only on a prescribed output base), would be better consistent with the compensation principle and have minimum effect on resource allocation. Difficulty arises, of course, in estimating its quantity per farm, per unit basis perhaps being the more nearly politically acceptable method. Direct payments of this general lump-sum nature were somewhat represented by the "parity payments" of the early 1930's and the conservation reserve income transfer starting in 1956, but both of these were directed also to production control.

Values and Compensation Method

Direct payments leave greater power to the market—in erasing surplus stocks, in bringing forth a more appropriate mix of farm products with less historic proportioning, and in farm output level—than support price-storage which allows attainment of the same compensation level. To the extent that resources so awarded remain in the industry, they still invite some "overage" of factors in the industry, but their product can be swept away by market-free prices. Elements of direct payment could be added, however, which would not retard but would catalyze migration of labor and capital.

For example, the individual given the same right to lump-sum payment if he stayed or left agriculture would not weigh the compensation in his marginal calculation of transfer to other industry. With or without the lump-sum payment, if made on "once and for all" basis, marginal gain or change in income would be roughly the same in shift between industries. The lump-sum might provide him with funds for transfer, if he could not otherwise collect enough. But even if direct "once and for all" compensation tended to cause them to remain, farm families could be given their choice: a given amount if they remained in agriculture, but this plus a bonus if they migrate. Paretoan optimum conditions would be favored, no person moving unless doing so increased his welfare. Those who suffer disutility from accepting subsidy payment, direct or indirect, could also have Pareto optimum: they need not exercise the right to it, whether they remain on farms or leave.

Our quantitative example was with annual payment, the discussion immediately above with "once and for all" single payment. Either could be used. Difficulty with "once and for all" payment is in establishing its quantity. Theoretically, a series of annual lump-sum payments has the present value, L, in (11.5) where A_i is income deficit in the ith year to be compensated and r is the appropriate discount rate, the compensation to extend for n years.

$$L = \sum_{i=1}^{n} A_i(1 + r)^{-i} \tag{11.5}$$

The difficulty with annual compensation payment is in establishing how long the payments "ought" to run. The "once and for all" lump-sum payment would be preferable to the annual lump-sum payment in encouraging resources to leave agriculture, but the annual attachment is no stronger in holding resources to agriculture than equal compensation under price support and surplus storage.

Perhaps a question of values attaches to compensation method. Is it true that the U.S. farmer believes a subsidy or compensation to be just or desirable only if it comes through the market place? The equivalent of subsidy or price level goal is attained by other economic sectors through various mechanisms of the market which do not show up directly as tax payments and as transfers among groups. Protective tariffs, marketing orders for fruits and vegetables, monopoly production and pricing, and even farm support prices cause transfers to take place under the label of market quantities and in a manner not directly apparent to consumers and taxpayers. The transfers to producer groups favored by these institutions could take place by allowing prices to drop to their free competition market level, with taxation and subsidy to replace them.

(Such a transfer of income from consumers to producers of electrical equipment would have saved the stiff fines and jail sentences imposed against firms of the latter in 1961 for monopoly conspiracy.)

Some of the heavy public discussion of direct payments implies them to be restrained by value orientations, although the method has long been used for airline mail services. Further research is needed on this value problem, or its interdependence with political stance among groups conflicting along a contract curve, and on possible reluctance of farm producers to have subsidies directly labeled in cash quantity (versus having them less apparent through the market). It is not impossible that Brewster's work ethic creed in values, "one fails to deserve esteem . . . if easy ways . . . (are) selected in employment of choice,"[1] does have relevance. There appear to be instances where farmers favor direct payments, and others where they favor market-oriented income transfers.[2]

SUPPORT PRICES AND NONRECOURSE LOANS

Support prices based on parity or historic price levels, loans without recourse to make them effective and public ownership and storage of surpluses have been the main policy means since 1930, with the direct instrumental goal being that of higher prices. As a means to compensate farmers for unfavorable distribution of gains and losses stemming from technical advance, the price-support/loans/storage road requires a greater outlay for a given level of compensation than do direct payments, or allows lower farmer compensation from a given level of treasury outlay. This is true because a large portion of funds under the former goes into administration, supervision and in investment for commodity storage. Too, where it is not accompanied by supply control, part of it becomes embodied in the greater output it encourages, with an important portion of this being drained out of agriculture into the nonfarm input industries which provide the resources for the over-extension of output. This complex of means may provide certain "windfall gains," however.

The mammoth accumulation of stocks in the 1950's provided both visible evidence—in magnitude of both treasury dollars and grain storage bins—that "something had to be done." The only variable with "give" related to foreign disposal of commodities. This use of surplus stocks was not costly to the public—they owned them anyway. Accord-

[1] John Brewster, *Value Judgments and the Problem of Excess Capacity in Agriculture*, USDA Farm Econ. Res. Div. Mimeo., May, 1960.

[2] For example, see L. Soth, *Direct Government Payments to Farmers. Policy for Commercial Agriculture; Its Relation to Economic Growth and Stability*, Joint Economic Committee, Washington, D.C., 1957. Some other studies also indicate specific groups of producers who have favored direct payments: D. E. Hathaway and L. W. Witt, "Agricultural Policy: Whose Evaluation?" *Jour. Farm Econ.*, Vol. 36. A discussion of some direct payment alternatives also are discussed in G. E. Brandow, *Direct Payments Without Production Controls*, Economic Policies for Agriculture in the 1960's, Implications of Four Selected Alternatives, Joint Economic Committee, Washington, D.C., 1960.

ingly, greater flow of food went to nations with hunger, such as Southeast Asia and the Middle East. This might not have been so had the public had to appropriate funds for this purpose, in addition to those appropriated for farm programs and foreign aid. Still, elements of indirect "windfall loss" clung to this same line, in the sense that foreign policy goals were sometimes submerged to that of dumping surpluses.[3] (Also, see discussion in Chapter 17.)

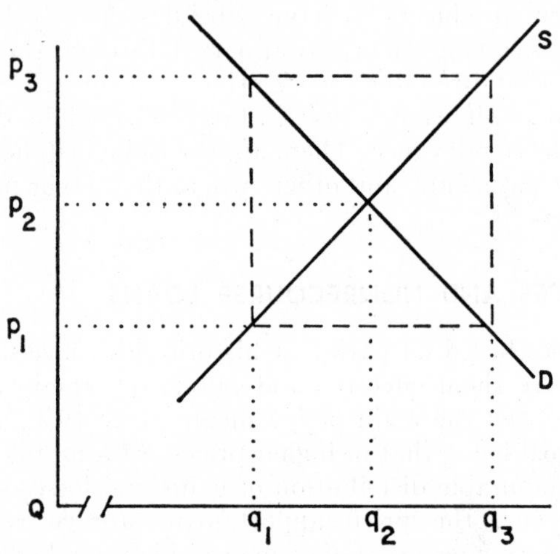

Fig. 11.1. Commodity Cycle Basis in Support Price and Storage.

Stability Mechanism for Aggregate Agriculture

Price supports and storage work best for commodity cycles such as those of hogs and crops which fluctuate in the cobweb manner of Ezekiel.[4] They also apply for somewhat similar phenomena: fluctuations in production due to the stochastic nature of weather variables. In respect to the commodity cycle, there is the case of supply elasticity greater than demand elasticity in respect to price, with exploding effect on magnitude of quantities, and also of supply elasticity less than demand elasticity, with dampening effect and convergence towards stable output and price.[5]

In practice, exogenous variables interact with those endogenous to the cycling mechanism, never allowing production and price to swing to positive and negative numbers of infinite magnitude, or to stabilize at a slumbering equilibrium. With knowledge of limitations in fact, we illustrate

---

[3] *Cf.* H. N. Carroll, *The House of Representatives and Foreign Affairs*, University of Pittsburgh Press, Pittsburgh, 1958, pp. 34–63.

[4] M. Ezekiel, "The Cobweb Theorem," *Jour. Polit. Econ.*, Vol. 47.

[5] G. W. Dean and Earl O. Heady, *Changes in Supply Elasticities and Supply Functions in Hog Production*, Iowa Agr. Exp. Sta. Bul. 471; this illustrates tendency of fluctuations to grow for hogs, with demand elasticity decreasing and supply elasticity increasing, but not under given supply and demand functions as in our example.

the adapted role of storage and support price in a case where complete convergence and complete explosion are not in sight. We start with "kickoff" price and output at levels of p_3 and q_1 respectively in Figure 11.1. Naive expectation models and "distributed lag" response, as used by most farm producers of cycle commodities or the latter would not exist, lead to output of q_3 and decline of price to p_1 in the following period.[6] Under demand with price elasticity less than unity, and elasticity declining greatly with quantity over the demand function, extreme fluctuation repeated over and over will lead to smaller revenue than if output and price were stable. But this need not be true under exploding or dampening cycles, or even with uniform cycles and change in supply and demand functions. Even under particular circumstances where demand elasticity is not too low relative to supply elasticity, fluctuation can bring greater revenue than stability.[7]

But supposing elasticities and lagged response are of a nature to cause fluctuations which reduce average revenue over time, in comparison to stable output, and that losses among producers who sacrifice from cycles outweigh gains among those who benefit, the aim of support price would be this: Support price would be set at level p_2 and when output is q_3, the storage authority would subsidize (boost) prices to the extent of p_1p_2, taking quantity q_2q_3 off the market under commodity storage activity. This one step, in our simple static example, would stabilize price at p_2 and output at q_2. But suppose exogenous forces cause "breakout of the system" and output of q_1 and price of p_3. The storage authority wouldn't allow this to happen to price, however, with the cycle resuming force. Quantity q_1q_2 would be moved from storage to the market, with price remaining at p_2 level and further cycling averted.

Neither weather nor economic variables distribute themselves in the symmetrical manner discussed above, either in 2's or 100's of time-series observations. But the logic has been illustrated even if the task of implementation is more difficult. Where the variables of concern are stochastic

---

[6] See Earl O. Heady, *Economics of Agricultural Production and Resource Use*, Prentice-Hall, New York, 1952. See Chaps. 15 and 17 for indication of models used by farmers and their consequences.

[7] If we start with the demand and supply functions in (11.1) and (11.2) respectively, for example, and suppose a "kick off" price of $.2a$ and output of $.6a$, the total revenue is $.12a^2$. Under the static "next year's price equals this year's price" expectation model, output will increase to $.81a$ in the second period and price will decline to $.095a$. The total revenue for the latter combination is only $.077a^2$. The average revenue for the two periods is $.099a^2$. If production and price were stable at the equilibrium levels of $.8a$ and $.1a$ revenue would average $.08a^2$ per year—an amount smaller than the average of the above two periods under fluctuations.

For four periods, revenue under year-by-year lagged response to price is $.893a^2$; whereas it averages $.8a^2$ for stable production and prices. But after years 3 and 4, the cycle converges on equilibrium, output and price averaging essentially $.8a$ and $.1a$ respectively in periods 3 through 6 (prices in periods 3 and 4 are $.10025a$ and $.09999a$ respectively while outputs are $.7995a$ and $.8a$). Even though this situation exists, some basis in costs (of production and processing) from fluctuating prevails as an argument for lessening instability. See Heady, *op. cit.*, pp. 524–34.

in relation to weather, averages and rules can be approximated to prevent mammoth swings in prices under yield variations. This was accomplished in the 1950's with support prices. However, stocks carried accumulated into giant magnitudes, instead of at size for "averaging." The tendency of support prices aimed at stability to get politically intermeshed with compensation payments when supply growth exceeds demand growth is the great weakness of the system. Perhaps at some time in history, the two elements of policy can be separated in the market and the public decision process. The time is yet to be seen, however, for any U.S. procedure of price support or forward pricing.

Storage and support mechanisms apply most readily to durable commodities as grain and cotton, less to meat, eggs, dairy products and other perishables. More costly and ample storage is required for the latter, but they have possibilities greater than exercised in past decades. For perishable commodities where weather is not the root of evil, more education and outlook for price expectations and planning, to bring understanding of cobweb phenomena and improved planning process to more farmers, could help stabilize the cycle and lessen investment required for storage of stabilizing stocks. For durable commodities, the restraint is less the ability to accomplish the storage task, and more that of separating the stabilization and compensation facets in political determination. Gustafson has provided us with some rules, in terms of the social welfare function, for gauging the size of stocks to be carried in evening inter-year grain supplies to meet weather fluctuations.[8]

Carryover stocks required are of two types: those of a "pipeline" nature which flow through the system in maintenance of continuity in processing, distribution, feeding and retailing, and those to give stability over fluctuations in yield and acreage of inputs. Stocks for these two purposes can cover some range, with opportunity for the market mechanism to do a moderate amount of "evening out" in supplies and prices. If absolute stabilization of quantity flowing to the market, and effect on price, were attained, carryover would have to be immense—large enough, and carried long enough, to cover "once in 50" deficits of the magnitude during droughts of the 1930's. The marginal cost of carrying such large amounts for such long periods is too great, if compared with the discounted marginal gains of the same. It has been estimated that "pipeline" stocks of corn, for example, need to be about 150 to 200 million bushels, and total or "normal" stocks for both purposes need to be about 15 percent of normal domestic consumption and exports. Hence, the "normal" carryover for feed corn would have been slightly over 500 million bushels, and all feed grain about 20 million tons, over the 1950's. Actual carryovers were more than twice, and on the verge of attaining three times, this amount.

Gustafson's precise rules for feed grains take into account the probability distribution of yields, the social value or welfare function and the costs

[8] R. L. Gustafson, "Implications of Recent Research on Optimal Storage Rules," *Jour. Farm Econ.*, Vol. 40.

of storage. They specify the rules for optimal storage policy, namely, that which maximizes the sum of discounted expected social gains over an n-year period where gain in each year is total social value minus storage cost of the carryover. He specifies two rules applying to two specified sets of conditions. Rule 1 supposes storage costs of 10 cents per bushel, a 5 percent interest or discount rate and an elasticity of "quantity used with respect to marginal social value" of −.5. Rule 2 is based on storage costs of 4 cents, a 5 percent discount rate and an elasticity of −.3.

The "computed rules" or specified quantities to be carried over, indicated as carryover per acre of feed grains, are detailed in Table 11.2 for each situation. These rules, however, provide for even lower carryovers than specified above. The previous figures were those which gave a "reasonable" averaging out of absolute surplus or deficits to stabilize prices, without account of discounted social margins or particular distributions of "weather runs." Storage policy to provide reasonable stability to farm prices would provide quantities of somewhat different magnitudes than those to maximize total social welfare, and would allow considerably different magnitude of price fluctuations. In general, stocks would be larger and price fluctuations smaller than those indicated by Gustafson's figures. His figures also, partly since they are aimed more at maximizing the social welfare functions and less at farm price stability, would allow stocks to drop lower in a poor year following run of average years and carryover to be larger in a high yield year following average years.

TABLE 11.2

QUANTITIES PER ACRE TO CARRYOVER AT SPECIFIED AVERAGE PER ACRE YIELDS OR SUPPLIES WITH INTEREST RATE OF 4.5 PERCENT

Bu. Per Acre	Rule 1	Rule 2	Bu. Per Acre	Rule 1	Rule 2
29......	0	0	38......	4.44	7.01
29......	0	.07	40......	5.89	8.66
30......	0	.77	42......	7.38	10.34
31......	0	1.50	44......	8.89	12.08
32......	.55	2.25	46......	10.45	13.83
34......	1.74	3.80	48......	12.02	15.61
36......	3.05	5.40	50......	13.63	17.42

Gustafson's upper limit carryover under rule 1, exceeded with probability of only .1 in weather expectation, would require 420 million bushels of corn equivalent plus 150 to 200 million bushels of pipeline stocks. This quantity, much above his quantity specified as average carryover with probability of .73, would be more realistic for purposes of price stability (but might be too high for maximization of discounted social welfare). For purposes of price stability, a range of 500 to 700 million bushels of corn equivalent for pipeline and stability purpose appears desirable, considering costs of storage, at rates of utilization for feed grains in the 1950's and as an average over years. For feed grains, carryover would be allowed to drop to the approximate level of pipeline stocks in years of smallest output and to withdraw all surplus when output exceeds annual use by 500 million bushels of corn equivalent, trend taken into account. Similar relative quantities needed for wheat and are much less than recent periods when stocks attained levels equal to or greater than annual production.

The large carryovers in grains developed, of course, because storage policy was used mainly as means of compensation, thus submerging its character as a stability mechanism. Numerous people looked upon these large stocks and their treasury carrying costs as the fundamental problem of the food industry. But this was untrue. They were indeed a heavy social problem, but served only as material evidence of the more fundamental problem, namely, supply capacity of agriculture which had grown to rapidly exceed rate of demand growth. Liquidation of surplus stocks, with policy elements of the kind in force during the 1930's to the 1960's, would not have solved the problem of large output based on short-run factor supplies of low elasticity. Neither did the stocks depress market prices in important degree—they were immobilized from the market. Mainly they represented a social dilemma: public costs growing to large magnitudes without solution of the capacity problem which gave rise to them. Accumulation of the stocks killed the pain stemming from excess capacity, but it did not eliminate the cause of the pain.

Man is not omnipotent and weather is not accommodating in prediction, as also is true for purely economic variables. Therefore, man will never predict and stabilize exactly on the target as in Figure 11.1, or as prescribed by storage rules. This is true particularly for aspects of fluctuation growing out of economic change which interact with other variables. But a scheme of forward prices, with the logical purposes outlined in Figure 11.1, would do so more than the imperfections which accompany a pure competition market where producers are at the mercy of weather and other variables.

Politics are rather the more important prediction (or, perhaps it is lack of knowledge of farmers, who do not understand difference in program purposes) which keeps a purely stabilization policy from being adopted. Forward pricing was recommended even before the great depression.[9] It has been given considerable refinement in concept and purpose in later decades.[10] It was used for hogs, wheat and other commodities for reducing uncertainty and encouraging greater output in World War II. Forward prices provide footing for developmental policy in countries such as India. For the goal of stability and greater certainty in planning, attempt would be made to predict and announce forward prices at equi-

---

[9] See Business Men's Commission on Agriculture, *The Conditions of Agriculture and Measures for its Improvement*, Washington, D.C., 1927.

[10] *Cf.* T. W. Schultz, *Redirecting Farm Policy*, Macmillan, New York, 1943, Chap. 5; and D. G. Johnson, *Forward Prices for Agriculture*, University of Chicago Press, Chicago, 1947.

librium levels before the time of decision and resource commitment by farmers. Supplemented by storage to even supplies, attempt would be made to keep prices effective for planning purpose, the projections modified with new information and not taken as inflexible historic restraints on consumer preferences, technical development and factor prices. Proponents of forward pricing would also use them for countercyclical purpose over business cycles, jutting them above equilibrium levels in depression to help stabilize income.[11] However, the main offense for business depression is at the national front, and not on the contracting farm flank.

Stability for the Individual

Stable commodity flows into the market and prices floating at peaceful stability levels would not eliminate fluctuations attending weather which fall on individual farmers. Even in years of average output and prices, some producers have yield failure and cannot claim a portion of aggregate placidity. Public crop insurance is a policy means to attain the goal of income stability for such random variables. It has been attempted for three decades in the U.S., without widespread use or success in terms of actuarial standards. It is provided, of course on a commercial basis for insurable contingencies such as those of hail and related phenomena. But for all-risk insurance, covering major variables such as weather, it doesn't appeal to private firms. Taking even fairly large producing areas, the relevant observations do not square too closely with the type phenomena needed for insurability, namely, a large sample, independence of observations and lack of control and prediction by the owner.[12] Too, all-risk insurance has not spread to crops of regions where the distribution of weather outcomes or observations provides a "sample in time" whereby the individual farmer can effectively establish probabilities and "carry his own insurance." This possibility is at a minimum for the beginning operator who sometimes is "wiped out" as soon as he starts.

Insurance lacks attraction where it is based on past history and does not sufficiently account for yield trends due to technical development. Farmers who progress in yield with technology will not insure; those who do not progress tend to insure, causing losses in actuarial accumulations where their yields vary more than the average. Insurance does not have great attraction where great variability of some regions causes "actuarial costs" to be at levels discouraging farmers of the area, particularly where indemnities are based on averages and do not account for variation among farms. Finally, where premiums in high risk areas are kept low, being supplanted by higher premium rates in regions of lower relative variance in yields, farmers in the less risky areas are little inclined to participate. All-purpose crop insurance, where weather is of proper characteristics, could be made to work. This is true only on a basis of a large

[11] Schultz, *ibid.*

[12] For further discussion of these and other points, see Heady, *op. cit.*, Chap. 17.

enough sample in respect to time and space and if it were used purely for stability purpose—entirely devoid of elements to transfer income among individuals and regions.

Instability of agricultural production and prices of the kind discussed in this section are not the major foundations of U.S. farm problems; the distribution of gains and losses under economic development and chronic poverty are. To eliminate the latter two would accomplish little in respect to the instability problem, or vice versa. Hence, we turn back to support prices and storage as a means related to goals of compensation.

Support Prices, Loans and Compensation

Support prices, loans and commodity storage have been used in the U.S. largely for income transfers or compensation. While they have stabilized prices of certain storable products, with the public adding an infinitely elastic demand at support levels exceeding market clearance, they have not had stability in the above manner as the basic goal. This complex of policy elements is luxurious in its costs as a means of accomplishing compensation, particularly where it is not accompanied with supply control and leads to large-scale accumulation of stocks. Under technical change and factor prices encouraging supply to shift more rapidly than demand, storage and prices supported at levels of previous periods will cause output to exceed consumer demand and market clearing levels. This is *a priori* obvious in theory; it is *ex poste* obvious in all experience, the size of treasury costs and storage accumulations in the 1950's being sufficient evidence for any doubters.

Looking back to equations (4.1) through (4.20) and to Table 4.1, it is obvious that technical change increasing marginal productivity of factors is expected to lead to an "overage" of output, if price support mechanism is used to retain the previous factor/product price ratio. Similarly, given the production function and a decline in real factor price as for fertilizer from 1940 to 1960, commodity price held at a level to maintain a previous factor/product price ratio also will add to "overage" in output. The effect is illustrated in Figure 11.2. Starting with original demand and supply functions, D_1 and S_1, supply changes to S_2 and demand to D_2, the rate for supply being greater than for demand. Hence, short-run equilibrium price declines from op_3 level to op_2 and output increases from oq_1 to oq_3. Under inelastic demand, the total revenue op_2oq_3 is less than op_3oq_1. If historic price is used as the support level, price at level op_3 is guaranteed under the new supply conditions. But at this price level, short-run equilibrium output is oq_4, rather than oq_3. If loans without recourse are available to farmers at level op_3, demand will allow only quantity oq_2 to clear the market. Hence, a quantity equal to q_2q_4 will move annually into storage, with continuous buildup of stocks. If compensation were provided only to cover loss in revenue, it would be set at magnitude $op_3 \cdot oq_1 - op_2 \cdot oq_3$. If it were to cover price depression on all produced at new equilibrium quantity, the general attempt of past

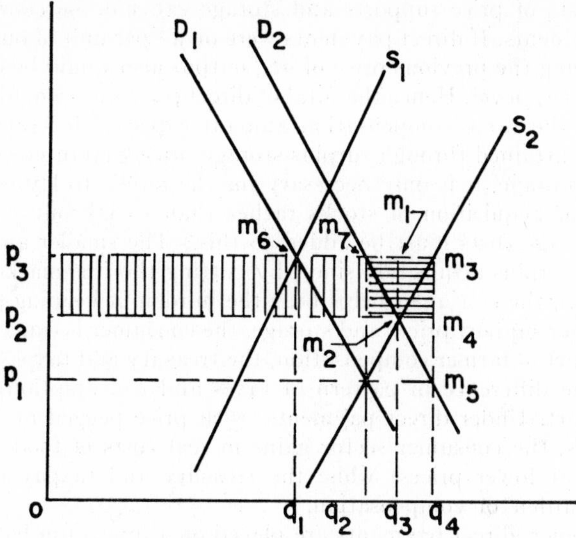

Fig. 11.2. Support Price and Commodity Storage in Compensation.

price supports, it would amount to $p_2p_3m_1m_2$. But without supply control where farmers produce oq_4 at op_3 price, compensation becomes the larger amount $p_1p_3m_3m_5$ where we suppose that prices are supported at the previous or op_3 level, or make up the difference between op_1 and op_3. The actual public outlay in withdrawing stocks from the market to maintain a market price of op_3 then becomes $q_2m_7m_3q_4$.

To this must be added annual storage costs of carrying q_2q_4 quantity. If storage per unit is m, total appropriations or treasury outlay for the year must be $q_2m_7m_3q_4+mq_2q_4$. In the second year, with the same amount added to stocks (leaving weather and yield variations aside at this point), the treasury outlay becomes $q_2m_7m_3q_4+2mq_2q_4$, to allow appropriations for stock acquisition and storage costs for two years of accumulation. The annual outlay in n years thus becomes $q_2m_7m_3q_4+nmq_2q_4$ and the total outlay is the summation of these annual amounts. The storage activity thus promises eventually to become a major cost. The compensation method could be much lessened if the surplus were burned rather than stored (forgetting now about any salvage value of the surplus). With q_2q_4 quantity burned, market quantity would be held back to oq_2, taken off the market at op_3 price, and with the costs of storage saved.[13]

[13] Burning or destroying surplus stocks of commodities such as wheat is considered to be inconsistent with a value held by many people. This value found its greatest expression in the outcry against "killing little pigs" in the 1930's. But this twinge of conscience, held for destroying wheat and feed grain stocks, does not prevail for plowing under lettuce and destroying fruit annually under market order control of supply.

The costs of price supports and storage can now be compared with direct payments. If direct payments were on a "per unit of output" basis guaranteeing the previous price of op_3, output also would be expected to increase to oq_4 level. Hence the total of direct payments would amount to $p_1p_3m_3m_5$, the same compensation amount expected for support prices which are attained through surplus storage price guarantee of op_3. However, for storage, it is only necessary for the public to lay out $q_2m_7m_3q_4$ directly for acquisition of stocks rather than to lay out $p_1p_3m_3q_4$. (Of course storage costs must be added to this.) The smaller amount is required in surplus acquisition since, by cutting the free-market quantity back to oq_2, the consumer helps bear the burden of keeping price at op_3 level. Under support prices and storage, the consumer is expected to bear a larger part of farmer compensation, the treasury and taxpayer (considering some difference in pattern of taxes and consumption) bearing a smaller part. Under direct payments, with price pegged at op_3 level in both cases, the consumer sector gains in real costs of food (more food available at lower prices) while the treasury and taxpayer bears the greater burden of compensation.

If, however, direct payments are placed on a lump-sum basis, and are not tied to magnitude of output, the total treasury outlay required is only $op_3m_6q_1 - op_2m_2q_3$ (as compared to $p_1p_3m_3m_5$ where direct payments are based on a per unit basis to provide the previous price level) where the goal is simply that of providing producers with revenue at the previous level. For lump-sum compensation in this manner, the treasury or taxpayer bears the full burden. The method will cost the treasury less than price supports and storage, where the latter (1) involves storage over a long period of high storage costs and (2) there is no close "salvage value" in use of stocks. Price supports and storage can cost less than lump-sum compensation if stocks need not be carried long and have demand in outside markets with sale at only slight reduction of price below p_3.[14]

For one comparison let us return to the supply and demand equations in (11.1) through (11.4). Under lump-sum compensation to guarantee the same revenue after change in supply and demand, the required public outlay is $.017a^2$. (See previous discussion.) Now suppose that price support and storage are used to maintain the original price level of $.1a$ in Table 11.1. Since farmers are expected to produce $.960a$ at this price level, a quantity of $960a - .8a = .160a$ must be taken from the market and stored to guarantee $.1a$ price. The public outlay to do so is $(.160a)(.1a) = .016a^2$. This amount for public acquisition of stocks is less than the $.017a^2$ required for lump-sum payment. The public acquisition will cost more than lump-sum compensation if storage costs and sales loss exceed this difference of $.001a^2$, but less if storage and sales costs are below $.001a^2$.

[14] One aspect of resource imbalance, in a conventional sense, also should be mentioned. With lump-sum direct payments and oq_3 output, aggregate allocation of resources would be more consistent with technology, factor supply conditions and consumer preference than price support-burning or storage-price support resulting in $oq.$ output in Figure 11.2.

SUPPLY CONTROL

If the public desires compensation transfer for agriculture geared to an intermediate goal of a previous or other price level, and wishes to minimize the treasury costs, the most efficient method is supply control. In Figure 11.2, if output is restrained to oq_2, price level of op_3 is retained. No product moves into storage and the only costs involved are administrative. This compares with treasury costs of: $p_1p_3m_3m_5$ if compensation is on a per unit direct payment basis to guarantee op_3 price level, $q_2m_7m_3q_4$ plus storage costs if compensation is through support price and storage and $op_3m_6q_1 - op_2m_2q_3$ if compensation is through lump-sum payment to guarantee previous total revenue.

We have been discussing treasury costs only. Obviously some one pays the higher price in both cases: in supply control, the higher food cost is distributed over food consumers, roughly in proportion to expenditures on food; in direct payments, the subsidy is distributed over taxpayers, roughly in proportion to tax payments. In the former, supply control, cost tends to be retrogressive relative to consumer living level; in the latter, it is more progressive to consumer income. Without supply control, equilibrium consumer outlay for product is $op_2 \cdot oq_3$, with supply control and old price it is $op_3 \cdot oq_2$. The consumer pays the difference. Under direct payment by lump-sum method, the difference between $op_3 \cdot oq_1$ and $op_2 \cdot oq_3$ is paid by the taxpayer. Given a society goal of compensation and "peg" to the old price level, which is best? The answer depends on the criterion for evaluation. If the objective is to obscure the difference through the market, as is done by other firms and industries which manage prices and output, if value orientation says that transfer has to be through market mechanism and if there is no negative value orientation to controls, supply management would be selected. If transfer need not be covered up by market mechanism, if producers greatly value freedom of decisions and of planting and have no objection to direct subsidy, if it is believed that cost should be borne progressively with income of taxpayers rather than progressively with food expenditures by consumers, and if preference is for a system allowing resource allocation best paralleling competitive markets, direct payment of "lump-sum" nature would be selected.

Method of Supply Control

Methods of supply control can be many, ranging from tight restraint on inputs to tight restraints on output, or modest approaches to either. In a welfare economics and values context, the major division in control programs is between compulsory and voluntary programs. Freedom of decision can be considered a commodity competing with level of income: Some farmers have lower income under the aggregate freedom which accompanies greater output and lower prices in the market. But other farmers have greater income under aggregate freedom, their ability to out-compete the masses causing the two "commodities" to be technical complements.

The fact that these two distinct groups persist gives rise to much conflict over farm policy. To one group, more supply control—less freedom—means greater income. To the other group, more freedom—less supply control—means greater income. Hence, to move to either more or less freedom is equivalent to a move along the contract curve in Figure 8.1. Economics has no gauge to indicate that more freedom to one group and less income to the other group, or more income to one and less freedom to the other, guarantees aggregate welfare gain. However, supply control programs can still be organized in a manner allowing movement to Pareto optima, without forcing a value judgement or necessity for utility measurement, as long as an "outside group" (taxpayers or consumers) provides method and funds of compensation and wishes to effect it. Here the rule is: make certain that no one is made "worse off," while some are made "better off." Voluntary supply control is specified over compulsory supply control under this rule. The condition specified can be attained by viewing production control in the general framework of supply: Individuals are able to sell their opportunity to produce the commodity, supposing that they can retain or market this opportunity depending on the choice which provides greatest gain to them. Those who so select to sell their opportunity to produce do not have a choice imposed on them, as also is true of those who do not choose to participate and give up no freedom.

This route to compensation and supply control cannot give rise to battle over trespass on freedom or utility level. The system is efficient also in the sense that it considers closeness of alternatives or marginal substitution rates, and also draws out those resources of lowest productivity in farming. It also provides for attaining a positive level of output reduction at lowest cost, by taking first those who offer it at lowest price. But on a purely voluntary or "negative supply" basis, it must relate to resources. If a farmer sells his "right to produce commodity only," as attached to his person, and moves out while another takes over his land and capital, supply restraint is not attained. But in the concept of supply, any magnitude of output reduction desired—any degree of restraint on output through input reduction—can be attained depending on the level of price paid for this "product."

While U.S. farm policy has had output restraint as a major element since 1930, the effort has always been so feeble and half-hearted that it has never been of noticeable effect—not even in keeping up with the rate of supply advance from technical change. The two programs of American society, of investing in research and education to increase output and in supply control to reduce output, appear to present an interesting conflict in goals. However, as is pointed out in Chapter 16, they actually can serve as consistent means of promoting economic development while giving farmers equitable opportunity to share in the growth to which they contribute.

Previous attempts to reduce output have been on both a voluntary and compulsory basis. Marketing quotas on wheat, acreage allotments on tobacco and similar restraints voted on other crops were examples of compulsory restraints in the 1950's. Acreage allotments over a wider range of crops in the 1930's represented an earlier attempt. Marketing associations have sometimes been able to work out successful output restraints for particular commodities; as have dairy farmers in selected areas under federal milk marketing orders. Voluntary participation in the "supply concept" was represented by the soil bank initiated in 1956, with bid by farmers for the rate at which they would withdraw part or all of their land from production. The massive public effort has been output control resting on land input. Programs of the past have variously been those requiring rigid acreage quotas applied to all farms (as in wheat and tobacco), those encouraging fractional withdrawal of acreage from production by all or millions of farms over the entire nation, those allowing withdrawal of whole farms over the entire nation and those allowing whole or partial farm withdrawal in concentrated regions.

The main "input and output control" attempted since 1930 has been to shift part of the land from basic crops on millions of farms. Land could be shifted from "basic or commercial" crops of the region to those not so classified. Cornbelt farmers could withdraw land from corn and plant it to soybeans or grain sorghums. Plains farmers could shift from wheat to feed grains. Cotton farmers could shift to feed and other crops. Programs of this type have no real basis for being called control programs. They had some little effect in reducing surpluses of wheat and cotton relative to absence of a control program. However, they also diverted part of the surplus from these crops to an even greater surplus of feed grain.

Under this type of program, we find the following results between 1945–49 without control and 1954–58 with controls allowing shift among crops: Wheat acreage in the Northern Plains dropped by 10 million acres between the two periods and feed grain acreage increased by 2 million acres. A decline of 25 percent in cotton and wheat in the Southern Plains was accompanied by a 12 percent increase in acreage of feed grains. For the United States, wheat acreage decreased by around 20 million acres and cotton decreased by nearly 5 million acres. However, total feed grain acreage increased by around 10 million acres, even though corn decreased by 10 million acres and a considerable amount of land shifted to urban and forestry uses.

These control programs only caused a greater "swell" in the surpluses of feed grains, while relieving slightly the pressure, but not the surplus, of wheat and cotton. Even in the Cornbelt, diversion of land from corn to grain sorghums and soybeans partly or entirely nullified the reduction in corn acreage. Studies show that for typical rations, 1 pound of soybean oilmeal has a marginal rate of substitution of 2.7 pounds of corn in a hog ration, 2.5 pounds in a broiler ration and 2.3 pounds in a turkey ration.[15] Feeding trials show that a pound of grain sorghums substitutes for approximately .9 pound of corn. With substitution rates of this

---

[15] Iowa Agr. Exp. Sta. Bulletins 409, 442, 443 and 444. Also see Earl O. Heady and John L. Dillon, *Agricultural Production Functions*, Iowa State University Press, Ames, 1961.

magnitude, control programs which shift acreage on many farms from one feed grain to another, and actually increase feed grain acreage in some regions, have no logical basis for being called control programs.

Even programs which allow diversion of land from grains or row crops to forages, with the latter used for livestock as allowed in early decades of attempted supply control, do not necessarily promise reduction in livestock output. An important question in the feed grain economy is whether land diversion schemes reduce livestock output, rather than whether they simply reduce feed grain quantities. The very great majority of feed grains is utilized through livestock and the price of feed grains in the market, aside from price supports that peg them at other levels, is derived directly from the price and income, and indirectly from the quantity produced and the relative demand for livestock. We can illustrate the conditions under which programs to shift land from grains to forages will or will not reduce livestock output, a crucial quantity in the feed grain-livestock economy.

For a region such as the Cornbelt, an aggregate production possibility curve or relationship such as *AB* in Figure 11.3 exists. Basically, it represents, given the state of technology, all the possible combinations of grain and forage which can be produced from the supplies of the various soils in the region. To the right, this curve slopes upward, indicating that as more forage is produced from a greater proportion of land in forage and a smaller proportion in grain, more grain also will be produced. Over this range of outputs (rotations or land use) forage and grain are complementary. It has been shown from experiments that, in the absence of

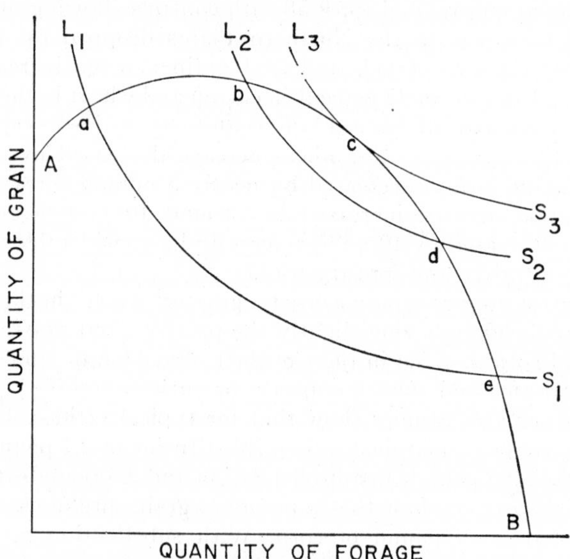

Fig. 11.3. Feed-Livestock Production Potential Under Land Shifts.

certain types and levels of fertilization, Cornbelt rotations which include some forages will produce more grain than if the entire land area is planted to corn or grains.[16] The percentage increase in yield per acre more than offsets the percentage reduction of grain acreage in the rotation.

But at some point in land use and cropping patterns, the relationship becomes competitive: A larger acreage and greater production of forage comes at the expense of grain output because per acre increases in grain yields (due to improved soil fertility, etc.) fail to offset the percentage reduction in grain acreage. A control program which causes an acreage shift from corn to forages, starting from a point on the upward sloping portion of the curve, would actually cause feed grain output itself to increase over a period of years—and thus would allow a greater output of grain and livestock from the same land area.

Sufficient data are not available to measure our current and past status in respect to these conditions. But it is entirely possible that the farms which mainly participate in voluntary control programs of the kind under discussion fall within this complementary range. Surveys indicate that rented, cash-grain farms are mainly attracted to these types of control programs. Rented farms with frequent tenant changes and imperfect sharing systems are the ones where continuous corn rotations are emphasized. Hence, land diversion programs which provide them with economic incentive for planting some forage can bring about an increased grain production (i.e. a movement up the positive sloped portion of the curve AB) from fewer acres over the rotation cycle.

However, presence of a complementary range is not required for livestock output to increase under grain acreage reduction. Even if grain output is decreased with greater forage output (the opportunity curve is negatively sloped only), a curtailment in livestock output is not guaranteed. A given amount of livestock can be produced with an infinite number of feed combinations. Thus for any particular level of livestock output, production contours or isoquants such as L_1S_1, L_2S_2 and L_3S_3 exist. Each of these represents a different quantity of livestock output and the various combinations of grain and forage which will produce this output. Thus the smallest livestock output level, indicated by curve L_1S_1, could be produced with the many combinations of grain and forage which could be "read off" the curve. The same is true for the larger livestock outputs indicated L_2S_2 and L_3S_3.

Suppose now that the land use pattern existing is one which gives the output combination of grain and forage indicated at point *a* on the production possibility curve AB. If these outputs are used for livestock feed, the level of livestock output indicated by L_1S_1 can be attained. Now, if a land diversion program is put into effect which increases both grain and forage to the level at point *b*, this same combination of feed will

[16] Quantitative indication of these relationships and production possibilities is included in Earl O. Heady and Harald R. Jensen, *Economics of Crop Rotations and Land Use*, Iowa Agr. Exp. Sta. Bul. 383.

allow the greater output indicated by livestock output curve L_2S_2. Current knowledge of substitution rates in crop production and livestock feeding would suggest that this outcome is physically possible and very likely, starting from the land use base on which our control programs have been projected. But even if the initial starting point were *b* on curve *AB*, in respect to grain and forage output, a land diversion program which changes the feed combination to the smaller grain output and the larger forage output indicated at point *c* would allow livestock output to increase from the level indicated by L_2S_2 to the level of L_3S_3. The curve L_3S_3 denotes, under the assumption of crop production possibilities and feed substitution implicit, the highest livestock output possible from the given land areas. The two curves are tangent, indicating that the marginal rate of substitution in crop production is equal to the marginal rate of substitution in livestock feeding.

Of course, if the land diversion were severe or large enough, livestock output could be reduced. Starting from point *a*, the combination of feed outputs would have to be shifted to the extent of point *e* before livestock production would be reduced. Starting from point *b*, the combination would have to be shifted to point *d*. The magnitudes of acreage change under programs of the past have not been great enough to attain combinations of the latter type, and studies suggest that they may have been within a range allowing a greater output of livestock, and probably a greater output of feed grains. In any case, the quantities suggested by Figure 11.3 need to be known in much greater detail than held true in implementation of previous production control programs if a program is to be structured to actually reduce grain and livestock output. To be sure that a grain acreage control program can reduce livestock output, the two sets of marginal substitution rates mentioned above need to be known. There is no basis to indicate that this knowledge has been available or used in programs of the past.[17]

In a later chapter, we wish to return to the "supply function aspects" of reducing inputs and outputs. Regional adjustment of agriculture, as suggested in Chapter 7, is ahead for American farming. It does, however, need to be structured to consider human resources other than those of agriculture in regions where important shift needs to take place in the product mix and in the input of labor and capital resources. Control programs in the "supply function" context of voluntary participation and Pareto optima can be used for these purposes. This complex has supply response operating or motivating through positive award and opportunity of people. Supply response, in withdrawing land and shifting product mix, functions similarly in an open market where returns are driven down and people give up farming for other pursuits. In the latter case, however, Pareto optimum need not be reflected because of the income reduction involved and the motivation is based rather on negative opportunity for people.

[17] For added notes relative to the effect of acreage control on distortion of production possibility curves, see Heady, *op. cit.*, Chap. 8.

Our discussion above has been in terms of input control. We now turn to output controls as in marketing quotas. Marketing quotas represent a compensation method, if we prefer to call it that, wherein the higher level of income, above that which would otherwise prevail, is distributed at a cost among consumers rather than over taxpayers. It is a method which requires small treasury outlay, as compared to surplus acquisition and storage or voluntary production control where participation is brought about by payments to effect withdrawal of land or other resources.

If price level op_3 in Figure 11.2 were the instrumental goal, under short-run supply and demand conditions giving op_2 price and oq_3 output, the objective of marketing quota would be to restrict output to oq_2, giving op_3 price. The gain in income would come through the market with no treasury costs except for administration and policing—the latter perhaps large for products such as feed and livestock. The system could be Pareto-better for consumers in the sense of giving them as much or more food per capita at equal or lower real price over time and also allowing technical advance so that fewer resources are required in agriculture and more of nonfarm products can be produced. In the Pareto-better sense for agriculture in aggregate, it could also give more of two things: more income than otherwise and allowance for freed resources under technical change to move to other industries and provide farm families with more of nonfarm products. But a question of distribution of gains and losses does arise within agriculture, in a manner differing from the "supply concept" of production restraint where only those who choose participate, those preferring freedom remaining outside the program. In the case of marketing quotas, all farmers would participate under compulsion, even though some value freedom over income. Thus the Pareto condition that "all are left as well or better off" would be negated for those with a high value on freedom.

Marketing quotas, as a means of income protection where farm production capacity exceeds demand potential, have been proposed for major aggregates of products. They are used by farmer selection in the case of milk, under milk marketing orders, as a means of restraining output to levels allowing attainment of particular price and income objectives. They also are used quite widely for nuts, fruits and vegetables, under marketing agreements and orders provided in state and federal legislation.

To illustrate how marketing quotas can simultaneously promote economic progress and allow benefit to consumer and producers, we resort to simple algebraic illustrations, employing a particular equation form (but with the same conclusions applying for other forms under the elasticity coefficients which surround agriculture). We suppose a single aggregate product and concern ourselves with the industry and not with firms. The analysis is short run in the sense of certain resource fixities and production restraints. Production decisions and income generation take place in a series of short runs directed towards the orthodox long run of economics, but highly linked and uniquely in existence. To simplify the analysis and ease the task of "following," we use numerical elasticities quantities, rounded in the neighborhood of some for agriculture in the short run of the 1950's.

The demand function is (11.6) where Q_d is quantity, P is commodity price and c is a constant.[18]

$$Q_d = cP^{-.4} \tag{11.6}$$

$$Q_p = \pi X^{.8} \tag{11.7}$$

$$X = \pi^{-1.25} Q_p^{1.25} \tag{11.8}$$

The industry production function is (11.7) where Q_p is output, π is a constant reflecting a short run of particular technology and resources specialized to agriculture and X is short-run variable resource. (See discussion of equations 1.1 to 1.5 for method.) From (11.7) we derive the resource requirements equation in (11.8), indicating the magnitude of factor needed to produce a particular output. Supposing that agriculture responds roughly to price stimuli, we derive the industry marginal cost function where P_x is the price per unit of X. Following, we derive the supply function in (11.9) where P is the price of product.

$$Q_s = .4096\pi^5 P_x^{-4} P^4 \tag{11.9}$$

$$P_1 = 2.41^{.227} c^{.227} \pi^{-1.1365} P_x^{.909} \tag{11.10}$$

Equating demand (11.6) and supply (11.9) functions, we define the equilibrium price in (11.10). Substituting equilibrium price (11.10) into the demand function (11.6) provides the equilibrium quantity, Q_1, in (11.11) defined in terms of the original production coefficients and state of demand.

$$Q_1 = 2.41^{-.091} c^{.919} \pi^{.455} p_x^{-.364} \tag{11.11}$$

$$X_1 = 2.414^{-.114} c^{1.149} \pi^{-.682} p_x^{-.455} \tag{11.12}$$

Substituting Q_1 for Q_p into the factor requirements equation (11.8), we specify total inputs, X_1, in (11.12). The magnitudes Q_1 and X_1 refer to a given short-run state of demand and production technology.

A new short run arises, one step away from the first but related to it

---

[18] This constant c in (11.6) has the value below where N is population, I is per capita income, P_0 is price index for nonfood commodities (actually a series of such P_i would be desirable) and T is time to allow changes

$$c = rN^{b_1} I^{b_2} P_0^{b_3} T^{b_4}$$

in preferences not related to population, income, and similar variables. For the time being, however, we consider these variables to be fixed and define a particular short run in respect to food demand. We might consider the π in (11.6) to have the value below where the Z_i, except one being varied, are fixed in different magnitudes in the short run, with some at positive levels to represent a particular state of technology.

$$\pi = sZ_1^{\beta_1} Z_2^{\beta_2} \cdots Z_m^{\beta_m}$$

since certain resources remain fixed. We suppose the new production function to be that in (11.7) multiplied by Γ where $\Gamma > 1.0$. Also demand increases in this second short run through multiplication of (11.6) by λ where $\lambda > 1.0$. These continuous types of short-run change characterize agriculture. Resources with low mobility and reservation prices remain in the industry over a succession of interrelated short-run periods even though their return is less than comparable resources in other sectors.

Suppose marketing quotas are to be established allowing attainment of a prescribed price level and growth of income of farmers as they contribute to economic progress. Many levels of price would do so, but momentarily we select the equilibrium price in the previous period, namely P_1 as defined in (11.10). Substituting this price into the new demand equation, (11.6) multiplied by λ, the annual output, Q_2, allowed by the price target of (11.10) becomes that in (11.13).

$$Q_2 = \lambda Q_1 \tag{11.13}$$

$$X = \Gamma^{-1.25}\pi^{-1.25}Q^{1.25} \tag{11.14}$$

$$X_2 = \lambda^{1.25}\Gamma^{-1.25}X_1 \tag{11.15}$$

This level of output is used for our example as the aggregate quota for the product. Under the conditions set forth previously, it is the total production quota which, under the new demand, will give the price level of (11.10), even though technology has changed to that represented by the production function in (11.7) increased by Γ proportion. For the particular algebraic conditions, output or quota level is the old equilibrium output increased by λ proportion.[19] Given this annual quota level and the new resource requirements equation in (11.14), with the latter reflecting technological change between the two periods, the resource input under quotas is X_2 in (11.15). This input quantity will produce the quota in (11.13) but maintain the price level in (11.10). Hence, inputs and costs will decrease if technical improvement is sufficiently large relative to demand growth.

If Γ is larger than λ, inputs and costs will decline: consumer's food needs are met with fewer resources, and farm income can increase because of both increased total revenue (more product sold at the same price) and decline in total costs. Obviously, incentive to increase the magnitude of Γ relative to λ exists and economic growth is encouraged just as if quotas did not exist. But even where Γ and λ are equal, farm income can increase as demand quantity grows to (11.13). The actual standard of comparison for income gain from the quota system should not be that of output in (11.13) and input in (11.15), against those in

---

[19] The relation of Q_2 to Q_1 grows out of the fact that Q_2 has the value in (a).

$$\text{(a)}\quad Q_2 = 2.41^{-.091}\lambda\pi^{.455}c^{.919}P_x^{-.364}$$

The relation of X_2 in (11.15) to X_1 exists because of (b)

$$\text{(b)}\quad X_2 = 2.41^{-.114}\lambda^{1.25}\Gamma^{-1.25}\pi^{-.682}c^{1.149}p_x^{-.455}$$

(11.11) and (11.12), with price geared at P_1 in (11.10). Instead it should be against the quantities which would arise under market-free equilibrium of price, output and input. These quantities of the free market are indicated later in (11.19) and give, under certain magnitudes discussed subsequently, a smaller profit than Q_2 output, X_2 input and price at P_1 level in (11.10).

Industry incentive in improving technology and promoting general progress could be greater than previously, since each improvement increases profit, whereas under market-free conditions and low price elasticity the aggregate effect of innovation is a short-run decrease in revenue and net income. With demand growing as indicated and price held at the level in (11.10), the amount of resources required in the absence of technical change would be (11.16), an amount always greater than (11.15) where technical improvement takes place.[20]

$$X_3 = \lambda^{1.25} X_1 \tag{11.16}$$

$$\Delta X = (1 - \Gamma^{-1.25})\lambda^{1.25} X_1 \tag{11.17}$$

Thus a contribution which farmers could make to general economic progress by improving technology, under the restraint that price be maintained at the previous equilibrium level, has been defined. This gain to society, ΔX, is the resource savings represented in (11.17). The savings of $1 - \Gamma^{-1.25}$ proportion of resources, under technical improvement as compared to its lack, is attained in meeting the demand quantity of (11.13).[21] This proportion of resources is "freed," against no technical change, for other products: to allow society a greater total mix of goods and services, or for more of other products at lower prices. But farmers also have positive gain from this contribution to technical improvement and general economic progress. Four industry net profit equations can be defined which allow expression of this gain:

$$N_1 = P_1 Q_1 - P_x X_1 \tag{11.18a}$$

$$N_2 = P_1 Q_2 - P_x X_2 = \lambda P_1 Q_1 - \lambda^{1.25}\Gamma^{-1.25} P_x X_1 \tag{11.18b}$$

$$N_3 = P_1 Q_2 - P_x X_3 = \lambda P_1 Q_1 - \lambda^{1.25} P_x X_1 \tag{11.18c}$$

$$N_4 = \overline{PQ} - P_x \overline{X} = \lambda^{1.146}\Gamma^{-.217} P_1 Q_1 - \lambda^{1.149}\Gamma^{-.682} P_x X_1 \tag{11.18d}$$

These include (11.18a) which is industry profit before change in demand or technology; (11.18b), profit with change in demand and technology but price retained at the original equilibrium level; (11.18c), profit with

[20] The magnitude in (11.16) supposes the new demand as a basis of indicating resource savings and one Pareto-type of gain to consumers where technological change does take place as against that where it does not. Under the price elasticity conditions of the farm industry, greater aggregate income from demand increase would come with no technical advance.

[21] Our comparison is in meeting the demand quantity in (11.13), where we suppose growth in consumption with population and income, first where we do not have technical change as in (11.16) compared with the case where we do in (11.15).

change in demand, no change in technology and price retained at the original equilibrium level; and (11.18d), with change in demand and technology and with price allowed to move to a new equilibrium or market-free level consistent with the new demand and supply functions. (In the first three equations, commodity price is at the P_1 level, but in the fourth equation it is at the level of the new equilibrium of the market under change in technology and demand.)

Now comparing (11.18b) and (11.18c), with society gaining $1-\Gamma^{-1.25}$ proportion of saving in resources under the former as compared to the latter, farmers have this net gain: Gross income is the same but costs are less by $1-\Gamma^{-1.25}$ proportion in (11.18b). Hence, society in "freed resources," and farmers in cost savings, gain by equal proportions to obtain a given output level, as technical change takes place and quotas hold price to the original level. We have, then, a scheme which allows farmers to contribute to general economic progress but to gain from the process, rather than to be penalized under elasticity conditions of the market. There would be great incentive for farmers to adopt a new technology, saving costs and resources because the quota would restrain output sufficiently to maintain price level and insure profit.

Output can be increased to match population growth and still allow gain in farm income. The price target need not be held at the prior equilibrium level to benefit farmers from contribution they make to economic progress. If the quota were managed properly, output could increase, absolute inputs could decrease, price of food could decline and farm profits could increase under sufficient rate of technical advance. An income goal, rather than a price goal, could be used with the price and quota level set accordingly. This modification would allow a degree of flexibility since consumers could "remix" their food and nonfood commodities, while still guaranteeing an income gain to farmers for their contribution to economic progress.

We have been comparing the gain to consumers under a situation where technical change does or does not take place. Dropping this comparison for the moment, we return to the case where demand and supply are (11.6) and (11.7) respectively. Before technical change, we have the equilibrium price, output and input of (11.10), (11.11) and (11.12). After technical change and demand increase and price held at (11.10) level, output and input are (11.13) and (11.15) respectively. Now obviously, if Γ is greater than λ, techniques improve at a rate faster than demand; total inputs will decline although "demand quantity" has increased to (11.13). Consumers have more commodity at lower total input requirements, allowing some resources to be shifted to nonfood commodities. Farmers have more gross revenue from the same price and greater output and increased net revenue for this reason and because cost of inputs also have decreased. The gain, allowing an increment of utility to both consumers in general and farmers, is of Pareto type. The decrease in resource requirements and the increase in farm income represented can cause both groups to "be better off."

In effect, we have moved from point m in Figure 8.1 to a point within the shaded Pareto area. Neither, of course, is in "best off" or optimum position in the sense of movement along a contract curve and gain at the expense of the other. Farmers would be "best off" if they formed a monopoly moving output and input below and price above levels such as those specified in (11.18b).[22] Consumers would be "best off" or in higher utility position (if great degree of monopoly does not interfere with resource allocation in the economy generally and they place no disutility on the relative income position of farmers) under a market-free equilibrium for the changes in technology and demand such as that represented in (11.18d), which has the corresponding prices, output and input in (11.19).

$$\bar{P} = \lambda^{.227}\Gamma^{-1.137}P_1 \tag{11.19a}$$

$$\bar{Q} = \lambda^{.919}\Gamma^{.455}Q_1 \tag{11.19b}$$

$$\bar{X} = \lambda^{1.149}\Gamma^{-.682}X_1 \tag{11.19c}$$

As we see from these quantities and from (11.18d), revenue and net profit will decline if Γ (technical change) is large relative to λ (demand change). The value of Γ must not be greater than approximately $\lambda^{1.7}$ if revenue is to remain at a level as high as in (11.18a) before technical change. If Γ grows more rapidly than this where prices are market free, consumers will gain in more food at lower prices but producers will sacrifice in income. Price will decline below the level of (11.10) if Γ is greater than $\lambda^{.2}$ But obviously, quotas could be arranged which let price drop below (11.10), with consequent gain to consumers, but retain net income gain to producers in the sense that supply is held in check (so that in effect Γ is less than $\lambda^{1.7}$).

But just as consumers would be best off if prices and output were turned loose in the market, they would similarly be best off if prices in the steel, petroleum, electrical equipment and other industries were flexible and market free, rather than managed, and if there were more firms and greater competition in these industries. Under inability of interpersonal utility comparison, we cannot specify an increase in total utility in either of the two cases: where farmers are made best off by forming a monopoly, but at a cost to consumers in level of price and pattern of resource allocation; and where consumers are made best off by market-free prices and output, but at a cost to farmers in income. Increased aggregate welfare can be guaranteed, however, where both groups are made better off. Both can be made better off, consumers

---

[22] The market price, quantity, and input magnitudes corresponding to (11.18b) are (11.10), and (11.13) and (11.14) respectively. The market price quantity and input magnitudes for (11.18c) are respectively (11.10), (11.13) and (11.16) where technical improvement is not supposed for (11.16). The price output and input quantities corresponding to (11.18a) are those in (11.10), (11.11) and (11.12).

through resources "saved" to be used elsewhere (or even in reduction of food price) and farmers through more revenue and lower costs, for the conditions outlined above.

Marketing quotas to accomplish income gain as above for farmers, but still allowing economic progress for consumers, would involve no treasury costs except for administration and policing—as in marketing orders applied variously over the nation in milk and as applied particularly to fruits and vegetables in California and Florida. They would parallel or be similar to the "self-administered" price and output programs used in major nonfarm industries, claimed to help profits and safeguard against the vagaries of "over competition." Progress does take place under marketing orders and "self-administered" plans of major nonfarm industries, as mentioned in several previous chapters. But large treasury cost is not involved, as in producing surpluses and storing them for agriculture. The consumer, rather than the taxpayer, contributes the difference in major nonfarm industries where prices are not market free.

Allocation by Regions and Persons and Distribution of Gains

Marketing quotas for inputs or outputs can be set on a historic basis with attachment to land, as they have been for tobacco, wheat, cotton and other crops. In this case, surplus profits, or returns to factors above their supply price considering their particular attachment to agriculture, become capitalized into land values. The historic apportionment is "inefficient" in the sense that it restrains technical advance on farms and regions where it comes to have special advantage (but is no more "inefficient" than in the quota systems which emerge under oligopoly, "follow the leader" and market-sharing arrangements of other industries).

Quotas also can be attached to the person or business apart from its resources, as is often done under marketing orders for fruits and vegetables. They can be attached to a particular resource, such as cows in the milk marketing orders of California where the quota takes on value in sale of cows. It is not necessary, however, for them to be maintained on an historic basis. They can be made negotiable, as can be true of any kind of allotment system even if resting on resources, with sale in the market.[23] Accordingly, more efficient farmers or regions can purchase them from the less efficient, allowing production to become concentrated at the point of greatest comparative advantage. Similarly as technical change breaks out more rapidly in particular regions, these regions can purchase quotas from other regions.

---

[23] See W. W. Cochrane, "An Appraisal of Recent Agricultural Programs in the United States," *Jour. Farm Econ.*, Vol. 39, for an early discussion of negotiable aspects. For other aspects of quotas see R. L. Clodius, "Opportunities and Limitations in Improving Bargaining Power of Farmers," Center for Agricultural and Economic Adjustment, *Problems and Policies of Commercial Agriculture*, Iowa State University Press, Ames, 1959; H. W. Halvorsen, "Direct Management of Market Supplies " *Economic Policies for Agriculture. Implications of Four Selected Alternatives* Joint Economic Committee, Washington, D.C., 1960.

In a manner, this scheme, when applied to either output or input quotas, has an advantage in helping some farmers move out of agriculture. Selling their quota value, perhaps in discounted magnitude approaching (11.5), they have a lump-sum quantity to finance the shift to other products or to move out of agriculture. As a method purely for compensation purposes, marketing quotas (or input allotments) with negotiable characteristics do not negate the market mechanism in allocating resources: They allow more efficient farmers and regions to specialize in commodities, encourage improved technology and reduced resource requirements for a given output, allow fund acquisition and movement from agriculture by those who select to acquire their compensation in lump-sum fashion and migrate rather than remain in farming. Prices and the market would still have as much power over these adjustments, and others. But aggregate output of farm products would be restrained below short-run level prevailing under market-free prices.

The problem of determining quota restraints for either inputs or outputs, depending on the type of supply control, is difficult. Without some precedent, it involves pure power politics, perhaps with "semi-equilibrium" and nonequity sharing as explained for equations (9.9) through (9.13). This likelihood typically leads to a historic start. Negotiable quotas for inputs or output allows eventual departure from this pattern, however. But even though the initial allocation problem is difficult and political, sometimes because it represents conflict along the contract curve in Figure 8.1, it seems to be attainable in many instances—even if not always on an historic basis. It has been worked out with degree of placidity allowing "control of marketings" under fruit and vegetable marketing orders, in major milk markets and in informal, "self-administered" market-sharing arrangements of selected nonfarm industries.

Evidently "rules of the game" can be established to allow distribution of some gain to all members of a producing group. Still, conflict and inability to bargain except along a contract curve may be one basis of major conflict in application of effective compulsory marketing quotas or input restraints to commodities such as hogs, wheat and feed grains. Those who oppose quotas may obtain a much larger share of market revenue through lack of controls; those who favor them may gain a larger share by controls allocating a portion of input or output restraints to each producer. It may be this more than the freedom issue which causes conflict in selected cases of quotas. Few rumblings of lack of freedom are forthcoming from those highly commercialized farmers who produce under quota allocation by marketing orders of fruits and vegetables in California or in the major milksheds over the nation. Neither do all large oil firms decry lack of freedom under the various quota systems which they employ. Negotiability of quotas or input allotments removes, of course, freedom restraint in the sense of limits to production: acquisition of quotas through the market allows any farm or region to up its output.

Transfer of Quotas and Allotments

If the only ingredient of agricultural production were a wave of the wand of Demeter, Goddess of Agriculture, complete freedom to produce would be accorded anyone in her favor. But this is not the nature of agriculture, and freedom to produce in unrestrained manner is lacking for many persons who would be farmers, as well as many who are. Right to produce exists only when farmers purchase it, through obtaining land under title of ownership or under monetary contract for its leasing. Too, capital in its agricultural forms must be purchased to use with it.

After these titles, rights, contracts and prices are attained and paid, farmers have unrestrained right to produce in the quantity desired. Having a basic input or output restraint in quota, but being able to enlarge it by purchase, they would be operating under a somewhat similar regime of freedom. In both cases they must pay a price to obtain the right and flexibilities of quantities arising from their decisions. Quotas do not place restraint on freedom of production, but only require a price for unrestrained production and greater sharing of market revenue where they are negotiable. This is true for the quotas going with cows in the Los Angeles milkshed or with land in Carolina tobacco areas. In the absence of any quotas, farmers are free to produce any quantity they wish or can from a given collection of resources and a particular technological state. Under absolute quotas, they are free to use as few resources as they wish or as is possible, given the quota and the technological possibilities. Both are freedoms: one in the case of maximizing against upper restraints in resources and inputs, the other in minimizing against upper restraint in output.

Negotiable output quotas or input allotments provide a setting not unlike the "self help" or organizational procedures employed by nonfarm industries where price competition does not prevail exactly and market-free prices do not reign. It is obvious in industries such as steel, petroleum, automobiles and others that "homogeneous short-run" price comes to prevail and competition is not typically over price. Price is established and competition is in share of the market, or in new products and technology. Firms can buy part of this market quota, the total consumer demand at the established price, through greater advertising, public relations and various promotions and investments. They can sell shares of the market by investing less in these activities. But the fact stands that the process is one of acquiring market share at a cost, where aggregate quantity and market price are more or less given, and is not unlike the sale or purchase of negotiable quotas and allotments.

While much conflict over quotas stems from competing economic interests of various groups within and surrounding agriculture, it also must be true that some resistance is value oriented. Most university professors have "built-in values" causing them to vigorously denounce any force restraining "freedom to produce." Farmers are not always dissimilar, even though the product is quite different.

Quotas Under Market Orders

Marketing quotas are not foreign to the American farm scene. They have had widespread use over particular commodities and locations. Too, negotiable features have prevailed for some time, tied usually to such resources as cows and land. Marketing quotas best apply and have had widest use for commodities where the market is concentrated to a particular point with opportunity to control the product which flows into it, or where the adapted production area is small with facility in organization and control agreement by producers.[24] It works least well where both the markets and producers are large and are dispersed widely over the nation.

Marketing agreements and orders had their forerunner in cooperative marketing associations of the 1920's. These groups, depending on voluntary organization and control, found that without enabling legislation, they were unable to attain the desired controls in quantity and quality. Producers who participated held up the price umbrella for those who did not participate. Evidently, legislation and an extent of governmental participation were necessary for success of marketing orders to control quantity and quality.

Federal and state legislation has provided this extent of government participation for commodities covered. Federal legislation was first provided in the Agricultural Adjustment Act of 1933. It was extended under the Agricultural Marketing Act of 1937, with the volume and price connotation as follows: " . . . through exercise of powers conferred upon the Secretary of Agriculture . . . to establish and maintain such orderly marketing conditions for agricultural commodities in interstate commerce as will establish, as prices to farmers, parity prices. . . . "

Federal legislation provides for "orders with marketing agreement" and "orders without marketing agreement." Marketing orders are not forced forever on a group of producers, nor are they allowed to select just their desired course of action and no other. They can vote orders out, just as they can vote to initiate them. A *marketing agreement* is a voluntary arrangement between an authorized government agency and individual producers and handlers of a commodity in a particular area, with terms of the agreement binding only on those who sign it. In contrast, a *marketing order* is uniformly applicable to all producers and handlers of the product once it has been voted in by the above rules. Marketing orders have come to dominate marketing agreements, although the latter set the historical precedent. A federal marketing order, the mechanism for volume control, can be initiated only when handlers with 50 percent of the volume handled and two-thirds of the producers in the specified area

---

[24] For detailed description of market orders and agreements, their extent and particular implications, see S. Hoos, "Economic Implications of California Agricultural Marketing Programs," *Jour. Farm Econ.*, Vol. 38; *Contribution of Marketing Agreements and Orders. Policy for Commercial Agriculture, Its Relation to Economic Growth and Stability,* Joint Economic Report, Washington, D.C., 1957.

approve. In terms of population, milk price control thus extends to a major portion of the nation. Its pricing is dominated by public regulation highly similar to that of public utilities in general.

In addition to federal legislation, nearly two dozen states have marketing programs with somewhat similar purpose. California had initiated such legislation as early as 1933 and has moved forward on the broadest front in terms of farm commodities and number of producers included under marketing agreements designed to have impact on quantity, quality, price and other provisions affecting the supply of the demand for, and the orderly marketing of, food commodities.[25] One reflection of this legislation and its purpose is included in the following statement by the director of the California Department of Agriculture:

One might think that this remarkable increase in farm productivity would enable farmers to become extremely prosperous. However, that is not the way it has worked out. The net farm income has decreased by 30 percent since 1951, while urban consumers have benefited by getting more food of a better quality, at a cheaper price. . . . These figures are reflected in a comparison of the years 1929 and 1958 for quantities of food which could be bought with one hour's wages. . . .

	1929	*1958*
Loaves of bread	6.4	11
Pounds of steak	1.2	2
Pints of milk (delivered)	7.8	16.8
Pounds of butter	1	2.9
Pounds of bacon	1.3	2.7
Dozens of eggs	1.1	3.5
Pounds of potatoes	17.7	33.8
Dozens of oranges	1.3	2.8

Even if the individual farmer could make exact production and marketing plans and carry them out, he would not be able to make a significant impact on the supply or demand of the market in which he sells. Because of the infinitesimal proportion of the total supply of a commodity produced by any one farmer, he can not, by himself, bring about a higher selling price by cutting back his production, for this would not cut back the total supply by any measurable amount. Moreover, his output usually becomes a small and unidentifiable part of the supply marketed under the brand name of some other person. For these reasons, the individual farmer, unless he takes joint action of the kinds I will mention later, has little or no opportunity to influence the demand for his product. . . . California farmers recognize these problems and have adopted methods of working together to improve their marketing positions. One kind of group action by farmers is the use of the cooperative association as a bargaining agent in selling their farm products. . . . There are several such associations in California which have attained a very important position in the determination of prices and other terms of sale by negotiations on behalf of their members. . . . Special legislation and the services of governmental agencies have also been utilized. Under the authorization of the California Marketing Act, agricultural producers are taking joint action on marketing problems by adopting marketing order programs. . . . Such programs may be designed to control the volume or quality of the product marketed, to provide for advertising and trade stimulation, to control unfair trade practices, and to

---

[25] For detailed explanation of California legislation and market order arrangements see: *California Agricultural Marketing Programs*, Calif. Dept. of Agr. Bul., Vol. 45; *The California Marketing Act of 1937*, Extracts from the Agricultural Code of California, Revised to September, 1959; and Sunkist Growers Inc., *A California Adventure in Agricultural Cooperation*, FCS Circular 27.

provide for research. . . . At the present time, there are 34 California marketing programs, several of which have been in operation for more than 20 years. . . . In conclusion, I feel that the farmer cannot prosper and our independently operated type of agriculture cannot be maintained unless there is brought into existence a condition of planned supply.[26]

Evidently, marketing agreements and controls work adequately and to the income advantage of producers where they are used. This fact may cause producers such as those producing milk in the East and fruit and vegetable producers in the West to have little interest and some scorn for the types of supply control and surplus storage programs used since 1930 for grains and cotton.

With a marketing order, an industry or group of producers provides means for regulating and affecting the marketing of a commodity. Under quantity control, quotas can be allocated to producers—as they are in fact. Certainly the basic purpose of marketing orders is to regulate quantity moving into market channels and price to producers, although provision also is included for quality regulation, advertising and promotion, research and similar activities. Federal marketing orders have orientation to quantity and quality control for the specified products, but state orders more generally include the other features and not all state programs allow quantity control. For example, California legislation covers more than two dozen commodities but with volume or quantity control only on such commodities as early apples, asparagus, lemon products, dry-pack lettuce, lima beans, cling peaches, fresh fall and winter pears and Delta white potatoes. Marketing orders generally differ between milk and other commodities, with direct price setting for milk, accompanied by supply restraints in quantity and/or quality regulations. The price effects are brought about indirectly through supply restraints or quotas for other commodities. Quantity restraint is reflected back to producers in quotas of commodities which they are allowed to market, with acreage adjusted accordingly or a portion of the crop destroyed if output exceeds marketing quota of producers. Hence, plowing under of lettuce and destroying peaches is a common occurrence for California producers. While the stated objectives of marketing orders and agreements are various, the real intent is to control supply, expand demand and improve returns to farm producers.

CONTROL, MARKET POWER AND PARETO OPTIMA

Supply control under marketing orders can be looked upon partly as a general compensation scheme as outlined previously, with Pareto-better conditions allowed in retention of some gains of progress by producers but with relative resource savings from new technology and lower real prices for food passed on to consumers. As much as anything perhaps, they are means of placing market or bargaining power in the hands of producers who otherwise, as "pure competitors," operate under the in-

[26] Charles Paul, Director, California Department of Agriculture, Speech to Clovis, Calif., District Chamber of Commerce, March 23, 1961, "California's Stake in Agriculture."

come instability characteristic of a pure competition market where *ex ante* expectations and plans lead to mass *ex poste* "overages" in upward and downward swings of output.

In addition to bargaining power with some control on market volume and price, marketing orders have been effective in lessening instability stemming from extreme seasonality of production. Not only has greater price stability been attained within the year, but also that growing out of price wars and fluctuation through the commodity cycle has been lessened. There is no indication that marketing orders have been used to create pricing conditions characteristic of pure monopolies for the selected commodities to which they have been applied. This extreme is impossible for individual categories of food commodities. There are too many substitutes for a particular vegetable, fruit or nut crop, just as there are numerous substitutes for industrial commodities produced under oligopoly and near-monopoly conditions where extreme price level encourages substitution of other materials and services. Not only does one food commodity have substitute in other products, but also substitute exists in the same commodity produced at other locations. The effects of long-run price competition in major production allocations cannot be reduced effectively by marketing orders, although they can bring an important degree of short-run stability to particular farm sectors. If one group of producers is "too successful" in attaining price goals through marketing orders, it is almost certain to be faced with competition (1) from producers in other regions and (2) from other commodities which compete in consumption. Since marketing orders best apply for perishable commodities moving directly to consumption or processing, produced by farmers with a homogeneity of interest located in a small area, they have much less promise for commodities such as wheat, feed grains, cattle and hogs. In the realm of feed grains, which serve as both inputs and outputs, the task of policing marketing quotas would be complex and costly if, in fact, it can be done.

Conflict in Restraint

Some detail has been added in this section on marketing agreements and orders to emphasize their existence on a fairly widespread magnitude, and as indication that there is great variance as to the expressed kind and degree of decision freedom desired by American farm producers. In addition to output and quotas of the type represented by marketing orders, there are also those represented by input quotas which producers of wheat, tobacco and cotton have voted upon themselves.

Imposition of these supply controls on themselves by farmers and commodity groups under the voting mechanism, while other farmers and organizations vigorously protest output and input restraints, have various implications, one being that a conflict of interest exists along a contract line such as that of Figure 8.1. And this is very likely true for commodities which have wide spatial adaptation and changing comparative advantage by region. In these cases, quotas distribute gains to some and potential or relative losses to others, without opportunity for trades. Attainment of the loci of tangency of indifference curves as in Figure 8.1 means that all cannot be lifted simultaneously to preferred positions. Quotas can be favorable to farmers with few resources and no volume expansion possibilities, and unfavorable to those with capital for extension of supply. (Some opportunity in expansion is still allowed under numerous marketing orders and under all quota or allotment systems wherein sale and purchase of resources or output restraints is possible. As explained in Chapter 14, other output quota systems may distribute the gains of control more in the direction of large producers.)

Conflict along the loci of tangency also occurs for commodities such as feed grains: While some farmers are sellers of feed as a commodity, others are purchasers of it as a resource. Also, milk producers in feed deficit areas of the East can gain from milk marketing orders which support and control price and volume of this commodity, but "have their freedom trespassed" where similar restraints are applied to feed grains. Finally, feed grains are grown widely, as general substitutes for other crops which may come under quantity or volume controls. They thus become the "general commodity of trade or compensation" (a method of "side payment") among regional groups which, in effect, give up some of one commodity to gain more of another. Hence, each regional group which gives up acreage of cotton, wheat or vegetable and other commodities moving directly to consumers wishes to have more acreage of feed grain, as in giving up some of X to obtain more of Z in Figure 8.1. Feed grains thus become the outside commodity (along with price support and direct subsidy) used to compensate the group where it otherwise would be made "worse off" in restricting acreage and output of its particular commodity. But this procedure, with feed grain as the trading commodity or method of "side payment," does not give recognition to all groups in position of being reflected gains and losses under such trades.

Besides direct economic conflicts of the type outlined above, differences in values per se might help explain the extreme conflict over supply control and freedom reflected by farm groups: Value differences do not themselves require an "either or" choice. The two sets of indifference curves in Figure 8.1 can have entirely different slopes, but still allow exchange and increase in welfare for both individuals or groups. But this is a case of continuous functions with divisible quantities for substitution and rearrangement. The real value conflict arises less under these circumstances, but more under cases where resources are not involved, the opportunity is discrete and only "one or the other" state can exist. The "belief or not" in a particular God is such a case. Does the supply restraint-freedom conflict for U.S. agriculture reflect discrete and ideological difference of the latter type? Or, is it more nearly the economic interest conflict outline previously?

To the extent that individual values alone are involved in quota restraints on supply, procedures may still be possible which allow Pareto optima in the sense of "making no one worse off" because of the weight he attaches to his own "freedom to produce." Quotas could be established for those who prefer more income even at loss of some freedom. They would then receive the market price for their sales, plus a direct payment from the public. Those who select more freedom would not be given a quota and they would receive return equal only to the market price for the commodity. But the equity of the procedure might still be questioned: Quotas would have to be continuously restrained for the first group to offset growth in supply by the second group, if the system served to "hold up the price umbrella."

Pareto-Better Mixes in Farm Policy

The historical extent of input and output restraint used in U.S. farm policy may well be oriented to Pareto optima. Under democratically selected mechanisms, those preferring less freedom and more income or stability have been able to select output restraints. Hence supply restraints exist for products such as tobacco, milk, cling peaches and dry-pack lettuce. Other farmers who prefer freedom over income maintenance have been allowed to select more of the former and less of the latter (and some have gotten more of both because of their advantage in capital and managerial possessions). Then, it is entirely possible that the maze of farm policy of 1930–60, with its great variance in control and flexibility of production as selected by producers, was highly consistent with welfare maximization or improvement over the distinct groups which make up the total of the U.S. farm community. Variance in policy over commodities and locations, rather than homogeneity, likely characterizes Pareto optima and welfare maximization. In this sense the heterogeneous and apparent piecemeal pattern of policy of 1930–60 was not necessarily incongruous, except in those instances where it did not attain income or freedom objectives for those producers selecting a particular policy element.

FOCUS OF COMPETITION AND LONG-RUN SOLUTIONS

Input or output restraints to stabilize markets and effectuate compensation probably are favored over direct payments by some producers because they are less apparent and invite less public scorn and resistance, just as is true for nonfarm firms and industries which use managed prices to attain stability and insurance of resource return. Publicly regulated prices in the case of milk marketing orders which control volume, through quotas for vegetables and fruits, and acreage allotments for tobacco, cotton and wheat are all devices which help prevent the extreme fluctuations in price and income which normally attend industries based on many producers who must make decisions under imperfect knowledge.

However, quotas and allotments which are attached to marketable resources, or which are themselves marketable, do not eliminate competition, regardless of cry to this effect. Competition still exists; only the focus of its implementation shifts. Under market-free prices, competition impinges on both commodity and resource. Under commodity supply control, the focus falls on the resources and the allotment restraints. This fact is implied in statements by those who claim that input or output quotas eliminate competition but immediately state that they are ineffective anyway because they become capitalized into resource values. The fact that they do become capitalized indicates existence of competition.

Long-Run Solutions

Capitalization of gains from price and quantity control into resource values provides the precise reason why supply control and price support do not provide a permanent solution to the lag of farm income below nonfarm income. The historic and world-wide characteristics of this lag, illustrated in Chapter 3, rest on variables and coefficients which will never be overcome by compensation policies and programs using extra-market means to boost resource returns.

Income gain can be attained in the short run but it cannot be retained in the long run (aside from direct payment compensation attached in lump-sum fashion to the individual) for the simple reason that it becomes capitalized into nonhuman resources. With policy which maintains higher price and income, a given quantity of capital then simply buys fewer resources, giving no greater total income to the resource bundle than if the program did not exist, factor prices were lower and given funds purchased more resources. For this reason, supply control and price support programs provide compensation only for the moment. They do not erase the variables causing the historic lag of farm income.

Marketing quotas of negotiable character, spread globally and permanently over all commodities, would have similar effect: compensation for the immediate generation with resource prices eventually increasing, rate of return declining and original disparity returned. This "return of the wicked" will remain as long as the basic cause of the income disparity is the low short-run factor supply elasticity and other conditions explained previously.

Farmers, of course, live and plan in the short run. They wish programs which bring income comparability at the moment, with less concern for the structural explanation of the disparity. To the extent that their income position is worsened from rapid advance in supply over a series of interrelated short runs, this interest is consistent with need to create conditions which spread gains and losses of economic growth in a manner to guarantee aggregate welfare advance. Programs are needed to attain these conditions, to the extent that conflict in economic interests and values of farm groups and political interaction allows them. But at the same time, programs and aids are needed which help overcome the structural imbalances giving rise to this historic depression of farm income relative to nonfarm income. Compensation methods are possible which do so while still allowing mechanisms for greater stability of price and supply of agriculture. The two problems, (1) compensation to offset rapid short-run rush of supply beyond demand, with its nonsymmetrical distribution of gains and losses among producers and consumers and (2) historic lag of income because of low factor supply elasticity, are not the same. Compensation will not solve the latter, and increased factor supply elasticity is not a substitute for compensation in the former.

ALTERNATIVES IN POLICY

We have discussed alternative approaches in the realm of compensation policy, in the context of distribution of gains and losses to better guarantee aggregate welfare increase and in the manner of a goal which society evidently has attempted to accomplish. Our concern was mostly with the compensation goal, supposing desire of society to attain it, and less intensively with the stability problem.

There are, of course, additional alternatives in policy. One is reliance solely on the open market and the structure of pure competition, with their particular scatter of sacrifices and gains from technical advance and general progress in agriculture. Still society has rejected this, as a pure approach, through its investment in public schools, roads, police force and even production of new agricultural technology. It has done so in regulation of food and drugs, in attempt to control the business cycle and in provision of unemployment compensation and social security.

In agriculture, as in other sectors, the great strengths of the price and market mechanisms need retention and strengthening, supplemented by public policy where (1) national goals are not best attained by complete reliance on the market and (2) the distribution of gains and losses through the pricing mechanism are deemed by society to be unequitable and incompatible with guarantee of aggregate gain. Of course the free market mechanism could serve to squeeze surplus resources out of agriculture, given sufficient time and widespread bankruptcy of farmers. But there are methods whereby the pricing mechanism can be supplemented to better salvage the dignity and capital values of individuals.

Miscellaneous Policy Means

We wish to speak at length in later chapters of policy means to accomplish the complex of intermediate goals cited above. Here, however, it is apropos to list some worthy of consideration in purpose and objective, if not entirely in efficiency and acceptability.

There is not complete precedent in the past wherein society has provided full compensation to redress individual loss, especially that arising from technical and economic progress. Accordingly, there is a question of whether it should now do so in complete scale for agriculture. Yet a minimum and reasonable scale of compensation seems in order and is only consistent with the large public outlays of the past to accomplish this goal. Efficient compensation policy would emphasize positive opportunity.

Policy consistent with both economic advance and retention of some fruits of progress for agriculture would include the following elements, to be discussed in detail later: an improved flow of economic knowledge and understanding to farm people; compensation and loans to cover capital losses and transfer from agriculture; retraining and greater job guidance services to overcome inflexibilities of older persons; aid in purchase of housing and relocation; unemployment compensation during the period of transfer and other measures to overcome the fear and uncertainty of transfer.

Pure Compensation

Given compensation as a pure and single goal of policy, with little resistance to method, simple means could be used to accomplish this end. One precedent exists in current Social Security Administration machinery.[27] If we could make an approximate inventory of persons who should not or never will leave agriculture, and if society firmly believes that compensation is due agriculture because of the burden of economic growth falling on the industry, the age at which social security payments begin might be lowered from 65 to the appropriate level. This system would not tie the interproduct use of resources in agriculture to consumption and technical patterns of the past. Given the conditions that the persons concerned are those who should not or would not leave agriculture, the system would not freeze resources in agriculture.

Even if some "errors" were made in designation of individuals, or even if anticipations led some surplus labor to remain in agriculture, the misuse of resources would be less than under price policies where farmers must remain in the industry to receive parity subsidies. With the age for social security payments lowered to a particular level, it need not be left permanently at this level. It would be moved up progressively to reach 65, the level for the rest of the population. In other words, the rest of the farm labor force would be warned that the same arrangement would not apply to it when it reaches the lower age, but that if its income is low, advantage should be taken of special education or mobility subsidies with movement to other employment. This policy would be clear-cut in its composition and "cut off." It is, however, less likely in general acceptance than others which can be advocated.

---

[27] These notions and others dealing with compensation to redress gain and loss distribution to guarantee increase in aggregate welfare appeared previously by the author in the article: "Adaptation of Extension Education and Auxiliary Aids to the Basic Economic Problem of Agriculture," *Jour. Farm Econ.*, Vol. 39.

12

Income and Mobility of Labor and Community Development

SHORT-RUN FACTOR SUPPLY ELASTICITY is high for individual products of agriculture where technological production possibilities allow relatively high and constant marginal rates of product substitution. Instability of price and income of individual products results accordingly from the commodity cycles so generated. But short-run supply elasticity of factors is low for agricultural commodities in aggregate, causing farm income to lag behind nonfarm income. In the regime of low supply elasticities, two factors are most important: land and labor. The impacts of these low supply elasticities for agriculture in aggregate are somewhat different, however. Low supply elasticity for land has its most notable effect in causing a low income blanket to lie over all of agriculture. Low elasticity and mobility for labor cause particular individuals and strata of the farm population to suffer extreme income depression. Supply elasticity of labor has been high relative to that of land, but low relative to equilibrium conditions which would give labor returns in agriculture approaching those of other industries.

The mobility of labor does not solve the aggregate supply problem of agriculture as long as land sticks to production of the conventional mix of crops and labor is still underemployed. With an approximate halving of the farm work force between 1940 and 1962, agricultural supply still hung heavy over demand. As mentioned in previous chapters, this large outflow of labor was possible without check on forward advance in farm output because of several reasons: Labor has been highly underemployed in agriculture, allowing the work force remaining to handle the crops and livestock of those who left. Scale economies and the substitution of machinery for labor has furthered this opportunity. But the same time, land remained employed in the conventional crops because its reservation price for this complex is low and because price policy encouraged it to do so.

Outmigration which was large in absolute number, if not in magnitude relative to level of labor returns, aided the income position of persons who moved to favorable positions in off-farm employment. It aided those who remained and, with sufficient resources, were able to increase volume and realize scale economies more than offsetting price recession. But though these income gains went to individuals, the high "stickiness" of land in current uses caused depressed income still to blanket agriculture in aggregate and especially for the strata of farmers able to make neither of the two above adjustments.

Quite obviously, outmigration of labor from agriculture can cause resource returns, as an average for the industry, to increase through more complete employment of persons remaining, through increased marginal productivity in the conventional production function sense and through reduction in output. But withdrawal of labor inputs must proceed much further before it will have great effect in causing output to be cut back; raising marginal value productivity through an increase in the marginal physical productivity of labor and a higher commodity price taken together. Withdrawal of labor must become so great that it has important complementary effect (see Figure 14.1) in causing shift of land from more intensive crops such as cotton, feed grains and wheat to less intensive ones such as grass, forestry and recreation.

Outmigration of labor can be discussed and evaluated in respect to these aggregate aspects of agricultural structure, or in terms of welfare of individuals who might better their income and life outlook by occupational transfer. The two can, of course, go hand-in-hand. But the analysis also can look at the problem either in purely mechanistic manners or in human perspective: People as resources to be adjusted as levers in bringing about the equilibrating process, and as machines into which commodities are dropped through slots to register utility; or people who are individuals with human aspirations and frustrations. Our emphasis in this chapter is mainly on welfare of individuals who have opportunity and prospect for improving their position by occupational migration; recognizing, of course, that this is a necessary adjustment of agriculture if magnitude of inputs is drawn to levels allowing resource earnings to be favorable through the market. While decrease in labor input to draw factor rewards in agriculture to higher levels is one goal of migration and greater supply elasticity, an equally important goal is that of benefit to individuals who can and should migrate because of better opportunity thus attained. Hence, our discussion in this chapter is on the latter, recognizing that it is an important step in accomplishing the former.

If compensation policies are developed which award farmers for possible loss attached to aggregate economic progress, or which allow them greater market power and retention of a share of developmental gains through this process, the need for migration still exists. It exists because of the large number of farm families whose income is so meager that compensation can do little to lift their welfare; because technical advance and change in relative factor prices will still give rise to need in migration; and because economic expansion outside of agriculture will provide larger benefits for many people now in farming. Under efficient and politically acceptable compensation schemes, even should these be based on negotiable marketing quotas, the opportunity for people to capitalize in sale of these and to migrate to other employment will still exist. It thus is reasonable to look to compensation schemes, or their equivalent, which redress welfare sacrifices of individuals by aiding them in migration from agriculture. Possibilities then exist for aggregate national gain from progress, regardless of the initial distribution of gains and losses, which benefits the people directly involved in migration and also brings structural and resource balance to agriculture so that more favorable returns are possible through prices consumers are willing to pay in the market.

EQUILIBRIUM THROUGH DEMAND, SUPPLY AND CAPITAL AVAILABILITY

The persistence of labor returns in agriculture at lower level than elsewhere provides several propositions of relevance in explaining the difference. This underemployment of labor in agriculture, a chief cause of downward drag in average incomes, would not exist in a full-employment economy where capital and knowledge supply served effectively to transfer and reallocate labor of farms to other sectors. Demand for labor from the nonfarm sector and supply from the farm sector would balance (also against labor supplied from nonfarm farm sectors) to give employment of agricultural labor which lifts returns in farming to the nonfarm level.

But this timeless, perfect market exists neither for labor or the capital related to its transfer. Two time periods serve to obstruct the equilibrating process: One in which the demand blade prevents it and one in which labor supply, as affected by counterpart supply of capital and knowledge, prevents it. Given full employment, failure for enough labor to transfer prevails because the supply of labor moving from farms to nonfarm sectors does not fill demand, in discrete sense of number of people against employment opportunity. Labor supplied from farms is limited then evidently because (1) the supply of capital to cover transfer costs is limited, (2) the supply of knowledge about job openings, magnitude of labor demand and living conditions is too restricted, or (3) differences in real income persist, with labor supply restricted because of personal preferences and related elements or real income. In period of prevailing unemployment, transfer is restricted because nonfarm demand for labor from farms is insufficient. Employment is then rationed. A level of wages prevails in industry and cannot be "beat down by competing labor of farms" because labor price is determined through market bargaining power rather than by open market forces. Labor supply eligible to "equilibrate the demand" then is defined largely by institutional creation, only some from farms being able to enter the industrial force (or having to enter the lower-priced, nonskilled wage pool).

Both of these supply and demand circumstances have worked to restrain labor movement from farms. Farm policy per se can do little to cope with the nonfarm "labor demand blade" restraint in the one period. It can, however, affect the "supply blade" through policy directed at labor on farms, causing the labor supply function, in amount of labor furnished by agriculture to industry, to shift rightward and increasing its elasticity. Policy which does so automatically shifts the supply function of labor to agriculture leftward and increases its elasticity.

This chapter concentrates on the supplying of farm labor to nonfarm industry. The demand aspect outlined above is properly one of economic growth and fiscal policy at level of national society. The limited supply of capital going into education and guidance in rural communities restrains the supply of labor moving from farms to higher paid professions and skilled fields, relative to the supply moving from nonfarm household sectors to these same fields. Investment for these purposes in rural areas is limited because education has been based too greatly on the supply of capital in the community; various institutional restrictions preventing augmentation of capital supply for education from outside or national sources. Farm youth and labor thus are excluded from major opportunities for increasing their welfare beyond horizons possible in agriculture. These considerations represent the general complex to be discussed.

Opportunity of People

Policy of agriculture focusing entirely and alone on compensation and market power for people who remain in agriculture is negative. It stands to constrain future earning power and economic opportunity of an important strata of the farm population. It diverts attention from the many human resources which can be aided little or not at all by typical compensation policies and which have opportunity closed to them by price or production policy fixation. Many of the youth and younger persons of agriculture need opportunity opened to them in manner which cannot be done through policy which has focus only on support prices, marketing quotas and similar devices. Finally, even if land use and supply could be transformed to bring greater prosperity to the farm industry in aggregate, the large pocket of persons with few resources and low income would still exist.

Nearly the whole of agriculture making up the poverty sector is candidate for transfer, or erasure of poverty, in the next generation if not in this one. Subsistence at substandard consumer levels has too long been its lot, in one generation following another. Youth has lacked education, guidance and opportunity—falling back into the same lot as its parents too much in a sense of perpetuity. The initial reasons for this situation are now unimportant. Further describing of factor markets and plotting of statistics in pure descriptive sense is unnecessary and only serves to distract from the need for positive action to relieve the situation. Action is desired: in the sense of economics wherein movements to Pareto optima or Pareto-better conditions are possible, in bringing gain to individuals involved and in furthering the growth and product of the nation; in the sense of constitutional guarantee of opportunity to the individual; and directly in the sense of equity and distributive justice. Complete freedom and opportunity of the individual does not prevail as long as successive generations are forced into a cast which prevents their capabilities as resources and consumers from being fully developed.

The poverty sector of agriculture stands to gain relatively most from investment which increases their worth as resources and gives them greater employment opportunity under economic growth. Lack of opportunity for this sector of the farm population does not stem from economic progress. Their lot is only made more noticeable by progress. In the absence of progress and with constrained supply of farm products giving rise to aggregate prosperity in agriculture, the poverty problem would still prevail. It is not, of course, necessary that all such persons be transformed from agriculturist. Given their inflexibilities of age and abilities in farming, and with opportunities otherwise lacking in farm size expansion, some stand to prosper best in agriculture if sufficient numbers of others migrate and credit supply is made favorable.

The need for migration to provide improved economic opportunity does not apply in the poverty sector of agriculture alone, however. Occupational migration is desired for a large number of persons in commercial agriculture who could better their lifetime opportunity in income and welfare by shifting to occupations with rewards greater than those in store for them in farming. Even with the present number and sizes of farms in commercial agriculture, this is true. Johnson's projections indicate that opportunities for gainful employment of new farm operators will average less than 25,000 annually during the 1960's.[1] Against this number of openings, about 250,000 male farm youth will be entering the labor force each year.

Johnson's definition of gainful employment is operation of a unit producing farm products valued at $5,000 or more annually. Even against this definition of opportunity, only about one in ten farm youth could ex-

[1] Sherman E. Johnson, *Agricultural Outlook in the 1960's*, Mimeographed presentation, Outlook Conference, Washington, D.C. Nov. 1960. Karl Shoemaker (*Opportunities and Limitation for Employment of Farm People Within and Outside Farming*, USDA Fed. Ext. Serv. Mimeo. 1958) estimates opportunity for one in 10 farm youth in agriculture on units producing $2,500 or more gross value of sales. The $2,500 value is consistent with net incomes of about $1,500 or less, a meager quantity considering the general opulence in the American economy.

pect to have reasonable opportunity in the industry. But $5,000 gross value of output is extremely low, too low for most types of farming, and would leave net income too meager for acceptance at current per capita income levels. With average nonfarm family net income already above $6,500 the $5,000 value of gross sales defines economic opportunity which is too restricted for acceptance at current levels of national and per capita income. The number of opportunities providing favorable economic outlook in family living level and capital accumulation is probably less than one in 15 for male farm youth entering the labor force during the 1960's. Hence, as many as 230,000 male youths annually will, or should, be casting to nonfarm industry for employment. In addition to this must be added females entering the labor force and looking for employment, plus those who have already started in agriculture but have found their returns to be low.

Demand for Labor and Supply Elasticity in Agriculture

Increasing numbers of farm persons will turn to nonfarm employment at a time when a bulge occurs in the labor force because of the jump in the birth rates during the 1940's. The number of new entrants in the national labor force will average upwards of 2,600,000 per year during the 1960's, an increase of 40 percent over the 1950's. (The number of young persons reaching 18 years of age is predicted to increase from 2.6 million annually in 1960 to 3.8 million in 1965.) The number of new jobs created during the 1950's averaged about 2.3 million annually. Hence, without stepped up growth rate, competition for employment will be keen, disadvantage lying mostly with those having least preparation and knowledge of opportunities. Employment opportunity is predicted to increase in professional, technical, clerical, skilled, service and sales jobs, but to remain constant in unskilled jobs.[2] Hence, some unemployment is likely to prevail in unskilled jobs while relative shortages exist in professional and skilled positions favored by economic growth. Typically, a majority of migrants from farms have had to first seek or remain in unskilled employment, with approximately half the expansion in urban-industrial labor force between 1930 and 1955 coming through migration from the farm population.[3] Educational and vocational training deficiencies of rural areas (see Table 13.1) cause farm migrants to be at disadvantage in migration and nonfarm employment. This is importantly true for farm youth, but particularly true for persons of 35 years and up who have spent their entire life in farming and have had but little education oriented towards modern industrial employment requirements.

---

[2] *Manpower Challenge of the 1960's*, U.S. Department of Labor, Washington D.C., 1960. For return on educational investment, see G. S. Becker, *Investment in Education*, Nat. Bur. of Econ. Research, Annual Report, no. 39, pp. 38–40.

[3] L. J. Ducoff, "Trends and Characteristics of Farm Populations in Low Income Farming Areas," *Jour. Farm Econ.*, Vol. 37. Over the single decade 1940–50, 8.6 million persons, alive in both 1940 and 1950, were added to the urban labor force through net migration from agriculture.

Prospects in Migration

The strata of farm people with low present and prospective incomes thus are faced with two major disadvantages in economic opportunity: There is not opportunity for many of them in agriculture because of paucity of their resources or rapid technical development of the industry; they are at a disadvantage in education and skills in moving into the nonfarm labor force.[4] Their disadvantage in skills arises out of the fact that knowledge and abilities used for agriculture have little transfer value when shifted to other employment. Also their education has been too limited and of uneven quality.

In general farm people have been, and continue to be, at an important geographic and educational disadvantage in attempting to avert the penalties attached to economic progress in agriculture and to capture the premiums attending progress in nonfarm employment. Improvements have been made in rural educational facilities and more are in store. However, the fact remains that concentration is still too much in turning farm youth back into agriculture where opportunity is bleak for many; that the majority of school districts is too small to allow attainment of scale economies and specialization necessary in supplying labor for future developmental demands. Educational deficiencies continue to place farm youth and established agricultural workers at a disadvantage as they migrate to nonfarm employment. These disadvantages can be fully overcome only in a decade and a generation, but there is need for immediate effort in this direction.

Immediate public investment to lessen this void in development of the human resource can have quick payoff for the youth involved. More effective use of talents in older persons is more difficult and requires somewhat different action as is suggested by the data of Table 12.1. From the standpoint of youth and the more flexible portion of the established labor force in agriculture, there is need to turn their abilities in directions of professional, technical services and skilled operatives where economic growth of future decades will have its greatest demand for human effort.

---

[4] D. G. Johnson, "Comparability of Labor Capacities of Farm and Nonfarm Labor," *Amer. Econ. Rev.*, Vol. 43 (and "Policies to Improve Labor Transfer," *Amer. Econ. Rev.*, Vol. 50) estimates off-farm migrants to have income of 82 to 90 percent that of nonfarm people of the same age and sex group. By weighting the 1950 median income of the ten broad occupation groups by the distribution of all employed males, 14 years and over, he estimates average 1950 income at $2,699. The occupational distribution of male off-farm migrants, 14 and over, yields an estimate of $2,348, only 87 percent of the income for all males. An age correction yields an estimate of off-farm migrants which is 88.6 percent of that for all males (over 14). Johnson's adjustment indicates the male off-farm migrants, in 1950 might expect an income between 80 and 87 percent of the average in the total employed male labor force. This does not account, however, for persons who hung back in low paid farm work because skills did not allow them to take other than the lower end of nonskilled off-farm work, or for differences in age distribution of migrants. Those most inclined to migrate obviously are those with smallest realized disadvantage in doing so. The fact that farmers moving into non-skilled labor categories get only slightly less than their city colleagues does little to alleviate the fact that a disproportionate of the farm population finds its way into these low skilled categories.

Yet with established farmers and farm workers lowest in educational attainment, there is much less (and more frequently no) opportunity to train them to partake of premiums in major growth categories. Educational attainment of established farm workers varies greatly by region and economic class of farm.[5] It is highest, in the process of economic selection and interaction, for operators of larger farms generating fairly high incomes (exactly the group least likely to transfer) and of no particular need in transfer. The main public policy element for this group is that to provide stability and compensation where society deems this equitable under the realized distribution of gains and losses from progress.

TABLE 12.1

PROJECTED CHANGE 1960 TO 1970 IN JOB OPPORTUNITIES IN SELECTED EMPLOYMENT CATEGORIES AND AVERAGE EDUCATION OF PERSONS EMPLOYED IN CATEGORY IN 1959

Type of Worker	Change in Opportunities, 1960 to 1970	Average Schooling, 1959
	(Percent)	*(Years)*
Professional and technical	+42	16.2
Proprietors and managers	+23	12.4
Clerical and sales	+25	12.5
Skilled craftsmen	+23	11.0
Semiskilled operatives	+18	9.9
Service workers	+24	9.7
Unskilled laborers	0	8.6
Farmers and farm workers	−17	8.6

Source: *Manpower—Challenge of the 1960's*, U.S. Department of Labor, Washington, D.C., 1960.

Educational attainment and development of abilities is lowest, and extremely so, for farmers from the poverty class; especially Negro farmers and operators in regions such as the Appalachian and Ozark mountain areas. As outlined in Chapter 5, this income group is source of the greatest number of migrants. Educational attainment, and equality of the flexibility of skills, also is low for many older farm operators scattered throughout dairy regions, the Cornbelt, wheat regions and other commercial farming areas. This group also is one little likely to migrate and perhaps with most claim to policy which increases stability of income and provides compensation for any loss resulting from progress. The utility of living among community, culture and acquaintance of long conditioned attachment is not small for this group, as also is true for many middle-aged families with children. Move to nonfarm job and new community with higher money income, even with adjustment for price level, does not

[5] Labor from farms has a high (or equal) rate of substitution for nonfarm labor of the same capacity and education generally. The trouble is less that it so serves and may have similar returns where it finds its way into nonfarm employment and more that it isn't developed to find greater way into higher-capacity positions. For notes on substitution of labor, see G. S. Becker, *The Economics of Discrimination*, University of Chicago Press, Chicago, 1957.

guarantee welfare increase for them and provides a strong barrier to geographic migration.

The goal in adjusting labor force and increasing supply elasticity of this resource, even in sense of restoring favorable income in agriculture, is not that of transferring all persons out of the industry, as some discussions would imply. Instead, it is only to do so in extent which will cause factor return in this industry to be comparable with that of other sectors. The discussion of equations (5.1) through (5.19) illustrates the purely economic mechanics of the reorganization involved. But quite obviously those most subject to transfer, because of few resources and low income, are either youth or persons with least training and resources to make success in agriculture. For the same reasons, the latter group tends to become thrown in with unskilled laborers where return also is lowest. For many of the older persons in agriculture, this is no advantage since they have opportunity only in menial tasks and promise of living standard and real income, considering strong value orientation to rural community, at a lower level than in agriculture. Hence, they are not prone to migrate.

Even though education in rural areas is deficient relative to labor demands under economic growth, youth is flexible and can take with him ability and some elements of training with payoff in nonfarm employment. While many youth, and the majority of persons first established in agriculture who later migrate, end up in unskilled work, an important portion of young persons progress into managerial and professional positions. Data for 1952 show that of persons of the labor force with fathers in farming, 30 percent were farmers, 46 percent were manual workers and 24 percent were nonmanual workers.[6] In contrast, 32 percent of persons whose fathers were manual workers were employed in nonmanual work while 64 percent with fathers in nonmanual occupation were employed similarly (i.e. in nonmanual work). Yet 16 percent of persons whose fathers were farmers were employed in 1952 as nonfarm proprietors, managers and officials; a proportion exceeded only by persons whose fathers were in these professions, the figure for the latter group being 26 percent.

The older farm worker with skills calcified to the industry has little experience and special ability of great value to take with him, and often is even at great disadvantage in the unskilled laborer group. There are, of course, a group of younger persons already established in agriculture who have greater opportunity for income and family well-being in nonfarm employment. Their skills retain important flexibility, even though schooling of past decades did not necessarily develop talents in manner most consistent with future employment opportunity. They have opportunity to transfer and, by devious methods, to acquire experience and eventually work up into semiskilled, skilled or service professions. But they would have much better opportunity to do so if retraining programs existed to revive talents which have been latent and without exercise in the farm industry.

[6] For data, see S. M. Lipset and R. Bendix, *Social Mobility in Industrial Society*, University of California Press, Berkeley, 1959, pp. 21, 89.

PEOPLE INVOLVED IN TRANSFER

Potential candidates for transfer from the farm industry are people, and not inanimate resources. For this reason, their welfare and the payoff of employment which they might attain is equally as important as the benefits from their migration which seep back to those who remain in agriculture—benefits which might arise because of smaller output and higher price, fewer and larger farms with more resources per worker, or greater freedom in sense of fewer restraints on production. Policy to guarantee that their transfer insures them prospect of continuous and permanent gain is equally as important as that which provides the same elements in stability and level of income for those who remain to grow the crops and milk the cows. The problem is one of defining reorganization and shift which results in movement towards Pareto optimum, with both groups made better off. There is no basis in economics, humanitarianism or democracy for prescribing courses of action which make one group better off, but only at great expense and misery of another. Indeed, the certainty that more people would be made better off in nonfarm employment would lead to increased migration and better resource balance of agriculture.

Here we should indicate that our emphasis on labor up to this point has been largely its low supply elasticity to agriculture. This is the outstanding source of the century-long and persistent tendency of farm income to lag behind nonfarm income, in all nations where economic development has had long-term upward trend. There have been times, in a century, when employment opportunity did exist and the excess of labor in agriculture, as measured by its low returns, might have been wiped out, had it not been for the fact of its low occupational mobility and hence small supply elasticity to the farm industry. But it would be an omission to underemphasize the effect of limit in demand for farm migrants in restraining movement of labor from farms. Labor supply elasticity is low to agriculture relative to the magnitude of labor being released from, and underemployed in, the industry. Even while this is true, however, the supply elasticity of labor from farms to other employment sectors has been high over the last two decades. It has been sufficiently large that many more persons would have migrated had there been demand for their services. As Table 12.2 suggests, net off-farm migration has diminished greatly and even reversed in periods of industrial recession and unemployment such as 1958. Unfortunately, employment sectors with greatest growth in demand are not those open to farm migrants whose previous education and experience have failed to prepare them for these occupations.

In an earlier chapter, we explained that the farm industry, in bringing healthier resource structure and improving resource returns, depends particularly on economic growth and absence of major depression in order that more labor released from farms can be employed. Also we mentioned that this absorption process is much easier in a developed economy such as that of the United States where a minor portion of the labor force is in

TABLE 12.2

NET MIGRATION, MIGRATION TO FARMS AND FROM FARMS, AND NET MIGRATION AS A PERCENT OF THE FARM POPULATION, 1940–1958 IN THOUSANDS

Year	Migration Since Preceding April			Net Migration as a Percent of the Farm Population
	To farms	From farms	Net	
1940	819	1,522	− 703	2.3
1941	696	1,329	− 633	2.1
1942	822	2,246	−1,424	4.9
1943	824	3,799	−2,975	11.2
1944	1,095	2,658	−1,563	6.1
1945	916	1,480	− 564	2.2
1946	2,585	1,721	+ 864	(3.3)
1947	1,768	1,617	+ 151	(0.6)
1948	1,016	2,702	−1,686	6.5
1949	1,171	1,542	− 371	1.4
1950	995	2,309	−1,314	5.2
1951	597	1,899	−1,302	5.4
1952	643	914	− 271	1.1
1953	528	2,524	−1,996	8.8
1954	675	1,846	−1,171	5.3
1955	544	635	− 91	0.4
1956	461	1,595	−1,134	5.1
1957	475	1,051	− 576	2.7
1958	440	988	− 548	2.6

Source: Department of Agriculture, Agricultural Marketing Service, *Farm Populations, Migration to and from Farms*, 1920–1954, AMS-10, and Farm Population (annual bulletin AMS-80).

agriculture, as compared to the Indian economy where the portion of labor in the industrial sector is almost trivial relative to number of persons engaged in agriculture. Yet the ability of the U.S. economy to absorb further labor released from agriculture is not routine, even though industry with 92 percent of the labor force need absorb perhaps only another 2 or 3 million persons displaced from agriculture. With economic progress and growth in labor demand falling in occupations largely of skilled and professional ability, release of another two million persons, beyond the normal youth, to the ranks of the industrial unskilled does present problem of employment opportunity. Then, if particular facets of growth cause perpetuation of labor scarcity in highly skilled occupations but with 3 or 4 million persons unemployed in less skilled labor categories, as was true over much of the 1955–60 period, farm migrants will be at an extreme disadvantage—regardless of a national labor force mixed predominantly in direction of nonfarm workers. Not only is economic growth required for mass absorption of labor from agriculture, but also that released from the industry needs education and training so that less of it is dumped in unskilled ranks.

Opportunity and Dignity of People

The need, purpose and structure of policy to cope with excess labor resources in agriculture obviously deviates from that directed towards compensation of ongoing operators because of loss incidence growing out of rapid technical advance. In addition to youth from all income strata,

TABLE 12.3

FAMILY PERSONAL INCOME DISTRIBUTION BY NUMBER OF FAMILIES AND FAMILIES AS PERCENT OF TOTAL. 1958 (000)

Family Personal Income	Number Farm Families	Percent Farm Families	Percent Nonfarm Families	Farm Families as Percent of Nation
Under $2,000	1,777	25	6	33
$2,000–$2,999	834	18	6	26
$3,000–$4,999	1,242	26	24	12
$5,000–$9,999	1,160	24	47	6
$10,000 & Over	336	7	17	5
Total	4,749	100	100	—

Source: U.S. Department of Commerce. Figures are net family income before income tax.

migration from agriculture—as large as it has been—came particularly from low income strata in the 15 years following the end of World War II. Even then, a large pocket of low income persons still reside in agriculture; over two-fifths, as indicated by Table 12.3 with family incomes less than $3,000. Too, the lowest income groups of the nation are populated by farm people in disproportionate number. While migration has drawn many people from these ranks, the low income problem and its waste of human resources in agriculture has not been eliminated. In terms of numbers of persons, it is still exceedingly important, even though a portion of the strata is represented by beginning operators and older people. But as indicated previously, to solve this problem will not solve that of excess producing capacity of agriculture and possible society decision to provide mechanisms to restrain supply against demand or distribute compensation against the effects of production possibilities which advance more rapidly than demand. McElveen's figures, and those of the most recent census, show no decline since 1944 and an increase before then, in number of farms producing gross product of $2,500 or more at 1954 prices:[7]

1939 .... 1.9 million farms with sales over $2,500
1944 .... 2.1 million farms with sales over $2,500
1949 .... 2.1 million farms with sales over $2,500
1954 .... 2.1 million farms with sales over $2,500
1959 .... 2.1 million farms with sales over $2,500

The commercial farm problem still exists with major migration from low income groups; the poverty problem will remain in face of policy to solve only the commercial problem.

Development of Human Resources and Differential Migration Rates

Starting at current wealth and income levels of the United States under economic development, relative factor supply places premium price on labor, but particularly on labor embodying a large investment

[7] J. McElveen, *Family Farms in a Changing Economy*, Agr. Info. Bul. 171, USDA, and subsequent data from 1960 census. (The 1959 figures are in current dollars.)

in development of technical and professional skills. Studies in genetics and psychology indicate that distribution of inherent abilities in population strata of low income is not measurably different from those of high income strata. Human resources in lower income strata are highly unexploited and capable of much greater development in a prospective economic expansion period when the nation is faced with a shortage of trained manpower.[8] The archaic system of public investment in human resource development wherein local communities are expected, or protect the right, to finance the training force for the national economy places both a restraint on rate at which economic growth can take place and the personal fortunes of those who must feed from farm to industrial labor force. Not only, as indicated in Chapter 5 by Freedmans, do farm migrants end up in low income and status groups, but also their migration puts a disproportionate capital drain on local communities. Taves estimates the cost of rearing and educating a child through high school to be $20,000.[9] With half the youth leaving a community of 4,000 persons, the annual outflow of capital is a million dollars.

This syphoning of capital from declining communities to the broader growth stream may be greatly consistent with progress. However, a much greater proportion of the transfer in capital surplus might well take place in other forms, with general society investing more heavily in education and training and a smaller restraint thus falling on (1) the abilities developed in human resources which will migrate and (2) the future stream of benefits open to these persons, and to general society. Numerous studies have indicated the inadequacies of education in rural areas, resulting from obsolete dependence entirely on local and state finance.[10] Great unevenness exists among communities in educational investment per head because of variance in resources, tax base and bonding power. Too, educational investment still leans too much to economic opportunity as it is seen within small communities and areas. In the latter 1950's, expenditure per day-pupil averaged nearly $300 for the United States but ranged from a low of around $125 to a high of $400 among states, with the low figure falling in agricultural and southern states. The small investment in some areas causes many youth to drop out of school, equipment and buildings to be inefficient, teachers to be in short supply and proper curriculum to be neglected.

[8] For detailed emphasis on need for better development and utilization of untapped human capacities, see: *Goals for Americans. Report of the President's Commission on National Goals*, Prentice-Hall, New York, 1960, Part I and Chap. I.

[9] M. J. Taves, "Impact of Population Decline on Rural Communities," in *Labor Mobility and Population in Agriculture*, Iowa State University Center for Agricultural and Economic Adjustment, Iowa State University Press, Ames, 1961.

[10] For example, see: W. Rovetch, "Opportunities and Limitations in Education of Farm Youth," in *Problems and Policies of American Agriculture*, Iowa State University Center for Agricultural and Economic Adjustment, Iowa State University Press, Ames, 1959; National Planning Assoc., *Special Report No. 58*, Washington, D.C., 1960; and H. W. Beers and T. R. Ford, "Health, Housing and Education of Commercial Farmers in the U.S.," in *Policy for Commercial Agriculture, Its Relation to Growth and Stability*, Joint Economic Committee, Washington, D.C., 1957.

As material for mobility, youth present small problem. Provided with education and vocational guidance, they are readily drawn to growth sectors where value productivity and wages exceed those of agriculture. The main problem in respect to youth is to develop relative supplies of labor for various qualities and professions which mesh with growth in demand, and which do not mushroom supply largely in unskilled labor categories where growth is stalemated because of automation and the substitution of capital for labor (the latter under growth forces causing capital to be priced low relative to human effort). Agrarian philosophies and educational emphases, such as historically in vocational agriculture and 4-H work which have had major focus on turning youth back into agriculture, disfavor youth who have neither the capital, desire or managerial ability to farm successfully. Yet, the nation has gone through several decades in which this philosophy prevailed and rural youth were provided little other opportunity in vocational training or no national prospectus in growth trends and labor demand. (See Table 13.1.) Misery only results for the youth which is thus directed into agriculture, only to find five years later that he must transfer, with loss of income and underdevelopment of skills being the result. Policy which grinds alone on compensation and bargaining power for commercial farmers fails to focus on this important problem of people, not only for low income strata but also for youth and others of commercial farms.

Youth have relatively small problems in transfer costs as they enter the nonfarm labor force. Improved vocational guidance could, of course, effectively improve their geographical flexibility and diminish costs of false starts for them, as they swing from place to place in trying to match the supply of their talents with the demand for them. Young people have much greater mobility than older persons. Their future income stream is longer and, discounted back to the present, has greater current value. They are flexible in skills and attachment to the community and are in a better position, with few family responsibilities, to assume risks and uncertainties in transfer. Their transportation and relocation costs are lower. The skills young people can take with them are greater than the salvage value of those developed by older persons through farming, and they generally are at a "breaking point" as they leave school to enter the labor force. For the obverse reasons, age selectivity in migration leaves at home young persons with families, debtors and those whose previous job establishment has caused them to grow inflexible as resources.

Persons past middle age may migrate more readily due to dissolution of household, retirement and final attainment of financial security. Transfer costs, in money and real terms, are greatest for persons in the median of age range. If they own their own housing, inadequate as it may be, the same space costs them more in movement to new location. Transportation and subsistence for the family during the period of transfer adds to this cost, as well as does the process of liquidation of their assets and the transition period of unemployment and related activities and costs. While incomes are meager for many older persons short of retirement from the poverty class, and also for many from the commercial classes of farms, opportunity for them to improve real income is constrained through movement to city or new occupation. Typically their education is short, even in years of school completed, and resistance to employment of older persons, because of lack of trained skills as well as costs in employee benefits and inflexibilities in group work and new environment, causes them to end up in the most menial of tasks.[11]

Census data show that farm operators in economic class with gross income of $2,500 to $5,000 in 1950 averaged only 6.9 years of schooling. The amount was even smaller for older persons in the group. In contrast, operators in the group with gross income of $10,000 and over averaged 10.2 years. Money income and urban culture typically has less appeal in marginal utility for older and middle-aged persons than air of security in rural acquaintances and culture. While most rural communities are weighted with people of this age group and culture orientation, the best alternative for many of these people is to remain in the agricultural setting.

The "in between" class of persons who have established themselves in farming but still have flexibilities in skills and community adaptation, have brighter prospects in occupational migration. Their chief restraints are (1) costs of the type pointed out above, (2) guidance in matching employment, location and community to their abilities, (3) preferences for farm community and (4) degree of "rustiness" in particular knowledge and skills which have gone unused. If any group is particularly caused to teeter longer in agriculture because of the uncertainty of outside world and the availability of price supports and subsidies, it is this class. (Subsidies have been negligible in holding youth on farms, and unimportantly thus for older people.) It is doubtful that farm subsidies have been as important as lack of positive guidance and migration policy, even in holding the "in between" group on farms. Their migration has been rapid, next to that of youth entering the labor force, and it would have been even faster had employment demand not been so highly restrained relative to the supply of persons falling quite largely in the category of unskilled labor. Farm experience has provided resource of some transfer value to many of them; but for others it has not, or their more important talents lie in other directions. In contrast to youth, which has some opportunity in improved public schooling, formal training programs in rural areas does not exist for the "in between group." In the regions where total migration rate is greatest, the group of younger but established farm families with children has lowest migration rate; partly because of farm opportunity within the region but also because of the relatively greater cost of migration over longer distances. (See Figure 12.1 for indication of migration rate and distribution among age groups and regions.)

---

[11] For discussion of employment restraints of the older migrant, see Burton Seeker, "Business Views Labor Mobility Needs," in *Labor Mobility and Population in Agriculture*, Iowa State University Center for Agricultural and Economic Adjustment, Iowa State University Press, Ames, 1961.

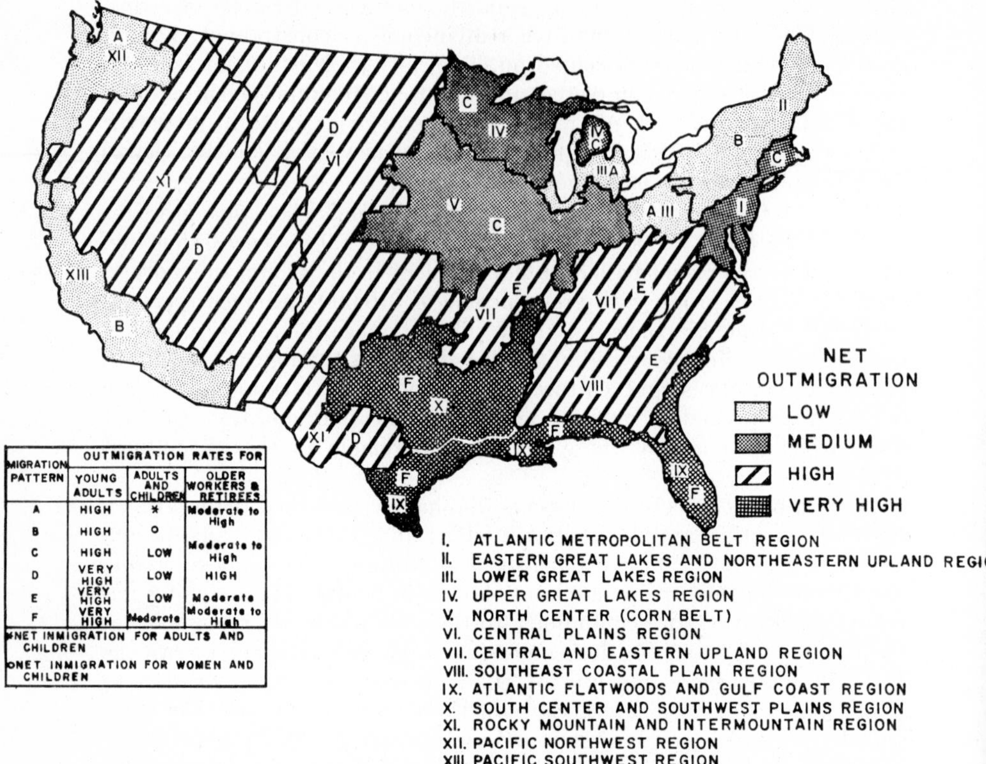

MIGRATION PATTERN	OUTMIGRATION RATES FOR		
	YOUNG ADULTS	ADULTS AND CHILDREN	OLDER WORKERS & RETIREES
A	HIGH	*	Moderate to High
B	HIGH	o	
C	HIGH	LOW	Moderate to High
D	VERY HIGH	LOW	HIGH
E	VERY HIGH	LOW	Moderate
F	VERY HIGH	Moderate	Moderate to High

*NET INMIGRATION FOR ADULTS AND CHILDREN

oNET INMIGRATION FOR WOMEN AND CHILDREN

Fig. 12.1. Net migration of the Rural Farm Population by Regions. 1940-60. (Also See Table 5.7.)

Equality in Opportunity

American society is based on the concept of the individual and on equality of opportunity for him. Freedom, a goal much discussed in respect to farm policy, depends on opportunity in exercise of choice and talents of the individual.[12] But freedom is "greatly unequal," being especially low for farm persons who have too little (1) capital and education for farm management success and (2) lack skill and knowledge to transfer to well-salaried nonfarm positions. Possibilities in contributing to national growth and income, and in attaining increased individual welfare, are limited for persons who have inadequate and below average resources for developing their capabilities. Farm people have been over represented in this realm of suboptimum development, throughout agriculture generally and in low income sectors particularly. Opportunity to better develop and reshape their talents and inherent abilities should be

[12] For emphasis of this point, see: *Goals for Americans*, Report of the President's Commission on National Goals, Part I, The Individual.

given many more in order that they can benefit most advantageously from nonfarm growth sectors in decades ahead.

With small farm labor force relative to national labor force, the need is more in relative gain to the individuals so represented, rather than in relative magnitude to which they can lift gross national product. The view is not that they must be ground into a mold and mustered into the market under the inescapable forces of the pricing mechanism. Instead, it is that many have talents which will thus reward them most and boost their their life satisfactions to much higher levels by being able to attach to these opportunities, rather than in being forced to become members of farm fraternity which supposes salvation only on farms under management of the market.

While the farm product and resource market mechanism can be reshaped to benefit those who will and should remain in agriculture, this reshaping cannot be the most positive hope of all persons born in agriculture and of all operators now in agriculture, especially those with magnitude of talents useful elsewhere and of capital promising no hope ever for success in farming. To turn to policy which can bend market mechanism with emphasis only on benefit to people if they stay in agriculture is as negative and backward as historic emphasis which provided only vocational education and guidance for return to agriculture. Not a few farm families of the United States have housing far below the standards of cows in Wisconsin and hogs in Indiana. To restrain the sons of these families, or even many of the farmers, to agriculture and use pricing policy to increase their income by 20 percent is trivial, against the much broader nonfarm opportunities open to them through appropriate investment in education and training, or compensation method which helps them in transfer from agriculture.

EFFECTS OF COMPENSATION POLICIES

Compensation policies of types used since 1930, and those discussed in Chapter 11, have little effect on the supply elasticity of farm labor in the poverty strata of income. The forces tying this labor to agriculture are not those which will be affected materially by market power, quotas, land retirement or other policies which might boost average per capita real income of American agriculture to nonfarm levels. Paucity of resources, and the very philosophy of the compensation principle prevent the poverty problem from thus being solved. Neither are farm youth from the higher income strata, as means are used to redress loss to commercial agriculture, very likely to be held inflexibly to agriculture by compensation policy. Melding of urban and rural cultures, the extent and effectiveness of modern communication, the widespread attraction of urban living and wage scales and greater vista for expression of talents has served and will continue to serve as the dominating force in drawing youth from rural communities. It is, in fact, extremely doubtful that farm policy has been influencial in diminishing the rate of transfer from farms since World War II. True, some farmers were able to thus remain when they would otherwise have had to liquidate and move. Yet others did move just as fast as information, industrial demand and employment opportunity allowed them. To have freed more from the embracing effect of farm subsidies would have had no effect in increasing number of nonfarm employment opportunities, a major restraint to migration, although the geographical pattern of shift might have been somewhat different.

As a sector of pure competition, against most sectors which are not, agriculture acts as it should in this academic context; namely, as a repository for the unemployed. Unemployed do not transfer directly from industry to agriculture, but the incidence of unemployment is the same in the sense that opportunity for off-farm migration becomes more limited and the preferences for youth and seniority rights prevail to pass major extent of unemployment back to established operators in agriculture. While price of farm labor is competitive in this sense, with wage flexibility so that people remain and continue employment in agriculture as their return declines, institutions and market power of other groups restrain them from stepping into the nonfarm market with full effect in pricing their labor at level to replace industrial workers.

The major structural problems of agriculture will be solved in the future largely through the occupational choices of farm children and young people. This is already proving true. Farm programs of the past decade have done little to retard the choice and mobility of young people. Migration of people from farms has been extremely rapid even in the presence of these programs. This rapid migration of labor from agriculture to nonagricultural work opportunities has been stimulated by the continued economic growth over the nation as a whole. Expanding nonfarm employment opportunities, at wage rates far exceeding labor returns on a very large proportion of the farms in the nation, have drawn labor, especially young people, out of agriculture. Perhaps the rate of labor transfer, from farm to nonfarm employment, has not been less than the amount which could be assimilated in an orderly way by industry and community facilities. Evidence is lacking to indicate that the mobility rate should have been significantly greater in the recent past, considering the rate at which nonskilled jobs were being created, the speed with which public services such as schools could be provided, the rate at which increased housing facilities could progress in industrial centers, and even the degree of economic instability and short-lived unemployment in postwar years. As mentioned in Chapter 5, lack of a more positive approach in counseling and guidance probably has been more important than acreage control and agricultural price policies in retarding labor from moving as fast as it could have, should slack have actually existed in employment opportunities, public services, and housing. Farm children of this decade, in making choice of occupation and social policy, will care little whether monopolistic production and pricing policies might increase their income should they select to enter agriculture, especially when the rewards to them from the same policies might be much greater in other endeavors and industries. It should also be remembered that where public compensation policy may have tendency to cause some, particularly older people in grain and tobacco farming, to "hold on," public development policy in research and education causes new technology to replace even more and cause them to leave farming.[13] A major accomplishment of public agricultural research and education, and factor prices favorable to the process, over the last three decades has been to free and displace labor from agriculture. These processes have replaced more people than subsidies have retained in agriculture.

Compensation policy in first impact makes it possible for incomes to be lifted when returns have been unduly depressed from rapid advance of technology and the supply function against inelastic demand and factor supply. Once initiated, it can keep this latter process from occurring at rates so fast that farmers fail to gain a share of their economic progress contribution. But once it has been initiated and has continued long enough to be capitalized into resources, or to be purchased outright if it is negotiable apart from resources, it has no, or little, effect on relative resource earnings. Capitalized at the same rate as assets of similar character and attachment, premium in price and income from compensation policy has no effect on relative difference in returns for farm and nonfarm employment for a new entry into farming, and no effect on absolute difference for a person already engaged in agriculture.

Taking the first for example, suppose that a farmer has assets producing income of $1,200 net, and the prevailing capitalization rate is 6 percent. (Also see the example in Chapter 10 emphasizing farm size expansion through recapitalization.) Under this combination, capitalized value of the assets is $20,000. A person able to muster $20,000 can purchase income of $1,200. Now suppose compensation boosts net income of resources by 10 percent. Assets of $18,183 which previously produced $1,091 in income will now produce $1,200. But capitalized at 6 percent, the assets formerly worth $18,183 now are worth $20,000. The beginner can buy no more resources and no more income with his capital than

[13] Considering the role of the tobacco enterprise as the main source of cash income on a large number of small, low-income farms, the short-run effects of compensation policy were those of holding some people on farms. On farms where both cash and real incomes are extremely low, and where part-time farming provides very little supplemental income, cash income made possible by tobacco allotments provides a necessary means of subsistence for some older persons. By causing the total tobacco acreage to be dispersed widely over many farms, many older farm people who are satisfied with "the rural way of life" are able to remain in agriculture. If the tobacco program were abolished, the competitive effects would remove this cash income source for many low-income families, forcing some to look elsewhere for employment. Furthermore, since many of these low-income farmers now are able to remain in agriculture because of the cash income made possible by their tobacco allotment, they prevent an expansion in farm size and an increase in productivity by other labor units in the locality. Abolishment of quotas would squeeze out many farmers operating small units who "hang on" because of the cash income from tobacco quotas. However, it is questionable whether many older farm operators who lack industrial skills (with their particular customs and value systems) would make important additions to the industrial labor force, or to the community life of urban centers.

previously. Hence, presence of compensation benefit can hardly cause him to select farming over other occupations. Similarly, an established operator with given differential of income against off-farm income, can now sell his resources and realize the same absolute differential by moving to other occupations.

It is likely that most of the more permanent effects of compensation through output control, marketing orders and quotas for sugar in Louisiana, tobacco in North Carolina, dairy cows in Orange County and lettuce in the Salinas Valley of California have already been so capitalized and their mobility restraints largely cancelled.[14] To be certain, individuals with capitalized effects of compensation or quotas would experience capital loss if they were dropped, and some more would have incentive to move out of agriculture. But to the extent that competition prevails for their resources, due to limited outside employment opportunity and knowledge, with farm labor and operators backing up in agriculture and looking for employment therein, assets would typically be sold to others who would retain them in production, partly as additions to other units but also as independent units.

Compensation policy elements are not the basic restraints to occupational transfer and more productive contribution of underemployed human resources to national economic growth and welfare goals. Conversely, initiation of negotiable quotas as a scheme of compensation, with some able to sell the future stream at capitalized value, would be direct incentive for many to "cash in now" and move to other occupations. Again we state that failure to effectively utilize agriculture's manpower rests more on negative policy in educational investment, in extension of education relating to job opportunities, in facilities for retraining and related activities, than on penalizing effect of farm compensation subsidies in historic magnitudes. These items, along with sporadic periods of unemployment in important magnitude, have held people to low income farms where their alternative was to accept meager compensation subsidy.

Rather than investment in surplus production and storage of grain and cotton under policy complexes of the past, a different set of production restraints and compensation method could have been used. These could have been more effective and/or less costly. Then, a large part of the real cost or amount (see Chapter 14) going into surplus production and its storage, could have been invested in education, retraining programs and improved employment services; thus making greater contribution in shift of more people to occupations of increased rewards to themselves.

Policies can be devised to provide (1) compensation to guarantee a positive-sum distribution of gains from rapid development of agriculture

---

[14] As an empirical study representing capitalization of subsidies into land values, see F. H. Maier, *et al.*, *Sale Value of Flue-Cured Tobacco Allotments*, Va. Agr. Exp. Sta. Tech. Bul. 148.

and (2) equity in opportunity for utilization of human capacities, labor mobility effects being of secondary consideration but a necessary complement, and need not be competitive or confounded in results. Policies have been but little so in the past, the greatest weakness being that little investment has been made in the category of increasing equity in general economic opportunity for people from agriculture.

POLICIES FOR DEVELOPMENT OF HUMAN RESOURCES AND LABOR TRANSFER

Diminution of labor input is an orthodox recommendation for solving the surplus problem of commercial agriculture. (It has the exceptions and limitations in time and factor supply elasticity discussed in previous chapters.) Policy which increases the supply elasticity of resources to agriculture should aid the transfer process, causing balance in resource returns of the market to be restored more readily. In the conventional tenets of farm policy economics, supposing economy-wide existence of pure competition and mechanistic resource allocation goals, this is a notable purpose. But equally in worth, the elasticity effect and restoration of economic balance can be a by-product of a more important purpose; namely, lifting the productivity, income and welfare of many persons whose prospects are better in nonfarm employment.

Whichever the viewpoint, policies are possible which can aid mobility, supposing that the nonfarm demand function for labor is sufficient to absorb potential migrants. Even where this is not true, policy can still put labor of farms on equal footing with that in urban centers; a condition lacking in the past because of variables in education, location and employment aids of differential magnitude for the two sectors. In the sections which follow, we discuss some policy alternatives for increasing labor supply elasticity, equally in the sense of mobility to increase welfare of people involved in transfer and for improving the long-run economic structure of agriculture.[15]

Education of Youth and Community Capital Supply

Equal footing in economic opportunity through more appropriate education is policy especially relevant for youth. The reasons why equity in personal opportunity is lacking in this respect have already been discussed. We add some summary notes, however, especially as these relate to existing public machinery for this purpose.

There is no principle in equity supposing that rural communities should make the full investment in education of labor resources which will become part of the production complex in other communities and locations. Neither is there a principle which says they should not do so if

---

[15] Numerous of the policy and action alternatives in this section were originally outlined in my article: "Adaptation of Extension Education and Auxiliary Aids to the Basic Economic Problem of Agriculture," *Jour. Farm Econ.*, Vol. 39.

they prefer. Largely, local and state groups have held to this preference and right. Unfortunately, however, local supply of capital for these purposes has been too meager, limiting the supply of professional and skilled labor which can be developed from farm youth of particular localities. Too much so, the productivity of capital in education is assessed by the locality in terms of endogenous employment opportunity. Why invest in education of chemistry and higher mathematics when they have low productivity in the neighborhood, lower than for vocational agriculture? However, labor resources are not restricted to the community after termination of community school and it is productivity of science and business in national community which is relevant.

While this productivity potential exists, it is not adequately assessed in the local community. The optimum level of investment in various educational fields within the community thus is entirely different from that of the national community. If communities and national society made calculation of optimum investment level in refined marginal form (and they do so in highly lagged and subjective manner), we would have the difference in level and allocation of educational investment suggested in Figure 12.2 where *A* is for the local farm community and *B* is for

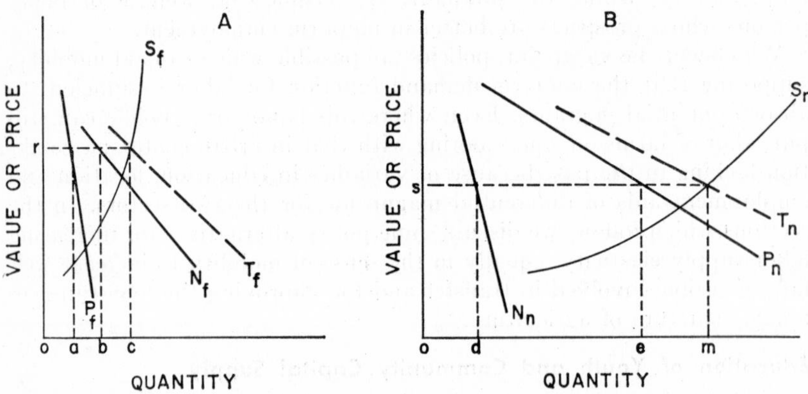

Fig. 12.2. Relative Supply and Demand for Investment in Education and Labor.

national aggregate. The marginal value productivity of capital invested in developing professional human services for the farm community is P_f, supposing that the professional services are used in the same community. The marginal productivity of investment to the farm community in nonskilled or "subprofessional" labor (including farm labor) used in the farm community, is N_f. The corresponding marginal value productivity functions for the national community are respectively P_n and N_n where we suppose productivity is measured across all sectors of the economy. Hence, each community has an aggregate marginal value productivity function, for capital invested in labor which will be used in the respective communities. These are T_f for the farm community and T_n for the national community.

We can represent each set of productivity functions as the payoff or demand in investment in human skills by the two communities. Productivity of investment in professional labor used within the farm community is high for small absolute quantities, but falls off rapidly when basic needs are met in doctors, dentists, teachers, etc. The farm community has little return on engineers, draftsmen and air pilots used within the locality. In contrast, however, the productivity functions are reversed for the national community, where we suppose more rapid growth and factor prices causing substitution of capital more nearly for nonskilled than for professional labor. The supply functions of capital for investment in education is $S_f(S_n)$, considering alternative uses of funds in consumption and production for the two communities. With relatively larger supply of investment funds for the national aggregate, the "optimum" level of investment in education and training is *om*, as compared to *oc* for the farm community. Investment can be made to realize lower value productivity at national level (*os*) than at farm community (*or*) level. The greater supply of capital available to education and the higher productivity of professional labor cause level of optimum investment to be relatively greater at the national level. Too, the largest proportion of investment is in professional education at national level while it is in nonskilled labor (perhaps vocational agriculture) in farm community.

Experience conforms to the theory elucidated. Local communities have high investment in vocational agricultural training largely because the supply of funds comes from national society; a point well forgotten by local communities who point with pride to the fine projects of their FFA clubs and the great uplifting it has brought to farm boys, but protest the lack of freedom promised by federal aid to education. The local community, where it alone makes the decision and investment, restrains investment in education while its productivity is held above levels preferred by general society and it invests far too little in nonroutine curricula and courses. Many rural high schools even lack a course in chemistry, biology or mathematics beyond geometry. The answer to the problem posed above is to integrate the supply of capital for educational investment at the local and state level with that of the state and national level (e.g. as outlined for equations 13.1 and 13.2). Not only can more educational resources thus be made available, but also these can be better resources in the sense of human and physical inputs devoted to education. Too, educational investment can be allocated more consistently with future demand for different occupational strata at the national level. Abandonment of the local philosophy of educational investment also can allow better attainment of scale economies in all fields of education—and better education.

Machinery or precedents already exist in many communities for turning education, training, and guidance in directions needed in future demand expansion for labor. Unfortunately, the concentration on vocational training in farm communities has been in agriculture and homemaking. (See Table 13.1.) Neither is splendidly adapted to skills and abilities needed for youth who will transfer to industry of growing automation and capital proportion. The emphasis in educational policy for agriculture has been that every farm boy should be made into a better farmer. The criterion of success for the Smith-Hughes teacher in many agricultural communities is the proportion of farm boys that can be enrolled in vocational agricultural classes. Given today's surplus of labor and income depression in many localities, the economic growth criterion for successful education might better be the opposite; namely, that farm youth be trained for other opportunities and guided from agriculture. As a minimum, education at this level should be broadened to explain the relative level of incomes in different sectors of agriculture, and of agriculture as compared with other employment. Given the high income elasticity of demand for prepared food, females might better be offered more courses in psychology; both for congenial association with their future working associates and to meet the modern day problems and challenges of housewifery. Both males and females in more communities could be furnished vocational training in trades distribution, industry and other areas allowed even by initial and existing federal legislation and appropriations.

Vocational agriculture has had as its focus teaching the boy to be a better farmer on his home tract of soil. In many cases, the individual and society would benefit if he were told why he should, and how he can, move from this farming location to another. But more important, vocational concentration should be on training farm youth who will not be needed in producing food so that their abilities can be better used for goods and services that have relatively greatest demand in a growing economy. To be certain, food needs of the future require that new farmers enter the occupation to replace portion of those who retire and otherwise leave the industry. The competitive prospects for future agriculture require that the farmer be even better educated and a more efficient manager than at the present. Agricultural education is required accordingly.

But it is just as important that, systematically, some boys be guided out of agriculture. The vocational agriculture courses taken by many leaving the farm provides them with little training and sometimes no skills for the products and services in which they become employed. The emphasis on vocational agriculture relative to trades, industry and distributive occupations is particularly great in the low-income areas of southern states. (See Table 13.1.) The value of this training is questionable for boys who will not return to the farm. In most agricultural communities there are several boys who must leave the farm for each one who will be needed for replacement, if agricultural production is to be geared to potential demand and economic growth. Human resources can be improved to a degree approaching the limit only if a much greater investment is made in occupational counseling and if vocational courses of a nonfarm nature are greatly increased. Counseling needs to begin with students entering high school, rather than as a main contact at time of graduation.

Historically, the main emphasis on youth in extension education also has been on farm skills. This activity is needed in the years ahead for the reasons mentioned above. But in order that a relatively larger portion of farm youth can have higher incomes and greater life satisfactions, as compared to subsistence on an undersized farm, 4-H activity needs to focus relatively less on how to fatten a calf for the fair and more on developing knowledge about, and interest in, economic opportunities on farms and elsewhere. Since there are many more boys than are needed as farmer replacement, specialists in youth work might best have vocational guidance as their central training. The challenge ahead is to help the individual predict, comparing different activities through which he can sell his labor services, the production possibilities that represent his makeup.

Prediction cannot end here, however. To tell the individual that he should follow farming because his production possibility curve extends further in this direction (i.e., that, representing his abilities, the marginal rate of substitution of farm production for other products is high), considers only half the relevant variables. If the price or returns ratio provides a revenue line with little slope towards the extreme of farming on the production possibility curve, the individual will have a higher return in the nonfarming activity. (See Chapter 13.)

Adult Education and Retraining

Adult classes in vocational agriculture schools now provide a basis for extending skills or retraining persons in agriculture. With the economic growth impinging on agriculture as it does, these same general facilities should be used to provide retraining for persons who are now engaged in agriculture but know about, or are interested in, opportunities elsewhere. Funds for these purposes were included for slump-areas, under the 1961 Depressed Area Legislation. They should be provided similarly for widespread areas of agriculture which suffer similarly from growth which is uneven for sectors and regions. Retraining of persons who can then leave agriculture is important, in areas where farms are small and income is low, for increasing incomes of those who will remain in agriculture. In fact it is equally as important as providing adult education to promote the skills of those who will remain: the latter often can increase incomes sufficiently only if others leave agriculture to allow farm consolidations and attainment of scale economies. In some instance, resources used in adult retraining for nonfarm skills could be provided by the same vocational agriculture instructor who conducts evening classes for farmers. Hence, resistance need not be encountered in "lessening the capacity" of current educational resources. Mainly, however, total educational resources need to be extended to provide a broader range of skill opportunities, for an activity that is as important socially as evening schools for farmers. Cost of subsistence during the retraining period might be furnished much as in "on the job training" following the last war.

The extension service should similarly redirect some of its work with young married couples. Farm and home planning and rural development programs should emphasize off-farm employment opportunities for resources, as well as reallocations of these same resources within the existing firm-household complex. The portion of the agricultural population with the high mobility potential is, of course, young persons who have not yet committed their abilities for a particular line and have not yet acquired a fixed set of skills. Next in flexibility are young persons who have started farming but have not pushed their roots deeply into the community; have long working lives ahead and still have enough youth to switch from one to another skill. Farm and home planning should, as is already true in some states, focus particularly on this group. A broad view of resource use and family welfare maximization is needed. From the family's standpoint, it is important to show them where they will have higher incomes and greater satisfactions in leaving agriculture, as it is to explain how some can reorganize production and consumption patterns to increase dollar profit and household utility on the farm. Planning should help those young families whose main hope for high income and utility level is not from compensation policies and quotas in agriculture, before their flexibility declines greatly, decide whether their capital and managerial assets best fit them for farm or other occupations. Refresher courses in science and mathematics, advanced short courses in these and similar scientific and vocational fields also could be offered.[16] Too, however, there is need for these extensions at point of impact in new employment.

Termination Compensation

U.S. society has precedent in providing termination payment to those released from particular employment. Such "mustering out" pay is tradition for armed services, as it is with many private firms. Its equivalent for technological unemployment or replacement also is provided in unemployment compensation possible between jobs under Social Security. Use of this principle, as capital investment to increase labor mobility and supply to nonfarm employment or as compensation reflecting recognition of a degree of technological unemployment stemming from advance of agriculture, could increase supply and elasticity of labor to nonfarm employment. In time of sufficient nonfarm employment opportunity and demand for farm labor, this policy might well have aided many persons to transfer, lowering total costs of programs and adding to welfare of selected persons.

[16] For the complex of problems involved in adult education in a progressing society, see: R. and William Peterson, *University Adult Education*, Harper and Brothers, New York, 1961, pp. 201–30.

Investment thus of the subsidy realized by many farmers during the 1950's, plus some of the capital invested in surplus grain storage—the rest going into resources for schools or developmental projects in the private sector—would have been much more productive and less burdensome on the farm public's conscience than the visible and large grain storage accumulated during the period. Such compensation mechanism could be on a choice basis, so that Pareto optimum is allowed, with persons accepting the alternative only if they believed their welfare to be so increased. Compensation and payment would be oriented around people as resources of possibilities in nonfarm employment, rather than as owners of resources tied in agriculture. The extent of labor withdrawal by this method, with individuals still making Pareto-better choices, could be extended to any desired amount, depending on the level of supply price acceptable to the public. Persons not preferring this choice could remain in agriculture to accept compensation through direct payments, quotas, etc.—or to accept the fortunes of the open market. All three alternatives, or more, could be used to allow choice and guarantee movement towards Pareto optima; a framework of pure freedom of choice in extent allowed by public outlay.

Magnitude and nature of these termination payments could be various, depending on the particular goals of transfer. One method would be to simply compute the value of subsidy in prospect over 5 years through other means; then offer approximately this sum at the moment for the person who wishes to retire or withdraw from farming, with limitation of a single payment and some provision for restraining use of his land. Or, payment might be calculated in terms of cost of liquidating assets, transportation costs, waiting period for employment contact, capital loss on assets and some aid in obtaining housing; the final mixture of compensation elements depending on public concept of equity and gain. (This scheme might appeal most to older persons, but social costs, considering differences in housing costs, might be less if some of these persons were to remain in present location and employment.) Where transfer did take place, provision could be made for locking land out of production if this is needed, desired or effective in restricting commercial farm supply. Or, the method could be tied in with a land retirement policy; a condition and precedent of termination payment which was closely approached in "whole farm" retirement initiated in 1957.

Cost of such a program would depend on level of compensation to be attained, supply of labor to be directed to nonfarm activity and extent to which the program is separated from or confounded with on-farm compensation, supply control and other types of programs. As a specific aid to persons whose welfare would be best advanced in nonfarm employment, the cost would be different—and less—than if it were used as a method to draw farm output down to level giving considerably higher farm commodity prices. Society would benefit more than in past programs where people have been subsidized only if they stayed in agriculture, payments have continued on indefinite basis and surpluses have continued to build up with capital investment required to store them. Farmers moving would be those in less advantageous position for farming. They would be persons benefiting least from public subsidy of research and education in agriculture. Undoubtedly, the system could be used effectively to remove two million farmers from agriculture in 5 years; but not necessarily with corresponding immediate reduction in output. As mentioned previously, migration must go far enough that labor input begins to serve in capacity of technical complementarity with land (as in Figure 14.1) eventually causing the latter to shift from conventional surplus crops to less intensive ones.

Transportation Subsidy

Cost of moving is a trivial capital cost for persons finding employment in their own community. It is a small and insignificant cost for a young person who has commitment for no others and who may look upon the venture to a new community partly as a consumption service providing utility, whether or not employment contract arises immediately. The capital cost is a function of, and increases with, family size, distance, and involvement in farming. It, plus the living costs during the period of transfer and employment location, can tax the resources of persons with small incomes and no savings. Hence, a means in between "mustering out pay" and passive employment services would be subsidy to cover transportation costs, perhaps on a once-and-for-all basis, to eligible persons moving out of farming. It might be especially effective in increasing labor mobility for persons making interregional transfer. Or loans could be made to cover transportation for moving and living costs until employment is obtained. This is a mechanism that has precedent, as does unemployment compensation under existing machinery. Although indentured servitude is not recommended as an acceptable mobility means, it drew a large proportion of immigrants to the United States and was, in effect, such a procedure. The indentured servant received his subsistence while he worked a contracted period of time to repay his transportation and upkeep costs. Another mechanism with experience behind it is the postwar G.I. on-the-job training. During 1942–50 payments provided living costs and retraining opportunity for persons who wished to make productive transfers of their skills and locations. We mention these to indicate again that the means required do not require any "revolutionary social measures," but generally are represented in public legislation accepted in the present or past.

The market for human labor functions much less perfectly than that for other animals, partly because private property is not allowed for the former. If a bull in Wisconsin has positive prospects of employment in Indiana, private endeavor will see that his services are transported to the latter location. Similarly firms specializing in relocation of animal services effectively invest and cause feeder cattle to be transported from Montana ranches to Illinois feedlots, then to packing plants and finally to consumer services in Boston. Although the end desired is not the same and the preference map of the individual involved is to be honored, man should be able to provide equivalent services for human resources which have consumers attached to them. The calculation to be made is one of the marginal utility and gain to be realized by the individual and society, and the supply price necessary in order that persons will offer their services for transfer with guarantee of family welfare gain. This alternative in choice does not make the supposition of the interpersonal utility measurement implied in shipping a person off to the Siberian salt mines.

Improved Employment Services

Labor transfer is possible and desirable, within a market framework where wage prices are established by market bargaining power, only to the extent that nonfarm demand for labor is of sufficient magnitude. Supposing periods with employment opportunity great enough to absorb greater supply of labor from agriculture, or to put it on more equal footing with nonfarm labor in ability to demand industrial employment opportunity, the means discussed above suppose supply of capital to serve in relation of technical complementarity with labor supplied from agriculture to nonfarm industry. We now turn to an additional quantity or resource serving in similar capacity; namely, knowledge of and about nonfarm employment opportunities. A large expansion is needed in services to inform people of job openings and personal adjustments required for new employment and new living environments. Emphasis should be on interregional job communication.

The existing facilities of the state and national employment services could, if extended to a broader basis, provide another means to supplement education and training in helping agriculture adjust to economic growth. The two are not substitutes for each other. Education and vocational guidance should be used to give individuals broad and long-run productivity and understanding of the working of the economy, and the prospects and needs in various industries and services. Employment services should provide much broader and more current indication of where nonfarm positions are. The federal employment service has over 1,800 local offices and is affiliated with state employment services. Yet it has no special program for farm people, except information on job opportunities elsewhere for migratory farm laborers. The employment services provide information on employer, location of position, hours of work, remuneration rate, job characteristics, expected duration of employment, local transportation facilities, requirement in union membership and general living conditions in the locality. The latter includes information on housing accommodations and costs, but nothing on community, sociological and other aspects. The set of information mentioned above refers to a specific area or geographic location, information for other areas being too costly for present resources of employment services.

Evidence suggests that employment service facilities have been inadequate or too little used in making geographic transfer and bringing greater perfection to functioning of the labor market.[17] State employment services, while concentrating on labor requirements of the locality, do provide some "clearing house" information with other localities. During the war period the federal service helped an important number of farm people find positions in rural and urban industries. Mobility during the war also was encouraged through provision of transportation costs and job guarantees. As an aid to the peacetime mobility required for agriculture, this information and the monetary and job aids need to be extended and made more comprehensive and detailed. Present employment services necessarily, because of fund limitations, are too little concerned in indicating the existence and conditions for off-farm employment for labor in agriculture.

Of course, some restrictive state and local legislation promises to stand in the way of using the employment services more effectively. For instance, scattered southern states have had laws that allow recruiting of agricultural labor, to be used elsewhere, only if a fee is paid for this privilege and if the county agent or other authorities give permission. Labor legislation in many states directly has discouraged migration of farm people. Except in New York, state and county residence requirements create hardships and barriers to labor mobility.[18] The most critical time for a migrant family is its initial period in a new community. The process of securing permanent employment and stabilizing the family's economic status at a satisfactory level may take several years. Therefore, even if alternative employment opportunities are known, the uncertainty of economic security and the lack of available welfare services in the short run tend to reduce mobility among an appreciable portion of the labor force, people who would consider a change in occupation and the locality of employment.

As a mobility aid, the state employment service should be expanded to emphasize nonfarm opportunities, more than alone on placement of seasonal farm labor. It could be relatively less a means of supply function in filling producers' needs and more a demand function for indicating employment alternatives for prospective migrants. The ideal would be a national "market clearing house," similar to commodity and stock markets, to reflect the location and nature of positions, wage rates and skill requirements. The prospective employee could be "fully as informed at the moment" as traders in the markets mentioned. This degree of "fineness" is impossible, of course, but it serves as a goal to be approached. These "market quotations" provided by the employment services could be complemented by information relating to consumption and the household, with the Agricultural Extension Service helping to

---

[17] See E. D. Smith, "Nonfarm Employment Information of Farm People," *Jour. Farm Econ.*, Vol. 38.

[18] Two articles indicating the difficulties families in new communities suffer as a result of state and local residence requirements are in *Parade*, Sunday magazine supplement to United States newspapers, Sept. 29, 1957, and Oct. 6, 1957.

carry information to farm people. The latter information should indicate the nature of living conditions and adjustments that might be required. Its purpose would be to prevent families from moving to places where their living patterns and social values would be inconsistent with those of the new community. This information would help prevent "waste motion" that otherwise occurs as the individual or family becomes discouraged and returns to the old community. It would help individuals to better find communities that match their own preferences and value systems.

Information and service should not be restricted to the "sending end" of transfers, but should be extended to the "receiving end" as well. A great deal of uncertainty exists as interregional transfers are made; in respect not only to employment opportunities, but also to making friends, finding housing, becoming integrated into a community and so forth. Lessening of this uncertainty at the "receiving end" would increase interregional labor mobility. This aid should be provided by a broad, well integrated national employment service. But again, as for most of the elements outlined here, a completely new machine need not be invented. This type of service, while far from perfect, has been used in helping to relocate Indians and in moving them from reservations to industrial employment. It has been used, at both sending and receiving end, in aiding migration of Puerto Rican labor to the continental U.S.[19]

Facilities of state employment services and extension services might well be joined in attack on some of the "intermediate run" problems of labor supply and demand and employment. For example research findings to predict possible impact of mechanization and other technology on farm labor demand and potential need for migration could be extended by extension services and used especially under guidance schemes which could be developed in employment services. Typically we have research to predict the results of technology on farms, supposing an operator who will "stay fixed." But we need estimates of broader impacts—interproduct, interregional and inter-industry substitution and productivity effects—of technological advance. Both public agencies could work more closely with schools in rural areas, the extension service to project longer-run outlook and the employment service to provide testing services and guidance at early time in student courses.

One problem of expanded employment service is that of getting sufficient resources and administrative sanction in extending certain activities now available in city areas to rural areas. Rural areas need, as much as or more than large city labor markets, services such as those provided in the latter, proficiency and aptitude tests for high school students and adults, and counseling aids for both. Provision of these aids to scattered

---

[19] The Puerto Rico Migration Division has 12 "receiving end" offices to help adaptation to cultural life and to locate in positions. See "Surprising Puerto Rico," *Look*, Jan. 17, 1961, p. 44.

rural areas is costly and difficult, but present transportation and mobility in this sense is as important as that of traveling libraries, and even in "getting the mail through." The experimental and intensive programs of the employment service in selected rural counties represent a significant step in this direction, if the productivity of limited resources is thus most efficiently defined. Effort in the initial experimental areas emphasized labor supply in terms of potential industrial development in the locality. Expansion of effort would need also to concentrate on connecting persons in specific localities with demand in industrial employment at various other locations.

Channels of information in respect to nonfarm demand for labor do exist outside of employment services. They have functioned quite well, having been the American tradition. The void in job communication through friends and relatives is somewhat less than that in vocational guidance services functioning in *a priori* manner to allow youth to anticipate future demand and absorb educational inputs accordingly; or, in guiding initial transfers from the farm labor force. In functioning efficiently, employment services as labor market devices would help to minimize undesirable migration and "false starts," as well as to guide those moves which are positive.

The crucial long-run need in balancing labor supply against labor demand is in supply of capital to educational and vocational guidance systems. This is a function relating to the public education sector, more than to the public clearing house represented by employment services. The latter is best adapted to serve in the short-run market, and thus for guiding persons who are directly entering the labor force, or those who are on farms and wish to transfer. In more positive mold, and given amplitude of budget and administrative opportunity, the employment services could serve in more positive fashion as *an employment service,* rather than under the negative connotation as *the unemployment service.* By itself, an employment service cannot create aggregate national demand for labor. It can, however, better inform potential farm migrants of the demand in various locations and occupations. Also, it can better inform employers of the supply of labor from farm sources.

DEVELOPMENT, EMPLOYMENT DEMAND AND LOW INCOME

Forces and policy leading to increased demand or nonfarm employment opportunity for farm labor must be viewed first, and over the short term, as a means of bettering the income and welfare position of persons at disadvantage in agriculture. Up to an important magnitude in shrinking of labor input, total output and level of price will not turn favorably towards higher income of agriculture. In 1960 numbers, farms and farm operators could be reduced by at least 2.7 million, leaving only slightly over a million, without crimping productive capacity of agriculture. (About 61 percent of all farms produced only 13 percent of all farm market sales in 1959.) Similarly, programs aimed at improving the on-farm opportunities of low-income or poverty-sector farmers must be looked upon as method specifically for enhancing their welfare, an important social problem in equity, or as a method of improving their position relative to other strata of farmers. To bring greater on-farm opportunity to their underemployed labor is not aid in solution of the over-capacity and surplus supply problems in aggregate commercial agriculture. The lowness of income, lack of effective opportunity in on-farm employment and generally restrained outlet for human capacities and talent in the poverty sector is cause for concern in social policy. Impact in causing labor to be more mobile, by increasing nonfarm demand for it, or by increasing knowledge of people on farms, promises to draw first and particularly on workers from low productivity farms with meager income and small contribution to national production.[20] The smaller proportion (39 percent) of commercial operators who produce the extreme majority of product (88 percent) are not mainly transfer candidates and will rest hopes largely in agriculture. They can readily take over the farms left by their low-income neighbors who represent 61 percent of farms. (In some localities of course, all farmers are in the low income category.)

Three particular groups are affected by sizeable reductions in the labor force. First is the group which moves from farming to nonfarm employment. To the extent that these persons possess little capital and operate inefficient units, transfer to employments of higher real incomes can increase their welfare. Second is the consolidating group which remains in agriculture. To the extent that they expand farm size and increase volume of sales and reduce unit costs relative to any decline in product prices, they also will gain from a reduction in the labor force. Third is the group which both remains in agriculture and is unable to expand farm size. Their relative welfare may be depressed further if product prices continue to decline because of continued growth in output. If time could be telescoped and this group could be inventoried, we would expect to find that it includes farm families unable to adjust because of age, health, skills, capital limitations, lack of knowledge, or similar considerations. It is this group especially that has claim to compensation to redress individual welfare losses growing out of general social gain from reorganization and development.

Several public programs have been attempted to ease low incomes of the poverty sector of agriculture. Those aimed specifically in this direction were the Federal Emergency Relief Administration of the early 1930's and its successors, the Resettlement Administration and the Farm

[20] This fact is substantiated by data presented in this and earlier chapters. Almost all of the decline in farm numbers over the past two decades has come from small low-income farms. The number of farms producing $2,500 and more of gross product (at 1954 prices) remained constant at 2.1 million after 1940 (a slight increase over 1939 made possible by liquidation of small farms).

Security Administration. These agencies carried a fairly vigorous program aimed at relief of poverty up to the early 1940's. Their programs had little focus on the commercial farm problem and its appeal in compensation. It has been suggested that orientation and action towards the poverty problem through these agencies were largely swept away by political struggle and power politics of farm organizations. McConnell suggests that one major farm organization which had its initial impetus in public support and program (i.e. through the agricultural extension service) was afraid that a second farm organization would be so favored through the Farm Security Administration and acted accordingly.[21] The politic process and maneuvering described in lessening the vigor of the FSA program appears to parallel the model mentioned in Chapter 9, namely, the goal in political process of maximizing power and control over others, with the farm organization of concern fighting to liquidate program and agency which fell outside of its control.[22] After respite in tackling the poverty problem, milder public attempt at community development was initiated in 1954 through the Rural Development Program, but through the extension service and interagency operation wherein power position was not threatened. This program was incorporated into somewhat broader community or area development activities effort after 1961.

Rural and Community Development Opportunities

Rural development, as a mild policy for tackling the poverty and equity problems of agriculture, cannot obviate the fact that labor is still in excess in much of the industry. In contrast to earlier attacks (through FSA, FHA, etc.) on the problem which assumed capital to be the restraining resource, the later development program more nearly assumes knowledge to provide the constraint. A rural area development program cannot cause incomes of all low-income farm families to be pushed, within the confines of the community, near the national level of per capita income. Neither can it alone materially lessen the on-farm underemployment of labor by all farm families. This is true because acquisition of enough capital and land resources for some operators to expand must cause others to be ejected from the industry. Yet the direction of such programs is appropriate to the extent that they (1) aid some farmers to expand to efficient operational size and increase their welfare and income and (2) guide others to nonfarm employment opportunity where their income and utility also are increased, both groups having welfare gain and Pareto-better conditions insured. Older persons who are entirely inflexible in move to other work, in managing more farm resources or in shifting cultural setting, might best retain utility level in continuing their present routine in agriculture. Most appropriately, rural and community development programs can aid in guidance of young opera-

[21] Grant McConnell, *The Decline of Agrarian Democracy*, University of California Press, Berkeley, 1953, Ch. 8.

[22] *Ibid.*, Ch. 9.

tors with some flexibility. These are persons whose future in income opportunity and development of personal capacities is largely "blacked out" unless they either move to other employment or extend farm resources to sufficient commercial scale.

Local development as a means of alerting all resources and facilities in a community is desirable. In essence, it calls upon the community to make predictions of its current production possibilities and how these can be extended by increasing capital supply to the area. But just as important, predictions for these production possibilities should be compared against those of the outside world. Many, if not the majority of, communities will have to look to outside demand for labor, and hence in migration of people, to erase poverty conditions on farms. As mentioned previously, this is true especially in concentrated low-income areas because the extremely small amount of resources per person. If all such low-income areas were gathered together in one location, the productivity of labor and income of people would differ but little from that of agriculture in Greece and similar countries. Fortunately, as compared to Greece, a much broader and more diverse national economy exists into which this labor can feed, however. This tie to national economy should not be submerged by communities purely through the existence of local developmental concepts and attempt to "keep the boys at home."

Local development is correctly a step in the needed direction of a general social policy as discussed in Chapter 10. We pointed out that solutions bringing relief to farm people often cause the same problem to show up in somewhat different form for nonfarm people of the same community; the latter being no less important as resources and consumers than the former. In "over the board" fashion, early objectives of rural development programs recognized high concentration of farm populations on few resources, inability of operators to make needed adjustments and underemployment of farm labor. They were oriented to helping farmers develop more adequate producing units, for counseling farmers in respect to nonfarm employment and for encouraging local groups in introducing industry to supplement farm income in the community.

Rural development programs originally concentrated too much on growth in local focus, supposing mainly that, for all communities, capital and managerial resources could be extended to improve income of farmers and that local industrialization could be developed for local employment of farm people. Local industrial development can successfully serve thus only where nature's endowment causes it to be productive and profitable. Where this is untrue, the community has little opportunity to lift itself by its bootstraps. Not all communities can be developing areas. In an economy as large, wealthy and diverse as that of the U.S., some must be developing communities and some must be declining communities. Development programs which prospect a community for 10 years, grubbing through industrial opportunities of great sparsity and holding people in false hopes, can only prolong misery and extend the time before income and welfare of families can increase more sharply.

All programs centered on community development and depressed area concepts are proper in recognizing the interdependence of the various sectors of a community and the equal worth of the people in it. The inter-group motivation which can lead to matching supply of various resources against their marginal productivities over various endeavors within the community is salutary and long overdue. The public has long invested in this process for physical resources: in mapping soil types by counties and specifying the collection of crop alternatives and yields for them. It is high time that we do the same at the local level for human resources and capital in its broadest meaning.

Developmental programs are desirable as social policy, but not specifically in solving the commercial farm problem of supply function shifting rightward faster than demand. In their very structure, they are designed to retain land in production but to make the resources used on it more productive. Their positive contribution in policy is promise in increasing income and welfare of low income persons (1) who remain on farms and (2) who migrate occupationally, with hope of spillover to non-farm people in rural areas of chronically low income. On an equity basis alone, there is no reason why any less of public funds should be invested in this group of low-production farm families than on equal number of commercial farms of larger output. In 1960, the number of farms with gross output value of less than $5,000 was roughly equal to the number of commercial farms with output greater than this. (Excluding noncommercial farms, the number of commercial farms with less than $5,000 in gross sales at 1954 prices was about two-thirds proportion of those with gross income greater than this amount.)

The low-income commercial farmer gains little from compensation policies. As mentioned previously an increase in land resources to allow income of some to grow to satisfactory levels necessitates that others forsake farming. But opportunity exists for these migrants to realize welfare gains in doing so, providing conditions of growth and employment can be maintained in the national economy and appropriate aids in transfer are made. The opportunity must be examined in national economic growth, however, simply because some areas must be declining communities in face of limited natural endowments and a structure of factor prices and consumer demands which favors growth at other locations of the economy.

Resource Flows

If the labor market worked perfectly, workers could migrate out of declining communities at the rate of job formation in growing communities. They would migrate to opportunities which provide highest real income to their labor. The rate of transfer would not be faster because of added costs involved for those who transfer but who do not find employment.

Of course, if the economy worked perfectly, supply of employment opportunities would expand likewise in growing communities to absorb labor as quickly as it becomes unemployed (or underemployed) in declining communities. In this general complex of flows and reallocations, the free-wheeling of the market works far from perfectly and is cause of great frustration and potential income foregone by individuals. More than that, lack of growth rates in expanding communities which keep apace of decline in other communities, or lack of knowledge of matching rates where they occur, causes actual income loss to fall on many individuals.

Growth of industry in communities and areas of underemployed farm labor, or where labor is replaced rapidly by the capital of new technology in agriculture, would ease greatly the reallocation process, especially for the older and less mobile strata of the farm population. Draw of industry outside of the community is not a sufficient force to cause migration of all displaced and low-income farm labor in communities lacking local employment opportunities. More labor would shift to nonfarm employment under local economic development. This is the hope of most small community groups. But the fact stands that a major fraction of rural communities just do not have the resources and locational advantages to cause local industrialization and growth in nonfarm demand for labor.

Spatial spreading of industry, a policy followed in certain planned economies, would give more opportunity to these stranded peoples. But over the long run, the cost of aiding transfer, as suggested in the policy means outlined earlier, is likely less than the marginal cost of moving industry in, and the products out, of more remote areas as a physical means of providing local employment. The tendency of industrial growth to continue concentration largely at large population centers suggests this likelihood, especially in light of lower wage rates which have prevailed in depressed rural areas, or in smaller towns.[23]

Local development necessitates flow of resources between and among sectors whether its emphasis is on growth of the community, the central focus of early developmental programs initiated, or on a broader national view of development. In the typical community orientation, which supposes farm enlargement and flow of displaced labor to locally-stimulated industry, it is expected that the elasticity of labor supply to agriculture will be increased, or the supply function of labor to agriculture will shrink, as result of increased nonfarm demand and price for labor formerly used in agriculture.

In the theoretical model, productivity of labor on farms should increase as its quantity is shrunk against land and capital inputs. But this

---

[23] *Cf.* V. W. Ruttan, "Potential in Rural Industrialization and Local Economic Development" in Earl O. Heady, *et al.*, *Agricultural Adjustment Problems in a Growing Economy*, Iowa State University Press, Ames, Iowa, 1958.

complex in equations of rural economic development becomes operative only if certain other relations exist with coefficients and variables of sufficient magnitude. First, the demand function for the final product to be "brought in" under development must be of sufficient magnitude, in order that the price function does not include coefficient declining too rapidly with quantity marketed. Otherwise, the derived demand price for labor will also fall rapidly with quantity of local labor used. But also, in order that the derived demand price for labor will not fall too rapidly with quantity used, the production function for the industrial commodity must be one without important restraints in natural resources and conditions and without rapid decline in marginal physical productivity of labor.

But this is not all in the system of simultaneous relationships defining extent of industrialization and nonfarm labor demand in the community. The nature of the capital supply function, defining the price of capital in different quantities, also will determine the net value product imputable to labor, and hence the demand price for labor. We also must know the supply price of labor furnished from nonfarm sources within the community and from sources outside of the community. Both are substitutes for labor from local farm sources. The story in many communities after bringing in a plant typically is this: the employees are not drawn from farm operator ranks, but from filling station operatives of general and specialized experience, from local supply of housewives who were former clerical workers or technicians, from persons in nearby communities who have had training and experience extending beyond that of low-income or commercial farm operators and from graduating high school students. In this case, the development program proves of benefit in demand for products and service of local businessmen, but not in demand for labor of local farmers. Finally, the supply function of capital for individual operators, who will remain and take over assets of those who do migrate occupationally, is not automatically enlarged by growth of local industry.

Within the above system of resource flows and supply and demand schedules, the greatest number of small rural communities in widespread and sprawling commercial farm areas such as the western Cornbelt, the Great Plains and grazing regions, will not be able to attract or develop the equivalent of an automobile assembling plant, although some regions of chronically low-income farms will do so because of their location. However, most of both types of communities will draw small-scale, sometimes-risky and seasonal enterprises somewhat oriented to farm products. They will use but a small portion of the local labor supply, with much more labor still having to migrate geographically, commute to larger industrial centers or continue in underemployment on small farms. Not all communities will fall in this setting, but enough will do so that rural and community development programs should be pointed to the outside economy, equally as to the local economy. With the latter fixation, the problem of the community becomes essentially that of a closed economy in an under-developed nation. It has an extreme shortage of capital, little initial industry and perhaps a large concentration of low-income farm people against meager land and capital resources. With emphasis on the former, however, the analogy becomes more nearly that of a less developed nation in an open world economy: where farm and other labor can move out into the larger demand realms and productivity sectors of world regions and capital can move over space to its location of greatest marginal productivity.

Rural and community development can upgrade local economies where the complex of relationships above has variables and coefficients defining growth opportunity, although the lift in income and welfare of farm families often will come with part-time farming operations and few farmers immediately relinquishing their assets to others. But over broad regions and in the majority of other communities, where it won't so serve, local development will need to take quite a different focus, with emphasis on improved schooling and guidance programs, the attraction of outside public capital for these purposes and the improvement of capital and management supply to farmers who go through the process of farm enlargement as land is relinquished by operators who transfer geographically. In concentrated low-income farming areas, and in those of medium-income levels such as much of the southern Cornbelt, this transformation won't come in 5 years. It will come only in a generation unless more vigorous policy is developed. Local development is a program recognizing the interdependence of sectors in growth, but thus far it has been a timid substitute for the larger investment needed in lifting the utilization of human capacities and in providing constitutionally-specified equality of opportunity for a significant portion of the farm nation's people.

Alternative Models in Communities

The emphasis in some communities can rightly be on local industrial development. The economic relationships—in supply of labor and capital, in demand for industrial products and services and in the production function for the latter—are favorable for utilizing much of the locality's excess farm labor. Development and the supplying of information, without transfer subsidies, can largely do the job. In others, however, this set of conditions is not favorable and concentration might better be on relative economic outlook of the community, vocational counseling and guidance, occupational training and transfer payments and services to send local labor out into other communities where development is favored.

We can use an overly simplified "one period" example to illustrate different outcomes depending on particular local circumstances.[24] (More

---

[24] The example excludes technical change on farms, lagged responses, resource supply response differing among demand sectors, the multiplier effect as industrialization boosts demands for products in local service industries, inter-period effects in growth and capital, and the simultaneous effects or interaction in supply and demand relationships of different sectors.

detailed algebra or geometry could encompass other community environments giving rise to still different outcomes.) Figure 12.3, representing developmental opportunities in a community, has three labor supply functions: S_n for that from local nonfarm households, S_f for that from local farm households and S_o, that which can be furnished from households from outside the community. The total labor supply from within the community is curve MS_t while the aggregate supply from all sources is MS_Σ, for the community. The demand functions for labor are as follows: D_n for local nonfarm industries, D_f for local farms and D_o for industries outside of the community to which labor may migrate. The total labor demand in the community is RD_t. If labor returns on farms

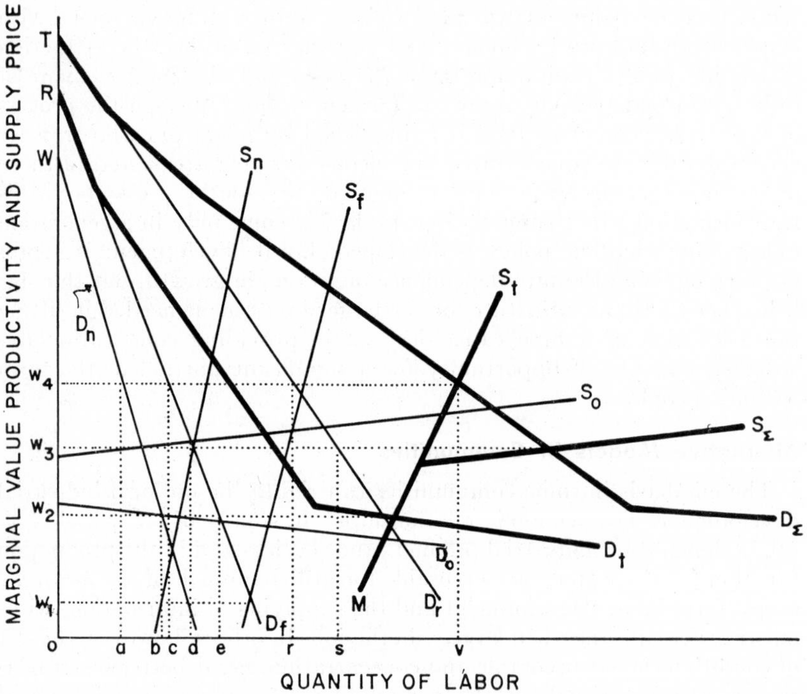

Fig. 12.3. Selected Relationships in Community Development.

were determined solely by supply of and demand for labor therein, wage return to farm labor would be ow_1. However, with full mobility between local farm and nonfarm sectors (the actual situation falling between these extremes), the equilibrium wage rate is ow_2 with *ob* of labor used in local nonfarm industry, *oe* used on farms while *ob* quantity of workers also migrate during the period.

Now it is hoped that a new industry or production sector with marginal value productivity or demand of D_r can be added to the community. If so, the total demand for labor now becomes TD_Σ. If the community could close itself off from other communities in labor supply, a hope of local workers is represented by supply function MS_t, but not a hope of merchants dealing in consumer necessities. The new equilibrium labor price or wage rate then would jump to ow_4, with *oa* employed in traditional local activity, *or* in new industry and *oc* on farms. In this case migration drops to zero and labor supplied from within the community realizes the total benefit of increased labor demand. However, if labor can be supplied from outside, as normally would be the case, the total labor supply function is MS_Σ and the equilibrium wage rate is ow_3 with *od* employed on farms and *os* in new industry, with no migration. (Actually, we would expect the D_n curve to move rightward from higher resource returns in the first case and with greater employment in the second.) The significant change in alleviating farm poverty is that labor return has been lifted from ow_2 to ow_3 and farm employment has declined from *oe* to *od* (most low income areas require a greater relative reduction than that appearing on the chart).

This is a fortunate community, faced with internal production function and net external or "outside" demand function for the new product helping to raise productivity and income of labor and "keeping all the young folks at home" (plus generating further demand for consumer goods from traditional local business—a first step in "chain reaction" or joint relationships not easily shown in a graph). But other communities are faced with quite an opposite condition where local production function, "outside" demand function and capital supply function from "outside" do not give rise to the marginal value productivity, D_r, for labor. In this case, the whole set of demand and supply relationships starts moving to the left. With the original supply functions S_n, S_f and S_t and the original demand functions D_n, D_f, D_o and D_t for a "first" period (where wage rate is w_2), this "chain reaction" of decline may develop: First, with migration lowering number of household, total demand falls from D_t to RD_o in a "next" period. Supply of local labor, because of decline of households, may also fall from S_t to S_f total; the resulting wage falling to level less than ow_2—a type of contraction in supply, demand and return of labor repeated in succeeding periods, with labor income supported only by "outside" demand function D_o. With further reduction in total labor demand to WD_o and total labor supply to S_n, the initial equilibrium labor return, ow_2, is restored. But income is still at its early depressed level, after having recovered some from even more distressed level, and total labor employment in the community has fallen from initial level of $oa+oe$ to *ob*. Here the community cannot lift itself by the bootstraps and policy must look "outward," with necessary informational and monetary assistance to aid outmigration and to help keep labor return from falling below the original depressed level of ow_2.

Whichever focus and direction eventually lifts welfare and opportunity in use of excess human resources of farm areas, it will lessen little the burden of supply capacity in commercial agriculture. Other policy must be used if the latter goal is to be attained. But as emphasized before, in large numbers of families and in great quantity of human resources represented for contribution to national society, solution of the low-income farm problem would appear to balance in urgency of solution with the commercial farm problem. This is not apparent, however, in magnitude and allocation of public appropriations, in number and subject matter of papers on policy written by agricultural economists, in equations selected for estimation and practice in inverting matrices by econometricians and in subjects brought to the surface for debate by national, state and local farm organizations.

13

Allocation of Resources in Education

THE NEED for education and training directed towards national growth potential of the future, rather than the agriculture of the past, has already been mentioned. Structural maladjustments in the farm industry will find their more permanent and minimum pain solution in the occupational selection of youth. Policy need not, of course, wait for the gradual replacement of one by another of overlapping generations. But the process of individuals giving up an occupation that partly fell upon them by birth for one matching other of their abilities is best accomplished by persons entering, or only shortly in, the labor force. Direction towards matching productivities of the resources that make up the individual with demands for these same services requires time for absorbing investment to develop them, however. Hence, for these reasons, it is useful to explore this facet of policy somewhat more deeply. Over the sweep of decades it will be the important policy in respect to potential welfare of people originating in agriculture, more so than all other policies aggregated together, for the particular population strata. Our approach is in a broad view of education as it relates to persons in agriculture, but is much more constrained than analyses examining the nation's educational system. Our focus is on education of the individual. A later chapter deals with the more specific developmental aspects of agricultural research and education.

The major contribution which can be made by agriculture to economic growth in future decades is through appropriate education of its youth.

Becker has estimated, for the entire U.S. and not for agriculture, the private return for high school education to be 19.2 percent, and return on college education to be 12.5 percent.[1] Return on all social investment in education is estimated to average about 10 percent, more than for the average returns of industry and agriculture. This education will be important as it prepares human resources to be efficient managers in agriculture, but more so in providing education and training adapted to the skilled and professional fields of greatest demand derived from economic growth.[2] Provision of more human resources to these fields will be a greater immediate contribution to national growth than upping the rate of output progress in agriculture. Improved education will be needed in agriculture so that diminishing returns won't be encountered in traditional inputs, with ratio of input to output in national food requirements increasing. This is true because farming, as other industries, increasingly rests on capital rather than labor and major human input for success being managerial and professional ability and because some, but smaller in proportion to the past, consumer gain can be made in releasing labor from agriculture. But the major direct contribution of agriculture to national economic growth will still rest on the training of youth who enter the nonfarm labor force. For this reason we need to look somewhat more deeply into the educational phase of resource allocation and development.

EMPHASIS IN EDUCATION

Research and educational programs directed to agriculture have been extremely successful in contribution to national economic growth. The latter, national economic growth, has indeed been a sufficient justification for these efforts. (See Chapter 16 for discussion of returns from investment in agricultural research and education.) The indirect gain or return to the society of consumers, not only in abundance and price of food but also in increased availability of resources for nonfood products, has outweighed direct gains to agriculture itself in recent decades. More of the investment in agricultural education and research will need to be justified in terms of national welfare and consumer return. If we accept these facts, and the facts have empirical basis, then education or research for agriculture needs some elements added and some change in emphasis. Largely the needed elements are those to help agriculture adjust to economic growth and to give people from agriculture a better opportunity to capitalize on favorable employment outlook from growth.

Education to date has been that which causes or forces changes in the

[1] G. S. Becker, "Underinvestment in College Education," *Amer. Econ. Rev.*, Vol. 50, and "Investment in Education," *Nat. Bur. Econ. Res. Ann. Rep.*, Vol. 39, pp. 38–40. Also see figures quoted from Becker's study in T. W. Schultz, *Education and Economic Growth*, Sixtieth Yearbook of the National Society for the Study of Education.

[2] For discussion of growth of supply and demand of professional resources in scientific fields, see D. M. Blank and G. J. Stigler, *Demand and Supply of Scientific Personnel*, National Bureau of Economic Research, New York, 1957.

structure of agriculture and brings about the need for adjustment. But it has left farm youth and their parents caught in the whirlpool of market forces, with little aid in adjusting to the changing structure which efforts in education and research have brought about. This void stems partly from a tendency to view agricultural research and education in an economic framework which is too narrow relative to their over-all social consequences. Typically, the framework viewed is that of relationships within the unit of the farm firm or household, or within a commodity sector. From the inception of major professional efforts for agriculture, including vocational training, the supposition has been that the beneficiaries are farm people, and only indirectly and incidentally the nonfarm public. A century back, this was more true, especially in terms of gain to agriculture. But it has not been the case since 1930, nor will it be in the 1960's. A main effect has been gain to the consuming public and an immense contribution to national economic growth. The gains have been real and important.

This, the contribution to national economic growth and progress, is broad over-all framework in which major research and educational programs in agriculture of the future need to be viewed and justified. The changing proportions of farm and nonfarm populations will require it. It is a framework which not only justifies continued and public support of research and education, but it also provides a basis for emphasis and structuring of programs to mesh with national needs in the future. Educational programs which rest on an economic growth framework will be much broader in structure than those which suppose agricultural education and research to have the single purpose of aiding people in farming to farm better.

The opportunities and needs in education for the future are not less, but are greater, in complexity than in the past. They will better recognize the relative shift in demand for products and the labor resources going into them than has been done in the past. They will guide more youth into nonfarm professions in response to changing structure of the economy. They will recognize that their success in increasing productivity of labor in agriculture has the very effect of reducing the labor force in agriculture. Finally, they will recognize that agriculture has become a complex and scientific occupation, requiring a richer mix in capital proportion, with need for education more in basic science and management and less in today's facts and do-it-yourself skills.

This regearing of education is necessary as new technology in farming replaces people and frees them for the labor force of other industries. As mentioned in Chapter 12, agricultural education, or even education in rural areas, of the decades past has had the main goal of turning farm youth back into agriculture, even when many had little hope of success and income in doing so. So great was this obsession that little else in vocational training has been offered in many rural communities. As Table 13.1 indicates, rural states have concentrated vocational training on agriculture, and this has been most true in those states where farm

TABLE 13.1

PERCENTAGE ALLOCATION OF VOCATIONAL EDUCATION FUNDS AMONG CATEGORIES (CENSUS REGIONS AND SELECTED STATES, 1955–59)

Region or State	Percentage Allocation Within Region or State for:			Percent Allocation of Region or State Is of U.S. for:		
	Agri-culture	Home ec.	Trades and industry*	Agri-culture	Home ec.	Trades and industry†
U.S.	31	30	39	100	100	100
New England	11	18	71	2.3	3.8	12.8
Mid. Atlantic	16	13	71	6.5	5.6	24.4
E. North Central	31	31	38	16.3	17.2	16.3
W. North Central	41	31	28	12.3	9.8	5.9
S. Atlantic	36	34	30	19.9	20.0	12.8
E. South Central	42	36	22	11.2	10.1	4.7
W. South Central	42	38	20	20.9	20.1	7.0
Mountain	32	32	36	4.3	4.5	3.6
Pacific	21	28	51	6.4	8.9	12.4
New York	13	9	78	2.3	1.7	12.0
Minnesota	38	28	34	3.1	2.4	2.1
Iowa	49	33	18	2.7	1.9	.8
South Carolina	44	36	20	2.8	2.4	.9
Georgia	44	40	16	4.8	4.6	1.2
Tennessee	37	38	25	2.8	3.0	1.6
Alabama	42	33	25	3.1	2.6	1.5
Mississippi	48	37	15	3.0	2.4	.7
California	19	26	55	3.8	5.7	9.1

Source: *Digest of Annual Reports of State Boards for Vocational Education to the Office of Education*, Division o Vocational Education, U.S. Dept. of Health, Education and Welfare, Office of Education (fiscal years ending in 1955–59).

* Includes Distributive occupations, nursing, area programs and other minor allocative categories.

† Trades and industries only.

income and opportunities are meagerly low. In the more industrialized states, where youth are better acquainted with occupations in industry and the professions, we find the greatest allocation of vocational education to occupations other than agriculture and home economics. It is in the low-income southern states and the midwestern agricultural states, regions where the migration from farm to industry has been at most rapid rates and will continue so, that allocations to vocational agriculture have been greatest. In both Iowa and Mississippi, for example, nearly half of all vocational education funds was allocated to agriculture in the period 1955–59. These two states allocated about 85 percent of vocational funds to agriculture and home economics.

This focus, for the great number who eventually find their abilities and capital situation to favor employment in other industries, has caused many to have vocational opportunity closed to them, or to stumble to it only after large financial sacrifice. Technical research and education has freed people from the industry, then left them stranded in agriculture, with emphasis continued on farming education to replace or free even more people from agriculture. It is obvious that most mechanical practices substitute for and replace labor. But biological practices serve similarly. Practice combinations which increase per acre grain yield by 20 percent substitute for nearly as large a percentage of the labor required to produce a given output. A combination of livestock practices which reduces the amount of feed to produce a given amount of meat or milk serves similarly.

Complete Educational Training for Farm Youth

Vocational education and 4-H training in agriculture have been efficient and successful as have other public educational and research programs for the industry. But all of these programs help change the structure of agriculture from within. This investment in agricultural training has shown all boys involved how to be better farmers and has given a better vocational opportunity to those with capital who could farm and participate in rapid advance. But while the vocational opportunity for some farm boys has been increased, the opportunity for others has been lessened as a result of the program. Under economic growth and rapid technological development, it is important to focus on vocational opportunities for farm boys who no longer have satisfactory alternatives in agriculture. We lack complete vocational and educational programs for farm youth until training is provided equally and appropriately for the greater number who have no promising future in agriculture. Farm youths have been handicapped seriously, in opportunity to capitalize on native capacities and abilities, by educational policy concentrated on farming.

As investment is made in education and research for agriculture specifically, we need to invest in services which help restore balance in both the resource and income structure of the industry. Two things are needed: (1) Research, education and programs which aid in increasing economic efficiency for farmers remaining in the industry needs to be maintained at appropriate level. Agriculture is a competitive industry. It will continue to be so, even with policies which lessen competition at level of commodity price, and farming can be conducted profitably only by those who have the proper abilities, skills and capital. Vocational training, education and a flow of information to operators who will or should remain in farming need to be continued for economic growth purposes. Young people need to be trained to take their place. This training needs to be even better than in the past, considering the growth in commercialization and competition of agriculture. It must rest more on basic knowledge and less on do-it-yourself skills. In the decades ahead, a greater proportion of farmers than in the past will need formal and advanced education in agriculture because of the growing complexity of agriculture. (2) A parallel effort is needed to educate more appropriately those forced or drawn from agriculture and to aid in the structural adjustment of agriculture. The larger adjustments in occupational and geographic migration and the activities which will facilitate them must revolve largely around the more flexible part of the farm labor force, namely youth.

With prospects for continued technological improvement and increases in output, the adjustment period for agriculture is going to extend for a long period into the future. Balance will be created as much by preventing young people, when their incomes and life satisfactions will be greater in some other occupation, from entering agriculture. We provide a positive service to these persons by training, informing and counseling them so that they make correct choices when they enter the labor force. We provide them a disservice if we encourage or allow them to enter farming, only to find out four or five years later that they have made a mistake and must switch from farming. In this sense, we need to consider vocational agriculture not as a self-contained educational program, but as part of a larger systematic vocational training program. For rural youth, as well as those in urban locations, we need counseling and training for those who will enter farming as an occupation.

One goal is to identify those who have the ability and capital to make a success of commercial farming in a competitive future. And competition will prevail. Programs which stabilize and support prices or provide quotas for each farmer still allow and encourage competition. The competition is in the pricing and purchase of resources and quotas to produce the output, if not at the commodity level. But an equal goal is to properly identify and train those who have neither the interest, ability nor resources to make a success of farming. Research and educational programs, financed from public funds, should have the effect of increasing aggregate human welfare. Never should they contribute to lessening the potential welfare of a large population stratum simply to allow projection of an institutional or educational structure of the past into the future, or in projecting gain of the persons who run such a program at loss to those who are misdirected in vocation. The need is not to eliminate successful agricultural educational and research programs of the past, because these contribute greatly to national economic progress. Instead it is to add program elements which facilitate the adjustments partly created by these research and educational efforts. We have an incomplete educational program for agriculture until we do so. We are subject to criticism until we provide vocational and counseling services which are as effective for those displaced from agriculture as for those trained to maintain the industry.

Aggregate Knowledge

Educational and research organizations directed at agriculture need to give more attention to the mass effect of their activities and the relationship of agriculture to the total society. They must broaden their view of the human resources in agriculture. These resources are not adapted only to agriculture, but represent humans with talents and possibilities which are often more important if guided into the services demanded by a wealthy and growing society. Through the educational system, they should be provided the opportunity and choice mechanism for selecting occupations on which rapid economic development places income premiums. In this sense, educational complex oriented towards people on farms needs to concern itself with areas given little emphasis in the past. It must turn its attention to the welfare of people replaced by technical advance in agriculture. It needs to turn its attention to secondary social adjustments, created in rural communities as farms become larger and population becomes smaller. It needs to concern itself with wider educational and employment opportunities for some rural youth than they have had in the past, just as it needs to emphasize improving the ability of those youth who will return to farming.

Increased scientific knowledge has stepped up the rate of technical change, causing applied knowledge obtained in vocational education to become obsolete more rapidly and with need for structuring adult education accordingly. Education for youth and families engaged in farming needs to be broadened, beyond consideration of improving the enterprise and increasing profits to an over-all view of agricultural industry in the national economy and of agricultural policies which are consistent with both economic growth and improved resource returns in farming.

Increasingly, farm people are of high literacy. They will make major choices in respect to private affairs in the market through decisions and prices to purchase resources and expand farm operations, follow particular consumption patterns or choose particular occupations. They also will make major choices through the voting mechanisms and decide for or against agricultural policies which affect the welfare of themselves and the nation. They function in a home and community setting which is more complex and less detached than previously. Choices for the business and household are more nearly joint ones, involving knowledge in both areas by husband and wife. Agriculture is much less unique and distinct as an occupation and way of life than in the past. Certainly these facets of change should be recognized in agricultural education for the future. No force has been much stronger, in the span of two or three generations, than education in diverting the personal distribution of income over the masses of the population. Labor of agriculture, particularly that in the chronically low-income and Negro-operator strata, has been long disadvantaged in this respect—as has agriculture as a whole.

With public education an investment subsidy to the individual, the the individual's ability to obtain a share of this capital and realize future premium earnings on it depends on his access to wealth and his ability to forego earnings while in school. This education investment or factor cost has been estimated at $2,240 for eight years of elementary school, $5,680 for four years of high school and $13,200 for four years of college at 1956 prices.[3] Of this total factor cost, 43 percent is attributed to earnings foregone through high school, and 53 percent through college. The person unable to go to high school and college misses about $10,000 in public capital investment in education. With high rate of return on this over his lifetime, the opportunity for capitalizing on public investment causes him large sacrifice as compared to other persons. But it is less the

[3] Schultz, *loc. cit.*

amount of capital that is important; it is more the opportunities which are opened with the education. Inability, and surrounding motivational forces, which force low levels of schooling on farm strata drives them into the lowest of unskilled employment opportunity, or to life on an inadequate farm.

Data on migrants from farms indicate great voids have existed in opportunity to capitalize on education services produced under public enterprise: For farm migrants in the nonfarm labor force of 1949, 8.5 percent of white and 30.8 percent of Negroes had less than five years of education, 35.2 percent of whites and 43.8 percent of Negroes had only five to eight years of education.[4] In the urban labor force as nonmigrants from farms, only 2.3 percent had less than five and only 16.1 percent had as little as five to eight years of education. In the farm population over 25 years of age, 20.3 of whites and 53.0 percent of Negroes had less than 5 years of education. In the farm population of the North Central region, 62.9 percent of whites over 25 years in age had less than a high school education; the comparable figure for Negroes in the South was 73.1 percent. Table 13.2 indicates that the labor force which does remain in agriculture has been at the lower end of the educational ladder, exceeding unskilled labor only very slightly in educational attainment.

ALLOCATION OF RESOURCES TO EDUCATION UNDER GROWTH

Economic growth takes place especially because labor is high in productivity and produces more than it consumes, because capital accumulation takes place and further increases labor productivity and because scientific discovery and knowledge also occur, adding to both labor and capital productivity. Education is an input or resource which thus leads to increased scientific knowledge and, hence, to increased labor and capital productivity which promote economic growth. But, since national economic growth causes change in consumption patterns, in allocations of the indivdual's time and even in his preferences and values, one of these variables cannot be considered as "exogenous," and determined outside of the system. Instead, education and scientific advance, national income and values or preferences are three "jointly determined variables," each determining what the magnitude of the others will be, or should be. There is not a "one way-relationship" between education (scientific advance) as the "determining variables" and national income and personal or community values as the "determined variables." National income and consumer values (preferences of people) equally determine what the level and direction of education and science can or should be. While education and science are sometimes carried on for the sake of "pure" ends, unrelated to the desires and preferences of consumers, they more often are directed towards the products, services and activities desired by consumers. This is true for education aimed at eventual employment

[4] D. G. Johnson, "Policies To Improve the Labor Transfer Process," *Amer. Econ. Rev.*, Vol. 50.

TABLE 13.2

EDUCATIONAL ATTAINMENT BY OCCUPATIONAL GROUPS, UNITED STATES, 1959

	Educational Attainment Levels			
		Percent with:		
Occupational Group	Average years completed	Less than high school	High school graduation	Some college
Professional and technical	16.2	6	19	75
Proprietors and managers	12.4	38	33	29
Clerical and sales	12.5	25	53	22
Skilled	11.0	59	33	8
Semi-skilled	9.9	70	26	4
Service	9.7	69	25	6
Unskilled	8.6	80	17	3
Farmers and farmworkers	8.6	76	19	5

Source: *Manpower Challenge of the 1960's*, U.S. Department of Labor, U.S. Govt. Print. Off. 1960.

of its student customers, in firms and industries producing the products for which consumers pay a price and provide employment opportunities. It also is true in large part for scientific research financed by the public, and particularly that financed by commercial firms which provides an important portion of our knowledge for education as well as the basis for development of products desired by consumers.

In this sense, growth in national income and consequent trends or changes in the pattern of consumer preferences are important in determining the structure and emphasis in education and science. As an input or resource used to attain the growth ends, to produce the goods and services desired by consumers and voters in a democracy, the structure and emphasis in education and science needs to be continuously adapted to conform with changes in national income and consumer preferences or values. Adaptations in education need to be in terms of the number of persons trained for the different occupational fields which produce goods and services, in terms of the nature and number of curriculum offered for this training and in terms of the educational methods fitted to both of the foregoing. But since change is continuous, emphasis in adaptation of education should not alone be on the number of persons trained for different fields, but also in developing flexibility of people so they can shift in occupational direction as economic change continues.

Alternatives and Competing Major Ends in Education

If we were to consider education solely from the standpoint of developing humans as resources, one of the numerous alternative ends outlined later, then an optimum procedure would be: to predict the level of national income and pattern of consumer preferences two decades hence. Then we would provide appropriate vocational guidance and curricula developing the proper number of persons to produce goods for these future demands. We would decrease the number of persons trained in some fields and increase it in others, with courses at secondary and college levels altered accordingly. We would increase numbers of persons and courses or other facilities in some fields, but by different proportions than in other fields. This would be the proper approach, if education were looked upon as an input designed to develop human resources in a manner most consistent with national economic growth and the maximization of consumer welfare. This should be an important basis for educational structure and change. But it does not provide a sufficiently complete framework for structuring education, since development of human resources is only one of the several possible ends to which educational inputs can be directed.

In fact, as national and per capita income grow and expenditure patterns and values of consumers change, it is possible that an increasing proportion of educational resources should be directed in directions other than development of individuals as resources. That is, while total investment in education may increase in the several areas, relatively more should be invested in the individual as a consumer, as compared to the individual as a producer of products and services. The reason is: the individual need not devote such a large portion of his time or exploit such a large portion of his energies for earning a living. He has a larger portion of his time and income for enjoyment, recreation and entertainment of himself.

Along with these changing patterns of allocation of time and income, it also is likely that we need to make relative changes in the educational system. For a very poor nation, it is essential that education be devoted to increasing the productivity of the individual. For a very poor person, the essential in education is that it provide him means for earning a better living. But for a wealthy nation and person, the goal and emphasis of education need not be alone that of developing the individual as a resource and preparing him to earn a living. We wish to explore some of these alternative ends on the pages which follow.

Some of the trends over past decades in allocation of more educational resources to development of the individual as a person or consumer, rather than in developing him solely as a resource, would seem positively consistent with growth in national and per capita income, rather than as a purely negative direction, as some extremists would lead us to believe. The issues being argued over education are partly those of whether we should be devoting efforts only to developing individuals as resources for our production machine, with less or no emphasis devoted to improving their ability to enjoy the rapidly growing per capita quantities of products and services coming forth from an industrial machine which "churns" at an ever increasing speed. Some would drop all courses and educational activities which develop the individual as a decision-making consumer of products, services and leisure which are growing in quantity as time and national income progress.

This is wrong focus for evaluating educational needs under economic growth. The error in allocation of educational resources isn't in this direction. Recent trends in education probably have been consistent with the needs of a nation which is already wealthy and is rapidly growing more so. Instead, the questions more appropriate for debate in education to develop human resources are as follows: (1) Are we allocating a sufficient amount of our growing national income to education for all purposes? (2) Of that allocated for purposes of developing individuals as resources, is it being used most efficiently, or could the same inputs be rearranged to produce a greater human resource and, hence, industrial product? (Certainly the last question is just as relevant for other ends to which education can be directed.)

Ends for Allocating Educational Resources

We now turn to the basic and broader ends to which educational resources can be allocated. With limited educational resources, these ends are competitive at some level of allocation to each. The important question isn't one of which single end should be included, with all others excluded. Instead, it is one of: What is the proper balance in educational resources, allocated to these several ends? As time progresses and national income increases, greater total investments probably should be made towards all acceptable ends, but relatively more to some than to others. Unfortunately, in this day of debate over education, sufficient attention has not been given to the existence of these alternative ends.

We do not attempt to discuss all possible ends for education. We simply point out some of the major ends which need consideration. Four major ends which might relate to criteria for determining the allocation of educational funds, and even in development of curricula, include using education for (1) developing a resource (2) bringing about a change in the pattern of personal income distribution, (3) using education directly as a consumption activity and (4) molding values of individuals in respect to ethical considerations, social organization, consumption patterns and other uses of resources.

THE END OF EDUCATION FOR RESOURCE DEVELOPMENT

Education could be approached purely from the standpoint of, with labor or the human as the material of relevance, a resource and its development, just as society might invest in the development or production of resources represented by bricks, concrete, animal breeding stock, steel, soil reclamation, manufacturing plants, etc. Education for this purpose is relevant as an end in a slave or dictatorial state just as it is in a democracy. A single dictator, or slave owner, receiving all the product of economic activity, would want to mold people into potential productive power, just as he would want to mold sand and limestone into concrete which has productive power, He would need trained engineers, technicians, herdsmen, doctors and others, if he produced a maximum product from available natural resources. The departure in interests for using education to develop or train human resources in a democracy or a slave (dictatorial) society is: In the one case, the relevant product and direction of education or training is specified by the community of consumers; in the other by the values of the dictator. But even though there is this difference, education can be viewed as an activity designed to develop people as resources with productive abilities, regardless of what the end may be or who specifies it. The resource development aspect of education is at the extreme in graduate training, where it is generally supposed that other possible attributes of education are already absorbed by the individual.

In using education to develop humans as resources, either in a slave, democratic or dictatorial society, two steps are important. First is measment of abilities. In technical terms, this is a matter of predicting the production possibilities, not as of now but as the potential after education, which make up the individual. After predicting the type of work for which the individual is potentially most productive, or in predicting which individuals will produce most from a given educational input, the person would be assigned directly to this area in a society concerned only with the individual as a resource, regardless of the individual's preferences. However, in a democracy, predicting the post-education potential which makes up the individual is only one necessary step in vocational guidance. The second important step is determination of the personal preferences and values which characterize the individual, and in guiding him into the educational field leading to the type of industrial activity which will maximize his own lifetime satisfactions and welfare, considering: (1) his productivity in various fields, (2) the price which the consuming society is willing to pay for these various products and (3) the relative value which the individual attaches to money income and what it will purchase, as compared to the nonmoney amenities which attach to different fields of work or production.

Optimum Education With Resource Development as Single End

As mentioned previously, debate in education has been focused on developing humans as resources; to increase the ability of people in producing a greater scientific and industrial product. True, this is desired, but we should not lose sight of the other possible and important ends around which education also can center. In a slave or dictatorial economy only the products specified by some person or group would be relevant in educating people as resources. The impact of education on income and its distribution and on the individual as a human and sovereign consumer would be disregarded. In a democracy we must ask ourselves: To what degree is or should our education be designed to develop people as resources as compared to other ends to which education also can be directed? Are we concerned only in using our educational facilities to produce resources, just as we might produce concrete blocks as resources? If we were to concentrate the same facilities on producing concrete blocks for the industrial purpose in mind, we would do so without flourishes which appeal to art, beauty or direct consumption aspects of the material resource. Some of the more technical educational institutions, or even technical curricula within less technical institutions, have had as a main or sole focus education for the purpose of resource development only.

If this were the only purpose of education for an agriculturist or engineer, we would try to make him into the best possible concrete block. We would feed him only the courses which mold him into a better concrete block, and take away from him all courses which relate to art, humanities, communications, and others which help him to understand himself and the people around him. We would take away all courses which help him make decisions, which will promote his personal welfare, which help him express his views as a member of society and which increase his ability generally for deriving greater satisfaction from the goods, services, resources and life around him. From the standpoint of education for purposes of resource development only, we thus might produce much better human resources, to serve singularly as concrete blocks in our industrial machine. Historically, education for agriculture, at both high school and college levels, has been prone to lean in this direction with so much technical and laboratory work that the student has had little time for development in the "human" or "consumer" direction.

Undoubtedly, our educational system has not had insufficient attainment in developing human resources. Many people have gone undeveloped as resources because they have not had funds for education, or because given educational resources sometimes may not have been used most effectively. This has been more true in agriculture than in general society. But we can attain greater perfection in furthering this goal, even while we also are furthering other ends to which education can be directed.[5]

Relative Productivity of Investment for Development of Human Resources

Another aspect of education for resource productivity purposes also should be considered. It concerns the relative productivity of, or returns on, capital investment in the human agent as compared to material agents of production such as factories, machines and other forms of capital. Given the empirical evidence available, the returns from capital invested in developing the human resource through education is very high in U.S. society, higher than the average return for capital invested in material resources such as industrial machines and buildings in "more" monopolistic industries. (See Chapters 5 and 12.)

But more important is the fact that our society, composed as it is of private and public sectors functioning partly through the market and partly through government in allocating resources, has had no efficient

[5] Over an important range, various products or ends which can be produced in the human with education are complementary. To develop awareness as a resource often develops awareness as an individual or consumer. To go to college may provide "fun" as a consumer good as it also produces a better human resource. Greater development as a resource and higher earning power adds to consumption in the household, etc. But we are mainly concerned with other allocations here.

method of allocating scarce capital resources for education into those individuals where it has greatest productivity. At the levels of primary and secondary education, we do and should, particularly because of some of the ends pointed out later, provide some comparability in educational inputs for all individuals. In a purely "productivity and resource returns" context of education, however, we would allocate different quantities, and even kinds, of educational inputs to individuals even at the lower grade levels, not alone in terms of the ability of students to absorb them, but also in terms of the productivity of these inputs relative to the national product. The productivity of variable educational inputs allocated to or used for any one individual would depend upon the fixed collection of capacities (resources) which make up the ability of the individual. This collection of "fixed resources," or basic ability obviously affects the productivity of variable inputs of education which may be invested in the individual.

As an example, we would suppose it to work out in the manner of variables in (5.14). If X is variable capital in education, the marginal productivity of and magnitude of this variable will depend on the "fixed" magnitude of Z, the basic capacity resource of the individual. With a large "basic or fixed" collection of capacities in one individual, we might invest twice as many educational inputs in him, before the marginal productivity of the last input dropped as low as that for a person with less capacity and receiving half as many educational inputs. Too little is known empirically about differentials in productivity of capital in educational form, depending upon the abilities of the individual who is the recipient of education. From the pure resource or productivity pole of education this productivity criterion would be paramount in determining which students receive how much education. It would be the only criterion in a slave or dictatorial society where education might be pursued only for the ends of developing human resources to satisfy preferences of the slave owner or dictator. Even, then, it also has importance in a free society concerned with resource development, economic growth and greater human welfare, but it should not serve as the only gauge for specifying the kinds, quantities and persons for whom investment is made in education.

Some Problems in Allocating Capital

Obtaining an optimum allocation of investment in education is more difficult than obtaining an optimum investment in other forms of capital or resource development in an economy such as that of the United States, for the following reasons. Where undeveloped resources such as mineral deposits, land and factory locations exist, and there is sufficient demand for the product of these resources, private investors can commit capital to their development and realize a return through the pricing system, representing the value which consumers attach to the products of the resources. But this procedure is much less possible for undeveloped human resources which promise high capital returns. Consumers may reflect a large demand for the services of these undeveloped resources represented by youth who have ability but lack funds for sufficient education and training. Yet the person who has capital cannot invest, through education, in development of resources represented by another individual and conveniently realize a return on his capital. This is true even though capital productivity is high when used for these purposes, higher than when invested in farms or factories. Consequently, he uses his private funds for other forms of capital investment or resource development which have a much lower return. Hence, the opportunities for development of the human resource depend largely upon the funds available to the individual, through his family or through public taxation and investment.

Because of these imperfections in the capital market, particularly in ability of funds to flow into education of persons where capital returns are high, a great disparity in capital returns can exist between (1) that invested in the human factor and that invested in other agents of production, and (2) that representing differential educational investment in different persons. An important need is to improve fiscal and market mechanism so that these disparities can be lessened and improved education can contribute to a greater national product. No major sector stands to gain more from such investment and improvement in educational allocations than people in agriculture. As indicated elsewhere, they have had too little opportunity, or have partaken too lightly, in education.

Yet even within present machinery there is room for improvement in structuring education to meet the productivity or resource criterion, in increasing the national product, while still allowing other ends to have claim in the allocation of educational resources. In the majority, our higher education has been allocated more to those who have a large enough collection of capital assets to allow them to purchase a portion of the total input provided by the public, than to those who have a large enough collection of intellectual assets to cause the same input to have greatest marginal productivity. True, an important quantity of costs of education are publicly subsidized. This is almost entirely true for elementary and secondary education, and opportunity is roughly similar for all children in a given locality—but not among localities such as those of high or low income and rural or urban locations. Even college or university educations are partly subsidized with open opportunity for those who can pass entrance tests to attend tax supported or other public institutions. The opportunity is open, however, only to those who have, or can arrange, the necessary finances for the larger portion of the costs which are not subsidized. From a purely resource or productivity framework of education, there are multitudes of high school graduates who do not have funds for higher education, or who have never been guided in this direction, but whose ability would cause educational inputs to have a greater productivity than for many who now find their way to college. A disproportionate number of the former are to be found on farms where income, spatial and school quality variables serve as barriers to college enrollment.

Public measures such as the National Youth Administration of the 1930's and the postwar G.I. programs helped ease this situation, as also do the National Merit Scholarships and certain other federal aids. However, a mass of human abilities is still not tapped by these programs, and it may become increasingly necessary to apply productivity criteria in determining to whom and by how much shall inputs of higher education be devoted in the future, should extreme international competition in economic and political affairs and the paucity of educational funds continue.

Allocation of Education to Students of Different Abilities

A more stringent application of productivity principles to allocation of education to different persons, depending upon their intellectual ability, generally would not mean that higher level education should be withheld entirely from all persons with low ability. This might be true if the only goal in education were resource development, the production function of education were linear (we would educate only one person then) and funds for education were extremely limited. But where funds are not this limited, productivity criteria, even under the resource development end, would specify allocation of educational facilities to those of less ability, even at the college level.

Certainly educational investment per person is subject to eventual diminishing returns. Suppose that investment in one individual is subject to diminishing returns, and that investment of the first, second, third, fourth and fifth $1,000 of public funds allocated to education returns, per $1 of investment, $20, $15, $10, $5, and $3 respectively for the person of high ability and $5, $4, $3, $2 and $1 respectively for the person of low ability. Then, if society has $5,000 to invest in education, its return will be greatest if four units of $1,000 are invested in the first person and one unit of $1,000 is invested in the second person. Current pressures on education tend to overlook this principle.

Or, if we wanted to retain some simplicity but express our general concept in more refined manner, we could do so as follows. We can do so in consideration of the national outlay for education and specify allocations among regions and communities in a manner to maximize the value of social product from this quantity, in contrast to the current pattern of allocation where funds are in paucity amounts in some states and communities but are in ample quantities in others. Or, we can use the same principle as it applies in allocation of educational resources among individuals. We will follow the latter context, recognizing that the concept and principle applies equally to the former.

We have n individuals whose productivity can be developed through education, with Y_i being the level of resource or product developed in the ith individual and X_i being the quantity of educational inputs or outlay allocated to him. Supposing that a functional relationship $Y_i=f_i(X_i)$ exists, as it certainly does, in developing the product of education in each person, then we have the general condition in (13.1).

$$Y_t = \sum_{i=1}^{n} Y_i = \sum_{i=1}^{n} f_i\,(X_i) \tag{13.1}$$

We wish to maximize Y_t, total educational output (or resource developed in education). It is the sum of that developed in each individual, Y_i, over the n persons. But we must add the restraint represented by

$$\sum_{i=1}^{n} X_i - X_t = 0$$

where

$$\sum_{i=1}^{n} X_i$$

is the sum of inputs allocated to the n persons and X_t is the total quantity of inputs or educational resources available. The sum of resources allocated to the n individuals thus cannot exceed X_t, the total amount available.

Substituting the actual production functions $Y_i = f_i\,(X_i)$ into (13.1) for Y_i, we can take the partial derivatives of Y_i in respect to all X_i and equate them to m as in (13.2) for the n persons.

$$\begin{aligned} \frac{\partial Y_1}{\partial X_1} &= m \\ \frac{\partial Y_2}{\partial X_2} &= m \\ &\vdots \\ \frac{\partial Y_i}{\partial X_i} &= m \\ &\vdots \\ \frac{\partial Y_n}{\partial Y_n} &= m. \end{aligned} \tag{13.2}$$

Solving for X_i in each equation, we then would have specified the amount of education to be invested in each person (or community of the nation in the former context). The values of X_i so determined represent the amounts to be allocated to each person (or region) if the marginal productivity of education in individuals is to be equated at level m and the product of education is to be maximized. Recognizing that $Y_i = f_i(X_i)$

varies between individuals depending on their abilities and motivations, the X_i would take on different values for different individuals. They would not be determined to provide *just exactly* four years of high school of four years of college to each of the n individuals. We have oversimplified the problem, particularly in terms of the measurements implied and in summing the Y_i as they relate to time and discounted values. We don't expect the school superintendent and the state or national administrator of education to readily put the principle into empirical application. But we have re-emphasized our point. Thus, in general, the magnitudes $X_1, X_2, \cdots, X_i, \cdots, X_n$ will not be equal because the productivity of education as input in producing resource or benefit will not be the same for all individuals. From the standpoint of resources and their productivity, the principle is not to provide equal education of each, but to equate marginal productivities of resources allocated to education of the n individuals.

There is nothing magic or unique about 12 years of elementary, secondary and high school and 4 years of college. These are archaic institutions selected with imperfect vision from historic precedent. Institutions in education suppose, for example, that the inputs going into education over time for one individual are technical complements and limitational nature: "Four years of them are necessary and the product is complete exactly." It can be argued, of course, that although students typically obtain a "four-year dosage" at all schools, the input actually differs because high schools, universities and colleges (or different curricula within the same high school or university) are of different quality. But regardless of this situation, education is not discrete in the sense that everyone *must have exactly four years* before it has value. The functional relationship between educational input and its product is continuous, and not discrete. Hence, a better allocation of resources in education might well take place if we educated more students for 2 years, and also more for 5 or 6 years; if we had more junior colleges and technical schools in rural regions. For resource development per se, the application of this allocative principle to students of different abilities, and the structuring of education accordingly, would call for more students receiving differential quantities of college education than we now have.

THE END OF EDUCATION AS A CONSUMPTION GOOD

Education can be viewed from the end of a consumption good or service, or an activity contributing directly to this end. (Again, this end relates especially to higher levels of education.) There are obvious extremes in this regard: the Saturday afternoon football game, the junior prom, the riding course and similar collegian activities appended to educational institutions differ little, if at all, from goods such as beer, potatoes, mountain hiking, doughnuts, the world series and others consumed by the noncollegian. But aside from such unique consumer goods and services as these, produced only by educational institutions, a college education per se also can take on a consumer characteristic. Students can select a richer mix of resource development relative to consumer development or vice versa, depending on the college or university they attend. The "price" paid for going to some "name" institutions by the wealthy is perhaps mainly for the personal and consumer satisfaction so derived. The pure "goodness" of having gone to college, enjoying the act for itself, is important to some and represents a consumer activity, just as does an afternoon at the art gallery or eating a steak dinner. In some strata of society, one could not say "that in fact he had consumed," unless he possessed a college education. It would be sad, indeed, should college students not enjoy these by-products of the educational plant. But, the main products of public educational plants can hardly be justified as consumer activities. There is no reason why the public should subsidize education as a consumer good, any more than it should subsidize the price of potatoes, beer, fishing or any other consumer goods used directly by the consuming population at large, particularly since the persons who can partake of college as a consumer good ordinarily are not "financially pinched."

This is not to say that education should be withheld as a consumer good. It should be produced for this purpose, just as any other consumer good for which there is a demand by consumers for "enjoyment of the service itself." But for consumption purposes it also should be priced in the market in terms of the demand for and supply of it, as in the case of potatoes and television sets not subsidized by the public. In other words, this type of education (education as a consumption good) best fits the private schools where the full cost of the good can be incorporated into the price the consumers pay for it.

THE END OF EDUCATION FOR DEVELOPING THE INDIVIDUAL AS A CONSUMER AND DECISION MAKER

Another possible end of education relates to the individual as a consumer, but in an entirely different context from that outlined above. Here the purpose is to help the individual better to understand himself and better to unravel his values and wants as a consumer so that he can increase satisfactions and welfare over his lifetime. The purpose also is to allow him to identify his goals and objectives and to provide him with decision-making procedures and methods so that, from the limited resources and income which he possesses over his lifetime, he can raise himself to higher utility or satisfaction levels. But in development of the individual as a consumer, the sovereign unit in a democracy, the responsibility of education transcends a mere understanding of the individual by himself. It requires that he understand himself, in relation to others, and the interactions that take place between the decisions of different individuals and groups. He needs to know, and to be able to apply, choice or decision-making principles both as an individual and as a member of society if the welfare of the consuming society is to be maximized.

Likely, it is in this area that many of the more technical institutions, including land-grant colleges, have devoted too few resources. One question which might be posed here is: Should education be used to develop the individual only as a resource, or only as a person (consumer)? The answer is quite obvious, and in a different direction. We can increase the individual's welfare by aiding him through education, both on the consumption (human) and on the production (resource) side. Given this fact, curricula should contain courses aimed in both directions. Only if we were concerned with training technicians as pure resources, would we withdraw them from all courses which also develop them as humans and consumers. The optimum pattern of allocation of educational resources between these two important ends still needs further analysis. Both are important in a democracy, a fact that might well be overlooked in a hasty effort to remold the nation's education system. Available evidence, particularly that relating to (1) income elasticities of demand for important groups of products and services and (2) changing patterns of expenditures as incomes progress, would point to a relative need (consumer desire) to have a greater proportion of resources devoted to the "consumer development" aspect of education as national and per capita incomes grow. This may not require an absolute reduction in the "resource development" aspect. Both may be increased as our national income grows. It is not impossible that, as income of our society doubles, we will wish to have more than 12 years of education through high school and more than 4 years for a bachelor's degree in college. Consumers no longer are satisfied with the amount of travel, housing facilities and home furnishings consumed 50 years ago. Why should they be satisfied with the same number of years of elementary, high school and college education?

THE END OF EDUCATION FOR IMPOSING VALUES ON INDIVIDUALS

Education can be used to mold value systems of individuals. Activity related to development of the individual as a consumer or entity with values can tread a slippery path between (1) true education and (2) propaganda or dogma. In the case of the first, the problem is to provide information, knowledge and principles which allow the individual to form his own values, and to understand the consequences of different sets of values and the courses of actions which might attach to them. For educational activity with purposes of propaganda and dogma, the end is the molding or imposing of values on the individual. Certainly higher education in a democracy, even that portion directed at developing the student as an individual, should not have the central end of propanda. Although it is doubtful that some direct effect in shaping values can be entirely eliminated from educational systems, the emphasis at higher levels of education in a democracy should be, apart from society's interest in developing resources, on the approaches outlined previously for developing the student as a sovereign individual, rather than in imposing values on him.

EDUCATION AS AN END IN AFFECTING INCOME DISTRIBUTION

Education can be used for changing or maintaining the pattern of personal income distribution. Development of a broad system of primary and secondary education quite early in the history of the United States, with relative equality in opportunity of participation by youth, rested importantly on a concept of equity in income distribution. Certainly the pattern of personal income distribution has been, is and can be altered by the types, quantity and quality of education available to different income groups. The poor can be kept in a state of poverty by withholding education from them. The position of the wealthy can be retained by restricting, through price or other rationing schemes, education and closely related information of relevant types for this group. Education can be structured to restrain the number of people entering a field, and hence to enhance the incomes of those who are employed in it.

On a broader basis, the relative differential in per capita incomes between highly developed and underdeveloped nations is partially a function of the amount and availability of education furnished to people by these nations. The same can be said for different regional, occupational and social groups within a nation such as the United States. As mentioned in Chapter 5, we view the lack of social overhead capital for these purposes in the poverty sector of agriculture as the reason for their continued maintenance in this status. If the students of Kentucky mountains had the same educational inputs or services, in course development and in widening the horizons of the individual, as in Palo Alto, California, or Manhattan, Kansas, the local population would soon thin and lessen the poverty problem.

The main resource of the majority of people is their own time and ability. Education can erase income differentials only to the extent that it develops these abilities in people who own few or no capital resources. Over a wide sector of the population, the (1) focus of education on developing the individual as a resource to further the national product or (2) focus of education on improving the opportunity for impoverished groups to obtain more income, are complementary activities. This is true in the sense that there now exist large numbers of persons who have (or whose parents have) low incomes but who have abilities which are not being fully developed by the educational opportunities afforded them. Helping persons to develop these abilities can increase their personal incomes and, at the same time, augment the national product. But the two are not complementary over all ranges of educational resources which might be directed to them. Some individuals of low income have limited ability, and the productivity of educational investment for them is low in comparison to persons of higher income and ability in whom it also might be invested. Here the two goals of education are competitive and, where educational resources are limited, society must decide (1) over what range the two are complementary and (2) at the point where they become competitive, the portion of resources to be allocated for attainment of either end.

Equality of earning ability and income cannot be guaranteed through education because people possess different amounts of capital and ability. Even if there were no difference in capital, education still could not guarantee equality of earning ability because of differentials in native ability. But even within these constraints, education in the United States is not optimally geared to generation of equal earning ability or opportunity of human resource, differences in capital aside. Data indicate no significant differences in the native abilities of persons born within different income groups. Yet equal opportunity to develop native ability is not generally afforded by the educational facilities and services available to these different groups. Even at the elementary level, equal opportunity to develop talents is not provided. Physical facilities, teaching materials, academic personnel and auxiliary services are generally less adequate in poor as compared to the more wealthy sectors of urban people; they are less adequate in rural areas where income is lower than in urban areas; they are less adequate in farming regions of extremely low income than in the more prosperous agricultural areas.

The contrast is even greater at the level of higher education. Roughly, the ability of the student to claim both public and privately financed education is progressive relative to his, or his parents, income, and retrogressive relative to the extent that his income position can be lifted by education. Two measures have tended, of course, to alter this condition, namely, the extension of college entrance examinations and public and private scholarships. However, these two measures have not been sufficiently intensive to alter the fact that college education is open mainly to those who have the income to buy it. Even if college enrollment were open only to those who might pass highly restrictive qualifying examinations, and even if higher education were provided at no cost to all such persons, country-wide equality of opportunity to improve earning ability through education still would not exist. This is true because education is not equal at the elementary and secondary levels, and students from different occupational groups, income classes and geographic regions would not be provided equal background for passing entrance examinations.

Historically, in democratic nations which have experienced economic growth, the evidence points to a tendency for relatively more of education to be structured towards attainment of greater equality in employment and income opportunities. Perhaps there are nations on Mars so wealthy that they provide college costs free to all citizens. But the

United States, the wealthiest nation on earth, has not been able to muster this quantity of resources for education. Hence, historically it has devoted relatively more to resource development and related ends. Yet we are certainly moving towards a greater proportion allocated to increased equity in income opportunities. We have a long way to go, even at the elementary school levels. However, the evidence does suggest that this end does, and will, receive greater emphasis as national income and wealth progress further.

Fiscal Implication

The income distribution facet of education has somewhat different fiscal implications than do the resource and human development facets. Generally, any sector of society can make decisions in respect to resource and human development aspects of education within its own group and can invest accordingly, given the resource or financial restrictions which it possesses. Yet a low income sector is much less able to push education for the purpose of changing its income position relative to other population segments. For these reasons, elements of an educational program aimed at greater equity in human employment opportunities and the pattern of income distribution depend especially on intersector transfers (equalization) of funds for school finance.

As is well known, the tax base or capital and opportunity to attain scale economies in education by low income and rural communities is not sufficient that they can develop economic opportunities, through education, at the level of wealthier communities. But the practical appeal to wealthier communities, for greater underwriting of education in less favored communities, rests mainly on opportunities for developing unexploited abilities in human resources and for promoting regional or national economic growth. Many wealthy communities or sectors of society may look favorably upon tax funds drawn from their own group for transfer to a school district in a less favored economic or geographic location if the transfer develops more scientists, engineers, etc. from the mass of students in existence. Fortunately, the products of resource development and higher income for persons of economic disadvantage are complementary products under transfer with initial focus on the former. Improvements in the structure of school financing which provide aid to low income communities for these purposes also can promote a more equitable distribution of employment opportunities and income under economic growth.

TYPES OF EDUCATION IN RELATION TO ALLOCATIVE NEEDS AND CHANGE

The analysis to this point has been largely in terms of the major objectives towards which education should or can be oriented under economic growth. The educational ends outlined do, however, have implications in other directions, such as curricula construction. The relevant curriculum, in the context of this analysis, is not solely a function of the subject-matter field, but depends also on the extent to which scarce educational resources—both public and private funds and the time of the student—are to be allocated to such alternative ends as resource development and human or consumer development, or the extent to which total education inputs for both purposes can be increased, with a growing proportion allocated to one of the other end. However, rather than to go into details of curriculum construction, we turn our attention to problems of allocating educational resources and student time between fundamental and applied courses, as they relate to the development of the production possibilities and flexibility of the individual.

First, of course, it can be questioned whether highly applied education, in the sense of pure memorization of today's facts, qualifies as education. If this were the foundation of education, then the efficient educational method would not include classroom instruction. Rather all relevant facts should be published in a huge encyclopedia, with an efficient index. The user of facts would then have a collection at his command, much greater than his mind could ever absorb from memorization in formal courses. But the utility would be even greater: It would be convenient if education were a discrete phenomenon in the sense that "once it is surrounded, that's it—there isn't more." But science does not come in this finite form. Knowledge must be considered as a continuum whereby (1) technical and economic change is generated and causes incomes to grow accordingly, (2) the relative wants of consumers shift and require a redirection in the use of people and resources and (3) previous knowledge and skills of people and the material forms of other resources are made obsolete. Thus we can't educate a person "for his life," in 12 or 16 years of school. He can only be given a foundation for learning, upon which he builds further as knowledge changes or increases. At best, he is given a framework for changing his previous knowledge, skills, values and choices.

Farm buildings last over the life of a human. The forms in which they were built became obsolete in the past with technical and price changes. We can destroy a farm building when it becomes obsolete, just as we can discard farm machines which become outdated. We now recognize that it often is better to invest in flexible buildings, whose use is more adaptable, than to build highly inflexible ones. We can't "scrap" an individual as change comes about. But through education we can provide "built-in" flexibility. Even if change in total didn't come about, we would still need flexibility of the individual, since his hope and experience is to start one job and elevate himself or shift to others which require different abilities and concentration. Here, then, we have a problem: What portion of educational resources should be devoted to applied and fundamental training? Generally, it is the fundamental training which provides for flexibility since, while the facts may change, established principles remain the same. Today's facts are soon obsolete. The student who memorizes today's national income, farm real estate values, planting rate, egg marketings, recommended feed rations or insecticides finds that this knowledge is, because of scientific and economic change, out of data a few years hence, if not before he graduates. Then why have him devote his limited time, for purposes of examination, in committing these facts to memory when the same material could be provided at less cost in the form of an encyclopedia of facts (which might be kept up to date by appropriate inserts)? The highly practical and useful facts could be provided to more people at lower cost by this method than by more complicated classroom paraphernalia.

Flexibility in Abilities and Training

With this qualification, we turn to some propositions about fundamental education as it relates to the production possibilities of the individual over his lifetime. We forward the proposition that broad education in basic principles, in contrast to pure fact memorization in a narrow curriculum, provides for flexibility in production possibilities as the individual ages and the world about him changes.

To place the proposition in sharper focus, we turn to Figure 13.1. We suppose that the potential human resource—the student—starts out with an initial set of possibilities represented by the opportunity curve

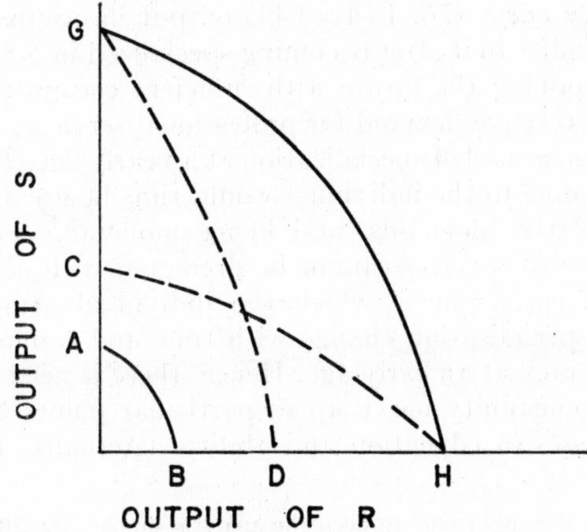

Fig. 13.1. Production Possibilities Under Education.

AB. This curve indicates the output which he can produce per period at the time, in occupations *S* or *R*, if he uses his abilities for either or for various combinations of the two. Opportunity or production-possibility curve *GH* represents his potential, after time progresses and he has received the available amount of education. But it is a long-run production-possibility curve, meaning that this set of opportunities is open only before the skills of the student are committed to specialized training. The first important function of vocational guidance and counseling is to predict this long-run curve and determine whether its slope is great or small. Unfortunately, guidance infrequently goes this far and, when it does, it too frequently stops with this step. The second important function of guidance should be one in economic forecasting or predicting the relative prices which will exist over a relevant time period for activities *R* and *S* when the human resource has been fully developed. The occupational choice, and hence the education which is relevant, then would be prescribed by the slopes of the production possibility and the relevant price for human services in the two occupations, if income were to be maximized in the relevant time period.[6]

Let us say that the appropriate choice for one individual becomes occupation *S* (technical engineering). Education is completed and the human resource is engaged in producing *OG* units of the product or service and none of the other. However, the long-run opportunity curve *GH* no longer exists, since it is only a planning curve representing the possibilities before resources and talents are committed to specialized form for one or more occupations. Opportunities now become defined by short-run production possibility curves such as *GD* and *CH*. Now if the individual should decide to shift from specialization *S* to specialization *R* in his field (i.e., from technician to production foreman or from engineer to manager), he cannot attain a productivity of *OH* as suggested by the long-run opportunity curve *GB*. Instead his output in occupation *R* will be only *OD*, if he shifts to it after becoming specialized in *S*.[7]

If we could predict the future with sufficient certainty, in respect to ability and the relative demand for professional services, we would start the individual on a road of specialization at an early age. The social product and the income to the individual would thus be greatest. But under change, the relative demands, and hence monetary rewards, for the product of different services cannot be predicted with certainty; or the relative values (preferences) which the individual attaches to either occupation or specialization change with time and cannot be predicted with great accuracy at an early age. Hence, there is need to retain flexibility in the opportunity curve up to particular points in time, as the student progresses in education and ability. (Actually, his alternative

---

[6] We have employed this model to keep the analysis simple. Actually, the production possibility curve might be converted to dollar units and the work preference of the individual could be represented by his indifference curve: with tangency of the two specifying the appropriate occupational choice. But even more realistically, we should use not a single time span, but a series of future periods with relevant quantities discounted back to the first. However, the simple model allows reflection of most of the relevant data and principles. In education, the production possibility curve also may have slope of decreasing rate; a point which does not alter our analysis in terms of long-run and short-run alternatives and needs in education. For example, see Earl O. Heady, *Economics of Agricultural Production and Resource Use*, Prentice-Hall, New York, 1952, pp. 275–90.

[7] But the error is just as great if he specializes in occupation *R* and then shifts over to occupation *S*; because, following short-run production possibility curve *CH*, he then produces only *OC* of output whereas he could have produced *OG* had he initially specialized in *S*.

abilities provide a whole set of short-run production possibility curves, starting from AB and bounded by or tangent to GH in Figure 13.1.)

Given inability to make perfect predictions, we wish to avoid errors and inefficiencies which result from specializing the human resource too early, as having it specialized in S, later shifted over to R and produce only OD (while under ability to predict he would specialize in occupation R and produce OH). To circumscribe errors in prediction and, consequently, inefficient resource uses such as this, flexibility in the production possibilities which represent the individual might better be retained. The optimum would be retention of GH through the individual's life. But while this potential curve exists at an early age, time and resources do not allow the individual to retain this long-run potential as he matures. Hence, broad specialization eventually becomes necessary in his career. However, change requires that he also retain flexibility of degree within his specialization, since scientific discovery and social change will alter the opportunities open to him and the environment which surrounds him.

Flexibility in possibilities is best attained by providing the student with general education and courses in fundamental principle and general science. He is thus better adapted to shift from one realm of specialization to another, if demand and monetary rewards or his preferences change to favor this shift. He is better equipped to change his skills and services as the nature and composition of production changes. He is better able to adapt his work habits, decisions and personal choices as he is confronted with change. We could provide some technical models outlining the possibilities here, but since they are provided elsewhere, we do not do so.[8]

FURTHER IMPLICATIONS IN AGRICULTURE

One needed change in emphasis on education for farm youth is in terms of development of this resource. From the standpoint of resource development per se, we need to make some change in our historic farm youth focus as "an agricultural resource only." This has been, in educational policy specific to agriculture, the main view taken of farm youth: to develop them as an agricultural resource. But with the types of changes outlined previously, stemming particularly from economic growth, we know that patterns of expenditures of consumers change as they grow wealthier. The technical innovations of agriculture and relative prices of capital and labor have caused the former to be substituted for the latter in meeting the nation's food needs.

A declining proportion of youth should be trained directly for agriculture, and educational resources should be shifted accordingly. We need to inventory the number of farm opportunities which will be available in the future and gear youth educational and guidance programs accordingly. An optimum arrangement would exist in identification of youth

---

[8] See Heady, *ibid.*

who have the ability, desire and capital to become efficient farmers. They could then be guided into farming, with education in science for agriculture which is more intense and appropriate than at the present. At the same time, we should identify youths who don't have these characteristics but have desires and abilities leading to comparative advantage in other occupations. They should be given vocational guidance accordingly. For those youths who can't or shouldn't become employed in agriculture, there is a relatively greater need than in cities for re-gearing education to needs in human resource development for further economic growth. An important amount of human resources represented by the youth of agriculture has gone undeveloped because schools in rural communities lack facilities for development of talents in science and industry generally.

From the standpoint of equity in income distribution or in economic opportunity, there also is need for improvement of rural schools relative to those of town and city locations. Developments in this direction are taking place through school district consolidation. Still, the fact stands over the nation that youths in many rural communities are handicapped in reaping the premiums from types of employment favored by economic growth because education and vocational training in rural areas focuses so little in these directions.

If education is to be used as a means of bringing about greater equality in economic and employment opportunities, it is best done by funds spread by the state over communities and funds allocated by the nation over states. This should be the case because less wealthy communities and states cannot invest as much in education and its facilities as can more prosperous ones. Here the challenge is to develop the latent capacities of individuals so that they can take advantage of favorable employment opportunities wherever they exist over the nation. The focus of agricultural policy on short-run surplus problems, and of agricultural economic analysis in this same direction, has caused the broader and deeper facet of education in rural areas to go unemphasized. While this may be true because of the long time span involved in increasing income of people from agriculture by this means, time does slip by. After all, more than 30 years have passed (since 1930) since price support and control programs were first initiated, but they are still with us.

14

Policies of Land Input and Supply Period

THE RESOURCE of lowest supply elasticity for aggregate agricultural uses is land. The commercial farm problem of supply against demand stems, in the short-run and intermediate period, more from low elasticity and mobility for this resource than others of agriculture. Low labor mobility more particularly causes the chronically low-income or poverty problem of the industry, although it also is part of the longer-run commercial problem wherein farm incomes lag behind nonfarm incomes. Our statement refers to the immediate or direct effect of low factor supply elasticities on income of farm strata. Even as labor displays considerable elasticity in movement to nonfarm employment opportunities in the short run, use of land input does not respond so readily. Pressure is strong for it to remain committed to agriculture in previous magnitude for the industry as a whole and even greatly for aggregates of crops which are close substitutes as resources and foods. Hence, it is true that while magnitude of labor transfer has been large since 1940, aggregate land input has remained much more nearly at previous levels for major grain and fiber crops.

With further advance in technology, and with capital representing it serving partly as substitute for labor and partly as greater input against given land area, output has not only been maintained but has increased at rate exceeding demand growth. As explained previously, this process has been possible because of the organization of agriculture in pattern of small producing units with a great amount of underemployed labor and some underemployed capital. Farm operators and their labor have been able to leave agriculture, with the particular producing unit absorbed by a neighboring farmer. The land has remained in production, typically in the same crops over the short run, operated by the neighbor with his previous supply of labor and machine capital, or with only small increments, amounts smaller than withdrawn by the operator who left the industry.

Underemployment and the particular organization of agriculture have provided a large amount of slack in the industry, so that much labor could be withdrawn without diminution in output. (As indicated in Chapters 4 and 5, the greater managerial inputs and capital of remaining farmers have actually allowed supply to increase as labor of farm operators has declined.) Sufficient withdrawal of labor would cause diminution in output, either in eventually causing employment of land to decline or in causing shift to crops with lower labor requirements. For particular crop, the situation is that illustrated in Figure 14.1 where curves y_1 and y_2 are isoquants indicating combinations of labor and land inputs which will

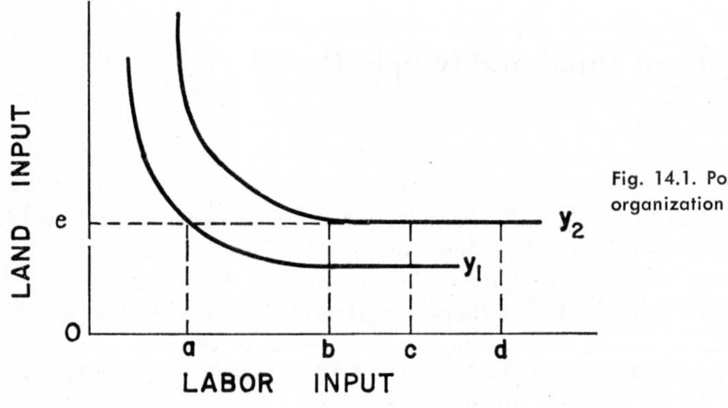

Fig. 14.1. Possibilities in Reorganization of Agriculture.

produce the specified levels of output in a region *or* for the industry. A given amount of land and labor, *oe* and *od* respectively, has been committed to agriculture. Consequently, output level represented by the isoquant y_2 has been attained.

Now, as some farmers leave the industry and their farms are taken over by remaining operators with underemployed labor, input of labor declines to *oc* but land remains at *oe*. Output can be retained at y_2 level, however, because of the particular structure of agriculture allowing the above rearrangement of resource inputs. The aggregate production function, under its particular institutional organization and with original labor input withdrawn in "lump sum" manner from individual producing units, is characterized by a portion of the isoquants with supplementary relationship between land and labor in the sense that the marginal rate of substitution between the two resources is zero. Zero rate of substitution extends back to *ob* input of labor. If labor resource declines below this level, land input remaining constant at *oe* level, output will then decline. For example, if labor input declined to *oa*, while land is held constant at *oe*, output will fall from y_2 to y_1 level.

In major U.S. grain regions, decline of labor has been mainly over a segment such as that between *b* and *d* on isoquant y_2. It has not been great enough itself, considering possibilities in reorganizing the structure of agriculture, to cause output to decline, with capital input in various forms remaining constant or increasing with new technology. Given further substitutability of capital for labor, and further extent for reorganizing agriculture as above, labor input can decline considerably more before it becomes a technical complement with land and capital, thus causing output to decline or be effectively restrained. As long as the land input remains essentially constant, output can be maintained, or even increased, with new technology.

The process of adjustment illustrated in Figure 14.1 is one which can increase the physical productivity of labor. With output at y_2 level, initial "gross physical product" per unit of labor is y_2/od. After withdrawal by *cd* it is y_2/oc. If, however, farmers who remain are able to use different forms of capital or technology to increase output against inelastic demand, the "gross value productivity" of labor will increase less rapidly, and not at all if output increases at sufficient rate. Labor input must decline by an amount which restrains output sufficiently to allow an increase in its marginal value productively, or to the extent that labor input is small in proportion to other factors, thus increasing the per unit value of product imputable to it.

Response elasticity of land to decline in commodity price is low for several reasons: In aggregate of agriculture the proportion of land needed for home and industrial sites and for public uses such as roads and airports is extremely small. At particular locations, the supply of land for these purposes is very limited and the price of the factor rises accordingly, with land also shifting readily to these uses with higher value returns. Yet demand from this source is so small that it has negligible impact on price of land in remote locations.

Given the magnitude of land supply, relative to demand for it in nonfarm uses over the nation as a whole, the reservation price of land in farm uses is practically zero. In respect to crops such as wheat, corn and cotton, the reservation price of land relative to supply of the resource for these uses is at the level of much lower alternatives such as grass and timber. Land will remain in agricultural production as long as the value of product forthcoming covers the short-run reservation prices of labor and capital which serve as its technical complements. Reservation prices for the latter resources are low for short periods but increase with time as the variables associated with labor mobility become more operative and as capital becomes used up or worn out (with its supply price then being based on outside industry and competition for resources, rather than on capital stocks on farms).

In the short run, then, land is able to command higher rents, as a result of surpluses and depressed price and with labor and capital accepting returns lower than in the general market, than over the longer run as supply elasticity of labor and capital increases. With lower rents, the value of land would be less and the problem of "level of resource returns" could be solved through restructuring of land prices. This is the general shakedown or adjustment which would be expected with "market-free" prices, following an abrupt change such as rapid increase in technology or removal of support prices or marketing quotas. Landowners must bear the cost of a decline in asset values or capital loss over the longer run, although this is not necessary in the short run as labor and capital remain committed to agriculture at levels of return lower than their long-run reservation prices. (Landowners also possess labor and capital, except under rented farms.)

This type of adjustment, with imputed return and land prices being at lower level as an avenue in solving the problem of "level of resource returns," does not, of course, obviate, the forces leading to transfer of labor out of agriculture. Decline in commodity price means directly a reduction in income for persons who own land, with the reduction continuing as a portion of asset values is thus melted away. Hence, remaining capital and labor of some families provide income low enough that they are encouraged to migrate. Thus in absence of inflation or scale returns allowing larger imputation to land under larger farming units, the direction leads to restoration of returns to labor and capital at a level more comparable to long-run alternatives in other industries. Compensation policies which modify prices, through price supports and quota systems, retard this decline in resource values and incomes, thus substituting "market management" for "open market" in solving the problem of "level of resource return."

Persistence of resources to remain in agriculture at low short-run returns pushes heavily on product supply, thus depressing family incomes. The problem is most severe for labor. But it also is important in respect to the short-run allocation of land among different agricultural crops or between farm products and nonfood services. Still, however, labor and land are linked economically, and the existence of excess labor in agriculture certainly has the effect of holding land to more intensive uses and in restraining its shift from surplus commodities. Contrawise, prices and tax structures for land, which are not geared to the services which the consuming society prefers from it, are also important in determining its employment pattern and the requirements or employment of labor as its technical complement. Policy or market mechanisms which cause a reallocation of land from surplus grain or cotton production to less intensive products such as grass, forestry and recreation also must alter the demand for labor in particular soils regions. It is, therefore, impossible to separate entirely the demand and allocative needs for land from that for the labor and capital resources which serve as either technical complements or substitutes with it.

However, the long-run needs of, and the problems in, diverting land employment differ greatly from those of labor. Relative to the needs and challenges in economic growth before the nation, land does not have the spatial opportunities of labor. Need or eventual demand in respect to labor is especially that of geographic and occupational migration, if economic development is to take place optimally and in manners which are consistent with development of potential capacities of people and with greatest opportunities in welfare increase of all persons. Opportunities in occupational shifts are much more limited for land and even then are geographically fixed. Hence, the means and alternatives for adjusting land and labor inputs do, at some point, part ways.

Public investment to bring about labor shifts over the long run, and in a manner consistent with fullest opportunity for youth, can best rest on such mechanisms as improved educational guidance, employment payments for transfer costs and market information facilities. Those for land, while affected by those for labor, must be of quite a different nature. The values of American society allow the institution of ownership in land, but not labor. Labor and individual, the motivating unit in our economy, are inseparable, and means which are publicly acceptable for adapting services of land are not similarly acceptable for labor.

Along with acceptance of ownership in land but not in labor, American society has been willing to offer a price for letting land remain idle. The "basic creeds" of American society likely prevent use of payments directly to agricultural labor for remaining idle, as a means for reducing or shifting farm output. In the 1950's emphasis of economists was on the relative surplus of labor in American agriculture, without parallel emphasis on the relative surplus of land inputs for particular products or aggregate output. The conventional remedy for solving the farm problem has thus been to "reduce the size of the agricultural labor force." Yet, in the short-run, reduction in the labor force places no important restraint on output because of the reorganizational opportunities already discussed. Migration of labor from agriculture does not simultaneously cause land inputs to shrink, or even to shift among alternatives. Remaining operators who use a richer mix of capital with land taken over from those who leave, typically obtain an even greater output from it. Past programs aimed at production control have focused on the land resource. They have been successful only in proving that the policy mechanisms employed for these purposes so far are ineffective in restraining output to any important degree. A maze of programs has been used which simultaneously subsidize improvements of land to (1) increase current production at the expense of the future, (2) pay farmers for withholding land from current production and (3) conserve the services of land for future periods. These programs are justified to the public partly or entirely under the heading of conservation, perhaps as a means of capitalizing on the favorable attitude, towards improving the intertemporal allocation of basic natural resources, which prevails in U.S. society.

While some features of land and labor resources committed to particular uses in agriculture are separable, problems in product output which stem from them have common elements in the realm of factor supply. To understand better the mechanisms most readily acceptable and of greatest effectiveness in adapting use of both resources, we must recognize the phenomena relating to supply and substitutability of either the resources or their services.

EFFECTIVE SUPPLY OF LAND

Technological improvement has had an important impact in increasing the effective supply of land over the last several decades. Physical stock of land has not increased but capital substitutes for it have been developed and have declined in relative price. This tendency of natural resources to become relatively less important in production is one outstanding trend of economic growth, although the process often is substitution of natural resource at one location or in one form for that in another location or form. The least advanced of societies rest their production mostly on natural resources. The more advanced societies are at the opposite extreme, not in the sense of lack of importance in natural endowment, but in the extent to which capital and labor are embodied in product relative to nature's materials.

The substitution process becomes effective as technical science uncovers the rates of substitution between the factors and as supply prices favor the substitution. This has indeed been the process of agriculture, with the supply price of phosphates, potash and nitrogen from concentrated deposits and sources serving to substitute for conventional agricultural land, other innovations of crop production serving similarly. The United States can, with modern techniques, produce the 1910 level of food output with a much smaller land input than at that date. It could meet the nation's demand for feed and food grains, cotton, vegetables and fruit with considerably fewer acres than were actually used as the nation's economy moved towards 1965. This is a salutary development and one which less advanced nations would like to attain, namely, knowledge that the effective supply of land has been increased so that its relative and real price at the margin has declined and the uncertainty of food shortage does not prevail for the normal planning period of society.

Each new form of capital or innovation which increases yield when used on given land serves as a substitute for land. This point has been illustrated in equation (2.24) and in Table 7.7 for fertilizer, but the same outcome holds true for improved seed, insecticides, irrigation and other technologies. The same effect is realized in livestock improvement which increases marginal rates of transformation of feed, the products of land, into food commodities.

As a nation, we have had specific and designed policy to develop knowledge of substitutes for land. Public expenditures in technological research for agriculture have dominantly been those related to materials or resources to increase yield per acre of land and per unit of livestock feed, both serving as effective substitutes for land. Then, with the passage of time and the improvement of markets and production functions in fabricating inputs, nonfarm capital inputs for agriculture have declined in real costs, encouraging further and indirectly their substitution for land (as well as for labor). The data on relative prices of factors in Table 2.10 emphasize this point, as well as does analysis in Chapters 5 and 7. It has not been development of technical knowledge per se, causing substitution of capital for agricultural land. Rapid increase in use of land substitutes has not "just happened," but has taken place because they have been priced favorably. The potential effect in substituting capital innovations for land has been encouraged also by policy which bolsters prices of farm commodities against the price of inputs which increase per acre output and thus substitute for land.

As we extend technological knowledge thus, we both increase the possible product from a given land area and raise the rate at which aggregate capital (due largely to its new forms representing innovation) substitutes for land. The long-run tendency for this substitution to occur is illustrated in the decline in farm land prices relative to the prices of farm products and relative to the price of other inputs.

Given a fixed supply of land, one would expect, apart from the offsetting forces mentioned here, population growth to cause land price to rise relatively. The same would be less true for inputs such as fertilizer, machinery and other items which might more nearly have a constant supply price (in contrast to land which would have a steeply rising supply price if we tried to increase it in aggregate). Yet relative to farm product prices, the real price of land has declined by almost 20 percent since 1910 (but since 1935–39, as indicated in Table 2.10, it has increased.) This decline emphasizes the relative increase in the "effective" supply of land services since the earlier period.[1] The real price (i.e. price of resource relative to price of farm products) of fertilizer has declined even more, or by around 35 percent, a development which has itself encouraged the substitution of fertilizer for land. In contrast, the real prices of farm labor, farm machinery and farm supplies in general have increased since 1910. The decline in real price of fertilizer has taken place not because it has been reduced in relative importance in the production proc-

---

[1] Land prices increased somewhat between 1910 and 1914. However, using the base period 1910–14=100, the index of farm real estate prices went up to only 227 over the period 1950–59 while farm product prices went up to 254.

ess (the opposite has held true) but because of technical improvement and competition in the fertilizer industry. The decline in real price has caused it to be "demanded" in larger quantities. In contrast, however, land is not used in larger quantities (its stock is fairly well limited) and has declined in relative price because other resources have increasingly substituted for it, thus increasing its effective supply against national food demand.

The product of agriculture is becoming less a function of the services of land and labor and more the product of the services of capital items representing improved technology. If we could measure the physical services of resources, we would now find each unit of farm output to embody a smaller portion of land and labor and a larger proportion of capital. The proportion of inputs represented by land has not declined as much as for labor in physical terms because of the restrained and inelastic supply function for land in aggregate. It appears in the data of Table 7.6, and over the broad sweep of time, that the proportion of value of inputs attributable to land was no more and probably less in the 1950's than in the decade before 1915. (Support price and subsidy programs emphasizing land undoubtedly increased the value of product imputed to it in the later period.)[2]

Using the data underlying Table 7.6, it appears that real rent to land in 1956–60, in constant dollars, may have been as much as 10 percent less than in the period 1910–14. The capacity of agriculture to produce is less limited by agricultural land area restraint and depends more on other sections of the economy. Capacity has been added through development and expansion of the industries which furnish the agricultural inputs substituting for land. This situation will continue, likely being accentuated by chemical and biological developments in prospect. While agricultural output once had an effective restraint defined by land area or a spatial limit, this is no longer true. Agriculture now is more similar to industries such as filling stations, department stores and others where space or area is not the major restraining force on output.

---

[2] For other indications of this same tendency, see Earl O. Heady, "Changes in Income Distribution with Special Reference to Technological Change," *Jour. Farm Econ.*, Vol. 24; T. W. Schultz, *General View of Natural Resources in Economic Growth*, paper for Conference on Natural Resources and Economic Growth, Mimeo. 1960; and J. R. Bellerby, *Agriculture and Industry, Relative Income*, Macmillan, London, 1956, pp. 295–98.

Some fluctuation has taken place in relative shares for resources, with computation and imputations based on either values of inputs or prices of factors. The definite clear-cut changes are for the decline in labor's relative share and the increase in capital's relative share, with the latter clearly coming at the expense of the former. Capital has much less replaced land in a physical sense, but relative to what would have happened in rents of land in absence of technical development and land substitutes, the change has been tremendous in holding down the relative value contribution of land, with apparently some decline, and certainly no increase, in its value contribution, with growth of population and food demand against land supply of extremely low aggregate supply elasticity. The figures we quote above exclude that portion of rent related to real estate and similar capital attachments of land.

The manner in which resource substitution takes place in "gross form" is again illustrated in Table 14.1. The shifts indicated cause the results of history to correspond closely with the models outlined in Chapter 7 and further indicate that forces of development are causing crop production to be centered more in the concentrated and intensive areas. As the data indicate, the substitution has taken place in all major farm areas. Output has increased and labor has declined in all areas. Fertilizer inputs, along with capital representing other techniques, a major substitute for land, have increased greatly, restrained only somewhat in the "older using areas." Over the 20-year period, land in crops decreased in four of

TABLE 14.1

PERCENT CHANGE IN OUTPUT AND SELECTED INPUTS BY FARMING REGIONS, 1939–60
(CHANGES ARE POSITIVE UNLESS INDICATED BY NEGATIVE SIGN)

Region	Total Output	Cropland Used for Crops	Plant Nutrients	Man-Hours of Labor
	(Increase or decrease—in percent)*			
Northeast	42	−21	106	−49
Lake States	52	− 3	1,379	−46
Cornbelt	59	8	1,146	−48
Northern Plains	136	6	6,780	−46
Appalachian	33	8	179	−49
Southeast	58	−34	164	−57
Delta	35	−25	339	−61
Southern Plains	60	−17	1,500	−55
Mountain	79	38	1,642	−39
Pacific	75	11	747	−56

Source: USDA Stat. Bul. No. 233, Revised September, 1961.
* Based on averages between the two periods, 1939–41 and 1959–60.

the regions and increased in four. However, even in the latter, fertilizer and other new technological capital still serve as substitutes for land in this sense: Level of output increased by a much greater proportion than land, and the original output could be produced with less of both labor and land. As well as illustrating the general substitution process, the data also indicate that land supply *for particular uses* does have an important extent of supply elasticity over an extended period and is not unrelated to labor input. The great difficulty comes, of course, in the short period when land tends to stick to its conventional uses.

We have a definite public policy for developing knowledge of resources which substitute for land, as well as for labor, in agricultural prediction —the systematic and effective public investment represented by the land-grant colleges and the USDA. This is wise policy and one to be selected by nations faced with population growth and inability to develop perfect predictions of future population and resource substitution possibilities. Even if they could develop perfect prediction, the need for increasing knowledge of potential substitutes at lower costs would be preferable in extent that these (1) lessen the constraint of conventional natural resources on supply and price of commodities and thus facilitate economic growth, (2) better explain the mathematical limit to which increase in food output can be pushed against fixed land supply and (3) insure against uncertainties of food supply and price in future time. But to the extent that this policy causes land supply to be burdened against food and resource demand at the present, and to have impact of causing short-run loss to land owners and cultivators, planned programs to facilitate shift in use of land to socially preferred activities are just as important as policy which leads to knowledges of land substitutes.

At the minimum, as effective supply of land is extended against current demands for food, policy of education and information should be initiated which aids in conversion of resource employment. At the maximum, policy would provide compensation to (1) cover loss in capital value of land and (2) labor training and transfer required to allow restoration of real income and assets to previous levels. In the sense of minimum policy based on Pareto optima and the compensation principle, there are two general choices: (1) providing compensation to cover loss in asset values and in transfer of resources to employment where real welfare is as great as formerly or (2) extending the time span over which the effects of resource substitutes are expressed and slowing down the rate at which shift in use of resources is made. Price support, land withdrawal and related policies of the previous decade have contributed to both, with the greatest effect perhaps being that of "buying time" in order that change was not turned loose on agriculture faster than families and resource structure of the industry could absorb it, or faster than allowed by the creation of nonfarm employment opportunities and public facilities required for efficient migration.

Agriculture would be in a much better income situation, under technical change and factor pricing which encourages substitution of capital for land, if occupational employment opportunity for land were as broad under economic growth as that for labor. If (1) production functions existed requiring large land inputs and (2) demand for nonfarm goods were of high income elasticity under economic growth, land-substituting effects of new technology would be quickly absorbed and income depression in agriculture would be spared. Demand for land in nonfarm uses would draw the resource away from agriculture, thus restraining supply of farm products. This process would, as is already true in selected local areas, cause land price to be raised in competition with farming (and draw some "fire" from agriculturists because of this fact).

Alarmists already point to the amount of land withdrawn year after year from agricultural uses for airports, highways, factory sites and residential areas. This fear is not economically well based. Jubilation, rather than anxiety, should meet this reallocation of the land resource from food and fiber products to other goods and services demanded by a society growing progressively in income and wealth. The reasons are numerous: First, withdrawal of land from production of food and fiber can help diminish the magnitude of the farm problem by curtailing put (but only slightly so because of the small input/output or transformation ratio involved in nonfarm uses of land). Second, these shifts in land use characterize economic progress. As noted elsewhere in this book, income elasticities of demand for food are low. But in contrast, income elasticities are extremely high for the land products and services mentioned above. Through land prices in the open market, consumers are indicating that marginal utility from services of land is greatest when some of this resource is shifted from food production. Through the voting mechanism, they voice a similar opinion as appropriations are provided for airports, roads and parks. Obviously, there is no "higher use" for land than this in a mature and wealthy society whose anxieties stem not from lack of food but from transportation snarls, shorter work weeks, congested living conditions, and related phenomena. For the benefit of the conservation devotee, land will indeed be preserved for the millennium if it is covered with a dome of concrete for these currently "higher uses."

RELATIVE SUPPLY OF LAND FOR DIFFERENT USES

Land is not in surplus supply in the sense that some of it must go unemployed. It is in surplus position mainly in the sense that the input sticking to the conventional mix of crops is too great. Supply of land adapted to feed grains, wheat and cotton has been effectively increased by development and supply prices of substitute resources. With demand inelastic and increasing much more slowly than increase in effective land supply, the tendency has been too great for the same amount of soil resources to remain allocated to these crops. With greater supply elasticity of land for these uses, and with greater mobility of land among major crop aggregates, supply price of crops such as grains and cotton would increase, with an accompanying decline in the supply price of crops to which land transfers.

What are the crops with somewhat higher demand elasticities under economic growth to which land might be reallocated, if its use were to be consistent with relative supplies and prices of resources and relative demands for commodities? We have already seen from the broad tentative model outlined in Chapter 7 that land would shift from these uses over a large expanse of the Southeast, the Lake States cut-over regions and the areas margined to annual cropping in the Great Plains. These are broad regions of adjustment, but smaller areas within broader regions of low supply functions would also be affected. Regions which are predominant and with deepest comparative advantage in feed grains, wheat and cotton (with shift westward) would remain devoted to these enterprises, but with the local variations mentioned.

Then to which crops could this land and its complementary resources be shifted? In terms of economic growth and prospective income elastic-

t would undoubtedly be in these directions over
y the open market. One product of land which has
city of demand under economic growth is recreation.
on recreation land and it will be relatively even more
population and income grow further and as transporta-
d mobility continue to increase. Unfortunately, however,
ted to recreation products is not always that which has
deeply in agriculture.

nd use yielding products with relatively high income elasticities is fo... try, for lumber and paper products. It is one that needs current planning for the greater population 40 to 50 years hence. Estimates suggest that not only will demand for forest products grow at greater rate than that for food products, but also that the real supply price is likely to rise unless more land and new plants are developed.[3] But because of time and discounting, forestry is an alternative that has little income attraction for individual farmers.

Another major alternative use for land withdrawn on a regional basis is forage and grazing. Demand elasticity most often is predicted to be considerably higher for beef than for pork or wheat. Yet even here a period of five years and upward is required before productive stands of native grass can be obtained on wheat lands and the collection of assets represented in grazing can produce an income. While there are direct costs involved in seeding and stocking lands diverted from grains, a major cost is the income that is foregone in the waiting period, and another is the income reduction in shifting from wheat under price support to grass-based farming.

The major problems of transferring land to commodities not in great surplus (and the reasons why supply elasticity of land to these surplus crops is low) are (1) the capital investment required in the transformation and waiting period and (2) the much greater thinning of population required over quite broad farming regions if agriculture is to be converted to these less intensive patterns. The low mobility and supply elasticity of labor relative to the magnitude of shift required is, at this juncture, important in causing short-run supply elasticity of land to be low for conventional crops. With shift in land resources concentrated much more than labor in particular areas and to specific crops (some labor from all segments of agriculture has been transferring out, even though concentration is greatest at particular locations), the income, investment and community problems are intensified at these locations. Too, while it may be less serious for forestry in length of transformation period involved and continuous growth in demand, the transfer promises to shift some of the problem of relative abundance in land resources to commodities previously less troubled with weight of output on price and factor returns.

---

[3] USDA Forest Service, *Timber Resources for America's Future*, Forest Resource Report No. 14, Washington, D.C., 1958.

Magnitude of Shift Involved

The magnitude of shift in land resource required to bring "approximate general equilibrium" in sense of factor returns in agriculture depends on many variables including: nonfarm resource returns and amount of labor drawn out of agriculture; future price of capital and extent to which it grows as a land substitute; whether land shifts in terms of optimality as expressed by its productivity in different uses, or as an average overall land quality; and other quantities relating to supply prices of resources and commodities. But the fact that too much land has remained committed to crops such as feed grains, wheat and cotton appears well established. The extent of overage in estimates depends on whether projected withdrawal involves land at its margin of productivity for particular uses or as an average of all land devoted to these uses.

We find the estimates varying widely in respect to method of transfer and quality of soil to include the following. Schnittker estimated 59.3 million acres, (including 28.6 million for wheat, 5.0 million for cotton and 28.7 million spread over the country in 1960 contracts of the conservation reserve) necessary to maintain prices at 1959–60 levels.[4] Johnson's figures, based on land average of productivity, projects up to 43.7 million surplus acres of land for wheat and feed grain in 1965, with about 19 million remaining under conservation reserve contracts of 1960.[5] Bottum estimates a surplus of 42.5 million acres of marginal land.[6]

The models illustrated in Chapter 7 indicate that 40 million acres at 1954 demand and technology level, with production allocated to regions for most economic attainment of discrete demand level and 10 million acres added for cotton, could have been released from feed grains, wheat and cotton. The models incorporating soybeans and cotton and considering technological improvements extend the "surplus" land for these crops to a "round" 60 million acres. The amount of "overage" in land input is a function of level of commodity price and resource return to be attained, however, as well as of method in diverting land. Estimates by Heady and Paulsen indicate, with 1960 factor costs, these amounts of land withdrawal for feed grains and wheat under varying price goals to be attained and methods of restraint: (1) For prices of $1.00 for corn and $1.15 for wheat: 26.8 million if the same proportion of land is withdrawn in all regions; 36.3 million acres if as much as 50 percent withdrawal of cropland is allowed in areas of highest per unit production

---

[4] *Economic Policies for Agriculture in the 1960's Implication of Four Selected Alternatives*, Joint Committee, Congress of the United States, Washington, D.C., 1960.

[5] *Agricultural Outlook for the 1960's*, 38th National Outlook Conference, Mimeo, Washington, D.C., 1960.

[6] A. C. Egbert and L. C. Dumenil, "Identification, of Nature, Magnitude and Physical Areas of Potential Supply-Demand Imbalance," In *Dynamics of Land Use—Needed Adjustments*, Iowa State University Center for Agricultural and Economic Adjustment, Iowa State University Press, Ames, 1961.

costs. (2) For prices of $1.30 for corn and $1.50 for wheat: 51.8 million acres if the same proportion of land is withdrawn in all areas; 62.5 million acres with the 50 percent restraint per region.[7] At 1960 time, an additional 5 to 12 million acres of cotton would have to be added to these figures, depending on the method of withdrawal and the price level to be achieved.

Rogers and Barton provide two sets of land "demand or requirement" figures for the year 1975, supposing a population of 230 million.[8] Their estimates are illustrated in Figure 14.2 and are based on use of only that technical knowledge existing at the present. Under their "attainable"

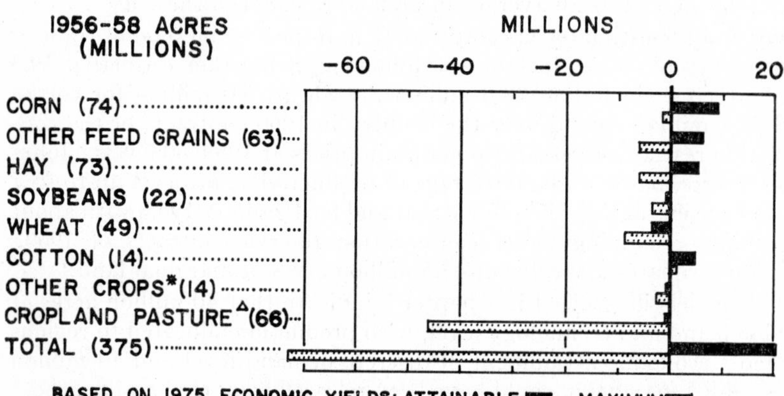

Fig. 14.2 Change in Acreage Required from 1956-58 to 1975 with 230 Million U.S. Population. (Source: Rogers and Barton, *ibid.*)

estimates, an assumption of practical use of present known technology and assuming capital and management limitations, total land required would exceed the amount actually used for crops in 1956–58 by 20 million acres. This land could come from various sources, including land in the conservation and other "reserves" in the early 1960's, pasture suitable for plowing, etc. In fact, if public land development went ahead at about the rates of the past, 30 million acres would be added to total cropland by 1975 through this means.[9] Under their "maximum" yield,

[7] "Retire the Excess Capacity? How much? Where? And at What Cost?" *Iowa Farm Sci.*, May, 1961. Also see *U.S. News and World Report*, May 30, 1960, pp. 104–6.

[8] O. R. Rogers, and G. T. Barton, *Our Farm Production Potential, 1975*, USDA Agr. Info. Bul. 233.

[9] H. H. Wooten and J. R. Anderson, *Agricultural Land Resources of the United States*, USDA Agr. Info. Bul. No. 140.

supposing presently known practice were used to their full profitability or economic level, land requirements would decline to 26 million acres fewer than the amount used in the period 1956–58. The latter level is economic and not a physical level of practice use. Physical potentials would allow an even greater reduction, against 1975 projected food demand. It is most likely, and even certain, that technology will increase up to 1975. Under increase in technology, Rogers and Barton's figures thus could be extended to a later date such as 1985 or 1990. (Without new technical knowledge by 1990, food prices would increase to levels drawing more resources into agriculture and allowing food demand to be met.) The most recent estimates of the USDA indicate that food demands of 1980 can be met with a shift of 51 million acres from cropland, as compared to land use in 1959.[10]

SUPPLY POTENTIAL

The time may come when agriculture will have greater difficulty in keeping the food supply function abreast of the demand function. This point in time will be one favorable to farm producers, causing the real price of food and rents of land to rise. Technical scientists are not willing to say that a mathematical limit is lacking in the rate at which technical capital can be transformed into food on a given land area.

Numerous uncertainties exist in this realm of supply and demand, including the possibility of artificial photosynthesis, chemical derivation of foods, medical findings relating to effects of livestock products (food products with high input/output ratio especially for land) on life span and heart disease, possibilities in world population growth and related demand possibilities. With these uncertainties, it is therefore prudent that society press forward in further development of knowledge lessening the uncertainty of upper limits in food production possibilities and in developing substitutes in the food production processes. This knowledge may have large payoff in 75 years in terms of real price of food to consumers. Even though this be true, however, distribution of gains and losses between consumers two generations hence and contemporary producers is not unimportant.

What is needed is policy allowing this generation of households to provide a hedge against real food prices of extremely high level in future time for a later generation, themselves gaining from lower supply price of food at the present, without causing welfare sacrifice by this generation of producers. The threat is not starvation, even with a much larger population, since the necessary mix of calories and basic food nutrients can be attained by change in diet to embrace foods with cheaper resource costs than those currently used.

The challenge under economic growth is to keep the real price of food, in mix of foods consumers prefer at high income level, from soaring to

[10] G. A. Selke *et al.*, *A Land and Water Policy*, The Land and Water Policy Committee, USDA Mimeo., Jan., 1962.

extremely high level in real price. This is not, as pointed out in earlier chapters, the threat during the 1960's or 1970's in the United States.[11] The supply of land is large enough that, given important magnitude of food demand increase, more could readily be shifted to crops which produce greater calories per acre. This shift could be accomplished with no, or very little, rise in supply price of food, considering that in 1961 nearly 30 million acres were idled under the 1956 Conservation Reserve Act while an equivalent acreage was idled in soil-building crops. And at this very time, surpluses were still being generated and added to government stocks.

The country also has well over 100 million acres of grassland and 105 million acres of woodland quite well adapted to cropping.[12] Fortunately we have more land which can and should be shifted into such uses as forestry and grazing. This total of land with little demand in crop production for the present, plus added technical knowledge and productive power from inputs furnished from nonfarm sources, provides a "contingency reserve" which can be drawn on, with the inputs shifted to crops and supply augmentation, should food demand increase to high levels. Obviously, then, policy is needed to guarantee safeguard in land resources and growth in production potential for future generations, in extent that the current generation attaches positive utility to future food supplies. But often, depression of current income and capital assets, resulting from pressure of food supply on demand as technical improvement increases production of resources with low short-run supply elasticity, causes part of this potential productive power to be lost through soil erosion arising from intensive cropping.

POLICIES OF LAND AND INPUT

National policy to restrict output has had major emphasis on land since 1930. This was the emphasis in the Agricultural Adjustment Act of 1933, the Conservation Reserve Act of 1956, the Feed Grain Act of 1961 and other production control programs enacted between and after these dates. Why has supply control had focus on the land input? There are several reasons. From the standpoint of practicality, identification of input withdrawn, although not its effect on production, is much easier for land than for labor or capital. It is difficult to imagine that an ac-

[11] For further summary of the short-run and long-run outlook in food production potential, see Johnson, *op. cit.;* Glen T. Barton and Rex F. Daly, "Prospects for Agriculture in a Growing Economy," In *Problems and Policies of American Agriculture,* Iowa State University Center for Agricultural and Economic Adjustment, Iowa State University Press, Ames, 1959; *A 50-Year Look Ahead at U.S. Agriculture,* USDA Mimeo., 1959; and R. P. Christensen *et al., Production Prospects for Wheat, Feed and Livestock,* USDA, ARS 43–115 and Rogers and Barton, *loc. cit.*

[12] *Cf.* "A 50-Year Look Ahead at U.S. Agriculture," *Food,* 1959 Yearbook of Agriculture, pp. 10–15; and *Water Resources Activities of the United States,* Committee on National Water Resources ,United States Senate Committee Print No. 12.

counting system could be set up to effectuate actual withdrawal of labor, when it can be substituted among time periods and is typically underemployed on farms. To identify any control or lessening of capital inputs, especially when it can take so many specific forms, would be equally difficult. In contrast, land is generally fully employed in some crop over a production season, has little substitutability between two time periods and is represented by particular units on each farm. Quantitatively, too, it is easier to establish historic base in land input, than for input of labor and capital or output in most products.

Control resting on land has political acceptability in the sense that it allows various sorts of "logrolling" procedure wherein trades can be made between geographic and commodity groups, but often with the effect of cancel in the control expected. (Logrolling does not, however, cancel trades to allow welfare increase. The latter may be augmented as intensity is expressed in the manner of Chapter 9.) At the farm level, the individual operator favors land input quota to output quota under the expectation that he can profitably substitute capital and labor for land, thus restoring or surpassing original output. On the regional level, commodity groups expect to substitute other crops for the one under control, thus restoring full employment of land resource where cross-compliance is not imposed. Control resting on land also has appeal in the sense that it can be placed under the label of conservation, thus capitalizing on the relatively high value which American society attaches to this end. The above is the general umbrella under which mass "production control" of agriculture has been attempted. Noteworthily, however, it has been unsuccessful, failing even to lessen output to the extent of growth from technological advance. It has been unsuccessful in reducing output because the loopholes and substitutabilities which lead to its great political acceptability also lead to its failure. Even under this wide range of substitutions, land withdrawal could effectively lessen supply—but only if initiated on a larger scale than over the three decades in experimentation.

Land withdrawal or control programs can have various intermediate ends. One can be to restrict inputs and lessen output to increase total revenue under inelastic commodity demand. Under this end, procedure can rest on compulsory or voluntary participation. Voluntary participation, with agricultural production vested in millions of producers, must rest on compensation. Otherwise, those who withdraw land to restrict price and improve income will sacrifice in return for gain to those who do not participate. If the end per se is production control, the extent of participation and the amount of payments to any producer who supplies his land to "disposal activity" should not be limited. If greatest possible production control from given treasury outlay is the end, resulting in greatest increment in price and income from remaining product in the market, land withdrawal should be allowed to come in a pattern which provides a unit of supply decrease at lowest cost. It should make no difference whether the producer supplying production control has large or small volume or receives large or meager payment. This fact is, however, often confounded with other intermediate ends of policy such as equity in income distribution and compensation to redress income position of producers who have had loss incident to gain of consumers. Consequently, payments have sometimes been limited, in order that they would be more equally distributed among producers, the production control end being largely dissipated in the process. Or, in terms of distribution of gains and losses, to prevent sacrifice of nonfarm persons in rural areas, upper restraint has been placed on land withdrawal on particular farms and regions to retard population outflow. Attempt to mix the ends to which diminution of land input might contribute, plus the loopholes provided to increase political acceptability, complicates attainment of production control as a means of attaining a higher income and of diverting a greater proportion of national income to farm producers.

Distribution of Costs and Gains From Input Reduction

Where compliance is compulsory, without direct or other payment to farmers who supply production control, the distribution and extent of participation among producers do make a great deal of difference. If some contribute only a small proportion and others a large portion to land withdrawal and supply control, the former gains in large extent and the latter in small extent from reduced market supply and higher price of commodity. But even under compulsory control, with each reducing land input by some constant proportion, the amount of production control supplied is not proportional to diminution in land input. Supply control proportional to land withdrawal, with all farmers diminishing land input by, say, 15 percent, would occur only if all factors of production were technical complements and constant returns to scale prevailed. In the widespread absence of these conditions and with production functions of individual farms which differ greatly in substitutability and output elasticity of resources, complete equity in contribution to and gain from compulsory control is difficult to attain. It would, however, be more difficult for other inputs which might be controlled. For example, control of fuel and machine inputs would hardly be restrictive on a tobacco farm but it would be exceedingly so on a Kansas wheat farm where it serves more limitationally with land. Restriction of fertilizer inputs would have less impact for a Great Plains wheat or sorghum producer who uses little or none of this resource than for a Cornbelt farmer who includes more of it in his resource mix for crops. It would have less impact, however, for the Cornbelt farmer than for the Southeast farmer where often a greater proportion of output is imputable to fertilizer than to land.

The method of input reduction thus does have important bearing on equity in the manner by which costs and gains of production control are distributed among producers. Even for a given resource, whether land, fertilizer or other, with input diminution by equal proportions among producers, the gain from control is much less relative to the cost for a producer using a large amount of resource under conditions of declining elasticity than for a farmer using less of the resource.

This point can be illustrated simply by supposing two farms have identical production function as in (14.1) where Y is output and X is input. The elasticity of production for (14.1) is the quantity in (14.2), indicating an elasticity of less than 1.0.

$$Y = 10X - .05X^2 \tag{14.1}$$

$$E = (10 - .1X)(10 - .05X)^{-1} \tag{14.2}$$

Now suppose that the input/output price ratio is 2.0, denoting that 80 input units will maximize profits under unlimited capital and correct price expectations. Suppose that one farmer (large) uses 80 units and has the corresponding output of 480. Another farmer (small) has limited capital and can purchase only 40 units of resource and has a corresponding output of 320.

Next, suppose that a program to lessen output through reduction of input is initiated, with resource to be reduced by 20 percent. The large farmer uses 64 units of input and has output, from (14.1), of 435.2. The small farmer uses 32 units and has output of 268.8. While both have reduced input by 20 percent, output has declined by only 9.3 percent for the large operator but 16 percent for the small farmer. This is a fairly obvious result from the elasticity equation and the fact that marginal productivity of the 80th input unit is only 2, while that of the 40th input is 6. Obviously, then, the cost of and gain from input reduction is not even the same for two farmers with identical production functions, producing the same crop without differential opportunity in substituting one resource or commodity for another. Under this condition of elasticity, the large farmer gains more, supposing reduced output increases price and income, relative to his cost in input reduction than does the small farmer. In fact, production control to restore a *previous level* of income can cause this *given level* to be distributed differently among farmers than the same previous amount established and distributed in the market.

In our case, suppose that income has declined from level of a previous time, with all farmers sacrificing in income. If input control restores income to its previous level, the large farmer will have more revenue than previously while the small farmer will have less. (Output quotas would have the same effect: A given percentage reduction in output would allow the "large" producer to decrease inputs by a greater percentage than the "small" producer. Hence, with both gaining the same proportionate increase in total revenue, the "large" producer would gain a greater percentage increase in net income than the "small" producer.)[13]

A linear homogeneous production function would result in gains proportional to costs for all producers and output reduction proportional to input reduction. In general, however, this is not the case because farmers have different amounts of capital and are at different levels in elasticity of output in respect to input. In simple terms, a farmer who is "in the trough of per unit costs" will generally have a smaller reduction in income from output diminution than one who is "high on the negative sloped portion of the cost curve," with a larger percentage increase in per unit costs as he reduces output. (See later discussion of Figure 14.3, page 542). Too, increasing marginal productivity, causing output reduction to be in smaller percentage than input reduction, is encountered even in control resting on land inputs because each farmer tends to withdraw acres in lowest order of productivity. (Also, see the discussion in Chapter 7.)

Even in simple concept of the farm production function, differentials in productivity and elasticity of resources cause unequal incidence of input control. However, we also have differential gain related to groups of farmers who largely buy feed grains, with opposite income effect from production control and increased prices, as compared to farmers who specialize in feed grain production and control.[14] Too, differential cost and gain arise where some farmers are, in equivalent, on the upward sloping portion of Figure 11.3 while others are "over the peak" and on the negative sloped portion (or some are at the point of tangence and some are above it even on the negatively sloped portion of the production possibility curve) for programs which allow substitution of a crop such as forage for another such as corn.

The problem of equity in distribution of gains and losses from reduction of land inputs is an important consideration in compulsory control programs. Within the farm sector per se, voluntary programs (where the pricing system is used to obtain desired level of land input and commodity output reduction) more nearly guarantee Pareto-better income conditions and equity in distribution in costs and benefits. In allowing the producer to exercise his own individual choice in "selling his production franchise," they also provide as much freedom—the much discussed goal of policy—as an unfettered market. No producer need join up unless he computes the gains from payments to be sufficiently greater than income and freedom foregone in placing land in disposal. But a voluntary pro-

---

[13] In the example used for (14.1) and (14.2), for example, a reduction in output by 20 percent reduces the "large" farmer to 384 and the "small" producer to 256. The inputs consistent with these outputs, from equation (14.1), are 51.8 and 30.1 respectively. Against the original inputs of 80 and 40, these represent input reductions of 35.3 and 24.8 percent respectively for "large" and "small" producers.

[14] But conversely, if output has increased rapidly and prices have decreased greatly (decline in total revenue) from progress, livestock producers will have gained at cost to grain producers.

gram with supply of land for withdrawal based on the pricing system will always have greater treasury costs to society than a program based on compulsion, which attains the same level of output reduction and price increase. Under compulsory program, the greater cost of food, supposing demand to be inelastic and output to be reduced, is borne by consumers only. For the same output reduction, under voluntary land retirement by pricing mechanism, consumers must pay the same cost, but the treasury cost of compensating participants also is involved.

If control of output through land withdrawal is given as an end, then society must make a choice in terms of (1) gain of greater freedom for farmers under voluntary control or (2) gain of smaller treasury outlay under compulsory retirement. There is, in addition, the equity problem mentioned above in allocating total reduction on a compulsory basis. This is a problem which applies equally to market orders or quotas and to compulsory land retirement. At the outset of a quota system, it is necessary to allocate the aggregate restraint among producers. As illustrated for equation (14.1), the cost of input reduction is greater relative to the gain from market price improvement for the producer with fewer resources and/or higher elasticity of production, whether this be because of capital applied to a given production function or because farmers use altogether different production functions or techniques, with quite different output response. In addition to the reasons mentioned in Chapter 12, this also is a factor causing market orders and quotas to have greater acceptance in the area of great homogeneity in production function and farming scale, and much less acceptance over the greater area where resources, techniques and factor productivity are much more heterogeneous and where wider differentials of gains exist in relation to costs of output control by individual producers.

Productivity Effect and Goals Attained

Land input reduction has no effect in lifting marginal physical productivity of labor—the "live" resource of surplus supply in agriculture—since about the same amount of the latter is used on a smaller amount of the former, particularly under fractional reduction in area of each farm. It is expected to and does, however, greatly lift the productivity of land remaining in production. In theory the reason is apparent. If we start with a production function such as that in (5.14) and hold a first resource at constant level while a second is decreased in magnitude, marginal physical productivity of the former will increase while that of the latter will decline. In a practical sense, especially where only portion of the land of each farm is withdrawn, use of the same amount of capital and the family labor on fewer acres will lower marginal and average productivity of these resources. But if funds previously used for fuel and other operating costs of land withdrawn are shifted to remaining acres, in the form of fertilizer and improved seed, land productivity will increase. This appears to be a strong force causing improvement of technology under land retirement as a portion of farms.

While labor is the resource of concentration in academic discussions of low productivity, production control programs of this type ordinarily do not have the goal of attaining resource equilibrium in the framework of the competitive model. Instead, they take plant and resources as given, and inquire how return to them might be increased in the manner of production and price management such as that employed in the steel, petroleum and other industries where surplus capacity typically exists and some resources are unemployed and of low productivity. Hence, production control programs aimed at this specific end must, given the objective, be evaluated in terms of other short-run criteria such as: how effectively they attain the conditions employed by these nonfarm industries; the cost of the control and price improvement attained; and degree of equity in the distribution of gains and losses from control.

The above are questions and phenomena just as amenable to economic analysis, given the particular intermediate end, as are the stability conditions of a competitive model. They involve application of exactly the same set of economic principles, alternatives for refinement in mathematical analysis, of concepts in minima and maxima, in application of institutional approaches, and in general "general stylishness of analysis" or "professional leaning." In terms of contribution to national economic growth, detailed analysis to bring the competitive stability or equilibrium conditions to agriculture, or to econometric prediction of relationships leading to it, has much less promise than analysis, rough or refined, designed to: lessen psychological and sociological barriers to greater productivity of the massive U.S. nonfarm labor force; lessen excesses in application of monopoly power; remove the many market imperfections which pace the national rate of economic growth below its potential; assess the social cost of advertising, an outlay larger than the net income of agriculture, in its purely offsetting effect; erase the poverty blight and low worker motivation in widespread section of cities and farms, with no unique cause in agriculture; better mesh employment opportunities for older persons with their potential in productivity—to mention only a few of many alternatives.

Progress and economic growth are generally preferred goals for agriculture as for the rest of the economy. But, as further detailed in Chapter 10, the marginal productivity of analysis to this end with extreme refinement for agriculture can be low relatively when great voids exist in analysis of equal intensity for other broad areas of extreme potential in furthering growth. Fortunately, however, policy means are available which allow both economic progress of the agricultural industry and growth in opportunity for development of individual capacities and abilities for those farm persons who have brightest prospects in a developing nonfarm economy; with simultaneous attainment in agriculture of the following conditions already attained by other industries: short-run price stability, competition and freedom, and equity of costs and benefits from policy results. It is less the lack of mechanisms—and more the political power struggle, conflict in group interest along the contract curve, and indecision over relative weight to be attached to different goals—which prevents adoption of a subset of policy elements. These would bring about simultaneous accomplishment of this particular end complex. There are of course, both complementary and competitive ends among this lot. But again the task is, selecting b_3 in Figure 8.1 as the production possibilities facing the community in respect to competitive goals or ends and the a_i lines as community indifference curves, to specify the optimum combination of ends by finding tangency point of an a_i curve and b_3.

This task is not simple for an individual confronted with only his private production possibilities and preference map. It is decidedly more complex for "aggregate individual" represented by the nation. Just as the individual often must experiment, and even find himself torn with conflict in decision and faced with error, so does the community feel its way slowly and in a wandering route. But over time it does move in these directions, not infrequently making choices in which it estimates gain to one group to exceed loss to another—in discrete choices where compensation is impossible or is purposely absent. No society can ever do otherwise.

Other Comparisons and Optimality in Mixed Strategy

Choice in respect to policy can be, and must be, among many intermediate ends which are far removed from the ultimate ends of life, liberty and happiness. Choice of production control method can be evaluated directly in terms of: minimization of costs in attaining a given level of output reduction and its accompanying price or income improvement; maximization of output control and income improvement from given program outlays; minimization of extent to which production policy is apparent to the public; maximization of extent to which producer control of output and price parallels that of other major industries; equity in the distribution of costs and gains of output control within agriculture alone, or between households of agriculture and other households in rural communities; maximization of economic progress while attaining specified level of supply restraint and price support; maximization of the intrafarm, interfarm and interregional, and even interindustry, efficiency in resource allocation within the constraint of attaining a particular output and price level; and others. Marketing quotas which are negotiable are more efficient than compulsory land withdrawal over all farms and regions in the latter or "constrained" sense of efficiency. Quotas allow transfer of production among farms and regions to locations of lowest input/output or cost coefficients. Similarly, voluntary land withdrawal operated as *supply phenomena through the pricing mechanism* is more efficient than compulsory withdrawal in causing output to be withdrawn where its supply price is lowest (or, conversely, where the supply price of commodities is greatest in relation to consumer location). While voluntary land retiral is a more costly mechanism to taxpayers than marketing quotas or compulsory land withdrawal where the same output and price goals are attained, it has greater "within agriculture equity" in the sense that only those need participate who assess gain to be greater than cost. It avoids the problems of equity within agriculture stemming from differentials in production functions and elasticities such as those discussed for equation (14.1). Yet, concentrating in particular localities where participation is free in the market sense denoted above, it brings questions of equity in gain and loss distribution between farm and nonfarm households. With solid blocks of farmers participating and moving from the community, under prices guaranteeing gain to them, merchants of the concentrated area are faced with loss. Yet merchants in other communities, where participation does not occur but farmers gain income from a smaller aggregate output and a higher national price, can sell a greater volume of goods and services and realize a welfare gain. Other comparisons could be made among control methods in terms of the various criteria outlined at the outset of this paragraph.

Existence of these different ends to which production control (or various degrees of it with one extreme being in market-free price and production) relate and have impact on different groups causes no pure strategy to be optimal in the policy game. Instead, a mixed strategy involving different methods of production control in use at the same time becomes more nearly and practically so. Undoubtedly, it is the need for choice and mixed strategy that has caused U.S. agriculture to have in existence at the same time: compulsory acreage control on tobacco; nonnegotiable marketing orders for fruit and vegetables; output quotas for sugar; marketable output quotas for milk (cows); voluntary land retirement through a semi-price mechanism for cropland in general under the conservation reserve; and pure freedom of the market for other producers. It is likely that this mixed strategy will have quantitative proof of optimality in historic perspective. It also is very likely that mixed strategy will be continued, but with a change in proportion to allow greater simultaneous attainment of price stability, farmer gain from contribution to progress, freedom in choice of alternative and economic progress itself. One necessary condition for simultaneous attainment of these conditions is, of course, that the control effort must be great enough to actually accomplish the control end. Another is that "marketability" and mobility of control restraints must be increased, in effect increasing the *marketable characteristics* of an institution devised to "lessen the impact of other characteristics of the market," or of *providing market competition for a control mechanism* which has been created to "lessen certain other competitive aspects of the farm commodity market."

Compulsory Land Withdrawal and Market Quotas

Output quotas and land retirement on a compulsory basis are similar in the initial equity supposition that costs or sacrifices to attain production control can be proportional to the gains from it. We have reviewed reasons why equity is not always easily attained in input or output quota levied by the same proportion on all producers. Between quotas and compulsory land retirement, equity in gross income gains and costs probably tips in favor of quotas in the sense that a quantity restraint is allocated to each producer without a method to circumvent control and redistribute or contort the planned pattern of gains. In compulsory land retirement, this is less so. If an operator has had practices or inputs per acre below the conventional optimum (i.e., marginal product of resources such as fertilizer and improved seed greater than the input/output price ratio), he can lessen the cost to himself (through output foregone) by extending his use of capital resources per acre—if he has access to financing. The farmer who has, by this criterion, been in an efficient position cannot do so profitably, except to the extent that price of commodity is increased by the control program.[15]

Under quotas, if total output is reduced by a given percentage to obtain a specified goal of price and revenue increase, then each farmer reducing output by this proportion realizes the same proportionate share of gross market revenue gain, if he produces his allotted quota. (See previous discussion, however, of net income effect.) Previous output is, of course, much more difficult to establish than previous land input, not only because of "counting difficulties" but also because of variance in year-to-year quantities relating to stochastic variables such as weather. An extremely difficult (if not impossible) quantity to determine, identify and police would be output quotas on feed grain where some farmers only sell it, some raise and feed it and some do both. An exactly equitable and enforceable output quota system may be impossible for such a commodity. This is the reason why market orders have had main application to more perishable commodities moving directly to market as consumer goods and lacking in "hideability" through storage and feeding.

In the pure sense of social costs and efficient resource use, marketing quotas have flexibility lacking in compulsory land or input quotas. Given a restraint on marketing, the farmer can produce his quota in least-cost method. In Figure 14.3, for example, the farm with a market quota in quantity represented by product isoquant q_1 could use the proportion of land and fertilizer represented by os_2 and of_1 respectively. However, a farmer restricted on land attaining the same output, would use os_1 of land and of_2 of fertilizer. With slope of the budget line representing the price ratio of fertilizer and land services, the market quota system would allow attainment of the isoquant at lower cost than the land retraction method. This is obviously the case for tobacco quotas. The same total output could be obtained at lower cost under a market quota than under the

[15] For equation 14.1, supposing inputs denoted by x to be those used per acre on land, the operator with 80 initial inputs per acre has less opportunity to circumvent production control through land withdrawal than the one with 40 inputs per acre, should the latter be able to obtain funds to increase inputs per acre on remaining land. However, if production control lowers the price ratio below the 2 of the initial situation of the text, the large operator could profitably use more inputs, if allowed.

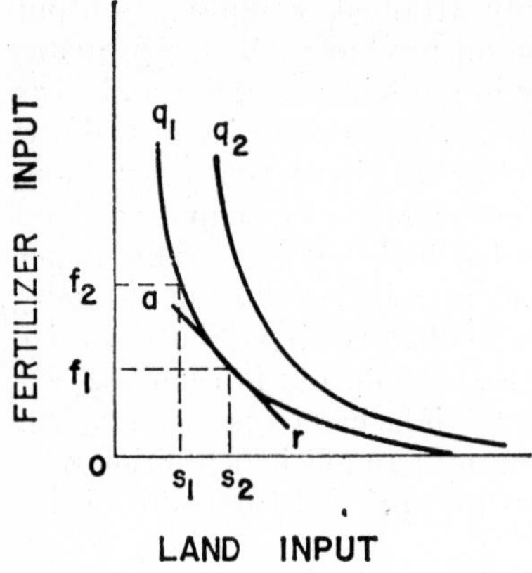

Fig. 14.3. Costs in Control.

present acreage restraint system. With acreage restraint serving as the means to bolstered price through output control and with consumer demand growing, farmers fertilize land very heavily. The result is a very low marginal productivity of the fertilizer input. Under output quotas, the same marketings of tobacco would undoubtedly be produced from more acres, fertilized at lower levels. Too, tobacco might become more highly mechanized, lowering the labor and total costs of producing a given quantity marketed. Mechanization of the tobacco harvest is possible, but results in some waste per acre. This nonmarketable waste would be easily allowed under an output quota where more acres could be produced at lower yield per acre. But with acreage restraint and ability to market the full output per acre, there is premium on hand methods which save all of the yield for market. In general, quantity quotas to attain given market supply would encourage more extensive farming, allowing (1) fuller employment of land which is in "excess" and can't be transferred to other industries and (2) lessening social costs in capital represented by fertilizer and similar inputs—materials using resources which have allocation possibilities to other products and services of the economy.

As in the comparison of voluntary and compulsory land retirement, quotas do have promise of net income gain proportionately greater for large than for small producers, even where the production function is linear but fixed costs are involved. The point is illustrated further in Figure 14.4. (We did not consider the effect of fixed costs in our example of equation 14.1.) The cost curve of main relevance in farming approaches curve *C*, being composed, within the season, of constant variable unit costs per acre for seed, fuel, fertilizer and similar inputs and declining unit costs of fixed resources such as machinery. Approaching the mathematical limit of constant variable costs per acre, the total cost per unit declines less with greater output, or increases less with smaller output, for large as compared to small volumes. (It can, of course, turn up in conventional *U* shape, but most farmers operate under the above conditions, given a curve eventually turning to positive slope. Here, we have not imputed costs to labor and investment capital of the farmer, thus allowing a margin between per unit price and cost.)

Now suppose two farmers, one with volume of *oh* and one with *od*. Both are given a quota 20 percent reduced—to *of* for the former and *ob* for the latter—from the original level. Price increases, from similar market quantity adjustment by the industry, from p_1 to p_2 level. Both farmers gain a gross revenue increment in proportion to their 20 percent reduction from their original output. But the gain in net income is much greater for the large producer, because reduction in output increases costs by a much smaller amount than for the smaller producer, whereas price increases by the same amount for each. (In our particular example,

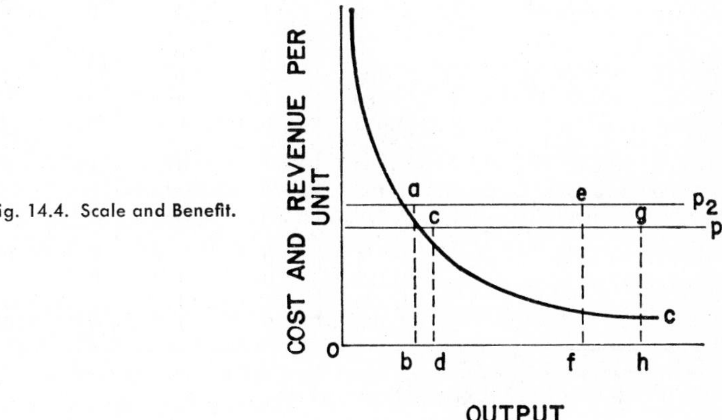

Fig. 14.4. Scale and Benefit.

the small producer even has reduced net revenue; he sells less output at about the same profit margin.) With fixed costs in fixed machine investment, the small producer may have a short-run increment in income above fixed costs, but fail to do so when he must replace machines which provide the "within year" fixed costs.

Impact on Land Values ·

Output quotas which are not negotiable apart from the land have the same theoretical effect as compulsory land retirement or input quotas in respect to effect on land value. The effect of returns from production control on land values, as measured in application to tobacco, was mentioned in Chapter 12. (The effect is the same in milk markets where the quota is tied to cows.) Here we wish to indicate a differential impact on resource values when output quotas are marketable apart from land resource. The expected effect is for the benefits of restrained supply and improved price to be capitalized into output quota, rather than being capitalized into land value.

TABLE 14.2

PROGRAMMING MATRICES ILLUSTRATING EFFECT OF CONTROL METHODS ON RESOURCE USE, INCOME AND ASSET VALUES

Activities in the "Program"*	Quantity†	Net Price (c_j)				
		$20	$23	0	0	0
		P_1	P_2	P_3	P_4	P_5
1. Land (P_3)............	100	1	1	1	0	—
2. Capital (P_4)..........	$2,100	20	25	0	1	—
3. P_1..................	80	1	0	5	−.2	—
4. P_2..................	20	0	1	−4	.2	—
5. $z_j - c_j$..............	$2,060	0	0	8	.6	—
6. Land (P_3)............	100	1	1	1	0	0
7. Capital (P_4)..........	$2,100	20	25	0	1	0
8. Acreage quota (P_5).....	80	1	1	0	0	1
9. P_3..................	20	0	0	1	0	− 1
10. P_4.................	$ 100	−5	0	−25	−24	−25
11. P_2.................	80	1	1	0	0	1
12. $z_j - c_j$.............	$2,392	9.9	0	0	0	29.9
13. Land (P_3)...........	100	1	1	1	0	0
14. Capital (P_4).........	$2,100	20	25	0	1	0
15. Quantity quota (P_5)....	3,840	40	48	0	0	1
16. P_3.................	4	0	−.2	1	0	−.025
17. P_4.................	$ 180	0	1	0	1	−.5
18. P_1.................	96	1	1.2	0	0	.025
19. $z_j - c_j$.............	$2,496	0	1.3	0	0	.65

* Activities at nonzero level.
† Quantity of nonzero level activities in the first column.

The difference can be illustrated by a simple linear programming example in Table 14.2.[16] We use the method to show the channeling of quantities through the production framework of a single producer, not expecting it to represent an aggregate industry, but with outcomes which do spill over with weakened effect into the industry. In the top of the table, we suppose two limiting resources, land (P_3) and capital (P_4) as indicated on lines 1 and 2. Two crop enterprises, P_1 and P_2, can be grown, the second being only a more intensive activity of the first, with the coefficients indicated in the respective columns. Net return per acre is respectively $20 and $23, with the annual cash costs of $20 and $25 on the capital row. The "optimum program" is indicated on lines 3 and 4

[16] See Earl O. Heady and Wilfred V. Candler, *Linear Programming Methods*, Iowa State University Press, Ames, 1959, Chaps. 1–4. The usual computational procedures have been used in arriving at solutions. Lines 1 and 2 provide programming situation without control and lines 3 to 5 provide its optimum solution; lines 6 to 8 provide situation with acreage control and lines 9 to 12 its optimum solution; lines 13 to 15 provide situation with output quota and lines 16 to 19 its solution. There is no P_5 activity for the first two situations, but, for the last two, P_5 serves successfully for land and output quota.

with 80 acres (units) of P_1 enterprise and 20 of P_2, land and capital being exhausted to provide a "net income before fixed costs" of $2,060 (line 5). Here, the imputed per year values of resources, before taxes and related costs, are shown in the dual solution on the $z_j - c_j$ row under P_4 (land) and P_5 (capital). They are respectively $8 and $.6. If the farmer had another unit of land, he could add $8 to net income (before taxes and other fixed costs). Another unit of capital would similarly increase his net income by $.6.

Now suppose compulsory acreage control is initiated. It requires a 20 percent reduction, or 80 acres are allowed to be planted as indicated by the added row (P_5) in the new matrix over lines 6 to 8 and the added column for its "disposal" (P_5). The "optimum" program is now indicated on lines 9 to 12, where we suppose a 30 percent net price boost, so that P_1 has c_j value of $26 and P_2 has c_j value of $29.9. The program changes to include 80 acres (line 11) of the more intensive enterprise, P_2, and none of the less intensive enterprise, P_1. Twenty acres of land (line 9) and $100 of capital (line 10) are left unused and "net before fixed costs" increases to $2,392. But now additional capital has no imputed value to the farmer (the zero in the "dual solution" under column P_4 on the $z_j - c_j$ row). Land per se has no imputed value within his year's farm operation (zero under P_3 on the $z_j - c_j$ row). However, a quota acre has an imputed value or price of $29.9 per acre ($P_5$ column on line 12), far more than land alone in the "free market" of the initial situation. It has this value because of the higher commodity price and the fact that quota per se restricts ability to gain a portion of this added revenue. Obviously, of course, if acre quota cannot be separated from land, this fact would cause the increment to be capitalized into the land with which each unit of quota is associated.[17]

Now suppose a market quota program establishes the same output as under the acreage control program above. (Also suppose that P_1 yields 40 bushels per unit or acre while P_2 yields 48 bushels.) With the prices as above ($26 for P_1 and $29.9 for P_2), with the quota row now having the associated disposal column indicated under P_5, we have the programming opportunities indicated over lines 13 to 15. The "optimum program" from this matrix is included in lines 16 to 19. In contrast to that of lines 9 to 12 with acreage quota, it now includes 96 acres of P_1, the less intensive crop activity, using all but 4 acres (line 17) of land. (Capital valued at $80 is saved in comparison of line 17 with line 19.) This is a lower cost method of attaining the 3,840 output level, and "net before fixed costs" increases to $2,496 as the quantity on the $z_j - c_j$ line (19). With output

[17] If land were allowed to shift to another, but lower valued, marketable product, the dual or imputed value of land would approximate this level. Without this alternative but the anticipation that quotas will eventually be terminated, land would take on some value under these expectations. We could develop and apply a programming model under these possibilities, with the resulting imputed, but lower, shadow prices or "duals" for land noted. However, we do not do so, for both this and the quota case, because the outcome would be apparent and we wish to keep the example simple.

quota limiting marketing and with land not serving as restraint, a unit of market quota has an imputed value (line 19) of 65 cents (in column P_5) while land has zero (in column P_4) imputed value. This outcome would be expected under marketing quotas which restrict output considerably short of land productive capacity.

Our example is extreme, within the bounds of a single producing unit. However, a quota serving as tighter restraint than land would generally take value away from the latter.[18] We would expect a negotiable marketing quota to take on value and land prices to decrease, nearer to "next closest alternative," with the quota having imputed value based on the farm purchasing it rather than the farm selling it.

Divorcing capital value of income from land in the manner of quotas would generally serve as incentive to increased labor mobility. This would be true more so than for compulsory acreage control since the tie among asset value, farm and individual then is loosened. The individual can sell his output quota and have money for transfer. He can also do so in selling land and its attached quota. But with output quota, he can sell its asset value while he moves and retains farm ownership as a "contingency measure"—a measure not possible under capitalized value of land quota. Further, output quota on unproductive land (and many low income farmers are on less productive land) would have greater market value than acreage quota. The quota could be transferred geographically to more productive farms and regions, with its asset value determined accordingly. This opportunity would, in fact, cause long-run concentration of output in regions with greatest comparative advantage. But with acreage quota attached to specific farm and location, its asset value is tied to the lower level of productivity at the less productive location since only neighboring farms can utilize it.

METHODS IN LAND CONTROL

Numerous different patterns of control of land input have been used or are possible, each having differential impact in equity of benefit and cost of control, and in treasury cost of the program if it is on a voluntary basis of producers supplying idle land at various schedules of price. Each method involves a different acreage to attain a given level of output control. The level of price and income improvement to be attained also has important bearing on the program cost and the acreage involved, supposing a given level of production control in any case. In the Iowa study cited earlier, these differences in annual program or treasury costs were obtained, supposing a voluntary program where individual farmers supply their land to the "idle activity," at a price just making it profitable for them to do so: (1) For prices of $1 for corn and $1.15 for wheat: 488 million dollars with the same proportion of land retired on all farms and regions; 352 million dollars with as much as 50 percent withdrawal allowed in high cost production regions. (2) For prices of $1.30 for corn

---

[18] See footnote above.

and $1.50 for wheat: 1,526 million dollars with the same proportion of land retired on all farms and regions; 1,403 million dollars with the 50 percent restraint by regions. These figures apply only to feed grain and wheat and do not include administrative costs.[19]

Over Regions and Farms

The main type of input, and thus output, control attempted between 1933 and 1960 was shift of a portion of the land on millions of farms over all relevant regions. This method has advantage in equity to nonfarm persons in rural communities (even if equity is assumed among farmers by voluntary retirement through payments guaranteeing against negative outcomes) since few farmers are led to leave the community and income increment to farmers may have "multiplier effect" to all merchants. In contrast, land withdrawal concentrated by regions encourages farmers to migrate, especially if withdrawal of entire farms is allowed. Hence, merchants and other service suppliers in the particular regions may sacrifice while those of "other" regions gain (supposing control to be effective and giving higher income farmers in "other" regions).

The "dispersed" method is less one forcing "drastic" change on an entire community. On the debit side, it costs more than a "concentrated" system because more productive soils, taken out of production with the least productive, have lower per bushel costs and greater profit per acre, land costs excluded, thus requiring greater payment for the farmer to forego production and cropping income. Also, the farmer withdrawing only a part of his land cannot reduce costs by as great a proportion as the farmer who "retires" all of his land inputs. Therefore, his supply price in providing "idled land" is greater. Output control through partial land input withdrawal allows the farmer to use more labor and capital on remaining acres, thus substituting for land and partially nullifying the output control effort. Too, surplus labor may be held on farms to receive payment of land withdrawal (although the actual effect may be weak against draw of outside employment opportunity). Finally, as soon as the program is lifted, retired land tends to move right back into production with all acres continuing under cultivation.

A similar approach is to allow or require entire farms to be withdrawn from production, with the restraint that they be spread somewhat proportionately *over all regions.* This method has the equity advantage mentioned above. It lowers program costs (supply price of participation) somewhat because all farm costs, except taxes and similar outlays, can be terminated on the "whole farm" basis. While it does not allow retirement concentration in the least productive areas, it allows the least productive farms in all regions to be withdrawn, lowering program costs below that of the "partial farm" method and allowing more labor to

---

[19] Net social costs would not be of these magnitudes because labor and capital would migrate to industries and location where they have greater value productivity. The regional model (A) explained in Chapter 7 is predicted to free, along with the land (if it went unused) labor amounting to 29 million man days and capital inputs of .5 billion dollars for wheat and feed grain.

migrate. The "whole farm" approach to input contraction and output control has a major advantage in this respect, if the criterion is that of greater labor migration from farms: The individual need not stay on his farm to realize payment, and he can boost income from off-farm employment. Encouraged to do so particularly are older farmers near retirement (who will generally stay in the community) and young operators. "Partial farm retirement" does not always lead to increased cohesion of labor to land, however. Evidence was that small cotton allotments in the Mississippi Delta were divided among the same number of sharecroppers in the first year but were consolidated to fewer families in later years.[20] Also, with partial farm retirement, use of machinery and labor is less efficient and operators are pressed to buy or rent additional acreage to offset this, thus pushing another farmer out of the industry.

Finally, the "whole farm" method does not allow substitution of labor and capital for land, as in the case where only part of the land is removed from production. If driven to zero input, land serves limitationally with labor and capital and no output is forthcoming. With "withdrawn" farms scattered among those farms remaining in operation, cessation of the control program will encourage the former to be incorporated into the cropping process of the latter. In a region where the whole land area becomes covered with grass and trees, with no croppers present, the tendency to put land back under the plow is much less, except when demand jumps to suddenly cover higher supply price of food. (The liquidation of storage, transportation and other facilities to service grain production aids the process when reduction is concentrated over regions.)

With land withdrawal allowed and encouraged on a "whole farm" and "whole region" basis, supply price to attain a given level of output control is lower than for opposite land reduction methods because of the reasons mentioned above. Also, for reasons already cited, the method serves as a greater catalyst to labor and capital outflow, as a limitational restraint in substitution of labor and capital for land, and in greater permanence of effect. It also is a method consistent with the shift in resource use which would be guided through the market by relative preferences of consumers and supplies of factors. In this sense, too, it stands to allow greatest contribution to furthered national economic growth, guiding labor and capital resources from regions where they are least productive in agriculture. Conservation also tends to be promoted since the least productive farmers and least productive lands have a rough correspondence to locations where water and wind erosion are most severe and the supply price for land input control is roughly lowest.

Land input reduction will not restrict commodity supply unless it is on a large enough scale and "has teeth in it." The 30 million acres in the

---

[20] See J. R. Motheral, "Impact of Current Natural Policy on Southern Agriculture," Proceedings, Southern Agricultural Workers, 1957; and E. L. Baum and Earl O. Heady, "Effects of Policy on Labor Mobility," *South. Econ. Jour.*, Vol. 25.

soil bank up to 1960 lead to trivial output control, not even offsetting growth in supply due to technical advance, because so much of it was largely derelict land or pasturage and acreage with low output. Even if all of the mountainsides in the nation were put in a "soil bank," supply of crops would not be restrained.

Under other types of land withdrawal programs, farmers were allowed to substitute one crop for another. For livestock and feeds, the alternatives were those outlined under the discussion of marginal rates of substitution in Chapter 11. Land inputs must "in fact" be withdrawn from production if output control is to be achieved, rather than simply be reallocated among crops which serve as substitute resources in livestock production or as substitute commodities for consumers. Where two commodities are concerned and one is put under acreage control while the other is not, both having inelastic demands, some gain in income from land can be attained by allowing shift from one crop to another—if production circumstances are favorable. The possibility is illustrated in Figure 14.5.

With an inelastic demand for both commodities, a total revenue surface exists as defined by the isoquants $r_1 \cdots r_m$, with maximum revenue attained when the level and mix of output for the two crops is that represented at point r_m. Suppose, however, that the short-run supply of factors provides the production possibility curve represented by AC. Given "approximate equilibrium" under this set of commodity supplies and the market demand structure or revenue surface, the level and mix

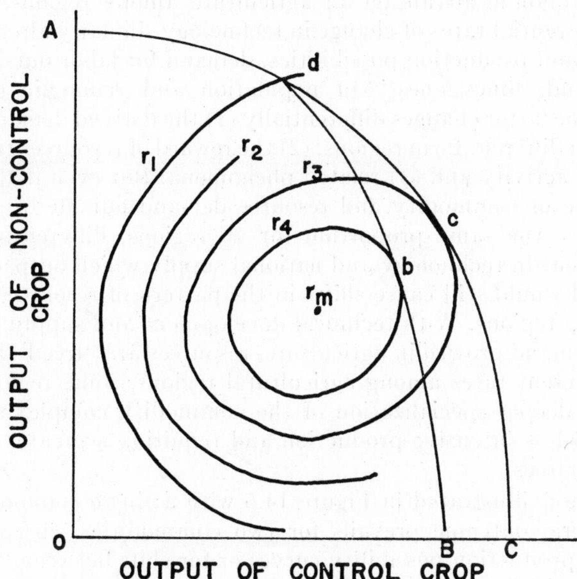

Fig. 14.5. Production Possibilities Under Control.

of crops is that indicated at point *c* with tangency of curves *AC* and r_3.

Now production control is initiated, withdrawing land from the "control" crop, but with no cross-compliance requirements preventing its shift to the noncontrol crop. The expected recombination is at point *d*, with less of the former and more of the latter crop. While land cannot be reallocated back to the control crop, labor and capital can be. Hence, a new production possibility curve arises, with a segment having lower marginal rates of substitution of control for noncontrol crops than formerly. It is *AB*, diverging at point *d* which defines the maximum amount of land which can be allocated to the control crop. But given the particular revenue surface, the revenue-maximizing combination is that indicated at *b*, with tangency of r_4 and *AB*. For the particular configuration of the curves, output of the control crop now far exceeds its expected production. (Ordinarily, we would expect the latter combination to fall somewhere between the proportions represented by *c* and *d*.) The control program has caused the crop mix to be forced to a higher revenue level, even though allowing one crop to be substituted for the other, if the particular competitive structure and factor supply inelasticity have held it to a lower level over "the revenue hill." (Optimally, for maximum revenue gain to aggregate of producers, the combination r_m would be selected under the supply control program.)

REGIONAL ADJUSTMENT AND EQUITY

Numerous reasons have been cited, indicating causes of change in the relative economic advantage of agriculture among regions. These include: differential rates of change in technology similarly altering supply functions and production possibilities, demand for labor outside of agriculture, and "unevenness" of population and economic growth by regions. The latter changes differentially (1) the derived demand for commodities in different farm regions, (2) the reward of resources transferring from farm activity and (3) related phenomena. But even if all variables on the side of commodity and resource demand outside of agriculture changed by the same proportion for all regions, differential regional improvement in technology and national supply which outpaces growth in demand would still cause shifts in the pattern of resource specialization among regions. With technical development and supply growth exceeding demand growth in agriculture, resources are "freed" from farming at different rates among agricultural regions, some regions sinking into even deeper specialization of the commodity complex and others shifting to less intensive production and requiring a greater outflow of labor resources.

The case is illustrated in Figure 14.6 with a single commodity. (The same general outcome prevails for two commodities with differential change in production possibility curves or for shift between "intensive" and "extensive" enterprises.) In Figure 14.6 region *A* has supply functions S_a and S_a' and region B has functions S_b and S_b' respectively before and after technical change. Total supply before and after change is S_t

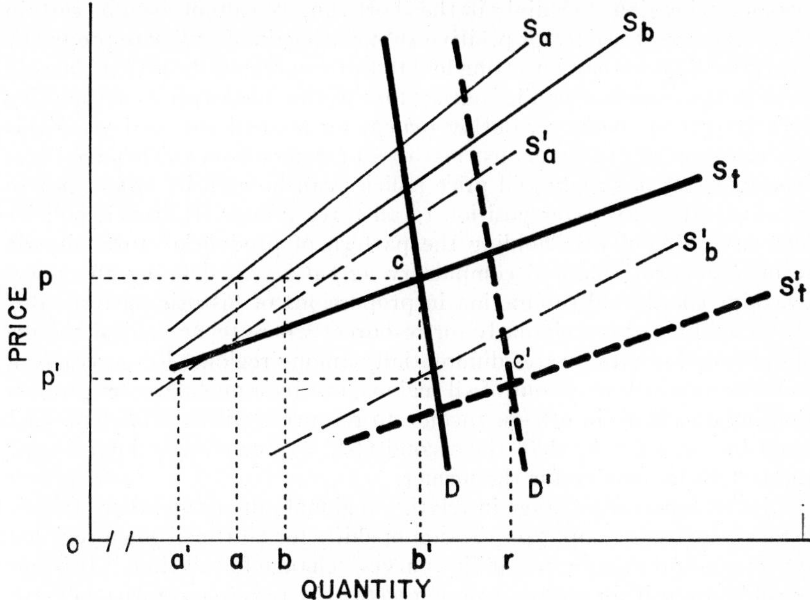

Fig. 14.6. Differential Changes Among Regions.

and S_t' respectively. With the total demand D before the change and D' after change (with differentials not subtracted for location and transport costs as a step in simplicity), we find that region A decreases output by aa' amount while region B increases output by bb' as price falls by pp'. Even without an increase in the marginal rate of transformation, region A will use fewer resources, but more so as the rate of transformation increases. Region B will use more resources if the rate of increase in average productivity is less than bb'/ob, but fewer resources if the increase in resource productivity exceeds this proportion. If production is to conform to factor prices, consumer demand and the state of technology, it is obvious that farming intensity will necessarily decline in the one region, but much less so, or even increase, in the other. This is, of course, the situation in U.S. agriculture, and while land is in surplus stock if applied to the conventional mix of products, it is not in excess supply (i.e., as a discrete number of acres not required) if diverted to less intensive uses in part. But as illustrated in the figure, although shift ordinarily is from "more" to "less" intensive products, land can remain fully employed with fewer resources applied to it.[21]

The distribution of gains from technical change and progress through the pricing mechanism obviously cannot be in positive quantity to every

[21] The equivalent of Figure 14.6 for n products and m regions would be represented with nm supply functions and n demand functions in both production situations (leaving aside nonfarm competing products in demand). Solution then would be in terms of inverting the coefficient matrix and solving simultaneously for all prices and quantities, with production within regions allowed to shift completely among products.

person and region. Certainly in the short run, we cannot even be certain that the aggregate effect is positive-sum, with gain of utility to producers in region B more than offsetting loss to those in region A, or that the gain to consumers, in the smaller outlay ($orc'p'$) for the larger food quantity (or) as against the larger outlay ($ob'cp$) for a smaller quantity (ob'), is positive-sum in utility against loss to all farmers from this change. Numerous types of supply and price policies can be used in an attempt to guarantee Pareto-better position to all three groups. However, policies will have difficulty in holding the pattern of production to a historic form. Nonnegotiable and compulsory *output quotas* defining an upper-restraint could hold production in proportions of historic pattern. But they could not do so similarly for resources where technological change alters transformation rates differentially among regions. Resources such as labor may still move out of all regions, but by a much greater proportion in some than in others. Income to resources will still be depressed more in the first (A) than the second (B), or income may increase for the latter and decline for the former.

Given permanent change in relative regional advantage, there thus is little reason to attempt "prevention of shifts for all time" when regional supply and production possibility curves "change for all time." It is impossible, even if for no other reason than that resource returns will still differ and resources will be motivated differentially among regions to supply their services to farm and nonfarm activity demand. More nearly, the problem (in light of the "upstream" duel against factor prices and demand, and against varying endowments by nature which cause differential productivity effects from new technology) is to allow and encourage progress in this sense, but with policy to guarantee positive-sum utility or income effect between consumers and farm producers. On the one hand, minimum policy may be that which restrains the rate of change so that it does not land with crash effect on regions of less advantage, but still allows change to take place. At maximum, it would provide compensation, allowing change but providing redress to those suffering loss, either or both through (1) monetary assistance and (2) aid in move to nonfarm employment where income of the individual could be lifted above the previous level.

Regional Shifts

At the turn of the 1960's, control and price support programs had been so long in effect, factor prices and productivities had changed so greatly and demand alteration had been so great that the policy-inspired equilibrium of agriculture departed considerably from that consistent with current production possibilities, consumer demands and national challenges. The problem then, as now, was to (1) restore a more consistent equilibrium, (2) further progress and (3) increase equity in distribution of gains from this process. (See the discussion of equation (7.9) and Figures 7.4 to 7.7.) Land in the conventional mix allocation to crop was surplus as mentioned above.

Numerous methods exist, in such situations, for bringing about equilibrium among regions more consistent with consumer demand and relative factor supplies and prices. Free markets is one. Turned loose in an unfettered manner, prices would cause a price "shakedown" with little immediate effect on production, but with more of the shifts illustrated in Table 14.1 taking place over time. Negotiable output quotas would accomplish the same, but over a longer time because of the period required for a market in them to develop, and because a decision period would be required for farmers in regions of low advantage to sell them without income sacrifice. Free market prices would have immediate price impact; marketable quotas would not. Free market prices would cause land in regions of low advantage to shift in concentrated manner because of the large *income penalty* imposed on producers. Marketable quotas would encourage the same, with land withdrawn from crop production in manner concentrated to low advantage areas, because of the *gain in income or the asset increase* in sale of quotas to more productive regions where they have greater value.

The third means for withdrawing surplus land from production in a manner consistent with regional comparative advantage, is voluntary land retirement with control or shift supplied in response to a price thus offered. The main "snag" in the free market approach is the problem of gains and losses discussed previously. This has special impact in the sense that while the imbalance of agriculture was a "product" of the entire industry and of historic policy, the brunt of costs in eliminating it would fall on nonfarm persons in those regions forced to shift from feed grains, wheat, cotton and similar crops to trees and grass. The free market approach has main loss burden for both farm and non-farm producers in rural areas of lowest comparative advantage; negotiable quotas has main long-run burden on nonfarm persons in the same areas. The main "snag" in negotiable output quotas is the initial problem in equitable allocation of total marketings back to producers, freedom in farm decision being allowed by actual broadening of the functions of the market to allow purchase and sale of these quantities. But the free market mechanism has this same equity problem on a very broad basis among regions.

But voluntary land retirement, with this resource supplied to "disposal activity" in response to price or demand offered by public policy, also has its "snag"—the cost of the program, an amount which can be sizeable as indicated previously. Yet the method is one for averting (1) inequity in spread of losses from overcoming imbalance suddenly through market-free prices and (2) difficulty in attaining complete equity in initial distribution of marketable quotas. On a voluntary basis of land retirement and supply control covering whole farms, individuals can evaluate their position, thus supplying land to these purposes only under a guarantee of welfare gain. Under an appropriate price schedule, land would be supplied in a manner concentrating its withdrawal from crops in the least productive areas. This pattern was partly reflected in participation through the 1956 Conservation Reserve Act. By 1960 the conservation reserve embraced 35 percent of all cropland in New Mexico, 12 percent in Colorado, 13 percent in South Carolina, 12 percent in Georgia,

10 percent in the Dakotas, 2.6 percent in Iowa, 1.5 percent in California and 6.2 percent for the nation.

The methods used in voluntary supply of land to crop withdrawal also could be various, as outlined in Chapter 7. Direct land purchase by the federal government was used in the 1930's, with some land still so managed. Others of the methods mentioned previously also could be used. But, until demand grew sufficiently, shift of grain land to grazing would push the income problems of crop farmers over onto ranchers; supply of grazing activities would be increased. Hence, all marketable use of land might be prevented in the short run, but with land eventually shifted to uses with greater prospect in demand. Methods employed could allow farmers to handle the land and the managerial problems in shifting it to trees or grass. But for many farmers a sizeable increment in capital investment would be required for seeding and/or stocking land. Shift from wheat to grass, a long drop in income, involves a large amount of capital for (1) more land to provide an adequate unit, (2) funds to stock and utilize grass and (3) to replace income foregone over the 5 to 8 years required for the shift.

Hence, a special credit program should be included in the "action bundle" to provide farmers with assets for making the shift. Two quantities are important in making such a program successful, namely, the rental rate and the time period. The annual rental rate should be high enough to make participation profitable on sufficient scale. The program should substitute for other price-support and income-supplementing mechanisms. At the end of a designated period, for example, prices could be turned loose in the market, aside from the stability programs discussed previously (but without throwing current surplus stocks on the market, should such exist). The amount of land so withdrawn would be expected to lift prices over aggregate agriculture from a depressed level and accomplish price goals in this manner. Economic progress would thus be greatly encouraged for areas remaining in production, a fact to be recognized in the amount of land withdrawn. Progress also would be encouraged in the sense that shift to extensive levels of capital and labor use in particular regions would feed labor out to other sectors, providing that employment opportunity exists.

The annual payment for rental of land or purchase of rights to produce specific crops should compensate for the shift to the alternative land use. Thus for land shifted from wheat to grass the rental or "rights purchase" rate would approximate the return from wheat during the first years, when income would approach zero because seedings were being established. It would be lowered as grazing was initiated. At the very minimum, contracts should be for 10 years or the period necessary in light of supply-demand conditions. A recommended rental period for wheat areas shifting to grass would be 20 years, in order to provide a planning horizon that favors participation and offsets the portion of capital value not represented by capitalization of support prices and subsidies. In either case, rental contracts could carry a renewal clause, allowing an option for extending the period at rates equal to those at the outset, adjusted upward in proportion to changes in the general price level. (Where rights were purchased, they could be held in the hands of the public as long as it so desires.) A credit program would be necessary and would serve as a technical complement to the rental or "rights" schemes, in providing funds for land conversion, livestock purchase, and other necessary investments. But it, along with the compensation method, would need to be so administered as to encourage and facilitate combination of farms into units of economic size for the new pattern of agriculture.

Community Equity and Costs

Voluntary land retirement so concentrated by region could be entirely equitable to farmers, participation being required only if individuals so selected. Farmers in other regions would lose no freedom, but would gain from higher price. But the problem of equity does fall, as explained above, on persons of rural areas. Equity would not be complete, unless appropriate aid is extended over nonfarm people of rural communities so affected. Here is the point where "complete social policy" rather than "just farm policy" must be involved as explained in Chapter 10. The numerous elements outlined in other chapters need to be incorporated in this "broader policy mix" and include the aspects of education, guidance, compensation, community development and others discussed in Chapter 12, with focus on human resources and their opportunity and welfare under economic growth.

Target date in the future should be set up to shift surplus cropland and regear agriculture by broad regions as suggested above and in Chapter 7. To accomplish it in a single year, even if under purely voluntary and complete "supply price" compensation, would cause change too drastic to be digested by particular communities where it concentrates. Hence, it could better be attained in step-by-step fashion, with announced completion data starting from a temporary program which restrained output over all areas.

Is the burden of cost too great under a voluntary program? The answer depends on the comparison. The U.S. public outlays for price and income support from 1930 to 1960 would have allowed purchase of all cropland necessary, with funds left over, and a problem which continues would have been earlier terminated. The data in Table 14.3 indicate that if the 8.1 billion dollar loss by the Commodity Credit Corporation alone had been used to purchase land, it would have allowed purchase of 81.5 million acres of land at $100 per acre. Land averaging quite high in productivity could have been purchased easily at this price, over the period. Perhaps a better comparison would have been realized costs of government programs. Using the 17.8 billion dollars largely for price support and 3.5 billion of that for conservation, since at least this portion was equally a subsidy to agriculture (and the remainder was for improvement of land which might also have been purchased), the total is 21.3 billion

TABLE 14.3

REALIZED COST OF U.S. AGRICULTURAL PROGRAMS AND REALIZED LOSS OF COMMODITY CREDIT OPERATIONS, 1956–60 AND TOTAL 1933–60
(Million Dollars)

Item	1956	1957	1958	1959	1933–60*
Realized costs of programs					
Primarily price support	1,461	2,714	2,655	2,028	17,753
Primarily conservation	301	406	494	579	7,001
Credit and related	49	59	57	70	1,619
Research and education	212	232	257	301	3,242
School lunch and donations	39	49	56	43	822
Total above†	2,585	4,059	4,044	3,542	34,183
Realized losses of CCC					
Price support programs	981	1,301	1,023	891	7,298
Commodity export programs	67	147	101	132	851
Total above	1,048	1,448	1,124	1,031	8,149

Source: *Subsidy and Subsidy-like Programs of the U.S. Government,* Joint Economic Committee, 86th Session 1960. Excludes 540 million for the Farm Credit Administration and 4,246 million for wartime consumer subsidies on agricultural commodities.

* 1933–59 for realized losses and 1933–60 for CCC losses.

† Rounding may cause total to differ from sum of elements above.

dollars. Hence, 213 million acres could have been purchased at $100 per acre, or 106.5 million acres at $200 per acre. Obviously, enough land could have been purchased, at prices lower than these, to accomplish the adjustment goal mentioned above. Purchase of fewer acres and outlay smaller than 21.3 billion dollars would have done so. Funds left over could have been invested in the broader social policy needs discussed previously. (The realized cost comparison may provide better comparison since the public would own the land under purchase or control it under rental. Hence, it could have realized offsetting revenue and capital value in appreciation of these assets—under inflation, growing trees or grazing fees.)

The program would, of course, exceed costs of a policy in marketable quotas, allowed to transfer among regions and to concentrate at points of greatest comparative advantage. Under quotas, exchange could take place in the manner explained for Figure 8.1. Producer in area of comparative advantage could exchange money for quota with producer in area of low advantage. The exchange could take place only in the case where both persons judge themselves to be made better off, with Pareto optima assured. Problem of equity in distributing gain ex poste to establishment of the system would not arise. Ex ante, however, the problem of equity in distribution of given quota among producers would. Also, although farmers in regions of low advantage could sell their quotas to those in regions of greatest advantage, with the former migrating and realizing gain accordingly, merchants and others servicing the area would still sacrifice (while merchants in the comparative advantage areas could gain), thus leaving the same problem as voluntary land retirement and free-market prices where compensation is not provided nonfarm people. But in this case, as in the other, the same minimum and maximum compensation alternatives exist for nonfarm people in rural areas.

Increasing the Functions of the Pricing System Through Policy

Programs do exist, then, which promise a workable degree of equity in distribution of program gains and which also can catalyze economic progress and aid interregional adjustment of agriculture. Which program is preferable depends on the wisdom, value and equity orientation of the people involved and their willingness to appropriate funds in sufficient magnitude. Equity considerations probably require not a "single type of program" but one with a strategy mix which guarantees equity or positive-sum result over all broad groups affected. Otherwise, as suggested in Chapter 9, the program is likely to be rejected by the public (as in argument of business people in rural areas against the conservation reserve land retirement method). We say "broad or major groups" because no reorganization is possible which provides equity in the sense of welfare gain to absolutely every person in every group. Only society can make judgments of programs which are assessed to guarantee positive-sum result in group utility where it is certain that some individuals or small groups will sacrifice. If all groups concerned predict positive-sum utility outcome to result from free-market prices, the alternative should be selected just as would any other method which attains this end.

The problem of policy is not to lessen the function of the pricing mechanism, but to make the pricing system work better in attaining progress and increase in aggregate utility of the national society. The best hope for any large and complex society is to use the pricing system where positive-sum and/or equity in Pareto-better outcome is assured. Where it alone does not guarantee these conditions, policy is needed to "shore it up," to bring about attainment of these conditions but still to allow maximum effectiveness of the pricing mechanism in maintaining an open economy which responds to the individual preference of its sovereign consumers, or to the aggregate desires of the community in public purposes. The other two programs, voluntary land retirement and marketable quotas, outlined above for regearing production to modern economic structure, do not do away with the pricing mechanism, but only add more functions for it to perform. In this case, then, does not policy have positive-sum effect in increasing the functions of the market and price mechanisms? Programs such as land retirement, diverting greater supply of land to uses other than commodities deemed in surplus, would be used to turn commodities loose in the markets. Commodities would be priced in a manner to let consumers better guide the relative allocation of resource; with the condition that the supply function would be restrained to a desirable extent by decrease in spatial extent of the farm plant. Prices free in this type of market could differ not at all in function and level from those operating in a free market where the supply of new technology might have been less. Would not both then be "free use of prices"? Had the public not "gone around the market" so greatly in socializing research and education, the supply of technology and the supply of commodities both would be less. Price would be higher accordingly. But this restraint would be undesirable and we would have a much smaller contingency reserve of knowledge and food. We prefer not to restrain research, education and knowledge, but to restrain supply by keeping standby production plant in the manner of regional adjustment mentioned above.

CONSERVATION PAYMENTS

U.S. society appropriated more than 7 billion dollars for soil conservation programs over the period 1933–59. In general, these appropriations, to the extent that they were truly for conservation, provide for greater future consumption at the expense of that in the present period. Funds allocated for conservation purposes mean greater taxes and smaller consumption of autos, clothing or other commodities of the present; or smaller consumption of other public services for which current tax dollars might also be used. Not all of these expenditures under the heading of soil conservation actually qualify as increasing conservation services, however. Soil conservation is an "acceptable label" for subsidies. Production control and price boosting programs have had a tendency to be put under this cloak. For example, the land input reducing program of the 1950's was designated as the 1956 Conservation Reserve Act.

Of the 1933–59 conservation outlays indicated in Table 14.3, nearly 75 percent went for monetary payments to farmers through the Agricultural Conservation Program. The payments were made to farmers who used more labor and capital inputs which were conveniently identified as "conservation practices." Viewing the relationships in equations (4.23) through (4.26), it is obvious that any policy which lowers the price of a factor should increase output. But the problem of true conservation is to increase supply in a future period with sacrifice of supply in the present period. The effect of perhaps the largest portion of soil conservation payments has been that of increasing production in the present period. The same analysis and statement can be applied to other conservation investments such as the technical assistance of the Soil Conservation Service.

Monetary and technical assistance (one provides money to the farmer for purchase of an input and the other furnishes him a physical input) can be used for true conservation or for boosting current production. Investment is made in true conservation activities if the practices are such as those which retard erosion and prevent salination of soils, so that they will be available in future time periods. But other investment under these programs simply cause greater inputs to be used currently on soils without a conservation problem. Monetary and technical assistance is provided, under the label of conservation, in California to improve efficiency of irrigation systems on level land, in Minnesota for draining land which is so flat that it accumulates water, in Illinois for fertilizing and liming land of zero slope, in Nebraska and Wyoming for putting down wells and developing irrigation systems, in Kansas and Texas for use of deep tillage and other yield improvement practices on flat land and for other output-increasing investments the nation over. Much of this investment has no relationship to preservation of future land productivity. Hence, total public expenditures for conservation could both (1) conserve more land for future purposes and (2) lessen pressure to increase output in the current period, if they were allocated differently.

Some of these investments are even the negative of conservation: If a parcel of wet land in Minnesota is not drained this year, it will still be there in 50 years (with more top soil deposited on it) and fewer of the initial soil nutrient supplies will be exhausted. Development of irrigation on Great Plains soils increases the rate at which phosphates and potash can be used from the soil—to increase present production at the expense of future production. Subsidy of irrigation wells in some localities increases water resources withdrawn at the present time, but lowers the water table and decreases production possible from it in a future period.

In addition to the above programs of developmental nature which have main effect in increasing contemporary supply of farm products, other programs do so similarly. Programs (involving more than a half billion dollars) leading to development of land for irrigation under the Bureau of Reclamation did so in the above period. Hence, in addition to the more passive investments in research and education, we make investments directly in inputs, or subsidize their costs, to increase output at the present. On the same farm, the nation has long made conflicting investments: one paying the farmer to curtail land and other inputs as a means of reducing output, and another paying him to use more inputs on remaining land to increase output. Here the ends and investments are pure contradiction.

More conservation could be attained with given public outlays, with reduced impetus to current output, or current conservation attainment could be had with smaller outlay, if conservation funds were allocated differently. Most importantly, distinction should be made between those investments which have a main effect of shoving the supply function of the current period to the right and those which shift only the supply function of future periods to the right. The optimum arrangement would be, considering current problems of production capacity and producer-consumer equity, investments which push current supply function to the left and future supply function to the right. Numerous such investment opportunities do exist (except major effort becomes confounded between investment in acreage and output quotas to restrain supply, and in conservation-labeled programs to augment it).

Perhaps the major opportunity, however, is in investments which are neutral in respect to supply function of the present period and retain the supply function of the future—safeguarding against the leftward movement in the future. This criterion should be used: Inputs used in one period which increase the supply function of the same period are *con-*

ventional inputs and should not qualify for conservation subsidy. In other words, the input can be used in the current period or future period, the effect on supply being the same in either. However, input which is required in this period to increase (or maintain) the supply function of future periods is a *conservation input* and should have the full public outlay for conservation. Investment thus must be made in terms of the nature of the production function in relation to the supply function. Programs which simply use subsidy to lower the factor/product price ratio and cause the farmer to use more of conventional inputs (those already in use), in order to drive the marginal productivity of the factor to lower level, are best labeled "production" or "supply increasing." Those which subsidize cost of a factor not in use, because its discounted factor/product price ratio has been higher than the marginal productivity of the factor in terms of its stream of outputs over future periods, but should be in use, are those for which conservation payments should be used. We have explained these concepts in detail elsewhere but will summarize essential relationships as they further distinguish between investments which increase the current supply function and those which augment or protect the future supply function of food.[22]

Without a criterion such as that mentioned above in respect to supply functions of different periods, there is no limit to the number of inputs which might be subsidized to increase supply or output in the current period. In the discussion which follows, conservation practices (resources) are only those which prevent diminution of output in the future from given resource inputs (retention of a given production function over time.)

In terms of our criteria, efficiency in the use of limited annual conservation appropriations is denoted by allocations which minimize the potential diminution of future production when given resources are applied to the land and which do not have focus on increasing present output. Irrigation, drainage, and weed control are not practices which are generally necessary to prevent a diminution in future production. If irrigation is not developed or improved on a tract of land now, there is nothing to preclude its initiation at a future date with an equivalent increase in production. A legume or grass crop used to prevent erosion or permanent deterioration in soil structure is related to production in the future. However, where these crops are used simply to boost short-run production of subsequent grain crops on level soil types, they hardly qualify for public subsidy if the objective is the maintenance of future productivity. Payments for liming materials and inorganic fertilizers for grasses and legumes on level land with the principal effect of increasing short-run yield and supply fall in a similar category. Subsidization of practices with no effect in preventing diminution of future production represents an inefficient use of public resources allocated for conservation

[22] Earl O. Heady, *Economics of Agricultural Production and Resource Use*, Prentice-Hall, New York, 1952, Chap. 26; and Iowa Agr. Exp. Sta. Bul. 382.

purposes (when processes which do lessen future production are taking place).

A similar analysis can be applied to SCS technical assistance. The first soil-conservation districts were generally formed in areas with the greatest erosion hazard and hence where a true conservation problem existed. Furthermore, a greater proportion of the SCS technical assistance is probably allocated to conservation practices (as defined here) than is true for monetary assistance. As the number of soil-conservation districts has expanded, however, the erosion hazards have generally been less critical, and a portion of technical assistance has been devoted to developing irrigation systems, drainage districts, and the like. Certainly the SCS technical assistance used for irrigation, improved rotations on level land, or drainage developments (where these are of a nonconservation nature) could better be employed where permanent deterioration of the soil is taking place. They would thus relate to conserving the production function for food and in restraining its supply price in future time period, rather than in causing current supply functions to shift to the right and lowering present food supply price.

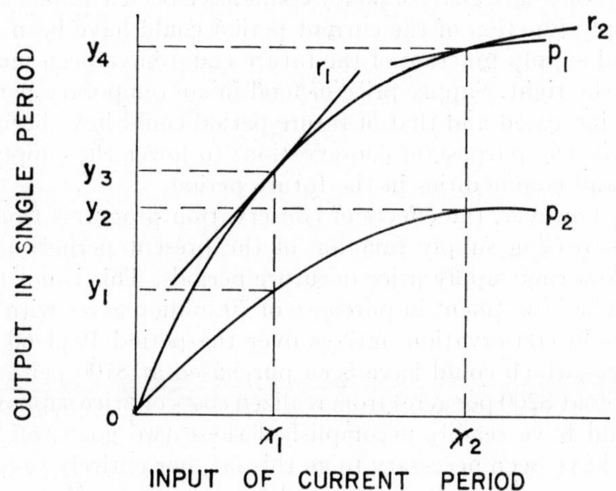

Fig. 14.7. Conservation Inputs.

Under our definition here, soil conservation refers to retention of a given production function over time to increase the conservation input which is necessary if conventional inputs are to have the same marginal productivity in a future as in the present time period. Hence, in Figure 14.7, inputs which increase output along a given production function, P_1, are conventional inputs. Increase from ox_1 to ox_2 along production function P_1 simply increases output of current period from oy_3 to oy_4. Subsidy of input has the effect of lessening the slope of factor/product price ratio line from r_1 to r_2, and in increasing the profitability of inputs which increase output at the present. In contrast, conservation inputs are those which are technical complements to retention of marginal resource productivity of conventional inputs at a level in the future production period equal to that of the present period. Hence, they prevent a drop from production function as from P_1 to P_2. For example, without conservation input, production from ox_1 input would drop from oy_3 to oy_4. Or, if the conservation input were not provided, extention of input to ox_2 would increase output to only oy_2, rather than to oy_4. Without question, much of the subsidy in the form of technical and monetary assistance of federal programs has gone into traverse of curve P_1, rather than in preventing fall from this function to P_2.

Given the current tendency of the supply function to shift more rapidly than demand, and with inability to predict demand magnitude a hundred years hence, it is preferable to invest in inputs which retain or extend the supply function of the future, rather than those which augment the current supply for food. The 7 billion dollars invested in conservation over the period 1932–39 alone would have allowed the public to purchase 70 million acres at $100 per acre, or 35 million at $200 per acre. Had this land been purchased and put to grass or trees, two important intermediate goals of policy could have been attained simultaneously: supply function of the current period could have been shifted to the left and supply function of the future could have been much better shifted to the right. Supply price of food in contemporary period could have been increased and that of future period could have been lowered. The latter is the purpose of conservation: to lower the supply price of resources and commodities in the future period.

Largely, however, the effects of conservation programs from 1940 to 1960, in increasing supply function of the present period, outweighed effects in lowering supply price in future periods. This is not necessary, however. The investment in purchase of 70 million acres with the 7 billion dollars in conservation outlays over the period 1933–60, plus 178 million acres which could have been purchased at $100 per acre (or 89 million acres at $200 per acre) from realized costs of price supports (Table 14.3), would have readily accomplished these two goals. Of course, it would not have been necessary to go this far, nor entirely to have sacrificed current supply to have attained future supply. We mention the quantities only to indicate the production possibilities in goal attainment which have existed from given public outlays in previous decades, and to re-emphasize the need for more permanent withdrawal of land inputs under an environment where current supply price of farm commodities is too low, and total input of resources in agriculture is too great to be consistent with desired level of farm returns, national income and economic progress.

It is likely that the above approach was not used in respect to a more efficient allocation of investment between food supply functions and farm commodity prices of current and future periods because (1) the public had insufficient knowledge of the basic supply and conservation problems of agriculture and of the inconsistencies in different policy means and ends, (2) political and interest groups pressed to keep programs oriented in particular directions and towards the present and (3) large-scale land conservation programs would have given rise to problems of equity between (1) nonfarm persons in rural areas (and farmers) of this generation and (2) general consumers of future generations. However, the actual public outlay from 1940 to 1960 would have allowed redress of such losses and attainment of general equity; or it would have allowed development of general social policy to assure positive-sum outcome from more effective integration of food supply in current and future periods.

POLICIES OF EQUITY AND PRICE

As mentioned previously in this chapter, policies can be developed to increase the number of functions which the pricing and market mechanism perform. These policies can bring equity in distribution of gains and losses from progress and desired economic reorganization, whereas some strata otherwise bear sacrifices posing negative-sum utility outcomes. They can help to erase major inefficiencies of the economic system which have accumulated from the past. They are public policies, designed and initiated by man who is master of the state and the institutions and mechanisms which function within it, in contrast to societies where man is the subject of the state and the mechanisms, market or otherwise, which operate within it and under its sponsorship. Marketable quotas increase the functions to be performed by the market, as also is true of voluntary land retirement supplied in response to a price offered for this purpose. The main policy problems are those of equity in distribution of gains and losses from policy or market impact. Under quotas, the problem is equity in initial distribution of aggregate market restraint; under the free market, it is a problem of equity in the distribution of gains and losses from ongoing variables in growth which cause opportunities and returns for some to grow, but for others to decay, as change takes place in technology and consumer preferences.

Restated, a major task of policy is to assure equity in the distribution of gains from progress. With attainment of this goal, there is no basis for further policy to restrain progress, in case measurement of progress embraces the complete range of goods, services and cultural attributes with positive utility to all consumers. Policy which goes beyond this general goal, to try to maintain a regional and resource pattern of agriculture drawn from the past, is inconsistent not only with progress but also with solution of basic problems of agriculture. As mentioned in Chapter 11, the "return of the evil" is certain in this sense: Policy which increases income at the present cannot remove the causes of low income and resource returns for the future where low relative factor supply elasticity is the basis. Surplus resources will remain, with transfer income capitalized into asset values and low return to future labor, unless the causes per se of low factor supply elasticity are removed.

15

Capital Supply and Family Farms

A PARADOX of agriculture is that for decades and centuries it has furnished capital aiding development of nonfarm sectors without a compensating flow of capital from the latter into agriculture. Yet it is an industry where the firm traditionally is short on capital. The paucity of investment funds is especially great in the poverty sector of agriculture, but the capital-supply complex of the commercial sector also differs greatly from that of the major nonfarm sectors.

Difference between industries in capital supply functions is not in material items such as machinery, fertilizer, seeds, insecticides and other specific forms. At the current level of economic development, these items of physical capital are supplied about as efficiently and freely to agriculture as to other industries, and in pretty much in the same competitive structure. The great difference is in the equity base on which capital funds and credit are supplied to agriculture. Traditionally, equity to which supply of investment funds is tied comes from within agriculture. Capital accumulation in agriculture has been almost solely a function of the industry. Recent studies indicate that no less than 90 percent of investment in agriculture has come from savings of households therein.[1]

As an industry declining in labor force and households, the steady transfer of people means that capital invested in the individual moves

[1] A. Tostlebe, *Capital in Agriculture, Its Formation and Financing Since 1870*, Princeton University Press, Princeton, N.J., 1957, pp. 3–5.

continuously to urban and industrial sectors. Also, farm plant shares of capital inherited by those who migrate has similar transfer, with persons remaining required to restore a portion of this value of assets from later savings generated within agriculture. Were agriculture an industry expanding in labor force and households and investment of the latter being beyond the supply indigenous to the industry as it was in the period of national settlement, capital funds would be supplied more from outside sectors. Or, if the farm labor and entrepreneurial force came equally from outside the industry, capital flowing out of the industry would only balance that flowing into it.

The nature of the capital supply function as it relates to the aggregate of agriculture does not restrain farm product supply against demand, thus causing pressure towards high real price of food. To the contrary, the capital market, both in respect to physical items and investment funds for the aggregate industry, allows and encourages adoption of new techniques faster than their effect in commodity supply can be digested by the indigenous structure of agricultural factor supply.

In nations at low stages of economic development, supply constraint for investment funds by individual firms and agriculture in total does have important impact on rate of technical advance. But in the United States it does not do so importantly for several reasons. Inputs of agriculture which are furnished from outside of the industry are generally more elastic in supply and less closely tied to equity of the household than those supplied from inside of agriculture. Investment funds are technical complements or limitational inputs with use of the physical capital items furnished from outside of agriculture. If farmers lack investment funds for farm machinery, they cannot purchase or use the latter. For this reason, firms which supply capital inputs to commercial agriculture have aided in expanding the supply function of investment funds for these particular purposes. Hence, capital restraints do not generally limit supply of funds for purchase of farm machinery. Dealer credit is available for fertilizer and seeds even for farmers in the lowest strata of income, but certainly at a high price or interest rate. Similarly, credit for chicks and feed is supplied by firms specializing in the supply of these resources to farmers through contract and integration farming.

The demand for these nonfarm inputs would be greater, and more of certain groups would be used, causing farm technology to be improved even more rapidly, if the supply function of investment capital to agriculture were more elastic. Yet the chain of relationships from (1) supply function of capital facing agriculture to (2) demand function for nonfarm inputs to (3) supply function of food products is not of serious consequence to the consumer. Relaxing the capital supply function to cause a more rapid expansion of the food supply function is not a pressing problem for American society. It is much less so than need in expanding the supply of capital to education in order that subsequent increase can take place in human resources developed and supply of skilled and professional labor can be expanded to growth industries. It might even be better argued that if the supply prices of investment funds and capital of new technology were increased "over the board" for agriculture, the commodity supply function would be restrained against an inelastic demand, and revenue of agriculture would be increased more than costs.

Why, then, is capital supply for agriculture a problem worthy of discussion? It is a problem of important magnitude in several respects. Capital supply phenomena largely cause the low-income sector of agriculture to retain its structure in times and locations when national industrial development otherwise is rapid enough and provides the setting for a much more speedy erasure of poverty. It causes investment for development of the individual to fall below the level desired in terms of national needs, future economic growth and the unexploited capacities of many individuals. It restrains the rate at which adjustment can occur in the structure of agriculture, especially in size and numbers of farms where resources per unit are inadequate for modern-day concepts of equity in living standards. It affects the freedom of some farm families. They are not equally free, with their colleagues of agriculture, to take advantage of technical change produced by the public and to maintain a given share of the industry's revenue. Those who are faced with an elastic supply function of capital with favorable price of investment funds indeed have greater freedom in the market than those who are not so blessed.

To the extent that the former group can increase its output at a sufficiently high rate relative to the increase in aggregate output and the supply price of capital, it can benefit from increase in production technology and food supply even though revenue to the industry declines. Finally, capital requirements for farming under continued economic growth, and the supply conditions which surround them, promise to have impact on institutions with long-standing value orientations. Family farms fall in this category.

CAPITAL SUPPLY AND EQUITY IN DISTRIBUTION OF PROGRESS GAINS

Equity in the distribution of gains from technological progress generated in public research institutions is possible only if farmers have a comparable degree of opportunity to capital. Otherwise, those who lack capital for innovating are left in the backwash of increased output, inelastic demand and diminished revenue. In equations (5.42) through (5.57) we illustrated that while the aggregate effect of increased output, at rate greater than demand growth, is decline in total revenue, producers who increase output by a greater proportion than the industry do gain from the process. Those restrained in innovation and who increase output at rates equal to or less than the industry bear the brunt of losses stemming from technological progress.

As agriculture becomes more commercialized and specialized, and as factor prices further extend the substitution of mechanization and its attendant scale economies for labor, this gap in opportunity between farm firms will grow. Those operating on a corporate basis, or with financial structure allowing access to supply of investment funds under comparable conditions, have greatest opportunity for gain from technological research. Those starting with low initial equity and dependent on capital accumulation through meager savings of households will be increasingly excluded from gains of publicly or privately produced research. In fact, it is upon this group that the costs of progress, over the total range of gains and sacrifices, fall with greatest weight. With speed in the rate of development and capitalization of agriculture, this burden promises to fall on a broadening group of farm operators. Equity can be restored, of course, through a wide range of policy means including: education, training and related services which give those squeezed out of agriculture the opportunity for comparable gain in employment by nonfarm industry; quotas which restrain output of all producers or allow those with least opportunity to receive compensation through sale of their producing rights; credit and educational policy which gives approximate equality of opportunity in capitalizing on the product of public research institutions; and others.

To the extent that credit policy is used for these purposes, it needs to be based more on prospects in productivity, and certain other of the rearrangements mentioned below, than on traditional attachment to owner equities. But just as education which turns surplus labor of agriculture back into the industry is undesirable, so is credit policy which becomes entangled in the nostalgia of pioneer farming and lashes people to agriculture when their best opportunity is outside.

The amount of capital necessary for initiation of farming on a scale promising success is approximately that required in training for the medical profession. Rather than credit policy to place this amount of capital in the hands of every farm youth, capital investment in education to train more for the medical profession is needed, given the rate of return on capital in the two sectors. Similarly, credit policy directed simply to keep middle-aged operators on inadequate units is not desirable when returns to the family would be greater in capital diverted to retraining them for employment and in underwriting migration costs for transfer out of agriculture. The transformation of low-income sectors of agriculture with meager productivity and family income to levels consistent with the over-all American standard does call for important credit aids in long-distressed areas. Only thus can small low-income farms be consolidated into productive units employing appropriate technology.

CAPITAL AND FARM SIZE UNDER ECONOMIC DEVELOPMENT

In discussion of Figure 3.1, we indicated that economic development itself would have called for change in labor/capital combinations, degree of mechanization and farm size—even had all machine technologies been known from the outset of civilization. This is true because of the increase in price of labor relative to capital in the long sweep that characterizes sustained economic growth. Without full initial knowledge of all physically possible technologies, they still tend to develop and are encouraged by the same set of price forces.

As labor grows in price relative to capital, it becomes more economic to substitute the latter for the former. Hence, there is growing profit in invention and supply of machines to replace manpower. With or without initial knowledge of all possible physical technologies, the different stages of economic growth call for different patterns of farm numbers and sizes and different labor or machine technologies. Suppose, however, that the over-all production function and its marginal productivities and marginal substitution quantities were known for all times as in equation (4.18). The input variables representing labor with "less" mechanization, labor with "greater" mechanization, etc. are known as illustrated in Figure 3.1. Focus thus is not on knowledge of the production function but on the relative prices of the factors which go into it.

In an economy characterized by capital scarcity, population pressure and general labor unemployment, the supply price of capital is high relative to that of labor. Even though the technical coefficients are known for machinery (mechanized agriculture), the least-cost and economically most efficient organization of agriculture leans in the direction of labor technology. With approximately constant scale returns or costs for labor-type technology, agriculture can be organized into smaller productive units without sacrifice in alternative social goals and economy of production. Given similar technical and management skills under labor technology, small farms operated independently can probably be just as efficient as large plantations or state farms operated with many laborers. However, as economic development progresses with capital becoming relatively abundant and labor becoming relatively scarce (agricultural production functions remaining constant and/or being fully known), the relative prices for capital and labor resources turn (Table 7.1) to favor substitution of machinery for labor.

With mechanization and "lumpy" capital inputs involving fixed costs, cost economies are much greater for increased farm size. Hence, with a decrease in the supply price for capital relative to labor under economic development, a transition from a labor technology to larger and fewer farms or a greater machine technology in agriculture represents the transition in structure of agriculture. Too, at a higher level of economic development and industrialization, the presence of increased employment opportunities and other social mechanisms for "producing" distributive and stability ends may be created.

Even without change in technical knowledge, growth of Asian economies to give per capita incomes and factor supply conditions approaching the U.S. level would call for transition from the "reform structures," farm sizes and labor technology which currently denote the social optimum, to an entirely different structure of agriculture. In this sense, given the production function, the optimum organization of farms in respect to size, numbers, capital requirements and technology in a broad sense is itself a function of economic growth and the conditions of capital supply. A different optimum farm size or technology exists for the various stages of economic growth. In a pure economic sense, this is as much true in communistic as in capitalistic economies. At stages of little capital and large population, labor agriculture is still optimum, even though it is organized into plantations or collective farms. But with growth, wealth and greater capital supply, mechanization becomes more the appropriate structure because it has lower real cost against the supply function of labor.

The extent to which farm size expansion needs to be an important concern in economic development of any country depends largely on (1) the rate of industrialization and the creation of nonfarm employment opportunities, (2) the size of the farm labor force and its potential contribution through migration and (3) the nature of resource economies in agriculture. Under lack of nonfarm employment opportunities and great underemployment of agriculture, national gain from farm enlargement and mechanization to increase labor productivity is small, if even positive. An increase in labor productivity simply results in unemployment for those released from farming. Of course, if farm enlargement not only increases labor productivity but also results in economies of capital, farm size expansion could contribute importantly to economic development even if the labor released has no other employment alternative. Questions of positive-sum utility outcomes and equity then arise unless mechanisms leading to distributive justice are created. Hence, the crucial question arises whether, under the relevant resource supplies and prices and hence the appropriate technology, important scale economies for capital do exist. A "strong hypothesis" is that they are "relatively weak" or nonexistent for the labor types of agriculture found in undeveloped countries, the technologies relevant for the conditions of factor supplies and prices where work force is large relative to the national capital. Economies may exist up to the limits of the typical buffalo, horse, camel or bullock team and associated implements. Effective utilization of these small "chunks" of capital is attained with a relatively small farm size. Larger farms largely are duplication of the land-animal-implement mix used on small units.

Factor prices in the United States are such that continued substitution of capital for labor will continue. Since capital of machines comes in large "chunks," with per unit costs declining over greater acreage, farms will continue to be larger. Already it is physically possible for a million farms, or ever fewer, to represent the food supply function of the nation. The trend will continue in this direction. Capital requirements will grow not only because of the large investments required in the "lumpy inputs" represented by large-capacity machines but also because the potential scale economies are possible only if the operator has the necessary amount of acres, animals and supplies to realize them.

Firm Demand for Capital and Credit Supply Structure

Given the existing and prospective techniques in agriculture and the relative prices of factors used in production, the individual farm's capital demand or requirement will grow greatly over future years. Even with some further decline in commodity prices relative to factor prices, this will be true because (1) of the larger amount of acres, animals and supplies over which scale economies of machinery and equipment extend and which are necessary to realize major cost advantages, (2) the productivity of many resources such as chemicals is still high relative to their costs for the individual farmer and (3) the suppliers of inputs will increasingly find themselves faced with the need either to increase the productivity of the resource they sell to farmers or to lower its price. A lower price means more inputs per farm, and fewer farms against a highly restrained or inelastic demand for food.

Greater knowledge of farm people, better adaptation of vocational and other education to current-day economic conditions and improved communication mechanisms for nonfarm employment opportunities also will lead further to a greater average capital input per farm. Too, the tendency towards increased specialization in farm management, partly as a result of the more complicated technology of production, also will favor a greater input and output per farm. Capital inputs or demand for the individual farm will grow much more rapidly than those for the industry, largely because the industry will retain a high degree of constancy against decline in number and increase in size of individual units. (See Table 2.8.) Growth in per farm use of capital and attainment of scale economies will tend to cause resource returns of agriculture to compare more favorably with those of other industries. But before this structural change is completed, in magnitudes which appear important, changes may be required in the capital market and in credit supply. Obviously a farm unit using $200,000 or more in capital, an amount now consistent with the technology and scale economies existing in major types of commercial agriculture, will have to surmount important financing problems.

Tradition in equity base of agriculture, mainly from families supplying labor to the sector, is not paralleled in other major industries. Corporate funds and common stocks draw widely over all sectors of the economy, and not particularly from households supplying labor. Typically, farm businesses have been initiated by the family providing the initial assets or credit backing to a son, each generation of firms starting anew in this process.[2] Inheritances drawn from capital accumulation within agriculture have been the main source of the "down payment" in purchasing land. This source of equity base is much less consistent with the tech-

[2] For more detailed analysis of the "life cycle" of farm firms, see Earl O. Heady, *Economics of Agricultural Production and Resource Use*, Prentice-Hall, New York, 1952, pp. 431–33. Also see papers in E. L. Baum, Earl O. Heady, and Howard Diesslen (eds.), *Capital and Credit Needs in a Changing Agriculture*, Iowa State University Press, Ames, Iowa, 1961.

nology and capital requirements of today than with those of decades back.

Growth of vertical integration may stem as much from these capital developments as from other reasons sometimes mentioned. But vertical integration is only one means for gearing institutional and market mechanisms more closely to modern capital needs and in causing the supply base for credit used in agriculture to be extended to nonfarm sectors. Others need to be investigated. Family corporations and equity financing may be of promise. The entire structure under which credit is provided to agriculture needs to be re-examined. Historically, the farm operator has borrowed funds, beyond his inheritance or individual capital accumulation to finance ownership. But he immediately established a goal of full equity and diverted savings into debt retirement. The goal underlying this procedure has been that of security for old age and retirement. The extension of social security coverage to farmers, the growing knowledge of farmers about nonfarm investments and related developments may remove the pressure for rapid and complete debt retirement.

The corporate firm makes no particular effort to liquidate its indebtedness on an amortized basis. Should credit be extended more to agriculture in a similar manner? Farm operators then might, where appropriate, utilize their savings to extend scale to a level more consistent with modern technology. Gain might well accrue to both farms as businesses and to lending firms, supposing initial loans to have an economically substantial base, under this demand-supply setting. In the absence of major business recessions and in a stable agriculture, borrowed capital should have no less productivity later than today. As corporate firms already suggest, why should debt be liquidated if the funds so obtained have a productivity greater than their price?

In orthodox economic context, farm firms should be encouraged to place their savings in enlarged investment, as long as the marginal efficiency of capital is greater than interest rates. Repayment would occur only after investment had extended to levels where they are approximately equal, and not necessarily then except to the extent that development leads to food prices which decline relative to factor prices.

If young farmers are to be given better opportunity for starting operations, or if established operators are to use the various capital resources in line with their relative prices and productivity, consideration needs to be given methods for extending credit more on the basis of capital productivity. Credit on this basis would allow a use of resources more in line with modern economic structure, as compared to the more conventional security basis of loans. Of course, risks to the loaning firm are no less important than risk and uncertainty to the farm firm in specifying the structure of the credit supply function. They depend on variance in management ability of individual operators as well as variance in price and production functions. Integrating firms have partly gotten around this difficulty by combining management aids or specifications with capital supply, to lessen the uncertainty of decision ability of the farm operator. A parallel development appears appropriate for other institutions and firms which supply credit.

Forces leading to larger and more elastic supply of investment funds to individual farmers do pose certain questions of policy ends and equity. Increase of the capital supply function to individuals promotes the growth or progress goal in the sense that it leads to greater capital use per farm, encouraged technical improvement, greater attainment of scale economies and smaller resource requirements of agriculture and the freeing of labor for employment in other industries. On the other hand, greater attainment of the progress goal promises to compete with other possible goals such as equity, family farms and, in the short-run, even aggregate level of farm income.

POLICY IN CREDIT WITH DEVELOPMENTAL EFFECTS

Credit policy can be directed towards such distinct ends as progress, equity and other constructs. As a mechanism to promote economic development, the function of credit policy should be to increase the elasticity of supply and lower the price of capital to farmers. Under these conditions, profit incentive is increased and rationing restraint is lessened, thus allowing purchase of inputs representing improved technologies and leading to economies of scale in resource use.

Numerous studies have indicated the impact of the uncertainty-capital complex on size of farms and agricultural practice or organization in commercial U.S. agriculture. Little direct analysis has been made of this phenomenon as it relates to small-scale, low-income farmers of the U.S., or to capital-short cultivators in less advanced agricultures. But certainly it places an even heavier burden on agricultural improvement in the latter cases and generally dampens innovation in technology and expansion of farm size. The "degree of uncertainty," even in the innovation of a new crop variety which does not increase capital outlay, stands to be great for a person whose meager income and food supply makes subsistence precarious in any year. With little or no reserve borrowing capacity in case of crop failure and with ability to predict and forecast new outcomes from innovations driven near zero by (1) lack of mobility to view outcomes on other farms at even short distance and (2) his lack of education, the low-income farmer or cultivator certainly must hesitate in substituting a new variety and method for one which has "proven the test of time in keeping him fed." Chance taking, when income is at the borderline of subsistence, is highly "unpalatable."

Game models tested in underdeveloped and subsistence agricultures against those of developed commercial agricultures would likely show the "strategies against nature" to be in the direction of conservative or Wald minimax types in the former and to be much less restraining in the latter. Perhaps more important are the innovations which involve the use of more capital. Generally it is agreed that Kalecki's principle of increasing risk is operative in highly commercialized U.S. agriculture.[3] Since the farmer is forced to underwrite borrowing with his own capital, the "degree of uncertainty," quite apart from interest rate or price of capital, reaches the "breaking point" as his equity is spread as a thin base under borrowed funds. Returns from further investment are discounted to zero where possible losses stand to wipe out his own equity and cease the life of his firm. The "breaking point" or discount of prospective returns to zero, for the low-income farmer and subsistence cultivator, relates more closely to the health and life of the household and to family members. The uncertainty restraint in capital use is much more binding here than for highly commercialized operators, even where credit sources exist and the capital supply function is not vertical.

Lifting the major restraint of uncertainty on innovation is difficult under low-income and subsistence farming. Largely, it can be approached from two directions: (1) improving the knowledge of outcomes from innovations, even to the extent of explaining the "worst to be expected" from new techniques, and (2) improving the capital and equity position of farmers. Sufficient progress in the latter would lessen the degree to which certainty for the former needs to be increased. Farmers could then "take some chances" and do more experimentation on their own.

In juxtaposition, the labor supply functions for agriculture in different countries, or farm sectors within a country such as the U.S., with various stages of development are highly similar in *degree* of elasticity and level of prices *relative* to other industries. In contrast, the capital supply function for agriculture is much less similar among countries and farm sectors, with the elasticity being higher and the supply price being lower in developed agricultural sectors relative to less developed farm sectors and countries. In purely theoretical and static context, the greater supply price of capital in less developed agricultures itself calls for a smaller product or yield per acre and unit. Lifting the static cloak to view the setting of decision under uncertainty, there is even further basis for less advanced techniques and lower yields on low-income and subsistence farms than on highly commercialized units.

Public policy to lower the supply price of investment funds has two effects: (1) It effectively lowers the prices of factors, encouraging their use to be expanded, since marginal productivities can be driven to lower levels in matching reduced input/output price ratios; (2) it lessens the cost of factors, thus increasing net income of producers even though they hold factor inputs constant. (Net income also will be increased from expanded factor use as long as the marginal product of the resources is greater than the price ratio.)

Public credit policy was initiated with establishment of the Federal Land Bank System in 1916. It was aimed at the broad commercial sector of American agriculture and undoubtedly had the general and initial aim

[3] Earl O. Heady, *ibid.*

of increasing net income as in (2) above. This was generally possible, with some segments of agriculture paying interest rates as high as 10 percent on real estate loans while other sectors of agriculture were paying only 5 percent and nonfarm sectors were borrowing at even lower rates. Perhaps this is still the main objective of credit policy and publicly sponsored credit facilities for agriculture. However, a lower supply price of capital to encourage economic development is itself hardly needed for the main commercial sector of U.S. agriculture. Attempt to increase income through subsidy or lower supply price of factors and investment funds logically has the same effect of higher support prices for these purposes.

If we turn back to equation (5.10), we see that the expected effect of lowered value for P_x, factor or capital price, is the same as increased magnitude of P, commodity price, namely, an increase in Q_s or output. Reduction in P_x shifts the supply function to the right while increase in P causes output to increase along a given supply function. For broad commercial agriculture there is little purpose in subsidized credit price as means of stepping up development of the industry. Rate of progress currently is as great as can be absorbed by growth in food demand and in nonfarm employment opportunities. Credit policy which lessens input price and extends aggregate output bears no promise in increasing the net revenue of agriculture. This is true in the extent that low price elasticity of demand for farm commodities causes total revenue to decline by greater proportion than reduction in costs through lower supply price of capital.

EQUITY FINANCING

Public credit policy for agriculture, such as through the Federal Land Banks, Production Credit Associations and Farmers Home Administration,[4] thus now has its greatest basis in bringing (1) equity of opportunity to agricultural sectors (2) aid in transformation of the poverty sector of the industry into a commercial sector to provide incomes consistent with greater equality of opportunity and (3) retention of family-based operations. Alone, it can do little to offset the trend to larger farms under economic development. Available to all farmers, it lowers the price of capital even further, encouraging more biological and mechanical inputs per farm, causing farms to become larger and less dependent on labor. Lower supply price of credit, particularly in the poverty sector where effective interest rates are considerably higher than in commercial agriculture, and a greater detachment of the supply of investment funds from equity, can have a relatively significant effect on income for low-income farmers; much more so than in cost savings for larger-

[4] Initially these were the following legislative acts: the Federal Farm Loan Act of 1914, the Farm Credit Administration of 1933, the Resettlement Administration in 1935, the Farm Security Administration in 1937 and the Bankhead-Jones Farm Tenant Act of 1937.

scale commercial operators who have highly elastic credit supply and low supply price of capital. Too, there is basis for public policy in credit where (1) certain scale economies in supply of this commodity is only thus attained and (2) the market for capital otherwise provides only a loose linkage between farm and non-farm sectors.

Separation of credit supply from its restraint in capital equity of the borrower is not a burden which should be relegated to private suppliers. They, like farmers who demand credit, are faced with the normal uncertainties of the agricultural production process. (Risk facing the farm producer in respect to weather and price also face the firm supplying him with funds to conduct production.) In addition, the private lender faces the uncertainty of the character of the borrower and uncertainty in demand for withdrawal of funds by his supplier. Equity financing in agriculture would lessen capital restraints from these sources.

Vertical integration represents equity financing, with funds coming from private subscription or sale of common stock outside of agriculture, a type of substitute for the same process within agriculture. This opportunity for equity financing of agriculture, through more elastic capital supply from outside the industry, is perhaps one of the largest forces leading to integrated farming. It may grow further because of this reason and because of the pull from the marketing end. In the integration sense, the supply of capital channeled to agriculture is loosened from the upper or institutional limits of owner equity which prevail for funds brought in through the traditional credit route. Substitute for farmer equity, in attainment of a given degree of certainty in supply of capital, is attained by integrating firms which bring in equity funds from outside of agriculture through a complementary supply of management aid and control. This mix of inputs perhaps provides the guide for needed public credit policy mentioned later, namely, the transformation of low-production farms to commercial units, capable of providing adequate income and dignity of opportunity for farm families, through improved supply of both capital and management. Policy mix to provide these ingredients, and approaching a scale for rapid effects, was perhaps represented in activities of the Farmers Home Administration in the 1930's and up to the mid-1940's. However, McConnell suggests that power struggle by farm organizations dissolved a framework which might have, with particular adaptations, speeded the end of the poverty sector in agriculture.[5]

Credit for Transformation of Poverty Sector

As mentioned above, credit is a major problem in converting the chronically low-income sectors of agriculture to commercial operations which can support families at income levels consistent with American capabilities. But important changes in capital, beyond those of land needed for farm enlargement, are required. Often capital invested in old forms,

[5] Grant McConnell, *The Decline of American Democracy,* University of California Press Berkeley, 1953, pp. 84–126.

such as buildings and equipment, is obsolete for these purposes of consolidation and farm improvement. Frequently, the persons migrating to industry or out of the region are those with the most capital and ability for making the transformations required.

Credit for transformation purposes necessarily should be broken far from the equity traditions of the past. In contrast to the historic philosophy of loans under FSA and FHA, credit supplied should have more the goal of developing a self-generating commercial operation, rather than a smaller-scale owner unit, capable only of generating income on the lower edge of comfort. To retain too many farms of the latter scale in the transformation of agriculture can only lead to family incomes which are inadequate when put to the test of economic progress and of opportunities for youth which fall short of their capacities. Notwithstanding these needs, transformation of the low-income sector of agriculture requires an extended time period and an integration of credit and educational services.

As pointed out in Chapter 5, technical knowledge and capital do serve as substitutes over a limited range of the isoquant map.[6] But over a wide range of combinations they are technical complements. These combinations perhaps best explain the fact that extension services historically worked with high-capital farmers—those who thus could profit most from the technical information retailed, as well as being the most "receptive audience."

Transformation of low-income farm areas to substantial commercial operations requires that a larger supply of both capital and management aids be made available and effective for operators who will and should remain in the industry. There are, of course, older operators of low-income areas who are potential neither in migration or greatly increased tempo in farm operation and whose utility would be lowered if they were forced into either. The attack on poverty structure through an extended mix of capital and management inputs must be directed largely at current and upcoming operators who have promise of managers; with other considerations in equity for those who must, unfortunately, remain underemployed in agriculture as the selected element of a set of low caliber opportunities.

Precedent for this operation does exist in the farm and home planning activities of the extension services, and the credit programs of the FHA. Unfortunately, however, either is inadequate by itself. Summed, they do not quite provide the aggregate of capital and management inputs required for the transformation. The educational aids are not now intensive enough and the credit constraints are still too rigid to allow rapid transformation to more effective commercial farm operations. A sizeable injection of capital is needed in these concentrated low-income areas, whether the goal be one of greater utilization of resources for national

[6] For other points in this complementarity, see Earl O. Heady, "Basic Logic in Farm and Home Planning in Extension Education," *Jour. Farm Econ.*, Vol. 38.

progress goals or for providing greater opportunity for the people represented. Capital is needed first in training and transfer of surplus labor to nonfarm activity. Next it is needed to provide the managerial aids and capital necessary for development of larger commercial farm operations. The second is undesirable without the first, since families are otherwise displaced from farms without a promising alternative. The first is unsufficient by itself, because it only leaves a void in land and families, with lack of necessary capital to tie them together in a productive manner.

PARTICULAR CAPITAL PROBLEMS UNDER CHANGE

In a highly developed economy such as the U.S., further economic growth gives rise to capital problems in two particular sectors of agriculture. One is in the poverty sector mentioned above. With capital accumulation, or the equity base which provides the maximum restraint in supply of investment funds, coming predominantly from savings of farm households, local industrialization and out-migration are not the full solution to the farm low-income problem. These developments do not place investment funds in the hands of remaining farmers in order that they can enlarge their farms and acquire the physical capital items necessary for efficiency of the farm firm and increased income to the household. Savings and household equity do not provide a sufficient base for the large investment required if farm consolidation is to extend to a level allowing elimination of underemployed labor even for a large number of commercial farms.

The other problem sector is that of areas where major shifts have to be made in the pattern of production in conformance with economic development and regional advantages. Regional adjustments from annual crops to grass and forestry, such as those discussed in Chapters 7 and 14 stand to lessen the demand for capital within the confines of the locations mentioned. Agriculture becomes less intensive in its use of capital in these regions, just as it uses more in other regions where developmental forces lead to greater physical inputs and output. With economic variables free in the market for a decade, America would see some of both: regions with declining comparative advantage, and supply functions relatively higher in the price-quantity plane, using a smaller aggregate of capital; regions favored by the obverse of these conditions and in favorable space orientation to realize higher derived demand for annual crops and fruits and growing populations using more.

But even in regions of contracting agriculture, decline in aggregate capital does not lessen the pressure for investment funds by the individual farm. This is true because shift among crops such as small grains or annual crops to grazing and forestry requires a considerable investment increment by operators remaining to make the transformation. As mentioned previously, these operators not only must obtain investment funds to initiate seedings and plantings but they also must acquire additional land to develop units which can generate adequate income. In shift to grazing, they must have capital for livestock and funds for household outlays during the several years when imcome is small under the transformation process. The investment problem is even more severe in the shift to forestry, and few individual operators can make the transformation while remaining as full-time farmers.

In major commercial sectors of agriculture during the 1960's, the complex of capital supply will not restrain commodity supply against the slowly increasing demand. Change over these sectors mainly means larger farms in order that prevailing scale or cost economies are realized. For rented farms, the underemployment of machinery and labor over much of the corn and wheat regions allows major expansion in farm size without a proportional increase in capital, or even with a very modest increment in investment per operator. Under land ownership and purchase, this is much less so. However, the stock of capital and access to investment funds in the concentrated grain producing areas can allow many families to leave agriculture, their units taken over by remaining operators, before capital supply stands to restrict the process of food supply advance. This is possible partly because equity for acquisition of investment funds has arisen with capital gains forthcoming from assets held under inflation. However, the picture may well differ with the next generation of farm operators: Scale of operations and capital requirements for attainment of major cost economies have not only grown but also capital gains from land value inflation promise to provide less growth in the equity base. Capital requirements or demand for investment funds by the firm will be closely intertwined with growth in farm size and scale of operations over the 1960's and 1970's. The supplying of credit may need to break away from certain foundations of the past if entry into the industry is to be kept free to a large number and if trend to larger-scale units is not to be rapid. However, insistence that larger numbers of youth enter farming, sacrificing training and employment in outside opportunity, needs to be avoided if looked upon simply as guaranteeing a nostalgic base of farming and a political strength which has already passed from the hands of agriculture.

EFFECTS ON FAMILY FARMS

"Family farm" is a term lending itself well to soap-box oratory. Many people discuss it but few can define it, or the definitions are as various as the persons. Early interest and meaning was quite concise: An organization of agriculture operated by individual families, rather than plantations or estates with herds of serfs or subsistence laborers, was preferred. These old plantation systems which prevailed in Europe and in the colonies of Africa and Asia are not now a threat in the United States, although this was considered to be an initial alternative to the family system of land settlement adopted for the United States. (See the Hamiltonian philosophy discussed in Chapter 1.) The alternative was inconsistent with the basic American concept, an attempt at constitutional guarantee of equality in opportunity and dignity in self-expression of the individual. It still is. However, the threat of this semi-slave state has itself largely disappeared, over most of commercial agriculture in the United States, as a function of economic growth. Labor is now too costly relative to capital for this structure of agiculture to be economic as the main national foundation of the industry. The potential of the system can be even further eliminated by investment in education which diminishes the pool of unskilled labor and which provides income and employment opportunity for labor consistent with the level of wealth and economic progress potential of the American economy.

There is not room in the U.S., given present knowledge of technology and capital prices, for an agriculture based on labor as the major input. National income and the forces of distributive justice are too great to ever allow this structure of the industry. The statements above about the strength of forces leading in other directions, are extremes for the moment, but not for the future. The modern-day equivalents of plantations and subsistence labor do prevail: in the structure of sharecropping with labor paid in kind, and in the labor camps of itinerant and imported workers in seasonal employment such as in the vegetable fields of California and selected other areas. But this is the minor structure of American agriculture, and the force of economic growth is in its diminution. Investment of capital in the individual, improved employment services and national economic growth which provides more productive opportunity can lessen the supply and increase the supply price of labor for these purposes. The latter itself, along with minimum wage income, can serve as stimulant to the invention of machine capital which substitutes for lowly skilled labor. The empirical evidence is at hand, for example, in the development and marketing of machines to pick nuts, fresh fruits as peaches, vegetables such as tomatoes and other perishable crops.

Perhaps it is less a construct which is desired and more one which is unwanted that leads to perpetuation of strong suppositions about the family farm. The unwanted construct is that of an agriculture resting on large input of laborers at miserable levels of wage, income and dignity. This potential and threat did exist in pioneer America, with large expanse of land for estates and large potential world supply of labor or immigrants such that many were willing to migrate under indentured servitude. In times of settling the American landscape, proprietorship in agriculture was a main opportunity in freedom of self expression and in reflection of individual capacities of the masses which flowed to agriculture. To have had agricultural structure built around large land units staffed by workers at puny wages would have meant a nation composed largely of serfs.

In contrast, however, current American wealth and industrial growth, and the accompanying large demand for professional and skilled labor, provides potential opportunity for individual abilities other than that of farm labor and entrepreneurship. The factor market itself no longer leans in the direction of a labor-based agriculture resting on serfdom and a large staff of hired laborers. Relative resource prices can depress this tendency even more as the human investments mentioned earlier are made and lead further to a decline in the supply of unskilled labor of low motivation. As mentioned previously, existence of labor-based, plantation agriculture rests on a large supply of unskilled labor, with low supply price to agriculture and few outside employment opportunities. Trend to larger farms with growing investment requirements is encouraged under factor market changes which alter resource prices and encourage the substitution of capital for labor. Typically, factor prices cause labor to become dear relative to machines and capital. Larger units are needed for realization of the scale or cost economies associated with capital and to provide adequate incomes under supply conditions which lessen profit margins.

Change of U.S. agriculture, in number and sizes of farms, is not yet as great as census statistics would lead us to believe. While farm numbers have dropped greatly and acres per farm, from 174 in 1939 to 302 in 1959, have increased greatly, this change in average farm size has come partly from exodus of many small-scale, low-income units, without a similar change in commercial farms having gross sales over $5,000. For example, if we had three farms, two of 300 acres each and one of three acres, the average size is 201 acres. If the small one disappears, the average size is immediately raised to 300 acres; the change in farm structure is "overly magnified." Of course, recombination of small units into one which produces more than this value causes number of the former to decline and number of larger units to increase. Factors from this side, leading to an increase in number of commercial farms, offset consolidations which lead to decline in numbers of the latter group.

While census figures do overemphasize the amount of change in farming structure, there has been considerable change, however. The number of farms with gross sales of more than $10,000 did increase by 160 percent between 1940 and 1960. As Figure 15.1 shows, there has been a definite decline even in farms selling $5,000 to $10,000 of product since 1944, with the offsetting creation of more farms selling $10,000 or more of product. This trend results from both inflation and farm consolidation. (See Figure 15.2.) The trend to mechanization and larger farms gives rise to the major capital problem of commercial agriculture. Under constant dollars and in relation to economic change, the capital requirement per farm is expected to increase from the $34,000 level of 1954 to nearly $70,000 in 1975.[7] The latter is an average for all commercial farms selling products in excess of $2,500 and already is approached or exceeded by state averages of farms in major wheat, feed grain and grazing states. But with change of the same proportions, capital requirements of $200,000 to $300,000 will be commonplace for many ordinary family farms by 1975.

---

[7] D. B. Ibach, "Economic Potentials of Agricultural Production," In *Dynamics of Land Use—Needed Adjustment*, Iowa State University Press, Ames, Iowa. 1961.

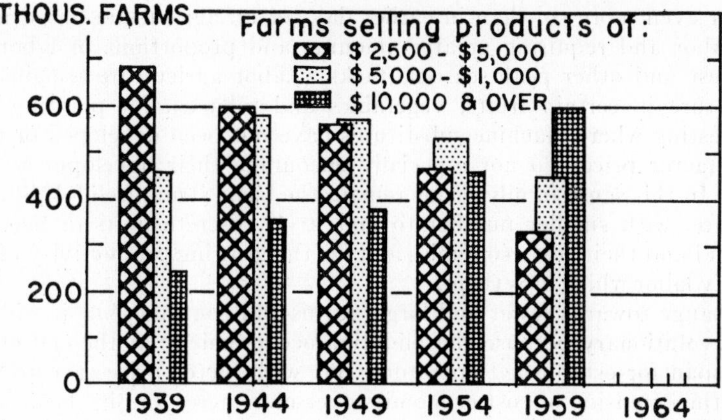

Fig. 15.1. Numbers of Farms Selling Specified Amounts of Product. Northern and Western U.S. (Source: U.S.D.A.)

This gradual trend to larger farms has not dissolved the family farm structure of U.S. agriculture. The proportion of labor force represented by family workers is greater now than 25 years ago. Hired workers as a proportion of all workers declined from about a quarter to a fifth between 1910 and 1960. Machine capital and larger farms have been slightly more effective in replacing hired labor than in replacing family labor. Larger units in acres are needed to realize attainment of the major cost economies of modern machines. Although these capital items do substitute for labor, a minimum or limitational amount of labor is required to operate them. The labor so used typically is that of the farmer and his family. In historic definitions of family farms, these units are as firmly

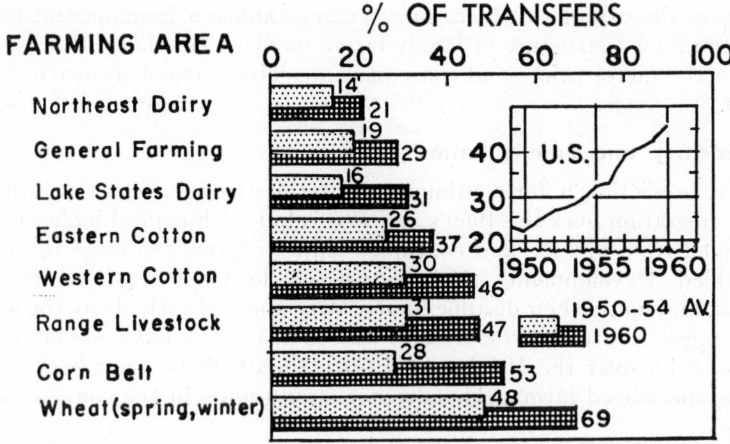

Fig. 15.2. Farms Purchased for Consolidation Purposes, 1960. (Source: U.S.D.A.)

so, or even more so, than in earlier days of an agriculture based more on labor and requiring greater amounts and proportions of labor for harvest and other peak seasonal tasks. (Labor agriculture remains the structure in certain fruits, vegetables and tobacco, for planting and harvesting where machine substitutes have not been developed or relative factor prices do not especially encourage their development and use.) In this sense family farms remain the basic structure of U.S. agriculture, with smaller number to match (1) discrete units of machine capital and their cost economies and (2) the growing productivity of the family labor which uses them.

Change towards fewer and larger farms will continue, but it will not be revolutionary because consolidation occurs chiefly at the end of the age span for established operators. But with factor prices accordingly and the extension of cost economies over more acres and in the absence of rapid inflation and capital gains as source of asset value and equity, initiation of farm firms becomes increasingly complex. This is true because each family farm firm typically has a life cycle in financing and capital accumulation, the firm most frequently being dissolved with the household and the process being repeated with each new firm-household complex. Retention of large numbers of family farms will be increasingly difficult with passage of time due to this set of forces. Developments in vertical integration which do allow diversion of national capital to agriculture through common stocks and equity financing, but by firms from outside of agriculture rather than from within, may increasingly provide the pattern over time as they thus overcome the typical restraint in capital supply to the individual firm of agriculture.

It is possible, in the elements forming the subset of agricultural policy, that an equivalent in equity capital needs to be aided in supply through public mechanisms, much in the manner that public mechanisms are now used to serve as a connecting link in the credit market. This statement rests on the extent to which society can establish a fundamental basis for retaining a structure of family farms smaller than those in prospect under the factor prices and consequent machine technology reached by 1980.

Democracy and Family Farms

Our prediction is for continuance of farm structure based on family farm operation over the 1960's and 1970's but with capital increasingly supplied from outside and continued shift to farms too large to be so classified. Developments of the future will lead only to fewer family farms, and not in their disappearance. Over much of agriculture the need is to upgrade size and resources so that family farms have adequate income. Still, over the 1960's and 1970's, there will be growth of more large, specialized farms which are not family units in the conventional sense.

The structure of family farms, and one we believe to be well established and likely of dominance for the 1960's and 1970's, needs to be evaluated as an end in itself, and no longer as an emotional means in insuring democracy and safeguarding individual rights. It is already too late to save American democracy through a foundation of family farms. With only 8 percent of the U.S. population living on farms, and with a large part of this represented by persons whose work and attachments are dominantly in the nonfarm sector, public choices have their major base and specification outside of agriculture. The trend obviously is not to less democracy and opportunity for the mass of individuals as number of farms and farm population declines. Rather than agriculture as a means to guarantee democracy for the remainder of society, the future may require that nonfarm population should better provide and insure the mechanisms of political freedom and economic opportunity for more persons now in agriculture, with wider spread of these basic rights to all groups in the industry.

Large agrarian populations did not prohibit growth of dictatorship and submersion of individual freedom in Eastern Europe.[8] To the contrary, democracy in the American sense was least preserved in these countries, and has been much more so in countries such as Great Britain where farm population dropped to insignificant proportion of the total. Soth reports polls showing farm people to be less willing than city people in upholding basic liberties of the constitutional system, rights of free speech, free press and freedom of religious observance for minority groups.[9] In this setting, agrarian structure and family farms should be evaluated as an end worthy of weighting against other more ultimate ends, rather than as means to safeguard democracy or similar constructs of society.

We believe that the family farm concept and certain, but not all, restraints which surround it, are most important in the sense of mechanisms to provide equity in (1) opportunity and (2) gains from progress; and that policy directed to these ends are more relevant than that which would "keep them down on the farm" simply for a voting majority and in disregard of income level. We believe that family farms must be gauged by how well they can provide opportunities to mesh with individual abilities and capacities of more people from farms.

Ends in Agrarian Structure

The goals of agrarian structure can be many, but three major ones predominate in social legislation favoring more farms of smaller size. These same three major goals may dominate in developed nations, less developed countries concerned with land reform and in Communist countries where small peasant units have been consolidated into large

[8] *Cf.* A. W. Griswold, *Farming and Democracy*, Yale University Press, New Haven, Conn. 1952, pp. 1–40.

[9] Lauren Soth, *Farm Trouble*, Princeton University Press, Princeton, N.J., 1957, pp. 23–24.

collective or state farms. But the relative weight given each goal probably differs greatly among countries in these various stages of development and democracy.

The three major goals of agrarian structure and land reform are: (1) Efficiency in the use of resources to produce food from a given collection of resources, or to lessen the amount of resources to meet food needs, (2) equity in the distribution of income and wealth or resources (i.e., to redistribute resources from persons with large holdings and wealth to those with few resources) and (3) attainment of social stability. These three major goals are not independent and universally noncompetitive. Land can be used in a manner to have more farms and a greater amount of distributive justice or political stability. The technology will then be one represented by small farms and large inputs of labor relative to land. If the creation of more small farms causes less food product from given collection of resources, the two alternatives are competitive. Or, competition between ends may result where tenants lack capital for adequate farming after they are transformed to owners. These two forces causing competition between ends in the short run can be overcome by public attack on the supply of knowledge and capital.

But aside from supply of managerial knowledge and capital, the technical nature of the production function is important in prescribing the long-run nature of the food and nonfood production possibilities in using farm resources. Given one set of production elasticities, goals of political stability and distributive justice could be attained without sacrifice in food efficiency. But under other conditions of the production function, the ends are competitive and the community must balance more food from given resources against agrarian structure and small farms.

First, suppose that the production function is, effectively for the relevant resources, of the nature in (15.1) where Y is output and X_i is input of the ith resource.

$$\frac{\partial Y}{\partial X_1}\cdot\frac{X_1}{Y} + \frac{\partial Y}{\partial X_2}\cdot\frac{X_2}{Y} + \cdots + \frac{\partial Y}{\partial X_n}\cdot\frac{X_n}{Y} = 1 \tag{15.1}$$

If management and capital resources can be the same in the long run after large holdings are subdivided, the goals of food efficiency and those of distributive justice or social stability are not competitive. The set of production possibilities arising under this condition is illustrated in Figure 15.3A. Starting from a level of food production and an amount of nonfood goals denoted at point s_1, large farms could be subdivided into smaller units. The result would be movement to point s_2 or to the limit s_n where other restraints place limits on gains in distributive justice or degree of political stability possible from subdivision of land holdings. The relative value which the community attaches to food or nonfood goals then would be unimportant in specifying the degree of goal attainment to be reached through agrarian structure. As long as a weight or value greater than zero is attached to these goals, the reform structure denoted by point s_n should be selected.

Given the technology currently found in many less developed economies, and favored by prices of labor relative to capital, it is possible that constant returns to scale do prevail or are approximated. Aside from managerial and farm practice skills of the operator, cost economies associated with farms of different sizes are probably small or effectively nonexistent for a labor-type agriculture. With high prices for capital relative to labor, labor-type agriculture is the most efficient in many less developed economies and the cost economies associated with mechanized agriculture are unimportant.

With food produced under increasing scale returns, the equal sign in (15.1) replaced accordingly, the production possibility curve denotes

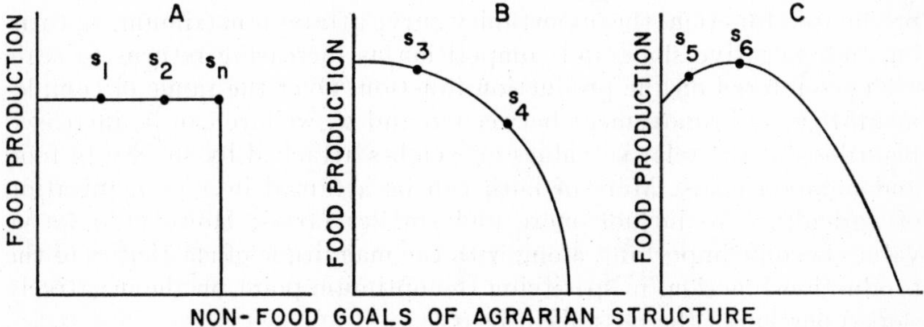

Fig. 15.3. Alternatives in Production Possibilities in Food Production Goals and Other Goals of Reform.

competition between ends, more like Figure 15.3B. (For a function with elasticities only greater than 1.0, the possibility curve is concave.) Agrarian structure to increase number and decrease size of farms, to attain more nonfood goals, necessarily causes sacrifice in food quantity produced from given resources, or requires more resources for given food. Undoubtedly, this condition prevails for mechanized agriculture in a highly developed economy such as that of the United States. Increase of farm numbers by four to allow more farming opportunities would require a smaller output from an equal collection of resources, or would require more resources for given food output.

The community or social value attached to the alternative goals or ends then is important in determining the particular welfare maximizing combination. If the family of community indifference curves has relatively little slope, denoting a high value on food relative to the nonfood goals, or the production possibility curve has great slope, the combination selected might be that indicated by s_3. But if indifference curves have a relatively large slope or the production possibility curve has little slope, the point (tangency between indifference and possibility curves) might be s_4. Obviously, the nature and elasticities of the production function are important, along with the values attached by the community to nonfood ends, in specifying the "type and degree" of optimal agrarian structure.

Given the orthodox production function of the economic text, the production possibility would be similar to that of Figure 15.3C. Over the range of decreasing scale returns, complementarity (positive slope of the opportunity curve) prevails between food and distributive or stability goals. By having fewer large farms, more food would be forthcoming from given resources. The large number of small farms would allow simultaneous attainment of other goals or products which result from this size complex. This situation might prevail especially where large estates or plantations are held by absentee owners only for purposes of inflation hedging, gaming, "attainment of aristocracy," etc.

At the collection of inputs defining constant returns for the food production function, the opportunity curve attains a maximum, s_6, turning to a negative slope and competition as increasing returns to scale are encountered on the production function. Over the range of complementarity, as in movement between s_5 and s_6, welfare can be increased regardless of the relative values or weights attached by society to food and nonfood goals. More of both can be attained in a reorganization of agriculture to include more and smaller farms. However, relative values become important, along with the magnitude of elasticities of the production function, in specifying the optimum point on the negatively sloped portion of the possibilities curve.

In the general framework above, even considering alternatives in values or weights attached to different ends, the stage of economic development and factor price relatives which arise have importance in specifying optimum agrarian structure. At low stage of economic development and high price for capital relative to labor, weight is thrown to labor-type agriculture without great scale economies and with more small farms being consistent with optimum structure. At high stages of development and high prices for labor relative to capital, mechanization becomes the base and with the greater scale or cost economies associated with it. The optimum structure, even against a given set of values or indifference curves, is one of fewer and larger farms. But also, when the food supply function moves rapidly to the right and the supply price of food is low, consumers may be so well furnished with food that it has a very low rate of substitution for other products or alternatives in agrarian structure.

This perhaps is the point already reached in U.S. society, with even the city person slightly engulfed in the nostalgia of "the good life on the farm" and some willingness to make investment which protects the small farm. Perhaps, however, it is less this and more the desire of farm persons to take advantage of urban life which leads to fewer and larger units, even among commercial classes of farms. Farm youth especially, in number beyond farming opportunities, wish the employment opportunities and the greater ability in expression of individual capacities in industry and the "good life of the city," rather than to remain and enjoy the nonpecuniary amenities of the farm.

And Land Ownership

If the problem of U.S. society were tardiness of the food supply function, need for reduced real supply price of food and greater response of production to price stimuli, then it would be best to encourage fewer and larger specialized farms. These are the units of highly specialized management where resources are less immobilized in family labor and fixed costs and profit maximization are the overriding motives in decisions. There is, of course, some trend in this direction of farm structure. But the fact that the food supply function has progressed with adequacy in terms of consumer benefit, and perhaps overly so in terms of positive-sum utility outcome in the distribution of gains and costs of rapid supply advance, causes society to lack impatience in this direction.

In the vein of family operation, the food supply function also can be advanced under extended farm ownership, providing that capital does not restrain the supply of operators so converted and the supply of materials for advancing technology. Leaving aside problems in time, uncertainty and related phenomena, we can illustrate conditions under which conversion of tenants to owners cannot only increase capital requirements of the farm firm but also can advance the supply function, a need momentarily more pressing in Indian than in American society.

Using a single variable resource for the sake of simplicity, the owner-operator can maximize profit under the condition of marginal product equal to the factor/product price ratio for each resource. Now contrast scale and technology for a share-tenant renting a farm fixed in acreage. If conventions of the rental market call for a $1-r$ proportion of product for landlord and r proportion for tenant while the tenant furnishes an s proportion (or pays s proportion of the price) of the input X_i, tenant profit is maximized if the X_i or inputs are used in the magnitudes of (15.2) expressed as equivalent in (15.3).

$$r\frac{\partial Y}{\partial X_i} = s\frac{P_i}{P} \qquad (15.2)$$

$$\frac{\partial Y}{\partial X_i} = \frac{s}{r}\frac{P_i}{P} \qquad (15.3)$$

If $s=1$ and $r=.5$, we have the ratio $sr^{-1}=2$. Hence, for maximum tenant profit, marginal productivity of the ith nonland resource must be twice that for the owner. The tenant can double the marginal productivity of the resource, given a production function identical to that of the cultivator who owns his land, by decreasing input of the resource. Hence, the optimum technology of farming, as represented by the mix of land and the X_i, differs for tenant and owner cultivator. Similarly, optimum size of enterprise or farm is less for the tenant. An industry composed of tenants would have a supply function to the left of that for an industry composed of owners. For example using the production function in (11.7) for both owner and tenant, and indicating corresponding owner supply as Q_0, the tenant supply function is that in (15.4), a quantity less in magnitude, depending on $rs^{-1} \neq 1.0$, than for the owner in (11.9).

$$Q_t = \left(\frac{r}{s}\right)^4 Q_0 \qquad (15.4)$$

Food prices would be, given a demand function, higher and consumption pattern of families would include a smaller proportion of food relative to other goods and services in (15.4) as compared to (11.9). Or, a higher level of prices would be required to attain a given level of food output and a specific technology and farm size.

Tenure constructs are possible, of course, which place tenant and landlord on the same footing in respect to supply function (as in making $r=s$).[10] Under forces of the market, ownership patterns in the United States have tended towards those which augment the supply function. From 1930 to 1960, tenancy has dropped by half, or from 42 percent in 1930 to slightly less than 20 percent in 1960. (These figures for the U.S. tenancy account for somewhat over 40 percent of farm operations in the major corn and wheat areas, but with some decline over earlier periods.)

And Capital Requirements

Farm ownership places, along with economic development and factor prices leading to mechanization and scale economies, a heavier burden on capital requirements. Similarly, definitions or legislation which place maximum constraint on particular input categories also may force farming into a position demanding greater capital inputs for a particular food supply. We illustrate this possibility with Figure 15.4. Typically, in terms of labor, family farms are defined in terms of a programming restraint on this resource: total labor input cannot exceed a specified proportion of the family labor supply. Hence, an absolute limit is attached to the per firm use of this resource.

In the main, farms in the United States do not approach this restraint limit because they use so little labor. Should they ever approach the limit, the picture would be that suggested in Figure 15.4. The positively sloped curves are isoclines denoting points of equal slope on successive product or income isoquants. Accordingly, they are expansion paths, indicating the proportions in which land and labor should be combined to attain each output or income level at minimum cost. In the absence of capital rationing and restricting definitions of family farms, expansion would follow one of these isoclines, denoting equal substitution and price ratios

[10] For details in this respect, see Earl O. Heady, *op. cit.*, Chap. 20.

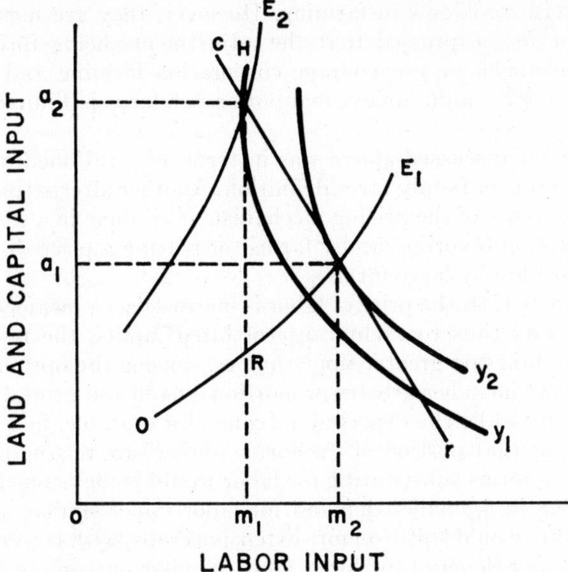

Fig. 15.4. Effect on Capital Demand and Input.

for factors, until the marginal value products of resources are equated with their prices. With limited capital, expansion should progress along the least-cost isocline until the iso-outlay or budget line such as *cr* is attained. In the figure, this involves inputs of om_2 of labor and oa_1 of capital and land. Output level is at y_1. A definition restricting labor input below this level might appear to also restrict land input per farm and allow existence of more farms. However, given the fact that farms generally do not use resources at levels equating value products and prices, a highly restricting definition of labor input can even push the firm to extensification of land use—and to fewer farms.

Suppose that the family farm definition limits labor input to om_1. The firm has the typical farm goal of pushing resource use and output to a level consistent (1) with a particular standard of living or (2) to the budget line defined by the funds available. If it wishes, or has funds, to attain the iso-investment line *cr*, it can follow the least-cost expansion path only to the restraining level R. Hence, to attain isoquant y_1 it must extend land input up the hybrid isocline RH. Attaining y_1 in this fashion limits labor input to om_1 but extends land and capital input to oa_2. Allowing expansion along the isocline E_1, labor input would be increased to om_2, but acreage would be lessened to oa_1, and more farms could exist. Conceptually, and practically if such tight restraints were placed on family farm definitions, the restraint would move the supply function to the left. It would thus help reduce surplus problems. But it would not create more farming opportunities. These restricting definitions do not pose near-term problems in farming. However, they are mentioned because of the fear expressed that the adjustments being forced by the market mechanism may encourage corporation farming and strangulation of the family unit, unless manpower per farm is limited by strict legislation.

The outcome discussed above was in terms of a rationed input to attain a constraint in family farm definition. Another alternative in checking farm size is use of the pricing mechanism, as is done in a weak manner through taxation favoring family farms (or placing a price disadvantage in land ownership by large farms).

If, for Figure 15.4, the price of labor is increased as a means of restraining its use, and thus to exclude use of hired inputs, the resulting iso-outlay curve takes on greater slope than *cr*, causing the optimal resource combination to include a greater proportion of land and capital and less of labor. This would be the expected outcome, for example, in a high minimum wage for that portion of California agriculture resting on seasonal labor. Capital forms substituting for labor would be developed and used, thus resulting in a smaller demand for labor under similar agriculture. Or, agriculture would shift to more extensive crops, with larger and fewer farms and lower demand for hired labor. Similar outcome would be expected with high minimum annual wage for sharecroppers in Alabama and Georgia or the hired workers of cotton plantations of the Mississippi Delta.

If we made the magnitude of P_x in (4.2) an increasing function of X for the firm, optimum input of resources (with all resources treated similarly) would decline, of course. Hence, we would expect more farms to exist, in supplying a given output of food. Per firm output would be less but also industry supply would be somewhat smaller and supply price of food would be higher, resulting in somewhat lowered demand and itself a slight restraint on number of firms. Increasing the price of land alone as a function of input magnitude would, of course, restrict size in a spatial sense, shifting agriculture towards more capital and labor in its resource mix.

In a family farm context, assurance of this structure is perhaps best attained, with a degree of efficiency and progress encouraged to give favorably to family income, in a price for credit and capital which incorporates the advantages of scale returns and equity enjoyed by larger units (i.e. putting small farms on the same or more favorable footing in respect to supply price of capital as large farms, rather than in changing the supply price for other factors between the two groups of farms). Where lower supply price of capital to all farmers is public policy, its main accomplishment is that of encouragement to economic development, and an extended supply function and output of food. In the realm of inelastic food demand, the stimulus of lower capital price in greater output may cause a reduction in revenue greater than the savings in costs due to lower credit price. Clearly, in this case, policy lowering the supply price of capital must be looked upon as policy to benefit consumers, rather than to bring gain to farm producers in aggregate during the short run.

Goal Mixture and Capital Needs

Problems in family farms, food supply advance and investment requirements present a complex admixture of possible means and ends. Promotion of family farming and ownership, by lowering the supply price of capital, can extend the supply function of food causing greater pressure on output and prices and itself place small farms at an income disadvantage. Or, family farm policies can increase capital requirements (e.g. as in Figure 15.4) under a stage of economic growth wherein demand of the individual farm for investment funds is expanding greatly, against relative constancy of the industry. (In the latter respect, see Table 2.8.)

Promotion of family farm and ownership ends will not mainly stabilize or restrain supply of agricultural comodities or vice versa, the two even being complementary under certain conditions. We look upon elements of capital and family farm definition (and the policy needs relating to them) more in relation to means than to ends. As means, policy oriented to them should have its main purpose in equity of: (1) providing greater opportunity in expression of capacities of individuals from farm families and (2) realizing a relevant share of the gains from progress as outlined earlier. We believe that it is farms resting more on the labor of the family and possessing the least of capital which bear the greatest burden of social costs associated with rapid technical development. Larger units, and especially those which expand rapidly with new technology and factor prices, can increase output more rapidly than price or profit margins decline, thus directly realizing gains from economic progress.

The alternative to a particular farm definition and size restraint is not transfer of farm persons to migrant labor camps or infusion of them into a pool of low-paid, unskilled labor. It can and should be an alternative of favorable nonfarm employment with opportunity in home ownership and greater ability for expression of skills and individual capacities. Given the opportunity, developed by capital investment in human resources as mentioned earlier in Chapters 12 and 13, most individuals would probably prefer the latter to life on an undersized farm unit.

The nature of scale returns, or the cost economies associated with farms of different sizes, will determine the extent to which further development and prospective adjustments to improve agricultural structure will strengthen or weaken the position of family farms. The family farm structure would be threatened if scale or cost economies extended over large acreages. We believe, and have supporting empirical evidence, that this is not the case. Given the fixed costs associated with modern machinery, substantial cost economies can result from some further expansion of small or modal sized farms. However, because variable costs of the agricultural firm eventually dominate total costs, cost reductions per acre eventually become minute as acreage continues to expand with a given power and machinery unit. When this *point* has been reached, no great cost advantage is realized by a larger unit. Generally, beyond this *point* on the per acre cost function, representing full utilization of labor and machine services in particular seasons of the year, further expansion must come from increase in discrete capital units. In other words, a second power unit must be added, largely as a duplication of the first one. In this sense, with major scale economies largely exploited by each discrete capital unit, there is little difference in per unit costs or resource efficiency whether the farm be of one size, or double or quadruple this size. But just as there is no disadvantage for the smaller unit, there is none for the larger unit. This set of relationships gives room for credit policy assuring equity without general economic sacrifice. Credit supplied, at supply price consistent with scale conditions of the credit market, to allow one farmer to expand to this point assures equity, which is not the case where he is restrained from doing so while another more favorably supplied with capital and credit expands to the quadruple size.

POLICY MIX NEEDED

Our analysis to this point has indicated that optimum farm policy cannot include a single facet. Instead, to insure economic progress and an equitable distribution of its fruits, a policy mix is necessary, with elements which contribute in preferred magnitude to the miscellaneous set of intermediate ends selected by society and the farm public. The ends often will be competitive and inconsistent if a single over-all policy attack is used. But by using a mix of policy elements, these conflicts can be minimized. For example, credit policy can be used to encourage family farms. But if it lowers price of this factor for all farmers, it is equivalent to decrease of P_x in equation (11.7), thus favoring an increase in output. Revenue of agriculture may decline, perhaps more than costs, from a reduced factor price.

Developmental policy which makes technical knowledge available to farmers at low or zero price has the same output increasing effect. It can benefit consumers at the expense of producers. Production control which has the effect of increasing P_x in (11.7) to agriculture, through payment for land which is not used for production, has the effect of decreasing Q_s in the same equation, thus leading to greater farm revenue but to smaller consumer surplus. Quota systems which restrain output for this purpose may appear equitable to some producers, but not to others, for the reasons outlined in Chapter 14. Public sponsorship of technical advance which has the effects through the market illustrated in Table 5.2 and over equations (7.20) through (7.31) can benefit owners of those resources retained in agriculture but represent cost to those rejected from the industry. Yet, as we have explained in Chapters 11 through 15, education, compensation and other mechanisms can be used to restore gain to one farm sector where it would otherwise bear cost of progress.

But the purpose of each policy element must be recognized and kept separate from others. Policy to bring opportunity of persons on low-income farms needs to be particular and not confused with other policy efforts. As we mentioned in Chapter 11, policy element aimed at compensation would pay a person according to his judged sacrifice, without upper restraint. Policy to restrain output would look as favorably upon inputs or "output rights" supplied by large producer, as that by small producer, for purposes of improving market price. It would not limit magnitude of participation by large and small operators. Policy aimed at family farms need not be confounded with that for other purposes, and certainly that aimed at developing the unexploited human resources in the poverty sector of American agriculture would be highly retrogressive to their income and farming scale. Capital investment for the better development of human resources in agriculture and to help increase the supply of talented labor is more pressing than capital policy to lower the price of factors and extend food output of farms.

16

Public Policy in Research, Education and Development

NUMEROUS PUBLIC POLICIES of the United States can best be termed developmental policies. They qualify thus in the sense that they have a basic effect in causing the commodity supply function to shift to the right and to become more elastic through effective (1) reduction of resource prices or (2) increase in the transformation rate of resources into products.[1] In review, the major developmental policies under this definition have been: land settlement policies keeping the price of land low; credit policy reducing the price of borrowed funds; payments and assistance, classified for conservation goals, lowering the cost of materials and technical advice for inputs which increase contemporary output as well as that of the future; reclamation, irrigation and related investments lowering the price of improved land to farmers; research and education lowering the real cost of knowledge to farmers and providing base for increasing the rate of transformation of resources into products. Other developmental policies could be mentioned, or compensation policies which had a by-product effect of increasing output could be cited, but this list includes the major policy elements.

The single most effective one of these policy elements leading to technical and economic development of agriculture over the first half of the 1900's was public policy of research and education in the technology

[1] In contrast, support prices aimed at compensation generally increase output along a given supply function. For example, reduction of P_x.in equation (4.26) causes the entire function to shift to the right, with ouput increasing against a given level of commodity price. In contrast, increase of P causes output to increase along a given supply schedule.

and organization of farming. In the last half of the 1800's, progress and rightward shift of the supply schedule probably came more from capital formation and extension of conventional inputs, than from technical advance. But in the first half of the 1900's, the major change came clearly from new technical knowledge and favorable price of this knowledge and the capital items serving to express it. Both are important: Without knowledge of new technique, lowness of price for material representing it is meaningless. With knowledge but with the price of the material so high that it cannot be used profitably, new technical knowledge would be ineffective in altering supply or output structure.

Public investment in research and education to develop and communicate new technical knowledge was a bold step in public policy. It was public action not since duplicated for other economic sectors. In other sectors, industries and firms are expected to, and expect to, conduct their own research. The public would, in fact, find itself confronted with vigorous resistance if it offered or began to conduct large-scale research in drugs, automobiles, television and similar products, with all findings quickly made public ahead of production scheduling and free to all possible producers and consumers.

Ordinarily, major research is carried on in the private sector, firms investing in and producing their own technical knowledge which they sell embodied in new and differentiated products. Research has come to receive an important allocation of resources and investment by large nonfarm firms and industries. They expect to produce knowledge and to realize a return on it. Encouragement of the process is left up to the free market and the play of prices. (See discussion of equations (4.21) and (4.22) in the differential role of prices in allocating research by private firms and public institutions.)

Decision of the American public to socialize research and knowledge for agriculture was a long policy departure from an activity generally left up to the market and private sector. The public implemented this policy by making appropriations to finance it; building institutions to produce and retail it; and hiring deans and other administrators to guide it, as well as other staff workers, as employees of the public. Without public intervention in the market to finance and produce research, the private sector would have found it more profitable to do so and would have increased investments along this line.

In some nations, it is indicated that while agriculture has made important contributions to national economic growth, new technical developments came particularly from private firms.[2] New technologies would have developed in the U.S. without socialization of agricultural research and education, but the process would have been much slower and the contribution of agriculture to national economic growth would have been less. (See Chapter 4 in respect to the real cost of technical knowledge to

[2] Bruce Johnson (*Agriculture's Development and Economic Transformation: Japan, Taiwan and Denmark*, Stanford, 1960, Mimeo., p. 110) uses Denmark as such a country, indicating that major effort in developing improved seeds came from the private sector.

producers and conditions favorable to its supply by the private sector.)

American society has thus been an active participant in economic development of agriculture even in recent decades. The amount it has been willing to invest in agricultural research has grown rapidly as indicated in Table 16.1. Aside from the ownership of resources in farming, no other nation has had a more direct and effective participation of the public sector in technical development and progress of agriculture. Development of agriculture has not been left to the free market. General society has invested heavily, and reaped high returns, from its direct intervention in promoting progress in the industry. It has had purposeful and well-administered public facilities for doing so. These facilities are represented by the agricultural colleges of the land-grant universities, and the corresponding activities of the U.S. Department of Agriculture. Like post offices, they are socialized services and facilities. In contrast to the post office system, however, where firms and consumers pay some price for the services used, the supply of services from the agricultural colleges is largely unrelated to the pricing and market system. The services to be produced, the funds to be used and the distribution of the product are determined by administrators who are public employees and by legislators who are public representatives. The creation and distribution of the services of the agricultural colleges respond only remotely to the pricing mechanism, and no more so than do the public sector products represented by other governmental services. It is therefore appropriate that the products of the agricultural colleges be analyzed and given direction in terms of the national purposes which are paramount in our society and for agriculture. Certainly the agricultural colleges have been, and are, an extremely important element of public policy relative to the industry. This has been especially true since 1920.

TABLE 16.1

PUBLIC INPUTS IN AGRICULTURAL RESEARCH AND EDUCATION, 1910-59, IN CURRENT DOLLARS (MILLIONS)

Year	Agricultural Research	Agricultural Extension	Vocational Agriculture
1910	6.5	—	—
1915	11.1	3.6	—
1920	14.5	14.7	2.4
1925	18.9	19.3	6.1
1930	31.6	24.3	8.7
1935	25.2	20.4	8.9
1940	41.3	33.1	17.0
1945	47.6	38.1	19.2
1950	104.3	74.6	38.5
1955	144.3	100.7	53.7
1959	225.4	136.0	66.7

Source: USDA and U.S. Department of Health, Education and Welfare.

Upsurge in Productivity

The tremendous upsurge in farm output and productivity of agricultural resources has come since 1940 as reviewed in Figure 16.1. Some of the major innovations relating to this large productivity increase were mentioned in Chapter 14. Other forces leading in this direction also should be mentioned. A large amount of new technology was accumulated during the 1930's depression when farmers lacked the capital to innovate and the factor/product price ratio was less favorable for these purposes than in later decades (although some important innovations did take place in the 1930's, with a more complete spread during the 1940's). But also, we should mention the larger investment and greater effectiveness of research and education following this period. Between 1914 and 1934, the agricultural extension service had been in operation less than 25 years. After that time, it began working with a "new generation" of farmers, a great number of these now being graduates of 4-H clubs and vocational agricultural education. Too, the extension services were themselves coming to maturity and had both better-trained persons and more effective methods in the decades following 1934. Much of the same also can be said about agricultural research, with important innovations, discoveries and adaptations coming out at increased rate following the depression.

Finally, we must mention the "stage of economic development" and the drawing of more private firms into research, communication and input processing. They could make investments leading to more rapid and homogeneous improvements. Starting in the 1930's, a "vast movement" took place, with input fabrication moving from farm firms to nonfarm firms. Common examples were power units, hybrid corn, fertilizer nutrients and similar innovations. As Figures 16.1 and 16.2 illustrate, the great upsurge in farm output and resource productivity parallels the steep rise in "other" inputs than land (real estate) and labor. The "other" inputs included especially materials representing new forms of capital uncovered by research. Few forms of nonland and nonlabor resources in use in 1960 were the same as those in use in 1930. (It might be argued that inputs such as livestock and feed grains are the same forms of inputs. However, the breeding stock and seeds used in producing livestock and feed grains were quite different inputs than in 1930.) With this large growth in capital inputs, private firms could dominate the supply of resources to agriculture. The quality and productivity of farm resources then could be increased more rapidly and effectively.

Given alone economic development and further commercialization of agriculture, growth in productivity rate of farm resources is not likely to slacken. Any slowing of growth in productivity rate is more likely to come from the biological limits of natural resources or endowments as capital inputs are increased against them. But as pointed out in Chapter 2, this biological restraint does not promise to restrict growth in farm output and resource productivity over the 1960's.

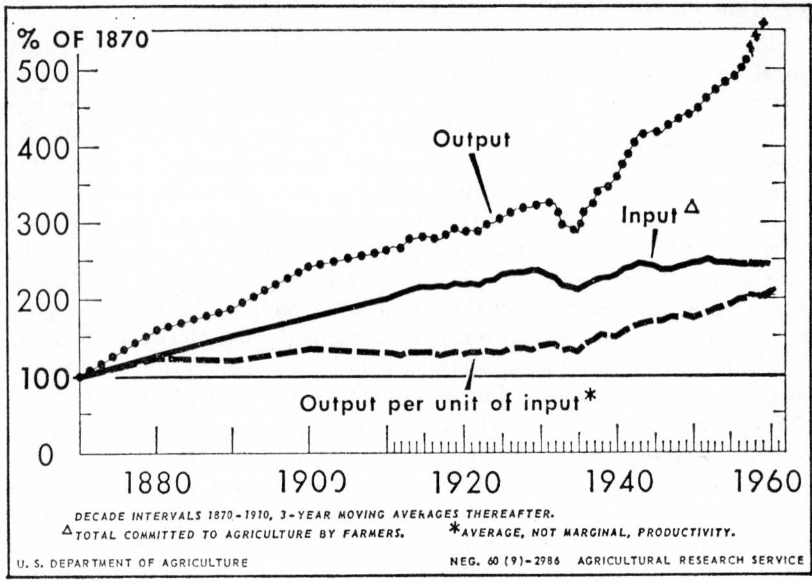

Fig. 16.1. Changes in Output, Input and Factor Productivity. U.S. 1870–1960.

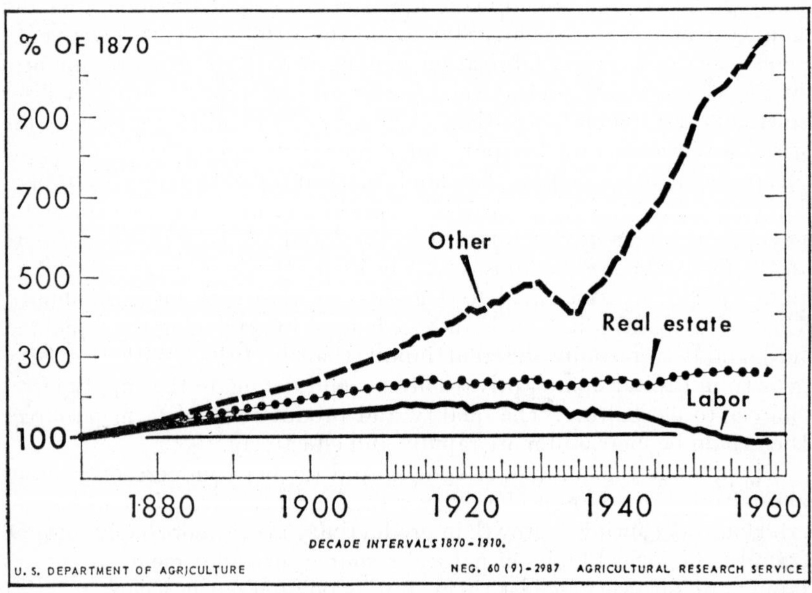

Fig. 16.2. Changes in Major Input Groups of Agriculture. U.S. 1870–1960.

RETURN FROM PUBLIC RESEARCH AND EDUCATION

Public research and educational institutions for agriculture have been generally well administered. With few exceptions they have had dedicated persons to guide them and they have been relatively free from political obstacles restraining them from their realized goals.[3] Their success in promoting the development of agriculture is now legend, not only in the United States but the world over. Other nations look to the system and wish that they could duplicate its developmental attributes. Given its conscious objectives, perhaps there have never been more efficient public institutions and investments, or at most very few. Farm output has more than doubled since 1910, but with nearly a halving of the farm labor force. Labor productivity in agriculture increased around 300 percent from 1910 to 1960. We are rapidly approaching the time when only 5 percent of the labor force is needed to produce the nation's food product, plus provision of some for export. Counting all farms and farmers, each worker in agriculture produces food for about 30 other persons; but considering only true commercial farmers who produce the very major part of output, the figure is more nearly 50 persons fed per farm worker—even allowing some exports. A nation can be wealthy only if a small amount of its labor force is required for food. In fact, the elementary step in economic progress is in developments which allow transfer from fields to factories and commerce. Per capita wealth and economic progress is extremely restrained in countries where 75 percent of the labor force is engaged in agriculture, such as in India or even greatly so where 40 percent of the labor force is so required, as in Russia.

The return to U.S. society on investment in public research and education to promote technical knowledge in agriculture has indeed been large. The payoff is not easily measured, starting from initiation of this investment. Difficulty arises in measurement because of problems in aggregation of commodities serving as inputs and outputs; in identifying research inputs and their outputs in both the private and public sectors; in evaluating knowledge which would have been "self generating" within the farm industry apart from public activity; and in others. But while there can be questions about the exact and specific level of return, there is no doubt that it has been extremely high. While the measurements serve as approximations and can give rise to technical questions of measurement, the data of Table 16.2 suggest some general levels of return. Over 50 years, output increased by nearly 110 percent with an estimated increase of only 22 percent in value of inputs, excluding taxes. The increase in annual capital was only slightly more than the decrease in value of labor. If the value of input per unit of output, considering output to be the same aggregate, had been the same in 1959 as in 1910, about $42 billion in total inputs would have been required at 1947–49 prices. Hence, we might consider the saving, comparing 1959 to 1910, to be the

[3] For notes on the politics of land-grant colleges, see C. M. Hardin, *The Politics of Agriculture*, The Free Press, Glencoe, Ill., 1952, Chap. 2.

TABLE 16.2

INDICES AND ACTUAL OUTPUT AND INPUTS OF AMERICAN AGRICULTURE FOR SELECTED YEARS, 1910–59, WITH VALUE OF INPUTS SAVED AT 1947–49 PRICE LEVEL (1910=100)

Year	Output Index 1910=100	Input Index 1910=100*	Actual Inputs Used at 1947–49 Prices†	Inputs Required at 1910 Productivity Rates (1947–49 Prices)†	Inputs "Saved," Actual Minus Required‡
1910.......	100	100	20.1	20.1	0
1915.......	111	106	21.3	22.4	1,032
1920.......	115	113	22.8	23.2	375
1925.......	115	114	22.9	23.1	281
1930.......	118	115	23.2	23.8	559
1935.......	118	104	21.0	23.8	2,734
1940.......	139	116	23.3	27.0	3,710
1945.......	156	119	23.9	31.4	7,507
1950.......	166	120	24.1	33.1	9,295
1955.......	185	121	24.3	37.3	12,992
1959.......	207	122	24.4	41.7	17,266
1910–59 Mean....	—	—	22.9	24.5	4,586

Source: Based on USDA data. (See Loomis and Barton, *loc. cit.*) Indices vary slightly from those in other tables and charts because of base of computations.

* Index of inputs excluding taxes and differs slightly from indices of inputs in other chapters where taxes are included.

† Billion dollars at 1947–49 prices.

‡ Million dollars at 1947–49 prices.

difference between this projected figure and the actual estimate for 1959. On this basis, the 1959 saving in resource inputs is approximately $17,266 million.

We cannot derive a lagged or dynamic model to relate research and educational investment in one period with its product in a later period. Data show a $225 million (current dollar) expenditure (Table 16.1) by the public sector for agricultural research in 1959. The expenditure by the private sector for agricultural research was about $240 million (current dollars) in the same year.[4] The average savings per annum in inputs, as computed in Table 16.2 were $4,586 million over the 50-year period 1910–59 at 1947–49 prices.[5] Using 1947–49 prices, the total public expenditure on agricultural research over this same period was $2,953 million. The corresponding public expenditures for education were $2,158 for extension, $982 million for vocational agriculture and $52 million for agricultural colleges. Figured as return on public investment in agricultural research alone, the average annual input savings in Table 16.2 represent a return of 155 percent on the total research expenditures over the period

[4] R. L. Mighell (*American Agriculture*, Wiley and Sons, New York, 1955, p. 130) places the figure at $140 million in 1953.

[5] Loomis and Barton (*Productivity of Agriculture*, USDA Tech. Bul. 1238) estimate the resource savings in 1957, comparing this year only against productivity gains of 1940, to be $9.6 billion. Comparing 1957 with productivity gains since 1910, they compute resource savings to be $16.3 billion when adjustment is made for purchase of specific items and taxes are included as inputs.

1910–59. If we add all public investment in agricultural education to research, saying that the research had zero productivity until it was communicated, the total public investment (at 1947–49 prices) in research and education, over the period 1910–59, was $4,145 million. The average annual input saving of $4,586 million is a 110 percent return on this total investment. If we estimate private expenditure on agricultural research and education to be a fourth of the public expenditure, the return is still 89 percent, and even 74 percent if we put private expenditure at half of public expenditure over the full 50 year period.

Obviously the return is much higher than these figures. There are several reasons: The expenditures on research are greatest in recent years and input savings or returns are increasing. The returns extend on forever, and those being realized now are from smaller annual inputs at an earlier date. Finally, the assumptions that the aggregate product was the same in 1959 as 1910 also cause savings to be underestimated. The product mix consumed in 1959 was a much more costly one in resources, to obtain the same level of food nutrients, than that of 1910. But even at returns of around 100 percent, or even of 70 percent, the social payoff is large. This is a return far above that of student education cited in Chapters 12 and 13, or the rates of capital return of the more monopolistic industries cited in Chapter 5. If inputs could be accurately measured against lagged productivity, the social return to the public investment, or all investment, in research would indeed be high. This would be especially so for particular innovations. Griliches estimates the return on research for hybrid corn, an extremely important innovation, to be in the neighborhood of 700 percent.[6] Research in general undoubtedly has a return well over 100 percent.[7] (Hybrid corn is one successful venture. Others requiring investment are not always successful; some which are successful have a lower payoff.)

Research, education and communication of new technology has been productive elsewhere in the world also. In Asia, Japan represents a nation of high relative economic development. Given factor supplies and prices which still favor technology resting heavily on labor, it has an agriculture which has high technical and economic efficiency. Smith indicates early interest in and spreading of knowledge in farm technology.[8] He indicates that progress was quite remarkable, during the Tokugawa period, from a combination in spread of technical knowledge, development of transportation and growth of markets. The use of fertilizers spread widely and the number of recorded rice varieties increased from 177 in the seventeenth century to 2,363 by the middle of the nineteenth century. Evidence indicates that there was widespread interest in improved technology and considerable discussion and writing in this respect even by peasants. As part

[6] Zvi Griliches, "Research Costs and Returns: Hybrid Corn," *Jour. Polit. Econ.*, Vol. 46.

[7] It is estimated that national rate of return on all research and development is 100 to 200 percent. See R. H. Ewell, "Role of Research in Economic Growth," *Chem. & Engr. News*, Vol. 33.

[8] T. C. Smith, *The Agrarian Origins of Japan*, Stanford University Press, Stanford, Calif., 1959, Chap. 7.

of this development, it is indicated that between the late sixteenth and seventeenth centuries, 398 new villages were founded in Musashi Providence, irrigation and double cropping were developed and rice output rose from 667,000 koku to 1,167,000. Johnson and Mellor report that per annum increase in food output in Japan was 2 percent between the decades of the 1880's and 1911–20, on a land area already fully settled, and labor productivity doubled.[9] They also report that the expenditures for agricultural research, extension-type activities and other "developmental" sources were of strategic importance in both Japan and Taiwan, with the productivity of agricultural labor for the latter increasing by 130 to 160 percent over a 30-year span and a threefold increase in sugar yields between 1901–10 and the 1930's. Kazushi's data indicate that real income produced in Japanese agriculture doubled between 1881–90 and 1911–20 while labor employed in agriculture declined by 10 percent.[10] Johnson indicates that in the 30 years, 1881–90 and 1911–20, Japan increased agricultural productivity by 77 percent, with an increase of only 21 percent in area under cultivation and an increase of 46 percent in yields.[11] Population increased by only 44 percent during this period and farm labor force fell by 14 percent.

Japan is a country where increase in agricultural productivity contributed greatly in capital transfer to nonfarm industry, as well as to rapid rise in food output and farming efficiency. The increase in agricultural output came with modest government investment in research and education, but an investment considered to be crucial.[12] Increase in capital inputs was very modest, or even small, against the increase in farm output and productivity of land and labor. The increase in product of agriculture provided a surplus for transfer to the nonfarm sector, in providing capital for economic progress. This process in Japan was indeed the equal of that in the United States.

We have ample evidence, then, that public investment in knowledge for agriculture and in knowledge of people in agriculture can bear high payoff, both in aid to general economic development and in value of resources to produce agricultural output at demand level. The United States provides evidence in the Western world and Japan in the Eastern world, both being in the vanguard of development over the last century for their general regions. Both illustrate a large increase in output without a corresponding increase in inputs, measured in most any manner. Abramovitz and Kendrick show similarly for the U.S. economy that only about one-third of the output increase between 1899 and 1953 can be

---

[9] B. F. Johnson and J. W. Mellor, "Contributions to Economic Growth," *Food Research Institute Studies*, Vol. 1.

[10] Ohkawa Kazushi, *Economic Growth and Agriculture*, Annals of Hitotsubashi Academy, 1956.

[11] Bruce Johnson, "Agricultural Productivity and Agricultural Development in Japan," *Jour. Polit. Econ.*, Vol. 34.

[12] Smith, *loc. cit.*, and Johnson and Mellor, *loc. cit.*

attributed to increase in input of land, labor and capital as conventionally defined and in physical measurement.[13]

The difference between growth in output and conventional inputs for American agriculture is even greater over recent decades. We have explained in Chapter 11 how exposition of knowledge of new inputs or their productivity effects and of their relative prices can lead to output increase which is more than proportional to value of inputs. Together it is improvement in general knowledge, as reflected in the forms, quality and productivity of capital and human effort, which allows progress in this sense. The public investment in research and education for agriculture had indeed been efficient and of high payoff for the American society of consumers. It remains so, and prospects are that it can provide further high return in the future. Society would have difficulty finding many investment opportunities in either the public or private sector, which had greater promise of return to consumers in general, than this activity which has been embraced as an active public policy. In terms of society returns, it is a public activity to be continued and expanded, until such time that it can be proven that sufficient other investments provide opportunity of such high, or higher, returns.

Input and Productivity Changes

Not all of the increase in output in recent decades can be attributed to technological change or improvement in resource productivity. Over early periods in the economic development of U.S. agriculture, greater supply of farm products was attributed mainly to increased input of resources. More land, labor and capital were used in extending the magnitude of the farm industry and its output. Even as late as the period 1870–1920, a greater portion of increase in farm production came from increased input of resources than from an increased productivity of the conventional resources measured in the aggregate and classical manner of land, capital and labor. However, as is suggested in Table 16.3, the portion of output imputable to productivity increases is much greater than that for input increases since 1920. Increase in output from productivity change is estimated to exceed by five times the output increase due to input change in the period 1920–39. The increase in output between 1950 and 1956 is estimated to come entirely from productivity changes, with the total value of inputs decreasing by 9 percent as a large amount of labor migrated from farmers and was not offset by a larger increase in capital items. Even for the period 1911–56, output increase attributable to technological improvement or productivity change is estimated to be double the increase in output attributable to increase in aggregate value of the inputs.

---

[13] M. Abramovitz, "Resource and Output Trends in the United States Since 1870," *Amer. Econ. Rev.*, Vol. 46; J. W. Kendrick, *Productivity Trends in the U.S.*, Basic Tables, Mimeo.; M. Brown and J. A. Popkin, *Measure of Technical Change and Increasing Returns to Scale*, University of Pennsylvania, 1961, Mimeo.

TABLE 16.3

CHANGE IN OUTPUT ATTRIBUTABLE TO INPUTS AND PRODUCTIVITY CHANGES AND AVERAGE RATES OF CHANGE IN OUTPUT, INPUTS AND PRODUCTIVITY FOR SELECTED PERIODS

	Percent of Output Change Attributable to:		Average Annual Rate (Percent) of Change in:		
Period	Inputs	Productivity	Output	Inputs	Productivity
1870–1911......	72	28	2.45	1.77	.67
1911–1920......	129	−29	.70	.89	−.19
1920–1939......	16	84	1.08	.17	.91
1939–1945......	34	66	3.05	1.04	1.99
1945–1950......	49	51	.81	.40	.41
1950–1956......	−9	109	1.89	−.17	2.06
1939–1956......	22	78	1.98	.42	1.55
1911–1956......	31	69	1.34	.41	.93
1870–1956......	56	44	1.86	1.05	.80

Source: Loomis and Barton, *op. cit.*, p. 9. Indices used above are based on 1947–49 = 100 with inputs valued on a constant dollar basis.

Technological improvement is the main phenomenon represented in productivity increases and is reflected in the manner explained in several earlier chapters. Or we might say that the main effect of public investment, or the public sector, in economic development of agriculture is in output increases attributable to increased productivity of resources measured in their aggregate and classical form as land, labor and capital. On the other hand, the major effect of the private sector is in increased factor input, especially in new capital forms, although the private sector also contributes importantly to productivity change in the research and knowledge it develops and in the more productive forms of capital which it markets in agriculture.

Without the new forms of capital representing technical change, output would be forthcoming only as inputs are extended for a given production function. Marginal and average productivity of resources would then decline. Agricultural expansion was readily possible as the nation was first settled and land, labor and capital could be increased largely in "true scale manner." After the public domain was fully settled, however, capital and labor were increased against a relatively fixed area or input of land. As expected for such a period when inputs are largely retained in conventional technical form, Loomis and Barton's figures show the average per unit productivity of resources to have declined in the period 1911–20. However, with momentum built up in agricultural research thereafter, productivity per unit of aggregate resource, with resources measured in the classical manner, increased rapidly. Increase in resource productivity has dominated increased resource inputs, in causing output to increase (i.e., the portion of output attributable to the two sources) since 1920. The very large increase in productivity came with the shift from horse to tractor power and the diversion of land from feed for the former to feed for livestock; with the introduction of hybrid corn, other new seeds and summer fallow; with the widespread use of fertilizer over much more of the nation; and with other important chemical, biological and mechanical innovations.

The public has not produced the inputs which have been physically transformed into output as the product supply of agriculture has been increased. It has, however, been the dominant factor in developing the concepts, forms and ideas of these innovations and in predicting their productivity effects. Once their forms and productivity effects have been predicted to be favorable, private firms then have been able to produce these inputs leading to increased productivity, and the final change in rapid economic development of agriculture under a fixed land area has been attained.

FOOD AND CONSUMER POLICY

At its outset, public investment in agricultural research had basic reason for being classified as *policy for agriculture*. It is now best termed as *policy for consumers*. Land supply had, in initiation of public research institutes for agriculture, been fairly well exploited, and opportunity to increase aggregate farm income through extension of land inputs at favorable price had largely disappeared.[14] The opportunity then existed for developing new forms of capital resources and raising the productivity coefficients of conventional resources remaining in use. As mentioned previously, the effect also was that of producing knowledge as a resource, with the public subsidizing its costs, through the actual process of producing it, and keeping its real price low to farmers. In this pricing effect, the relevant relationships led to an extension in output of agriculture and a rapid shift in the supply function (as suggested by a relative reduction in P_x in equation (11.9) or an increase in the elasticity or multiplier in equation (11.7).

But increase in the supply function and rapid increase in output also promised increased farm income under demand regime of higher elasticities in respect to price and income. Assuming that the demand regime allowed increased output to bring forth greater aggregate revenue and increased net income, public investment in agricultural technology represented policy element with a major gain to agriculture. This is exactly what it was expected to do. Under this demand regime, aggregate welfare increase was generally assured in the national community or society of consumers and farm producers (although certainly, there were specific groups which might have realized greater gains from restrained supply function and greater price of commodities and resources). Also under this demand regime, existing in an extent not easily specified, gain could be twofold, with distribution of benefit broadly to consumers and farm producers. Given a high rate of demand expansion, from immigration and high birth rate plus growth in income when this elasticity facet provided more growth opportunity than at present, the real price of food could be restrained and lowered; at the same time, revenue of farm output could

[14] For a previous analysis of public policy in these respects see Earl O. Heady, "Public Purpose in Research and Education," *Jour. Farm Econ.*, Vol. 45.

increase in the relative magnitudes explained in Chapters 1 and 3. Positive-sum outcomes in real income gain were thus more evident as between farm producers as a group and consumers. Gradually but certainly, however, the demand regime explained in Chapter 6 came about, with the effects in revenue and resource returns explained in earlier chapters.

With emergence of this stage in economic development and in related structure of supply and demand in farm products, the certainty of positive-sum real income gains, broadly between farm producer group and national consumer group, no longer existed. To be certain, consuming society continued to benefit in large magnitude through decline in the real price of food, and in the extreme abundance and variety of food produced with an approaching minimum of resources for this purpose. These gains to consumers are an important basis for further extension of the food supply function, and its interrelated lessening of the resource demand function in agriculture.

The ongoing consumer gains being realized and those in prospect themselves justify continued public and private investment in research and education on improved food production technology. This will continue true, as long as the return on this social investment is at the high levels set forth earlier, and until it drops much nearer to the levels of other conventional investments in either public or private sector. And should it ever drop to this level, further activity of the public in financing and producing improved food technology would still be justified, both in terms of equality of resource and investment returns and in terms of increasing degree of certainty and "food productive capacity contingency" in a world matrix with yet-to-be-established vectors in population, political and developmental space. One problem in guaranteeing that this public activity be continued at scale commensurate with its high payoff is broader knowledge for administrators of agricultural research and education, indicating the gain to general society and the need to so justify it and claim support for it. Appeal now should be made more to general society than to the farm sector.

The large gain to consumers does not, however, guarantee positive-sum short-run outcome in real income or utility to consumers and farm producers aggregated as a community. Nekby has made an attempt to predict monetary gain to farm producers and consumers from agricultural research.[15] He obtains negative outcome for producers and positive outcome for consumers. But while the estimated monetary gain to consumers exceeds the monetary loss to producers, a similar positive-sum outcome in utility over the two groups is not guaranteed (in the absence of compensation). Large forward press in supply against an inelastic food demand causes decline in revenue of agriculture as explained earlier. Without ability to make interpersonal utility measurements, we cannot be certain that the gains to consumers in lower real price of food (and not services incorporated with foods in the nonfarm sector) out-

[15] A. B. Nekby, *The Structural Development of American Agriculture*, Ph. D. thesis, Iowa State University, 1961.

weigh the loss to farm producers in revenue. Here we speak of sectors of agriculture such as those in feed grains, wheat and cotton where market orders and other supply restraints have not been effective in slowing the pace of supply growth so that an equitable share of progress fruits are retained with producers.

But even if we consider benefits to farm groups which have gained in managed supply to retain progress rewards, or producers of other sectors who have gained in ability to race output ahead of the industry average, we still have the problem of short-run distribution of costs and payoffs from farm economic progress. Gains to these producer groups, as well as to consumers at large, come at income sacrifice to farmers who are not in advantageous position to share in the fruits of this progress. Farm policy from 1930 to 1960 can, as has been mentioned in earlier chapters, be interpreted as recognition of possible negative-sum outcome unless compensation was arranged. Unfortunately, the compensation methods used were somewhat clumsy and costly, relative to alternatives which were available.

Certainly the philosophy of early public investment in agricultural research and education was in terms of *farm policy* and income, gain to consumers being secondary. This was appropriate, with the major part of the households then falling in agriculture. The gain to consumers was a "windfall profit," but one indeed of great magnitude and itself sufficient basis for public action. With the change in demand regime and the stage of economic development explained above, public investment in improved farm technology should now be looked upon as for purpose of *food policy* and major gain to consumers. This itself is important reason for public investment in the process. The accomplishments of improved technology as element of food policy have been great, but too little recognized by both the public and administrators who direct the public facilities which produce knowledge in new farm techniques. The public at large is only slightly aware of these efficient institutions and public investments, in extending food supply and in lowering its real cost. The product and contribution of these institutions is much broader than most staff employees recognize, but it is more to national and consuming society than to farm society per se. Nonfarm society would probably support agricultural colleges more heavily than at the present, and more richly than is now done by the farm population, if they had more complete knowledge of the origin and magnitude of these gains. The empirical evidence for this statement is at hand: Large industrial states with small proportion of population and income from farms often better support their agricultural colleges than agricultural states. In comparison to past decades, if appropriations are related to value of farm marketings, and as measured in relative increase in appropriations for agricultural research since 1920, agricultural research moved somewhat out of the farm states to the city states. This relative shift, now more or less stabilized, does not follow an "exact pattern" and has perhaps favored most those states with "more balanced" income from both industry and agriculture; as well as those with products having greatest demand elasticities.

The role of agricultural research and education in national economic development and food policy needs direct recognition, in relation to further opportunities open to gain by consumers and for general integration and systematization of over-all agricultural policy. In this vein, the agricultural colleges might best change their name to The College of Food and Agriculture. The land-grant colleges and the U.S. Department of Agriculture have performed well. Their creation was visionary, coming at a time when the goals of society were those of agriculture because the population was thus distributed. They now function in a time when the goals of agriculture are largely those of society because communication is so effective, income averages so high and farm people are a sparse portion of the total population. Economic growth caused gradual transition from a time when contribution of public research and education to farm families was dominant to the time when its contribution to consumers became dominant. This desired time path in redirection of gains from technical advance was not consciously planned. However, it was an optimum process, given the restructuring of society which accompanies economic development. It has been true, however, that a parallel restructuring of research and educational programs to mesh with this change has yet come about in only a few institutions. The outcome or product of publicly sponsored farm technical advance over the 1950's undoubtedly has been inconsistent with that believed to prevail by many staff workers in land-grant colleges.

The greatest marginal challenge to public research and educational institutions for agriculture in years ahead is not alone in figuring out how to organize activities for rapid progress in technology. They already know how to do this efficiently. The challenge is in devising research structures which allow digestion of new technology into the economic and social structure to give equitable distribution of gains over the population. Too little concern has been devoted to this problem in the past. Accordingly, some farmers have gained and some have sacrificed from rapid technological gains. Our society expects some penalty to attach to persons who do not take advantage of positive opportunity available to them in growing sectors. Most young people displaced from agriculture choose accordingly and transfer. Others in agriculture step up their operations, to increase output by larger proportion than price decline and thus profit. But there are many people who are not thus situated to adapt and who must bear the brunt of the costs of technological progress which leads to general national gain, sometimes at expense of farm revenue. Certainly the basic problem surrounding agriculture in the 1960's is: How can the rapid supply increase in foods be handled to avert major income burden in agriculture while still allowing the desired rate of progress and in diffusing gains of progress equitably over the population?

BASIS OF PUBLIC SUPPORT

Most less-developed nations do not ask why improved knowledge of agriculture should be promoted. The reason is obvious: to aid in economic development. As mentioned above, organized optimally for this purpose, public investment so allocated needs no other justification. There are, however, miscellaneous and less dirct reasons calling for public subsidization of research and communication of farm technology and organization. One more technical reason for public investment in such a highly competitive industry is: When expenditures have indiscriminate benefit and those who gain cannot be easily identified, public investment is justified. Similarly, where competition is so great that few innovation gains can be retained by those who produce research results, it may be necessary for the community to invest in it.[16] Private firms, of course, conduct research relative to agriculture where they can market a product and gain accordingly. "Early innovators" on farms also benefit from putting research results to use early. However, few firms could conduct research, and retain gain, on improved crop rotations and similar items of technology.

Having looked at some of the broader and more general reasons why publics may wish to conduct agricultural research and development, we now examine some of the more specific and pragmatic reasons. Many land-grant college personnel probably think of their effort as falling in one or more of these.

Alleviate Starvation Potential

This is a sufficient basis for emphasis on improved farm technology in India and similar countries where population presses deeply against current food production possibilities. Looking forward in 1860 and making predictions of the population-food balance over the next century, U.S. society had reason to be concerned about the period ahead. Population was increasing by a quarter to a third in each decade. Agriculture was making parallel strides in output through settlement and development of new farming regions; but the end was apparently in sight as settlement of the more productive soil areas was nearly completed. If future increases in agricultural output were to keep pace with population trends, expansion in the farm plant would have to come largely from a greater output per acre. Two possibilities existed: (1) use more labor and capital per acre (a more intensive agriculture) with techniques known at the time—and a consequent increase in land productivity but a decline in labor and capital productivity or (2) develop innovations which would increase the physical productivity of land, labor and capital alike. Decision was made by U.S. society to emphasize the latter. The decision was wise, and in the last century, population of the United States has increased by 550 percent. Agricultural output has increased similarly, with the major part of the increase in the last half century coming from technological improvement. Starvation has not been a threat, and food demand is not likely to press on food supply in the next half century.

Small Scale of Firm

A further firm basis for public sponsorship of farm technological advances is the small scale of the firm in agriculture. Individual farmers

[16] *Cf.* P. T. Bauer and B. S. Yamey, *Economies of Underdeveloped Countries*, University of Chicago Press, Chicago, 1957, pp. 160–65.

generally do not operate on a sufficiently large scale and do not have sufficient funds for organizing their own research units. In the first two and one-half centuries of United States history, relatively few industrial firms invested in research relating to agriculture. This was true because labor and land inputs dominated agriculture and fewer profit gains were possible from capital inputs developed for agriculture. The investment of industrial firms in technical innovations for agriculture has, of course, increased greatly in recent decades. Development of more and fundamental knowledge in these fields has led to the creation of new chemicals, biological materials and machines which could be produced commercially and marketed in agriculture. Consequently, industrial firms have increased their own investments in uncovering more discoveries. Factor prices and a farm industry resting more on capital inputs have favored this development. However, there are large areas of possible agricultural improvements or scientific relationships which do not result in easily fabricated, packaged and marketed material products or which do not readily lend themselves to patenting and brand promotion. In these areas particularly, farm firms are too small to carry forth their own research. They will continue to require publicly supported research.

Competitive Structure and Small Scale

Another possible basis for public support of farm innovations because of the competitive nature of agriculture is: Society evidently has desired that an important degree of competition be maintained in the American economy. These values are reflected in various types of antitrust legislation. They are related directly to agriculture in historic legislation favoring family farms. An essential characteristic of a family farm is: It is not large enough to exercise monoply power in commodity markets or in the labor or land market. Public sponsorship of agricultural research has likely helped to promote and maintain the competitive nature of agricultural firms. Farming improvements are more equally available to all farmers. This retention of competitive structure has helped maintain family farms, but with the effects of weak market power for agriculture discussed earlier. Farm policies have attempted to give the industry some monopoly power, but retain the competitive nature of the firm. When small-scale firms exist, they are not large enough to conduct research which realizes scale economies possible in this activity. This is itself a reason for group activity in research organization.

Increasing Farm Income

A fourth basis was that of increasing incomes of farmers. Whether or not aggregate farm income is increased or decreased, as a result of technological improvement, depends mainly on two things: (1) the price elasticity of demand for the particular product and (2) whether the technical innovation increases aggregate farm output. Our previous analysis explains the current outcome in respect to this goal.

General Economic Progress

The goal for public investment in agricultural research and education could have been primarily that of economic progress as explained above. This has been its important effect. It is the major basis for justification in the future. In this sense, however, it does need to be emphasized under the appropriate heading and in relation to food and consumer policy. It is possible that this basis for investment may broaden with world economic development and extended political understanding and facilities among nations.

Interregional Competition

Farmers of each region and state can and do look upon investment in research as a method of meeting interregional competition. While it may be known that food demand is inelastic, with decline in total revenue under increased output, a group of farmers forced to hold their output constant while those of other regions increased production, would find themselves to be recipients of a smaller share of a reduced revenue. On a competitive basis, they would be better off, although worse off in both cases, to increase output and have a larger share of the smaller revenue. (See the discussion of equations 5.42 to 5.55 on effects for those who cannot innovate.) In this sense, farmers of each state or region serve in the manner of firms competing with each other and under the necessity of innovation to hold a share of the market. Under the structure of American agriculture, this interregional competition does prevail and causes particular geographic aggregates of farmers to improve technology. Even under a quota system of agriculture, this type of competition would still prevail.

For the Sake of Knowledge

Agricultural research also is conducted for the sake of knowledge in itself. Man has always desired to know more; or parents generally want their children to have an enlarged universe of knowledge open to them. Society obviously is willing to make some investment to this end. As societies become richer, they come more nearly to look upon knowledge as an ultimate or consumption good and invest in it. But to the extent that they do so, emphasis is more likely to be on fundamental research and knowledge. While society may invest some quantity of public funds for this as an end per se, it is apparent that most fundamental research must serve as a means to ends such as those above. It is unlikely that the agricultural colleges will ever be able to justify themselves to farm and consumer publics largely on this basis. In major proportion, investment in improved farm technology needs to be justified where it has greatest contribution: as consumer food policy. It now makes a greater contribution to general economic progress than to farm gain. Relatively, however, its contribution to general progress is less than in earlier times, when farming used a majority of the nation's labor force and resources, and a larger proportionate gain to consumers was possible in the transfer of resources to other industries. As we mentioned earlier, today's farm technological research does not have its greatest promise for today's consumers who are well fed and have calories at low real price. It is for consumers in 1980 and 2000.

EQUITABLE RETENTION OF GAINS

It is in a free market that public investment in farm technological advance is largely an element of food policy. This is true in the context discussed: lower real price of food and reduced farm revenue under inelastic demand. Even when coupled with compensation policy which provides direct payments to farmers or price supports to accomplish the same, it represents food policy for consumer gain. The compensation or transfer payments, either directly or indirectly, simply represent means of redressing the position of those who otherwise bear the cost of this progress. Output is allowed to grow against declining revenue.

There are combinations, however, whereby public action to improve technology could be looked upon as element of farm policy, with focus on increase of farm income rather than on consumer surplus. If, for example, supply of food was restricted to maintain revenue under the inelastic demand that faces agriculture, farmers could innovate to reduce resource inputs and costs of given output. With output and revenue at constant level, technical advance lowering per unit requirements in resources and costs would increase net income of farmers. Any type of innovation which is economic in the sense of marginal cost less than marginal revenue could do so, even if it is a biological development such as new seed variety or fertilization to increase yield per acre. The farmer could simply use fewer acres, lowering costs of attaining output and revenue restraint and thus increasing net income. Hence, within this framework, advancement of technology in agriculture could have the end of farm income improvement and serve as a basis alone as farm policy.

Consuming society could also gain from resource savings allowed to transfer from agriculture to other industries. Still, it also is possible to arrange subsets of policy elements such that they provide even broader gain to consumers, while some gain of progress is retained for farm producers as a broad group. The supply restraint could be gradually loosened so that real price of food is allowed to decline, but not so fast that total revenue to agriculture declines, while farmers are realizing gains through relatively larger decline in per unit resource and cost requirements. (Some of the "saved resources" could also be transferred to other economic sectors as indirect source of consumer gain.) Pareto-optima or Pareto-better conditions thus are attained, with real income gain to consumers in aggregate and money and real income gain to farm producers in aggregate. A wide range of policy mechanisms would allow this, including the regional land reduction alternative or others discussed in Chapter 14.

Another alternative to these more direct supply restraints would be managed rate of technical advance. We illustrated in Chapter 7, equations (7.20) through (7.31) for particular forms of demand and supply functions, maximum rates at which production coefficients might be allowed to change against rates of demand increase, if specified goals in respect to resource use and prices of agriculture were attained. In equation (7.28), for example, technology could increase only at the rate $\Gamma = \lambda^{.2}$, where demand has the price elasticity of only $-.4$ and production elasticity remains at .8 under technical change for the particular algebraic form. (The equations and discussion in Chapter 11 relating to quotas and supply management also illustrate how technology can be furthered with gain to both producers and consumers.) Hence, public-sponsored technological advance at rates managed to attain these goals would be primarily farm policy, with food policy attainment being secondary but with Pareto-better conditions allowed in gains to both consumers and farmers.

Managing the rate of technical change is a more subtle mechanism and would not appear so directly as "market interference," as do quota systems for inputs or outputs, to check supply. Society, of course, does interfere with the market in this respect. It does not allow the market to generate all new technology, but produces it in its own institutions. It has injected technology, helping change the production function at a faster rate than demand has grown. Injecting it at exactly the rate consistent with profit maintenance under demand growth would be no more, and even less than at the present where the public supplies the technology without restraint, a mechanism of market interference. Obviously, however, management of rate of technical change to accomplish this end would be extremely difficult, much more so than other policy alternatives allowing the same attainment. Difficulty arises because the technological potential at a current time is largely a function of research inputs at an earlier period.

Data of previous chapters indicated that existing technical knowledge not yet in full use promises a regime of food supply burdening demand for the next one or two decades. This knowledge has already been partly dispersed and its withdrawal would be impossible. Difficulty also arises because an increasing proportion of research inputs are those financed by private firms. The outturn from these inputs would go on, likely at increased tempo because of profit incentive. Finally suppression of scientific knowledge is not an alternative of general appeal, particularly when it has high returns to general society, and even if guarantee of positive-sum outcome is not apparent over all groups.

Organization of Research for Progress

In some nations, the problem ahead is to organize research for agriculture which has urgency in possible return in national economic progress. This was an important basis for urgency, but unwittingly to those originating it, of research in earlier decades of the U.S. With approach of only 5 percent of labor force in agriculture, urgency for these purposes is now in other areas. But research could be organized readily to meet various sub-goals in general economic progress. Take a nation short on food "necessities" and with a paucity of resources for nonfood development. Developmental goal would be for technical progress and augmented supply function to increase output and lower price of basic food items while freeing resources for other industries. Magnitude of demand elasticity would be a criterion of some relevance for ordering research on farm technology. Research might be devoted especially to commodities with low price elasticity of demand, these being the commodities consumed in broadest expanse by the population and immediately needed to lessen hunger. Also, these would be the commodities engaging the greatest quantity of resources, and presenting greatest potential in resource savings for intersector transfer. This society, not concerned first with farmer income and welfare, would perhaps leave aside those commodities of more exotic nature and with high elasticities of demand in respect to price and income (except for export and exchange for greater quantity of necessities). In any case research promising greatest resources savings would be emphasized.

Now take a contrasting society. It is not concerned with consumer welfare and progress goals. Its only concern is in increase of farm income. Farm technological research in this society would be conducted generally only for commodities with price elasticities of demand greater than unity, plus certain other non-output increasing (to extent that these exist) innovations of an engineering nature.[17]

We can specify other organizations of technological research with criteria in economic growth where supplemental policy is not used to guarantee retention of some progress gains in agriculture. More than otherwise, emphasis in research and education of agricultural colleges over the past decades has been on innovations which increase productivity and output of resources specialized to agriculture. Stress on quantity has been greatest in research which increased yield per acre, output per animal or production per unit of feed. (The traditions and lore of agricultural science evidently have given more recognition to the worker who thus accomplishes, as compared to the one who develops, an improved quality or embodies a new service in a product.) This is the relevant emphasis when either (1) a nation's diet is near subsistence level and (2) the price elasticity of demand for food is greater than one. Neither of these conditions hold true in the United States. Hence, while the paramount emphasis in India is correctly increased yield per acre of staples such as rice, with smallest resource costs per caloric unit, this is not singularly true in the United States.

One set of criteria for ordering biological or physical research and

---

[17] For some of these classifications, see Earl O. Heady: "Basic Economic and Welfare Aspects of Farm Technological Research," *Jour. Farm Econ.*, Vol. 31; "Adaptation of Education and Auxiliary Aids to Solution of the Basic Farm Problem," *Jour. Farm Econ.*, Vol. 39; and *Economics of Agricultural Production and Resource Use*, Prentice-Hall, Englewood Cliffs, N.J., 1952, Chap. 27.

education in public institutions which are not part of the market in a private enterprise economy, is still reflected through quantities of the market, however. Income elasticities of demand quantities which can be measured and have practical empirical meaning, can serve as criteria. In effect, these quantities indicate that consumers who are well fed and have high incomes (1) take satisfaction of hunger for granted, with worry mainly of obesity, and (2) are more intensely concerned, not with obtaining "commonplace luxuries" such as food, electricity, running water, telephones, radios, cars and a 40-hour week, but with more "exotic necessities" such as hi-fi, automatic transmissions, power boats and automatic washers and dryers. They place no premium on greater physical quantity of food per capita as their income grows.

While the consumer places no premium on the quantity aspects of food, income elasticities show that he does place positive premium on the quality or service aspects which can be incorporated with foods. (See Chapter 6.) Income elasticities of demand, then, could well be used as one basis for ordering biological and physical research on farm products aimed at improving consumer and producer welfare in an economy as wealthy as that of the U.S. Directors of research might lay out before them, for the purposes focal to this section, the complete array of income elasticities for different agricultural products and for different aspects of products such as quality, quantity, service, convenience, etc. Research resources would then be allocated in terms of and relative to magnitudes of income elasticities of demand, weighted by the quantity of resources used for each product. Those products, qualities and services with highest elasticities are those from which consumers will derive greatest satisfaction as their income and total expenditures increase. For this very reason, they are the ones for which consumers will reward farmers most in profit as per capita income continues to grow. Certainly private firms are concentrating research in these very directions (i.e. growth industries) for the reasons mentioned.

Research and education are not purely stochastic phenomena, with chance occurrence relative to their initiation and outcome. They need not serve as exogenous variables, with their direction predetermined by conventions of the past or as by-products of a previous organizational structure. They can be geared to the present and prospective economic or developmental status of a nation. The probability of scientific discovery for a particular product, function or service depends on the size of the sample, the quantity and quality of research resources allocated to it. Quantitative guides, if recognized and used in the administration of research, exist even for gearing physical and biological sciences to the emphases specified by economic growth. An ordering of research in line with these quantities would not nullify the demand for particular specializations in agricultural science, but would only turn the direction of their concentration. For example, plant genetics would be just as important as before, but emphasis would be more on breeding to develop "inward quality and services," rather than quantity. Genes, heterozygote, recessive, dominance, mathematics, chromosome and other scientific concepts and phenomena which serve as traditions of the field would continue so. They would simply be used for more urgent social purposes. The challenge to plant breeding scientists need not be lessened. To the contrary, it could be increased since the quality-service aspects of plants have been less exploited and likely are more complex. The same would be true for the majority of specialized agricultural sciences. We have, then, one approximate basis for estimating the payoff and needed direction of biological research and education under economic growth, starting with a high level of per capita well-being and with further growth on income in sight. Undoubtedly it would call for sizeable increases in physical and biological research relating to food processing and manufacture in stages beyond the farm.

The discussion immediately above has been in terms of public research policy apart from all other policy elements. It is the realm in which directors of research operate, since they cannot individually initiate, legislate and implement other public policy. But where public research policy is linked with public output restraint policy, as discussed previously, any innovation which can reduce input per unit of constant output, revenue remaining constant and costs declining, can serve to increase aggregate farmer welfare. In absence of this linkage, however, elasticities of demand do become relevant criteria of ordering research to guarantee positive-sum certain outcome in attainment of Pareto optima wherein both consumers and producers are better off—producers in increased revenue and consumers in supply and real price of commodities to which they attach greatest marginal utility.

Emphasis on Social Sciences for Developmental Attainment

The criteria above serve as one basis for ordering research in the physical and biological sciences, with focus on innovating services of greatest marginal urgency to high income consumers and, hence, with greatest prospect for monetary reward to farmers. But if appropriate total goals are selected for research in the land-grant universities, growth criteria also relate to the social sciences. Research and education in agriculture have had significant effect not in increasing aggregate farm profits or in creating new and different food utility and service for consumers, but in helping to lessen the amount of the nation's resources required to produce food. Labor and other resources are freed from agriculture so that they can be used to produce schools, hospitals and roads in the public sector, and to produce houses, television, power boats and clothes dryers and the many other goods of "great marginal consumer urgency" in the private sector.

The agricultural colleges and the U.S. Department of Agriculture have been in the vanguard and have been major contributors to this facet of national economic development. They can well pride themselves in it. It has been a major reason for their existence, although it has not always been so recognized. But they should become more cognizant of this contribution and base appeal on it. They will have a broader role and financial support if they do so. They can tie cause and result together, a condition not well attained when justification and financial appeal is based mainly on contribution to farm profits. As indicated above, there is some empirical indication that this appeal and contribution can be recognized by the consuming public, the main sector to gain from the contributions to development by agricultural colleges under conditions of the market. Appropriations for the experiment stations and research services tend to be smallest, relative to value of farm production, the greater is the proportion of state income represented by agriculture. Between 1920 and 1955, agricultural research became concentrated relatively more in the industrial states, high population states or states having products with greater demand elasticities. (Also, states with small initial research investments were able to increase their percentage share of state research appropriations.)

But our main concern in this section is in the ordering of research and education and in gearing it better to national economic progress and guarantee of Pareto-optima or Pareto-better attainment in utility increase over producer and consumer groups. Emphasis on research for technological progress of conventional types (e.g., the quantity facet, as compared to the quality-service facet without regard to magnitude of income elasticities) is justified in the broad economic development framework outlined immediately above. For this purpose, however, it is not sufficient that the resources be freed through biological and physical innovations and then left stranded. Under this condition, they remain in agriculture producing a product. With low demand elasticities the result is surpluses and depressed farm prices, incomes and factor returns. Hence, if the general economic development goal is to be selected as the major justification of biological and physical research of conventional emphasis, it must be accompanied by equally intensive research in the social sciences, if the national development gains made possible by technical research are to be realized rapidly and fully, and if economic misery is not to impinge on those persons caused to become surplus resources as a result of rapid technological progress. Social science becomes an important technical complement with technical science for this goal of agricultural research and education. The former needs to be put on a footing with the latter, a condition which does not hold true in many land-grant universities.

Social science should not be increased at the expense of technical science, but rather increased in magnitude and financial support to the levels which have more often been traditional for the physical sciences. The two go along together for the basic developmental goal. Social science is needed to lessen economic pain for labor and capital resources caused to become surplus by technical progress. The benefits of these resource savings have no basis unless equal activity is devoted to aiding transfer of the "freed" resources to occupational and geographic points where they have premium under economic growth. (Too, there is need for more research and education on social mechanisms which allow this contribution through technical progress, and also allow farm producers to realize reward, rather than only short-run penalty, for contribution made to broad national consumer welfare.)

The investment in social sciences now needs to be large. Magnification of social sciences can actually aid and enhance the physical sciences. Without more intensive social science to help solve the surplus, excess factor and depressed income problems generated by rapid technical progress, technical sciences are much more likely to be restrained by lack of funds. Again, the question is not one of social science at the expense of technical science or vice versa. The problem is to develop total research and educational programs which are systematic in the broad national developmental sense. Here, social and technical sciences go hand in hand and one is needed more because of the other. Without the other, the one is much less meaningful in terms of social gains and justification and is much less likely to have adequate long-run financial support.

Technological research of the type normally conducted, and in a market environment with the traditional distribution of gains and costs, contributes to long-run economic progress by bringing about more output from given resources, or allows the same output from fewer resources or costs in agriculture. Hence, in the long run it allows a growing population or consuming society a greater output and variety of goods from the total available resources. Research of this kind is needed in agriculture in the traditional framework (1) to give farmers of one state equal opportunity with farmers of other regions to realize the potential of technological improvement, (2) to provide a basis for general economic progress and the benefits which generally accrue to consumers, (3) to advance general science and knowledge and (4) to enhance the position of a nation in the competitive world. But in accomplishing these long-run objectives in the normal environment, much of this research gives rise to short-run problems, since the increased output and increased resource productivity are not immediately "digested" into the national economy.

In the short run, increased output gives rise to surpluses which depress prices and incomes or cause some resources such as labor to become excess. With the long-run effects of research of the cost-reducing and output-increasing types desired and necessary for the above reasons, research is needed for: facilitating the "digestion" of potential gains from these other types of research into the general economic or industrial system; lessening short-run problems created by increased output and resource productivity in agriculture; bringing returns to resources in agriculture up to levels in other industries; helping to insure that the gains from technological advance from usual types of research are realized more quickly and fully by consuming sectors, including both farm and city families; establishing means whereby farm people can receive appropriate rewards for their resources under rapid technological progress and an equitable share of gains from progress; aiding in change of social structures appending both directly and indirectly to agriculture and altered by rapid technological advance and population change; bringing about a more efficient allocation or balance of resources within agriculture and between agriculture and other sectors of the economy, considering distribution of gains and costs of advance and "unevenness" in market power; and providing the factual basis for developing positive governmental agricultural policies consistent both with the welfare of farm people and over-all national goals. Generally these needs call for social science inputs on par of importance with physical science inputs.

Systematic Research Programs

It is highly appropriate that land-grant colleges make a systematic analysis of the effects of conventional research and educational programs on income and welfare in both the farm and nonfarm sectors of society; then, after this picture is more precisely established, they should outline the appropriate role and orientation of future research and education in a wealthy and progressing economy. This role is quite different from a century ago and from what many land-grant college staff members still believe it to be. A vigorous and well-supported research and educational program will always be needed, and the returns over the next several decades can be relatively as high as those over the previous century. But the support for this continued investment is most likely to be forthcoming if land-grant college personnel better understand the actual effects of their efforts and develop programs which are more complete and systematic in terms of these effects. Too, they will be better able to appeal for support to those segments of society which actually are the chief beneficiaries of the research, in contrast to the existing situation wherein large benefit accrues to consumers but appeal for financial support is made mainly to farmers.

Another reason also exists, causing this re-examination to be possible and relevant. The private sector of the economy now is extremely important and efficient in development and production of new agricultural technology. Likewise, it is efficient in communicating this knowledge to farmers; appropriately because knowledge serves as resource in the position of a technical complement necessary for productive use of material resources sold by private firms. Investment by private firms in communication, including salesmen, dealers, advertising and public relations likely exceeds that in extension agents and printed materials by the colleges. Too, if measurement extends far enough into fundamental research by private firms, the private sector investment in research for new farm technology probably exceeds the public investment. It is for this reason that underdeveloped countries cannot reproduce the U.S. public facilities for research and education, represented in the agricultural colleges and the U.S. Department of Agriculture, and expect development results comparable to ours over recent decades.

New machinery, ration supplements, fertilizers, improved seeds and even certain aspects of livestock breeding have come to flow largely from the private sector, which has illustrated great ability in applied research, especially in adapting fundamental findings to applicable forms for marketing as capital materials. Because of growing private sector contributions, public institutions for agriculture have an opportunity to evaluate the relative economic urgency of their contributions under economic growth and to divert effort towards those products or services of knowledge (1) apparently still subject to decreasing costs not realized in the private sector, (2) most consistent with the income and growth status of the U.S. economy, (3) not adapted for "package and sale" by private firms but of extreme importance for furthering progress in agriculture and (4) consistent with the actual economic impact of research and education on the various segments of society.

EXTENSION EDUCATION ADAPTATION

Large needs and opportunities also exist in adapting extension education to the economic growth status of agriculture and the nation. Extension is an important tool in helping lift nations of low stages of economic development, and also in helping to guide economic reorganization at high stages of development.[18] (Also see the educational needs discussed in the last section of Chapter 9.)

A basic need, serving as foundation in programming extension education, is for extension services to know that a major effect of their traditional activities has been to replace people from agriculture. As mentioned in earlier chapters, more potent feeds, insect sprays, fertilizers, seeds and other technologies substitute for both land and people in the agricultural production process. The faster these innovations are extended and adopted, the more rapidly are people replaced from agriculture. Then, do the extension services have educational responsibility for these persons displaced by their traditional activities? What goal exists on which this displacement is based? Are the persons displaced any less important than those remaining? Are information and services to ease their transfer not a minimum compensation need? These are questions which not only are appropriate but also can serve in providing direction and broader opportunity for the extension services.

Alternative Views in Purpose

Extension education can view itself largely in the economic and social framework of a century back: when the country was agricultural in the majority and public investment was used largely to increase farmer income. Or, it can view itself in the twentieth century setting, as an arm of general society with its main function to bring about lower real prices of food, to reduce resource requirements and to get these freed resources

[18] Bauer and Yamey (*op. cit.*, p. 217) indicate the need for public service to provide basic knowledge at low levels of development since private sectors often cannot develop and sell applicable innovations at a profit. This statement is even more applicable to problems of change and public choice on policy at high stages of economic development.

transferred to other sectors. It could proceed with the first without concern about positive-sum utility outcomes for all of society. Or, it could proceed with the second in the same vein, with gains from farm technological advance going to consumers, but costs falling on farmers in aggregate as revenue declines under inelastic demand. Let us review possible activities under these alternative "charters."

Several alternative goals could be selected as the focus of educational activities in land-grant colleges. The goal selected largely specifies the means. The means are reflected in the types of information carried to farm people, the types of specialists (animal husbandrymen, agronomists, economists, vocational guidance specialists, etc.) who are employed by the extension service, the relative amount of funds used in low-income counties as compared to high-income counties, the methods employed in contacting people and communicating ideas, etc. Means or educational patterns selected can be either consistent or inconsistent with the end held. Conflicts have existed, and do exist, between (1) major ends or goals which educational administrators use as the allocative focus of their program, (2) the means employed and (3) the actual ends attained.

Perhaps the most widely held goal of extension education has been to increase the aggregate income of farming. If this goal were the only relevant one, the direction of education activity and employment of specialists would be quite clear. Specialists would not be employed and information would not be communicated to increase output where the price elasticity of demand is less than 1.0. Unfortunately, the list of commodities with demand elasticities greater than 1.0 is very small. (See Chapter 6.) Hence, if the goal of extension activities were actually that of increasing farm income, and not necessarily that of maximizing the welfare of farm people, specialists would not be employed and information would not be extended for techniques that increase output of such commodities as wheat, corn, potatoes, hogs, many dairy products, peanuts, cotton, eggs and most other common farm products.

Physical specialists would be those with engineering emphasis, to assist in techniques that lower costs per unit but do not increase output. Biological specialists would not fit into this scheme so well, for although biological techniques lower costs per unit, they also generally increase output. Even an engineering innovation that has first impact in reducing total costs may lower marginal costs to an extent that output finally does increase. The point is that many of the activities traditionally emphasized in education are not consistent with increasing gross revenue of agriculture.[19]

If greater revenue to agriculture were the sole end of extension activities, the means employed are highly inconsistent with the goal. This

[19] Of course it is true that even though demand is inelastic, farmers who first adopt an output-increasing technique, and who do not produce enough to affect market prices, can gain from any type regardless of the demand elasticity. However, the emphasis of this paper is on macro adjustments and mass farmer reaction.

is not to infer the specialists in most types of technological improvement should be dropped from extension programs. As brought out below, this type of activity is consistent with other possible goals of extension activity, if other means are employed with it. However, it is generally inconsistent with the goal of increasing farm income in the free market where demand is inelastic and resources have low mobility. If this were to be the actual goal of extension education, emphasis should be on experts who would help farmers form monopolies and reduce output, at least to the point where price elasticity of demand becomes 1.0.

Maximizing the Welfare of Farm People

Welfare of people in agriculture might be increased generally by any educational activity that extends output where price elasticities are greater than 1.0 or lowers total costs but does not increase output for commodities with inelastic demands. However, welfare also can be increased by extending output for commodities with inelastic demands, as long as the reduced total revenue is redistributed so that the increase in utility to farm families realizing a gain is greater than the reduction to those realizing a loss. Suppose, for example, that output increases by 10 percent from a new technique while price declines by 15 percent. Although total revenue will decline, revenue will increase for farmers whose output increases by 20 percent, but decline for those whose output increases by only 5 percent. Of course, the difficulty of interpersonal utility comparison prevents any easy designation of which group of farm families might gain in utility relative to the loss of others. The activities in extension education do cause redistribution of income and assets. Historically, the effects of education in causing income to be redistributed have been more in the direction of farm families who have the highest income. This tends to be true because these are the operators with the capital for investment and for taking risks in new techniques, and they are easiest to contact.

The goal selected as the relevant framework for extension education not only provides the basis for determining the allocation of educational resources among (1) fields of subject matter specialization and (2) geographic and income strata of farmers, but also in specifying the communication methods employed. If the goal were mainly one of "providing educational services to those best equipped to acquire them" (usually farmers with ample capital and education), then communication methods could include only meetings at state universities and colleges, television programs and technical bulletins. The intended consumers would have time, foresight and funds for coming after the information. However, if the goal is one of maximizing welfare of farmers, with emphasis on increasing utility of farm families who have low income, the communication system needs to be quite different. It cannot be in terms of mass media. The low-income farmer may not have the funds for a television set or a trip to the state college meeting; he may not be able to understand a highly technical bulletin. The communication method more nearly needs to be one of "taking the educational input to the farm."

If general economic growth were selected as the central end or goal of extension education, the means for accomplishment might be various. Investment can be made in specialists to promote techniques for products with inelastic demands. With minimization of resource inputs for subsistence goods being a subgoal, the "lowness" of the price elasticity might be one relevant goal for allocation of resources to products and extension specialists. Educational resources then need not be allocated to conform with any income distribution pattern or framework of communication media, but should be used where their marginal productivity is greatest in increasing the output per unit of those resources that are mobile and can be used elsewhere in the economy. However, an important means, complementary with those means directed towards minimizing the amount of labor used in producing subsistence food products, is that of facilitating the movement of labor from agriculture, once it has been "freed." To free labor from agriculture and then leave it stranded is as inconsistent with economic growth as in not having freed it in the first place.

Selecting individual goals, such as those discussed above, allows selection of particular methods. They can be pursued with vigor when inconsistency between goal and outcome of means is not brought to question. The same is true where we attain one end with means efficient to it without concern of distribution of costs and benefits resulting from the progress or reorganization so fetched. But on the other hand, we can concern ourselves with the distribution of these gains and costs, and with possibilities of negative-sum outcomes when sacrifice to some groups may be larger than reward to others. When we become so concerned, then ordering of educational program in the vein outlined above for research programs becomes appropriate. Without policy linkage, we must look for educational activities which promise to increase farm income as well as consumer surplus, if our effort is based on farm policy and positive-sum utility outcome is to be guaranteed. If gain is certain only for consumers in lowered supply price of food, and loss to producers is certain through greater output and smaller aggregate revenue, the educational activities best serve as consumer policy. But with policy linkage as mentioned in a previous section, gains to both consumers and farm producers can be guaranteed and agricultural education again becomes an element of farm policy and general economic growth guaranteeing positive-sum utility gains.

Broad Needs in Education

Education is near the human resource and it needs to be handled accordingly, as emphasized in relation to phenomena of Chapters 12 and 13. Faced with further economic growth, extension services will need to concern themselves much more with people, and in aiding them to make both private and public decisions.[20] They need to lead the way in helping farm persons understand their individual capacities and means for most opportunity expression and gain from their particular abilities. As outlined in Chapter 12, much of this need is in direction of guidance, counseling and job information. Extension services have done well in providing hogs with market outlook. They need to do as well with people. The important educational need, as part of the extension service's challenge in and contribution to economic growth, is in providing knowledge that guides farm people to their most promising alternative in life. This activity has been submerged by the flow of technical information. It needs to be made a main focus of educational activities and can become the foundation stone of agricultural policy designed to solve income problems stemming (1) from both economic growth and a relative depression of farm prices and (2) from paucity of resources and true poverty of farm families.

The needs and opportunities in extension education were never as broad as at the present time. The extension service represents an educational mechanism of great value to society in its decision-making processes relative to changing structure and national needs under economic growth, for either group or individual choices. Whereas its traditions were established in gauging the possibilities for plants and animals, it can now do so for people. To be certain, it can and should retain activities which focus on technological improvements, since these have been part of the public investment returning the large progress payoffs mentioned earlier. But it can go much further. First, it needs to extend its services surrounding the individual much as it surrounded plants and animals in the past. This is part of guidance and counseling efforts already mentioned. Then, it needs to extend further to communities with these same processes, helping them to assess their production possibilities, in deciding to invest in local industrialization or to help surplus labor migrate. It needs to help individuals and communities see their interdependence and interrelationships with the national economy, with choices made accordingly in geographic, occupational and social commitment of resources. Finally, it needs to teach basic or general economic principles to people so that they will have tools for making evaluations and choices consistent with individual preferences and group goals.

In this latter respect, we re-emphasize the points made in Chapter 9:

[20] Grant McConnell reports that the land-grant colleges devoted little attention to people until the 1944 Land Grant Policy Statement. Since that time, of course, farm and home planning and rural or area development programs have taken effort more in this direction, as have orientations around the "scope report" and similar statements of philosophy. Political struggle revolving around possibilities of educational aid to the lower-income strata of agriculture also is discussed by McConnell (*Decline in Agrarian Democracy*, University of California Press, Berkeley, 1957, Chaps. 8–11). Soth (*Farm Trouble*, Princeton University Press, Princeton, N.J., 1957, pp. 88–94) suggests need for transfer of emphasis from the technical service activities for higher income farmers little interested in fundamental education to the more fundamental needs of distressed persons. He indicates that the technical services can be handled quite appropriately with mass media or as a marketable service.

People make choices through the pricing and voting mechanisms. Through the second mechanisms, they specify their selection of public policy. But often they operate in a knowledge vacuum, not knowing which ends are complementary or competitive, the predicted outcome of various means, the interrelationship between ends and means and other interrelationships within this general complex. So short is knowledge, that a policy choice often serves as a pure experiment: to try it out and see how it works. The decision-making process can be made more efficient where voters possess greater information. The extension services can provide more productive services for public choices, just as they have done for private choices. They can be objective in this process and thus gain wider public recognition and demand for their services. Given effort in this direction, they should have little concern with having to "burn the books" as result of the pressure and group antagonism mentioned earlier.[21]

Stage of economic growth gives rise both to need for these broader activities and to opportunity to engage in them. It is nearly a "natural law of economic growth" that increasingly, with passage of time, details of farm technology will be furnished by private firms. In early stages of growth and factor prices, agriculture rests mainly on labor—a commodity which private firms cannot process and retail. But with growth and change in factor prices, the transformation of agriculture calls for more of technology to be in the form of capital inputs which can be produced and retailed by private firms. They can and do invest heavily in retailing this practical knowledge to farmers. Extension services thus can be relieved of much of the detail of technical services and can devote an increasing proportion of efforts to (1) the more fundamental principles and knowledge in the physical, biological and social sciences and (2) the more urgent social decision and adjustment problems. A relatively higher public investment also is required to take a given amount of fundamental principle in biological and physical science, and general knowledge of social science facts and understanding, to people. This is true because the facts and principles so represented are not "packageable commodities," as in the practical findings of physical fields.

In accepting the broader and more fundamental educational challenge, extension services even can lead in the transformation of rural communities. As mentioned in Chapter 10, precedent can be set for communities by regional extension offices which provide activities broad enough for employment of more specialists. These specialists are needed in the extension of fundamental principles of biological and physical sciences. They are needed equally in the fields of social sciences: to provide guidance and to help families and communities to inventory their resources and possibilities, and to make decisions which are commensurate with their opportunities and capacities.

---

[21] For the problems, forces and methods encountered in handling "book burning pressures," see C. M. Hardin, *Freedom in Agricultural Education*, University of Chicago Press, Chicago, 1955.

THE BROAD ROLE AND APPEAL

The time has come, in fact, when the agricultural universities and colleges should see themselves in the broad framework of contemporary U.S. society and its problems. There is need and opportunity for greater role and support than at any time in previous history. The agricultural colleges represent resources not only for promoting domestic economic growth, but also for helping to attain the international goals and responsibilities of the nation. A responsibility necessary and assumed by the nation is promotion of economic development in countries of less progress. This responsibility and intermediate goal will grow in emphasis because of (1) growing world public opinion favoring freedom from hunger and self expression by all peoples and (2) interrelated world political and economic competition. In furthering these long-run goals, and if the broad public role should be taken seriously in agricultural colleges, personnel in both the technical and social sciences should be allocated much more to international problems. What is needed is not so much the "remote" inter-university relationship between U.S. and foreign universities, seldom considered to be an on-campus activity of most institutions, but rather an activity which is an integral part of on-campus efforts. Under more "direct" engagement, a research worker at one college would be assigned as directly to development improvements for a foreign location as is his colleague in developing an improvement for a particular county in the state. But this is a development, however important, which currently lies outside the financial and jurisdictional opportunities of states, either singularly or collectively. It must await intensification and clarification of national purposes and emphasis.

Somewhat strangely, many agricultural colleges have viewed research in foreign economies and development to be out of their realm. Such projects are completely subordinated to small local projects and are not supported at all in most states. This is true even though (1) most agricultural colleges consider themselves to be working in behalf of farmers and (2) the single major opportunity for increasing income magnitude (and justifying increased agricultural productivity) is in developing international markets and institutions to allow the hunger and population problems of other countries to be solved from the U.S. supply of food. If the sole goal of agricultural research and education were farmer income, it might be best attained by shifting a large proportion of personnel and financial resources over to this investigational area and in developing a breakthrough in large foreign market outlet for U.S. foodstuffs. In balance with other goals and among the relevant sciences, this extent is not needed or desired. But certainly more emphasis and work in this direction is needed.

APPEAL TO CONSUMERS AND PATTERN OF FINANCE

In a similar but less worldly vein, the agricultural colleges need to tackle the problem of broad national recognition, justification and support of the system, even to the extent of adding "food" to their title. This is a task which is not best accomplished by individual states, but by a comprehensive approach of the land-grant college system. It was less, or was not, necessary with initiation of the agricultural colleges when most of the population was farm. In another 25 years, the farm labor force will be less than 5 percent of the national labor force and net farm income may be only 2 percent of disposable personal income. The numerically great and economically significant sector of society benefiting from conventional agricultural research and education on technology will be the consumer, as it now is. One hundred percent of the population will have contact with the public institutions as food *consumers and households*, but a small and declining fraction of the nation's *resources and producers* will have any tie to the efforts of the agricultural colleges. Without wider recognition of this fact, and of the true role of the agricultural colleges, and without financial appeal and programs bent more in this direction, the institutions stand to face an increasingly difficult "uphill climb" in competition for public funds for these purposes.

Financing Gain From Technical Advance

Change is suggested not only in the over-all structure of technical programs for economic progress and consumer benefit in real food prices, but also is desirable in the regional pattern of specialization and financing of research and education. To the extent that demand elasticities were high enough to cause farmers in aggregate to benefit directly from technical advance and greater output a century back, it was highly consistent that farmers and citizens of farming states be asked to provide the main funds to support the corresponding research. They bore the costs and realized the gains, the latter in general exceeding the former. With a different status of national economic development and demand elasticities, and with the major beneficiary of greater output being the consumer, it is now less appropriate that farmers and citizens of the agricultural states be asked to finance research and education to benefit consumers in other states. This is, however, partly the pattern which exists for state funds used in research and education, the majority of funds going into technical improvement.

Should not a much greater proportion of funds aimed at technical improvement be obtained on a national basis, with the pattern corresponding more consistently to consumer concentration, then be allocated back to states on the basis of concentration in agricultural production, with research conducted accordingly? Or more specifically, should Kansas wheat farmers be asked to pay for technical research which benefits Bronx consumers and, through greater output, reduces revenue from wheat? Given the current day distribution of benefits from improved agricultural technology, an affirmative answer to the latter question would not seem appropriate. The preferred source and allocation of financing would (1) allow research and education to be emphasized and conducted more in line with the regional concentration of agricultural production over the nation but (2) allocate costs more consistently with the pattern of gain to consumers over the nation. In contrast to the "rough" trend of 1920–60, a relative shift in magnitude of agricultural research funds for agricultural states as compared to some industrial states or others of smaller proportion in farm/nonfarm mix in output, this pattern would result in a more productive application of the total national research investment. We are talking here, of course, about technical research in the conventional manner where there is not certainty of positive-sum outcomes, because gains of progress are distributed to some and losses fall on others. Under policy which guarantees mutual and simultaneous gains to consumers and producers (see discussion of earlier sections), the need is different. Some commodities and services have high demand elasticities and are not tied to state locations. This "farm" research can be conducted as readily in industrial states as in agricultural states.

American society has partly recognized this problem by appropriating funds at the federal level which are then allocated to states for research and education on commodities with inelastic demands, as well as for other products and services. These funds are collected somewhat in proportion to gain, through income and other federal taxes, and allocated back to states largely on a farm population basis. Yet major resources for research on these products come from states where they are produced, and not from states of consumers of the same products. Appropriations for research relative to the value of farm production tends to be highest in states with large consumer populations or large industrial output relative to farm output perhaps partly as a further realization of this gain, as well as for youth, family and gains from services and commodities with more elastic demands.

17

U.S. Agriculture and World Economic Development

WORLD AGRICULTURE presents the two contrasting problems mentioned earlier: An agricultural problem which arises because of rapid march of the food supply function, with its resultant depression of farm prices and factor returns; and a consumer problem and a high real price for food growing out of tardy progress in the supply function. The United States has been an example in the first extreme and India in the second. If food were scarce in the United States, as wealthy as it is, the demand price of food would be great and rewards to resources in agriculture would be high. But the converse would not hold true in the sense that food abundance in India would immediately make all cultivators rich; at least, not with the quantity of resources owned and managed by the typical Indian farmer.

If the Martian from our first chapter returned and viewed these consumer and farm problems side by side, he might ask the "naive" question: "Why can't the problem of deficit in food supply be solved by the problem of surplus in supply?" This isn't a strange question. It is asked by many "men on the street," both in food-surplus and food-deficit countries. But the question is naive in extent to which it does not recognize complicated international economic and political relationships. The problem is much more than a physical one, or a transportation model, involving the simple matching of bushels and tons in one country against consumption requirements in another. Countries which are potential recipients of aid in food, just as those which may provide it, have particular value moorings which tend to resist pure charity; or have reservations on the purposes underlying aid. Underdeveloped countries are more concerned with aid as it serves to a means in economic growth and income improvement, rather than as an altruistic end, or as a means to solving surplus problems of particular advanced countries.[1]

AGRICULTURAL POLICY AND FOREIGN POLICY

To obtain a perspective of agricultural policy in relation to foreign policy, we need to review the roles which food supply in the United States has had in filling world food demand. Early food exports were important in acquisition of foreign exchange and capital to promote industrial growth of the nation. Foreign demand allowed U.S. agriculture to expand profitably at a rapid rate over much of the nineteenth century, but world economic development and global summation of food supplies caused this export demand to shrink. Farmers were encouraged to turn to a "protectionist" policy, providing part of the political force leading to high tariff schedules. But with great export demand and rapid supply growth in food during World War II, the potential of the "world stomach" in absorbing U.S. food output has been reappraised by agriculture since 1940.

Growth in export markets helped allow agricultural supply of the United States to grow rapidly at favorable prices, with increased farm income, over the nineteenth century and up to about 1920. Foreign markets were highly elastic, as is true for the product of any one country which does not supply the majority of world exports. They were important to U.S. agriculture as it developed rapidly and drew resources into it. However, farm leaders took a quite different view of foreign trade in the 1920's. Proportionate supplying of international markets by U.S. farm products dropped greatly even as early as 1910. Although protective tariffs could not benefit them at the time, farmers, who had lost their battle for "cheap money" were encouraged to turn to the protectionist fold as far back as the 1890's. It has been suggested that they were convinced to do so by the emerging power group known as the "Captains of Industry," who stood to gain by high tariffs and restrained imports of industrial products.[2]

But the greatest turn in this direction by farmers came in the 1920's. Decline in U.S. exports undoubtedly caused them to believe this to be a major opportunity for "economic uplifting." During the first decade of this century, U.S. farm exports dropped by about 60 percent. While cotton exports continued to climb, 1910 wheat exports fell to a third of those in 1900. Beef exports fell to a fourth and pork exports were halved. The United States supplied these percentages of world exports in 1884–

[1] For viewpoints of aid in receiving countries, see B. F. Hoselitz, *Progress of Underdeveloped Countries*, University of Chicago Press, Chicago, 1951, pp. 259–69.

[2] M. R. Benedict and E. K. Bauer, *Farm Surpluses, U.S. Burden or World Asset?* University of California, Division of Agricultural Sciences, Berkeley, 1960, p. 141.

88: wheat, 36; corn, 44; beef, 43; pork, 71; and cheese, 28. The comparable percentages in 1924–28 were respectively 22, 6, 1, 29 and 1.[3] Proportionate supplying of world markets dropped even lower during the 1930's. The decline grew out of competing supplies from countries such as Australia, New Zealand, Canada and Argentina, the change to creditor position by the United States and restrictive trade policy tariffs on farm products; the latter lifted to unprecedented levels by the Fordney-McCumber Act of the early 1920's and the Smoot-Hawley Act of 1930.

The Trade Agreements Act of 1934 was a first "restep" in policy to lessen trade restrictions and increase international commodity flows. On the other hand, the price support and production control programs of the 1930's caused farm products of other nations to be substituted for those of the United States in world markets. Increase in cotton exports of other nations somewhat more than exceeded the decrease of exports by the United States during this period. It is generally agreed that the price policy programs were inconsistent with other U.S. attempts to expand foreign markets.[4] The AAA of the 1930's also provided for limited export subsidies to allow greater foreign sales of U.S. farm commodities. Exports jumped under the Lend-Lease shipments of World War II and continued heavy with reconstruction of Europe. Food represented only about 12 percent of U.S. exports under Lend-Lease, but it was enough to boost farm prices greatly under the regime of inelastic demand. The UNRRA program served similarly in increasing foreign transfer of food and boosting farm profitability at the close of the war. In postwar years, aid to food exports was given under the Mutual Security Act (MSA or P.L. 165) of 1951 and its amendments (particularly P.L. 665) which allowed for food shipments as "defense support" items. With early European recovery, foreign demand slackened and surplus buildup began. However, the Korean conflict erased these export losses and held demand temporarily high. But again in 1953, foreign demand slackened and U.S. farm supply began its rapid march ahead of both domestic and foreign demand.

It was at this time that greater reliance began to be placed on food disposal through foreign assistance programs: the Point IV program and its successors providing technical assistance; commodity grants and emergency aid to India and Pakistan, with provision of revenue forthcoming from sales to be used in promoting technical development of agriculture; Public Law 480 (P.L. 480) promoting foreign disposal of U.S. agricultural surpluses; and subsequent "Food for Peace" authorizations. Whereas legislation such as the Mutual Security Act served more as a general mutual-assistance program with friendly nations, Public Law

[3] See R. M. Stern, "A Century of Food Exports," *Kyklos*, Vol. 13.

[4] *Cf.* D. G. Johnson, *Trade and Agriculture, A Study of Inconsistent Policies*, Wiley. New York, 1950, and A. Hickman, *Our Farm Program and Foreign Trade*, Council on Foreign Relations, New York, 1949. Along somewhat similar lines, see A. J. Youngson, *The Possibilities of Economic Progress*, Cambridge University Press, Cambridge, 1959, pp. 245–65.

480 was from the start primarily a domestic bill using the foreign-aid program as a means for accomplishing surplus disposal. Sales of food under the Mutual Security Act were sizeable, with other countries able to use some of the funds granted them by the United States under this program to buy food. Restraint in disposal of food surpluses under this program existed, however, because so many of the participating countries were agricultural.

Under P.L. 480 sales, the recipient nation could retain the payment it would otherwise make and use it for selected developmental purposes or investment in mutual security. Sales under P.L. 480 were limited to commodities acquired by government with price support programs or deemed to be in surplus quantity, and emphasis was on expansion of foreign trade in U.S. farm commodities. Public Law 480 also included such provisions as these: developing new markets for U.S. farm products, promoting balanced economic development and trade among nations, aiding international educational exchange and the publication and translation of books and periodicals, collecting and disseminating technical and scientific information and others. Under the program, it became possible to conduct research, from payments held in local currencies, on improved marketing of U.S. farm products abroad, but not on methods of increasing the farm supply function of foods in underdeveloped countries.

As indicated in Table 17.1, an important portion (about a third) of U.S. farm exports went under provisions of P.L. 480 and other special programs over the period 1954–60; exports of wheat, rice and other surplus commodities through normal channels being adapted in nature accord-

TABLE 17.1

U.S. Farm Exports Under P.L. 480 and Special Programs and Normal Channels, 1949–60 (Million Dollars)

Fiscal Year	Public Law 480 Exports*				All Special Programs†	Total Exports	Percent of Exports Under Special Programs
	Title I	Title II	Title III				
			Donations	Barter			
1949–50....	—	—	—	—	1,969	2,986	65.9
1950–51....	—	—	—	—	1,202	3,411	35.2
1951–52....	—	—	—	—	584	4,053	21.1
1952–53....	—	—	—	—	532	2,819	18.9
1953–54....	—	—	—	—	677	2,936	23.1
1954–55....	73	83	135	125	931	3,143	29.6
1955–56....	439	91	184	298	1,417	3,496	40.5
1956–57....	909	88	165	401	2,003	4,728	42.4
1957–58....	660	92	173	100	1,451	4,002	36.3
1958–59....	730	56	132	132	1,351	3,719	36.3
1959–60....	815	65	107	151	1,400	4,527	30.9

Source: *Agricultural Statistics*, 1960.

* Title I sales are in foreign currency. Title II quantities are donations for emergency relief abroad. Title III quantities are donations in the U.S. and overseas and for barter to American processors who acquire strategic materials abroad and furnish them to the U.S. at a later date.

† Includes P.L. 480 and P.L. 665 with the latter sales also in foreign currency.

ingly. Of total U.S. farm sales, around 12 percent has been going for export. P.L. 480 and MSA exports amounted to about these percentages of total U.S. exports of the particular commodity in 1960: wheat, 75 percent; rice and vegetable oils, 60 percent; feed grains and cotton, 33 percent. Europe (mainly Spain, Yugoslavia, Italy, Poland and France) has taken about 40 percent of these special program exports, Asia (India, Korea, Pakistan and Taiwan) another 40 percent and Latin America and Africa together about 10 percent. These sales have not been in dollars, but in the currency of the importing country, mostly inconvertible currencies, with some food going directly as grants. These local currencies have not been converted to goods shipped to the United States but have remained in the countries or have been used for projects agreed upon by the government of the importing country and the United States. Up to 1961, most of the agreements were for a year's duration, although one was signed with India to run to 1964. A 1959 amendment to P.L. 480 allowed countries to use their payments for these surplus farm products as a loan, payable in 20 years at 2 percent interest. Up to 1962, no sales had been made under this provision.

Under P.L. 480, local currencies received for sales were placed in a U.S. account in the foreign country. The United States spends some for its own purposes (expenses for U.S. agencies abroad, embassy buildings, local military purchases, etc.), but most of it has remained simply on deposit for the United States. A small part (less than 10 percent) has gone to special projects including development of mining, industry, power, transportation, schools, etc. A little has gone for agricultural development such as irrigation projects and a trickle to research. But by and large, P.L. 480 and special programs have sent surpluses abroad, with foreign currency simply piling up in the recipient countries, or a fraction turned back to them for special or highly specific projects on which they agree with the United States.

Foreign aid programs with the partial, and perhaps dominating, goal of surplus disposal have been effective in moving crop stocks out of the country. Without these disposal activities, government storage in the United States would have been much greater. The data below indicate what the percentage exports were of production for three crops in the years specified:

Year	Exports as Percent of Production for: Wheat	Corn	Cotton
1925	14.3	1.8	48.3
1930	11.9	.5	48.7
1935	−4.9	−.4	56.1
1940	3.6	.4	7.5
1945	28.7	.9	36.9
1950	31.6	4.8	40.0
1955	35.9	5.6	14.2
1960	44.6	6.9	39.1

By 1960, the United States was exporting nearly half of the annual wheat crop, with most of this going under foreign aid programs. Feed grain exports had jumped too, but were still only a small proportion of annual production. Nations with hunger prefer grains serving as human food, rather than that serving as animal feed. Cotton exports had increased, but relative to production were still below the levels of the 1920's.

Long-Term Trends of Agriculture in World Trade

World economic growth over the long pull will not restore agriculture to its "previous place in the national economy." Agricultural exports have become a declining proportion of total U.S. exports, or of total international trade. The reasons are largely those stemming from economic development as explained in Chapters 3 and 6. With expansion in national economies and differential income elasticities of demand under per capita income growth, this trend will continue. As Table 17.2 indicates, farm exports, while increasing in dollar and physical volume in recent years, have become a minor part of total U.S. exports. (Also, see the data and estimates of Table 6.16.) This is true even though P.L. 480 has expanded disposal of surplus commodities. While greater food supply will be needed as nations develop their economies and experience population growth, the mix of goods in international trade will continue to shift towards a greater proportion of nonfood commodities. Even for develop-

TABLE 17.2

VALUE AND PERCENTAGE OF U.S. AGRICULTURAL EXPORTS IN TOTAL EXPORTS*

Period or Year	Agricultural Exports†		Agricultural Exports as Percentage of U.S. Exports	
	Total	Commercial	Total	Commercial
	(million dollars)		*(percentage)*	
1902–06	878	...	59.4	...
1907–11	974	...	53.8	...
1912–16	1254	...	45.1	...
1916–21	2856	...	42.6	...
1922–26	1950	...	45.9	...
1927–31	1621	...	35.9	...
1932–36	713	...	36.4	...
1937–41	679	...	20.3	...
1942–46	1976	...	18.9	...
1947–51	3469	1,563	28.1	12.7
1951	3411	2,201	27.1	17.5
1952	4053	3,157	26.0	20.3
1953	2819	2,273	18.6	14.7
1954	2936	2,225	19.3	14.6
1955	3143	2,281	21.1	15.3
1956	3496	2,140	20.7	12.7
1957	4728	2,724	22.9	13.2
1958	4002	2,702	21.4	14.4
1959	3719	2,419	21.5	14.0
1960	4526	3,127	23.7	16.4

* Source: *Agricultural Statistics,* USDA 1960: The Demand and Price Situation 1954–1960; The Foreign Trade of the U.S. USDA 1960.

† Total includes all agricultural exports while commercial includes only those not under government programs such as P.L. 480 and P.L. 665. (Commercial includes sales under international wheat agreements.)

ing nations starting from an early stage, the marginal social efficiency of investment and inadequate supply of foreign exchange typically places premium on import of capital goods for industrialization; or even for producing inputs which serve to develop agriculture.

EXTREME SUPPOSITIONS

Some policy advocates in the United States view the nation's surplus problem nearly as if it were a physical problem, capable of easy solution by shipment of excess products to foreign soils where the recipients can then drop their hoes and turn to building roads, schools, factories and the modern amenities of advanced societies. This picture of matching high development against low development is an oversimplification. It has appeal in politics and to the person who need speak only in grandiose terms and need not face the preliminary but necessary steps involved before this "magic wand" can be waved, eliminating the problem of Cinderellas in both rich and poor nations. But it is an important contrast worthy of much more intellectual effort and imagination than has gone into it in the past. Current speculation and hypotheses pose the possibility that the diametrically opposed problems of food surpluses and food deficits in different parts of the world will continue to worsen in the short run. At one extreme, it appears that the "break through" in agricultural technology and farm progress experienced in recent years by advanced agricultures will continue and surplus potential will continue for a decade or more. On the other hand, conservative estimates of near-term population growth pose food needs in some less advanced countries which exceed prospects of growth in food supply.

The threat of "population explosion," with people standing on each other's heads as suggested by extremists through national magazines, is not realistic. If national societies do not find effective market or institutional means of restraining supply of humans, the "iron law of subsistence" will do so. It is not likely that any major, or any but scattered minor, nations will allow food demand and food supply to progress to the point where physiological well-being of people declines to a miserly subsistence level. In this day of knowledge and enlightenment, it is certainly hoped that the problem of food is not one of averting retrogression whereby human nutrition worsens and approaches the subsistence level; but that it is the more positive one of managing food and agricultural resources against supply of households and labor, such that economic development can be best promoted and real level of living can rise the world over.

The latter is the hope of the world's population, rather than the first. Policy of a food surplus nation takes on quite different image when it is analyzed in this light, rather than purely an emotional appeal to avert starvation of helpless people. Aside from politics and poor social management, nations of this age are concerned with the more important problem of lifting real incomes, with more of industrial products as well as of variety in food, and with methods of attaining this goal. In fact, as Millikan and Rostow point out,[5] it is probably a misconception that revolt and political instability of less developed nations are the result alone of hunger and poverty; that relieving hunger by itself will reduce revolutionary tendencies; or that if people are only better fed, they are less likely to shift from one to another political camp. Revolt does not typically come from chronically destitute populations who, after centuries of the same, take it for granted that their lot is thus. Putting extra food in the stomach will not itself generate takeoff in economic development or, unaccompanied by other changes, guarantee a particular pattern of political advance in backward societies. Food to people who can't read is not likely to build up any great convictions in politics and economics. A first concern of most nations of low development is to "break away from the agricultural mold."[6] They need first to develop industry in their own country, so that the productivity of agriculture can then be increased to release people to nonfarm employment. Until industry can be developed at a rate fast enough to provide this employment, the concern with agricultural productivity is to move it ahead as rapidly as population growth and to keep the real price of food at reasonable level for consumers. An increase of agricultural productivity to release labor to industry is needed only when industrialization increases rapidly enough to absorb people from farming. As suggested in Chapter 2 and as illustrated in Figure 17.1, economic growth is characterized by a decline in agriculture as a share in the national economy. Nations at the lowest level of development have the major part of both their labor force and national income in agriculture. In nations such as India, with 50 percent of national income and 70 percent of population in agriculture, the hope is not to avert diminished nutritional standard through agricultural development, but to use industrial development to allow agriculture to decline in the national economy.

Food surpluses and deficit problems are not simple ones to be solved by transportation models in defining least-distance or least-cost flows against upper restraints of surpluses in some countries and against lower restraints of human nutrition in other countries. They involve more complicated structures in international politics and economics. More importantly, they involve political, economic and psychological structures within countries which are short on food.[7] Too, the problems of economic development and of bringing more tardy economies to the takeoff stage,

---

[5] M. M. Millikan and W. W. Rostow, *A Proposal; Key to an Effective Foreign Policy*, Harper Brothers, New York, 1957, pp. 19–22.

[6] In this respect, see the discussion by Richard Hartshorne, "The Role of the State in Economic Growth," pp. 317–19, in H. G. Aitken, *The State and Economic Growth*, Social Science Research Council, New York, 1959.

[7] For discussion of some of these political and planning problems and mechanisms, see E. S. Mason, *Economic Planning in Underdeveloped Areas*, Fordham University Press, New York, 1958, Ch. 4.

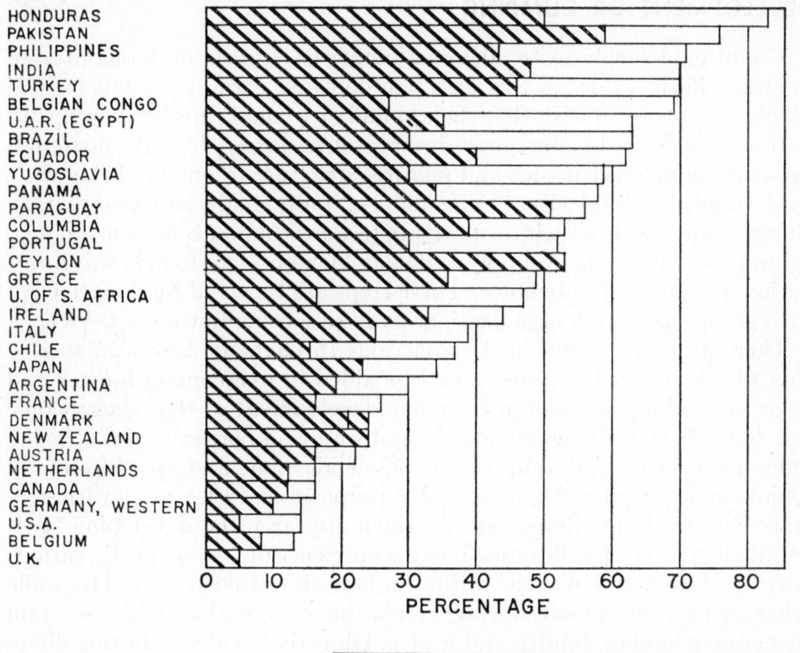

Fig. 17.1. Percentage of Population and National Income in Agriculture for Selected Countries. (Source: FAO. State of Food and Agriculture, Rome, 1959, p. 96.)

the foundation upon which most proposals for foreign food disposal are based, involves much more than food. In fact, it cannot be proved that food is the prime restraint to development by most countries which have yet had little of it. Most nations which have been given recent opportunity to direct their own political and economic destiny, or their political leaders, have foundations in values, aspirations, national morale, self reliance and basic creeds as important to them as to major nations which are in the maturity stages of economic development. This is one reason that it is not even easy for nations with surpluses to give food away. It is true that even most infant or less developed nations have pride and self respect which causes them to resist dependence on pure charity, or approaches to it, in times other than natural emergency.[8] A developed nation is not likely to win many international friends if it maximizes its image as a donor and savior of disadvantaged countries, without creating maximum ability or recognition of recipients to make their own contributions in its growth and development.

[8] *Cf.* Millikan and Rostow, *loc. cit.;* Benedict and Bauer, *op. cit.*, p. 141; and S. R. Sen, "Impact and Implications of Foreign Surplus Disposal on Underdeveloped Economies—the Indian Perspective," *Jour. Farm Econ.*, Vol. 42, pp. 1031–32.

DEVELOPMENT OR DUMPING

Use of food surpluses to alleviate hunger has appeal on humanitarian grounds. Basic values in this direction do cause earnest persons of food surplus countries to wish that their abundance could thus be shared with nations which are less fortunate in natural resources, historic surroundings, economic mechanisms and political structure to quickly bring their food supply to level eliminating misery. Individuals and groups take sincere steps and use their own private resources and mechanisms to help bring about matching of supply and food "demand" for food in this international context of imbalance. These steps are reflected by donations of such groups as church organizations and those contributing to CARE.

There also are deeply held convictions throughout American society that disadvantaged nations should be aided in overcoming hunger and being started on the road of economic development so that their people can have better living standards and enjoy opportunity in utilizing human capacities and abilities for these ends alone and apart from any nationalistic purpose. These are noble purposes and they mesh with general "worldwide public purposes" which appear to be developing. It is not likely that the public objectives or conscience of peoples in the various developed countries over the world will long allow them to stand by while other nations suffer food shortages and other deprivations which restrain elementary human dignity and health. Objective evidence in this direction is already provided in the lifting of restraints to self government imposed through colonialism and in investments in economic development of backward countries by even small but economically advanced nations over the world. The general world trend, albeit with difficulty resting in international politics, is to observe and promote the aspirations of people, whatever their nationality and location. It will indeed be beneficial if political and economic competition among advanced nations can be channeled into these types of investments, with positive productivity in human welfare, rather than into war productivity. Environment for development and progress of people over the entire world indeed exists if resources can be allocated thus. While chance for change previously seemed remote for peoples in many backward nations, they now see opportunity for social and economic improvement and aspire to it. Accelerating developments in literacy, mass communications and travel are causing enlightenment of people who were previously isolated. The world community is being drawn into closer proximity of desire and aspirations in education, social structures and economic progress.

Purposes of Aid in Food

But just as concern for economic development and elimination of hunger is a noble and humanitarian end, the same appeal can be used to oversimplify the problems of using food surpluses in international markets and to camouflage policy to get rid of domestic farm surplus problems. Like some other marriages, surplus supply and foreign disposal can be joined to cover up slips which occurred elsewhere. The United States is a wealthy nation and it can afford some "overinvestments" in farm policy which do not lead to a mathematical optimum in use of resources and institutions. It can afford delayed movement to desired community utility positions because of the complexity of decision processes through the political mechanism of a diverse but democratic society which emphasizes sovereignty of individuals. It does and can, for this reason, use domestic agricultural policies which are not optimum in the long-run context of values and aspirations by upcoming generations, or of values held by this generation for the one which follows.

Internally, the United States can afford certain group concurrences and "nonoptimum" uses of resources where imperfections in these activities are consistent with the political process allowing social evaluation of alternatives, policy testing of outcomes which have no *a priori* basis in prediction, and subjectively measuring group outcome in distribution of gains and losses from specific policies. Domestic farm policies which are publicly justified under one label but are directed basically to other ends can function temporarily in this setting without bringing human misery, submersion of general societal goals and major restraint to economic development. But they should be limited to this domestic environment, and not be shoved off on other nations under similar cloak. Political luxury possible for farm policy in a wealthy nation should be limited to its shorelines, and not mixed with its more basic and fundamental goals in foreign relationships and policy. Farm policy orientation which attempts to use supply capacity in manner best consistent with the nation's foreign policy and societal concern in optimum world economic development should be pursued vigorously. That which is only convenient marriage of surplus problems at home and food outlet elsewhere, and in conflict with optimal economic development patterns for less advanced nations, should not even have second consideration.

The type and manner of policy best suited to deal with international economic problems depends on the ends of the policy. Millikan and Rostow have posed these questions as a basis for gauging assistance programs and misconceptions about them:[9]

> Are economic assistance programs intended to win friends for the United States? To strengthen the military capability of our allies? To induce other countries to follow foreign policies to our liking? To reduce the appeal of communism to the poverty stricken? To benefit the United States economically? To induce healthy internal political development abroad? To raise living standards for humanitarian reasons?

To this list we might add the questions: Is surplus foreign disposal a means to "ship the American farm problem abroad," just as we were expected to "eat it up" under an earlier set of propositions? Is it convenient method of benefiting American producers? Does it have the fundamental purpose of fitting into optimal economic development programs of nations starting at low level and desiring rapid progress?

---

[9] Millikan and Rostow, *op. cit.*, p. 9.

Confusion over the extent to which portion of outpouring from the U.S. farm supply function can or should be used in assistance programs to less developed nations stems from differences in values, beliefs about facts and ends of economic interest groups. Some people press it in pure humanitarian hope. Some sincerely believe that it can or should be used as a primer in economic development of backward nations. Others support it in terms purely of their own economic interest, and policy proposals and legislation have both been made in this vein. Some groups who would call "foul play" should Canada or Australia pour their surpluses into the United States, or if U.S. legislators were willing to accept them, are not unwilling to dump farm surpluses in other countries, without concern over detrimental price and income effect on producers of other countries who also have surplus farm productive power or on producers in countries who might serve as recipients of surpluses.

Concept of "fair play," or expectation of retaliation, does prevent Americans from advocating outright dumping of surplus farm products. Dumping under the cloak of foreign assistance programs is more palatable to the same persons, however. Mortenson estimates that U.S. decision to export cotton in 1956 substituted for about 2 million tons from competing nations and lowered export revenue from the latter by about 350 million dollars per year.[10] Too, even where advocates restrain themselves in suggesting dumping (Public Law 480 states that surplus disposal should not impair the position of friendly countries) which might have serious impact on producers in competing export nations, they often worry little about any adverse price effects which surplus disposal might have on producers in nations which stand to become recipient of aid in the form of our surplus farm commodities.[11]

Frameworks of Aid

Currently the facts are too few to know exactly where and to what extent U.S. farm products can best fit into assistance programs which optimally promote growth of underdeveloped economies.[12] Undoubtedly there is opportunity for their use, but the exact extent and manner are yet to be determined over the long pull. To be certain, few countries are going to be interested in temporary blasts of policy and appropriations from the United States which provide them with both more food for a year or two and uncertainty thereafter. And this has been the mold of much surplus-oriented legislation. It has been entirely in terms of ephem-

---

[10] Erik Mortenson, "The Competitor's Perspective," *Jour. Farm Econ.*, Vol. 42. For an expression of sentiment in Australia on use of surplus U.S. food, see: Farm Foundation, *Increasing Understanding of Public Problems and Policies*, Chicago, 1960, pp. 77–8.

[11] For an early suggestion of negative price effects in recipient nations, see Millikan and Rostow, *op. cit.*, pp. 91–2. Also see J. S. Davies, "Food for Peace," *Food Res. Ins. Studies*, Vol. 1, p. 146; and N. Islam, "Foreign Aid and Economic Development. A Rejoinder," *Social and Economic Studies*, 1959, p. 285. Dumping is common practice under market orders for nuts. (See Benedict, *op. cit.*, p. 110.)

[12] For a discussion of aid in Latin America, see A. T. Mosher, *Technical Cooperation in Latin American Agriculture*, University of Chicago Press, Chicago, 1957, pp. 245–338.

eral appropriations, subject to cessation with the following year's appropriations. What nation would want, aside from initial building up of buffer stocks to alleviate distribution problems and exorbitant consumer prices in case of disaster, to build economic development on a product or resource lacking certainty and subject to withdrawal at momentary notice? To build diets to an improved level, then have their basis suddenly withdrawn would cause more political and psychological difficulties than leaving nutrition at a somewhat depressed level. Or, from the standpoint of resource allocation, no nation is going to draw resources out of agriculture to extend development in other sectors with the prospects that it would have to rush these resources back into farming at the end of a year—should food aid be withdrawn after the year's political campaign ends in the United States. Not even five years is a sufficient time span for a country to greatly incorporate food aid into its development planning. To do so efficiently, it needs 10 years as a minimum period and 20 years is preferred. Five years is only long enough to get resources in the midst of reorganization, and not long enough to attain major outpouring in product from this reorganization.

Use of surplus food in assistance programs can take on different molds depending on the end or goal of the program. For example, any one of the questions above poses a goal of assistance calling for a different disposal program.[13] The program optimum for one purpose is not thus for another. If the goal were simply that of getting rid of an embarrassing domestic problem, at least cost with conscience restraint that food must not be wasted and must be used by someone on the globe, we would give it to whatever nation would send ships to haul it away, at whatever price could be forthcoming. If this goal also were to be attained under constraint of "not losing our friends," the mold of the program would have to be quite different, and we would try to get as much food as possible into the hands of less developed nations. But if the goal were, from the limited capital funds available over the world for the purpose, that of maximum economic development of backward nations, we might have a quite different concept of where the latter nations should get their imports, and of whether they should get more resources for industrial development and less food from ourselves.

We can analyze food flows and foreign assistance in many different frameworks of optimizing. Suppose we selected a goal of maximizing, through economic growth over a given time period, the product of a less developed nation. Assistance then would be analyzed in terms of capital productivity for these purposes. Where food per se, in raising the ability of labor and augmenting its productivity, has greater productivity than

[13] As one example in interpretation of foreign disposal under P.L. 480, the Asia Team of the extension services had this to say (Farm Foundation, *Increasing the Understanding of Public Problems and Policies*, Chicago, 1960, p. 70): "Not only do P.L. 480 programs help people to learn to use U.S. products such as wheat, milk and feed grains but they also increase capital facilities and knowhow for handling U.S. type commodities . . . U.S. furnished aid wheat to the Japanese and taught them to eat it . . . and bread fits into the consumption pattern of a richer people."

any other form of capital, we would send food rather than other materials or capital funds. Where food still serves these purposes but a given amount of funds has greater productivity in form of fertilizer and technical knowledge, in boosting food production within the developing country, we would ship capital in these forms rather than as food. Where food per se does not restrain economic growth as much as development funds for industry, we would ship the capital in the latter form, letting the recipient nation use wise economists to allocate it over the economy in a manner to maximize national product and economic growth for a given time period.

This framework supposes maximization of internal growth of a less developed country, from given capital available from the United States, to be the goal of analysis. Under it, we would provide developmental funds to backward countries and let them buy their food imports elsewhere if food has the productivity mentioned above and if it could be obtained at lower cost of developmental funds to the United States, or the recipient country, than surpluses produced in the United States. There have certainly been cases where the same funds, represented by the subsidies paid to United States farmers to produce surplus, the government purchase of stocks and the storage costs of holding them plus transportation, could have bought more food for recipient countries if they had been used for purchases from the current output of other nations.

Another framework for analysis would be that which supposes we do not have imagination to choke off our surplus production and that it costs us more to store it than to give it away or ship it at subsidized price as assistance resource. Here we can view disposal in a Pareto-better sense, rather than one of a tight and pure mathematical maximizing of growth in backward country from given developmental funds. The analysis then rests not on whether the recipient nation is made *best off*, or even that the total community of nations involved be made so in attainment of highest point on a utility surface; but only whether both ourselves and the recipient nation are made *better off* in the "unanimous consent" manner discussed in an earlier chapter. Certainly some use of U.S. farm products in assistance programs must be so analyzed. Given political processes and inability to choke off the outpouring of farm production within the United States and the high storage costs and depression of public conscience which followed, the nation may well have made itself "better off" by giving food to nations with tardy food supplies. It is even possible that at times these surpluses have provided "windfall gains," in the sense that it would not have been possible, had it been necessary, to get specific public appropriations to buy food, or get it produced, and ship it to nations who needed emergency quantity to tide them over crop failure or in the lean developmental periods following initiation of partition or self government. The large stocks were already in existence and the American public owned them. Hence, it was unnecessary to go so directly to the public for greater appropriations which might have been resisted.

But this is not a convenient or efficient manner of handling the farm surplus problem in the United States. Effort should be made to divorce, and not marry up, problems of our own surplus capacity and needs in our foreign policy and in economic development of other countries. Where U.S. food serves as efficient resource for these purposes in the future, it should be so used. But where it interferes with these goals, we should use other means to solve our problem of farm surpluses. Perhaps one of the greatest dangers in U.S. foreign disposal is that food shipped under P.L. 480, Food for Peace and other programs will be classified in the total assistance and foreign exchange allotments for less developed countries, thus restricting capital items needed for other developmental purposes. Only where it can be shown that the food will not substitute for other claims in exchange, will not depress development of agriculture in the recipient country, will not displace exports from other nations and does not divert resources within the United States from more essential commodities for foreign development, can surplus disposal be considered a perfectly neutral program with no danger of sub-optimum or negative outcome in respect to development.

Basic Aid in Development

We may look at the simple Harrod-Domar type of growth model in (17.1) and inquire how U.S. food might best fit into promoting economic

$$dY = sk^{-1} - dL \tag{17.1}$$

growth of less developed countries.[14] In this equation dY is the rate of growth in national income, dL is the rate of growth in population (i.e. labor force), k is the ratio of capital to output per unit increase of these two items and s is the rate of savings in national income. Where population is increasing rapidly and otherwise $dL = sk^{-1}$, food supplied from the United States at low or no cost could allow dY to be nonzero. However, it would be only a stop-gap measure and no real takeoff would be generated in the recipient country. The more permanent aid to development would be in increase of the magnitude sk^{-1} so that $sk^{-1} > dL$ and income per capita can grow. A country such as the United States can do little to increase s for these purposes, since this is a decision largely in the country trying to accelerate dY. It can, however, help to decrease the magnitude of k through technical improvement or investment aids. As far as agriculture itself is concerned, emphasis should be as much, in true economic development aid, in decreasing k through the means suggested in this chapter and in Chapter 16; as on simply shipping food in line with excess growth in dL or surpluses in the United States. The latter is purely a step in humanitarianism; decreasing k is a fundamental step in development.

[14] R. F. Harrod, *Toward a Dynamic Economics*. Macmillan & Co., London, 1949; E.D., Domar, "Capital Expansion, Rate of Growth and Employment," *Econometrica*, Vol. 14; and H.W. Singer, "The Mechanics of Economic Development," *Indiana Econ. Rev.*, 1952.

Return on Use of "Fixed Surpluses"

If surpluses are taken as "fixed resources" with no alternative uses, or of negative return when held in storage at growing public cost, the investment representing them can be used with low payoff. If the same investment has different opportunities in development allocation for a later period, it has an entirely different payoff and needs to be compared with a more complete range of alternatives in domestic agricultural policy and foreign developmental policy. Considering the specified uses to which these foreign currencies, exchanged under Title I of P.L. 480, must be allocated and the uncertainty of their repayment or conversion to dollars, Schultz places the value of each dollar in P.L. 480 exports at 10 to 15 cents for the United States.[15] He places their value to recipient countries at 37 cents on the dollar, considering price elasticities of demand for surplus commodities and alternative sources of these commodities or inputs. These are extremely low values, for either the United States or the recipient countries. For the period represented by major disposal under the program, however, the "opportunity marginal cost" of the surpluses, and the dollars they represent, may have been near zero to both the United States and numerous recipient countries; to the United States because the surpluses would have been kept in storage generating even greater public storage costs and to recipient countries where equivalent of other development funds would not have been available.

Yet opportunity costs of these magnitudes are in the past. The important alternatives in the future are other developmental uses to which the same total capital might be put. In this sense, there is need to develop American farm policy which eliminates and restrains buildup of surplus supply and which frees the public capital so represented for more optimum developmental purposes. In this sense both goals might have been better attained had we paid U.S. farmers to cease production here, and travel to foreign countries to aid cultivators in their decisions. This is a needed emphasis, rather than adaptation of foreign assistance programs to the surplus producing capacity of American agriculture. In developing more optimum developmental and assistance policy, agricultural policy needs to be divorced from it, agriculture contributing to developmental policy only as growth needs in less developed countries so specify. This is a near-term framework needed for American farming and agricultural policy. The very long-term outlook and orientation, however, may well be quite different to the extent that sustained takeoff in economic development can be generated for nations which thus far have been restrained in growth and per capita incomes.

LONG-RUN DEMAND HOPE IN WORLD DEVELOPMENT

Potential in food demand of particular countries and of the world in aggregate depends on rates of population growth and income improve-

[15] T. W. Schultz, "Value of U.S. Farm Surpluses to Underdeveloped Countries," *Jour. Farm Econ.*, Vol. 42.

ment per head. Using these two variables as the major ones, and forgetting about the smaller quantitative effects of gradually changing preferences and real food price relative to other commodities, approximate annual rate of growth in food demand within a particular country can be represented as in equation (17.2) where Δ is the approximate growth rate in food demand, P is the rate of growth in population, E is the income elasticity of demand for

$$\Delta = P + EG \tag{17.2}$$

food and G is growth rate in per capita income. If rate of growth in food supply is greater than this quantity in a "closed economy," farm depression results; if food supply grows at a slower rate, consumer depression results. As mentioned previously, the value of E for aggregate poundage of food is near zero in the United States. Hence, the main variable affecting domestic food demand is P in (17.2). In other countries, however, the value of E is sufficiently large that national economic growth itself can generate considerable increase in food demand. The main concern in some nations of very small development, of course, is to keep food supply moving ahead as rapidly as P or population.

The need for rapid economic development and food supply in less advanced nations is thus fact. The existence of U.S. surplus supply also has been fact. To some persons, it also is apparent fact that food from the U.S. is needed to get this development on its way. This proposition has both basis and overanticipation. Temporary foreign disposal programs will not, however, solve the U.S. farm supply problem, unless the temporary program extends over 20 or more years and is organized on a larger scale than that conducted between 1955 and 1960.

For those who look to population explosion and growth of world consumers to alleviate the U.S. problem, there is little hope without economic development in the countries of rapidly advancing populations. A better hope in expanded demand for U.S. farm products might even be constant populations, but great economic growth in the specified countries. The reason for this statement is somewhat obvious in Figure 17.2. These data, based on national cross-sectional observations and serving under predictional limitation as conservative indication of differences for food in physical form among countries at various stages of development, indicate that potential food demand is indeed still great in those nations where per capita incomes are low.

Using Clark's measurements in International Units, the income elasticity of demand for food in aggregate is still of important positive magnitude in many densely populated countries with low per capita incomes. From this scale, we would expect Indians to have income elasticity for aggregate food of around .8. More recent figures based on more detailed observations even suggest that the elasticity is higher for certain specific categories of food. One belief is that income elasticity is as high as unity for expenditures in the most densely populated regions which approach subsistence incomes.[16] Certainly over much of the world, food demand can increase at a rate faster than population with stepped-up rate of growth and higher per capita income. This is in contrast to nations like the United States where food as a physical quantity has income elasticity of zero and domestic demand growth is limited to population. Table 17.3 illustrates the difference in income elasticity of demand in respect to expenditure on food in four countries at various levels in economic growth

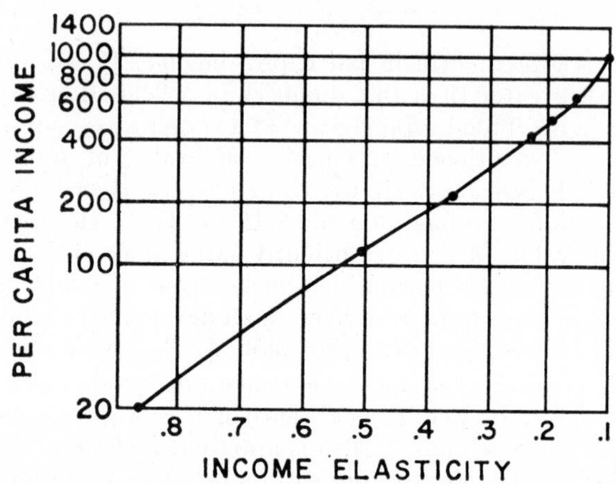

Fig. 17.2. Income Elasticity of Demand for Food (Farm Level) in International Units With Value of Dollar 1925–34 = 100. (Source: Clark, C. World Supply and Requirements for Farm Products. Jour. Roy. Stat. Soc. 1954, pt. 3.)

and per capita income. (Also see the elasticities in Chapter 6 for the United States.) Expenditure on food is predicted to have an income elasticity around .7 for Italy.[17] For countries where income of farm families is extremely low, expenditure elasticity is predicted to exceed that of urban persons with higher incomes. In any case, a less developed nation which has rapid growth in population, but no progress in income, is going to lack foreign exchange to buy commodities from surplus producers.

---

[16] C. P. Kindleberger, *Economic Development*, McGraw Hill, New York, 1958, p. 110. Other estimates are to be found in: N. Tsutomu, "Long-Term Changes in Demand for Agricultural Products and Income Elasticity," *Structure of Food Demand—Prewar Period*, Translation Series No. 1, Translation Unit Tokyo, 1959; H. S. Houthakker, "An International Comparison of Household Expenditure Patterns Commemorating the Centennial of Engel's Law," *Econometrica*, Vol. 25; and "FAO Factors Influencing the Trend of Food Consumption," *The State of Food and Agriculture*, Rome, 1957, pp. 70–110. The later study estimates an income elasticity, based on a rough international comparison, of .1 for calories except for countries with extremely low income. There are some populous countries where even caloric income elasticity is considerably greater than zero.

[17] A somewhat different set of income elasticities, but generally of the same high level, is indicated elsewhere. See A. J. Coale and E. M. Hoover, *Population Growth and Economic Development in Low Income Countries*, Princeton University Press, Princeton, 1958, p. 125.

TABLE 17.3

INCOME ELASTICITY COEFFICIENTS IN RESPECT TO FOOD EXPENDITURES FOR FOUR COUNTRIES IN SPECIFIED YEARS

	United States 1955		United Kingdom 1953–54		Italy 1953*		Italy 1953†		Japan 1955		India 1952	
	Rural	Urban	Rural	Urban	Rural	Urban	Rural	Urban	Rural	Urban	Rural	Urban
Total Food Expenditure......	.18	.39	.6	.7	.65	.58	.74	.69	.48	.6	.87	.79
Bread and cereals..	.01	.16	−.2	.05	.27	.21	.33	.20	.38	.2 (bread and cereals, starchy food)	.69	.33
Starchy food, etc...	.20	.16	.4	.05	...	...	...	...	−.55		...	...
Sugar...........	.02	.27	.9	.9	.78	.50	.92	.89	...	...	1.43	1.09
Pulses and nuts...	−.17	.16	...	...	...	...	...	...	.30	.65	...	...
Vegetables and fruits.........	.16	.36	.6	.6	.60	.67	.60	.79	.33	.6	...	...
Meat products...	.27	.31	.3	.3	.88	.71	1.25	1.07	...	...	1.15 (meat, fish)	1.26
Fish products....	.28	.24	.5	.0	.81	.63	1.06	.93	1.03	.5		
Eggs............	.01	.18	.7	.3	.50 (eggs, milk)	.38	.76	.78	.83 (eggs, milk, butter, fats)	1.3	1.86	1.53
Milk products....	.02	.28	.45	.1								
Butter..........	.17	.50	.1	.0	.81 (butter, fats)	.54	.83	.70	...	...	...	...
Fats and oils.....	−.13	−.02	.0	.0					.31	...	1.16	1.01
Nonalcoholic beverages.........	.06	.28	.2	.05	.86 (nonalcoholic, alcoholic)	.72	1.18	.95	.71	1.05	...	...
Alcoholic bev.....	.95	.85	2.0	3.3					1.27	.8	...	...
Meals outside the home.........	.92	.85	2.5	5.0	1.15 (meals, other foods)	1.29	.74	1.09	1.52	1.6	...	...
Other foods......	.22	.34	.7	.6					.54	.4	.93	1.01
Tobacco.........	...	...	2.5	3.3	.90	.78	.95	.48	.18	−.2	...	...
Clothing........	...	...	...	...	1.53	1.16	1.13	1.24	1.95	1.7	...	...

Source: FAO, *The State of Food and Agriculture*, Rome, 1959. p. 195.
* Central North.
† South.

Potential in Supply and Investment Alternatives

Great strides in economic growth over the world would result in solid advance in food demand. The potential in demand is extremely large relative to current U.S. domestic surplus food capacity of 6 to 8 percent; or to capacity of current surplus-producing countries. But whether this growth in demand would be filled in major part from nations with current surplus supply potential depends on the interaction of economic development and agricultural productivity of nations to be developed rapidly. In the short run the price elasticity of the food supply function has much greater potential of increase in nations such as Canada, the U.S., Australia and Brazil, as compared to countries where population is pressing against food production. Yet this need not hold true in the future to an extent equal to the past. If supply elasticity of resources such as technical knowledge, managerial capacity and capital can be increased greatly in less developed nations, a corresponding increase in the elasticity of the food supply function also will take place over the long run.

Comparing India and the Philippines with Japan and the United States, the relative physical base for increasing food supply elasticity is greater in the former than in the latter countries. Yet whether, and to

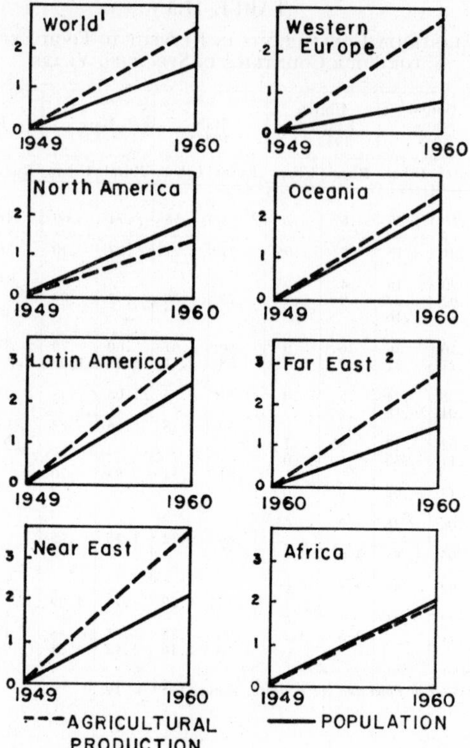

Fig. 17.3. Trends in Agricultural Production and Population. World Regions, 1949–60. (Source: FAO. The State of Food and Agriculture, Rome, 1960, p. 12.)

the extent that, emphasis is or should be on investment to extend food supply elasticity in the former countries will depend on the expected marginal efficiency of capital in farming as compared to other industries, as well as on certain nonmoney and more subjective evaluations to be made by the developing countries. We return to this point later. While the technological potential, against present performance, is greater in some less developed countries than in advanced ones, the rate of progress in output is still currently greater in the latter. As Figure 17.3 indicates, agricultural production has been growing more rapidly than population over most of the world, and especially so in Western Europe and the Near East.[18] Growth in output in these regions, and others where potential is great, may check the rate at which technical advance in the United States can feed into world markets. While production has only kept up

[18] Also see J. Marczewski, "Some Aspects of Economic Growth in France," *Economic Development and Cultural Change*, Vol. 9.

with population in Africa, the physical potential for increasing supply faster than food demand is high.

If per capita income grew rapidly in the short run, food demand in less developed nations certainly would grow more rapidly than the rate at which food supply in these nations has increased over recent decades. This increase in food demand would then spill over to utilize more of the supply forthcoming in more advanced nations and agricultures. However, the rate of per capita income improvement in less developed nations has been slower than the rate of growth in food supply in more advanced nations during the 1940's and 1950's. Consequently, food demand growth in the former has not alleviated surpluses in the latter. Not only has the growth rate been too slow to cause this, but also exchange and investment problems have served as restraints to mushrooming food imports by less developed nations.

If we view the population projections in Table 17.4, it is obvious that the world food supply function will have to increase tremendously or the

TABLE 17.4

WORLD POPULATION BY REGION 1800–1950 AND PROJECTED (MILLIONS)*

Area	Year					Percentage Increase			
	1800	1850	1900	1950	2000 (*est.*)	1800–1850	1850–1900	1900–1950	1950–2000 (*est.*)
World	906	1,171	1,608	2,495	6,280	29.2	37.3	55.2	151.7
Asia (exc. USSR)	602	749	937	1,379	3,870	24.4	25.1	47.2	180.6
Europe (exc. USSR)	150	204	277	393	568	36.0	35.8	41.9	44.5
USSR	37	62	113	181	379	67.6	82.3	60.2	109.4
Africa	90	95	120	199	517	5.6	26.3	65.8	159.8
Anglo-America	5	24	80	168	312	380.0	233.3	110.0	85.7
Latin America	20	35	75	162	592	75.0	114.3	116.0	265.4
Oceania	2	2	6	13	29.3	—	200.0	116.7	125.4

* Computed from: United Nations, *The Determinants and Consequences of Population Trends*, 1953, and *The Future Growth of World Populations*, 1958.

real price of food is going to push upward greatly in particular world regions.[19] This event would work to the advantage of resources in agriculture. Technological improvement and greater supply and lower costs of resources such as those mentioned above are variables which stand to increase supply and restrict increase in food price. The amount by which demand variables will change and cause greater demand for food exports from countries such as Canada and the United States depends on the extent to which agricultural productivity is increased in nations such as India, Pakistan and the Philippines, as well as in other exporting nations such as Japan, Burma and Indonesia. Given the constraints of developmental funds and foreign exchange, it is not likely that rapid developmental take-off in less advanced nations during the 1960's will itself

[19] See also: M. K. Bennett, *The World's Food*, Harper & Brothers, New York, 1954, Ch. 1. Coale and Hoover, *op. cit.*, pp. 34, 124, estimate that India food ouptut could be doubled in 25 years; but project population to 775 million by 1986 with fertility unchanged and to 589 million with a linear decline in fertility rates.

cause demand for exports from the United States to grow faster than the food supply function in the U.S. This situation held true in the 1950's, even as the U.S. stepped up foreign disposal under assistance programs.

FOOD DEFICITS

The problem of food in many underdeveloped regions is not that of producing enough of agricultural products to keep up with the demand increase associated with greater per capita income, high income elasticities and economic growth. Instead it is a problem of bringing level of food consumption up to minimum nutritional standards for the current population, or of meeting food needs for a growing population. In rather aggregate form, Table 17.5 indicates estimated 1958 daily food consumption in major world regions. These consumption rates can be compared against the following daily caloric requirements developed for the Food and Agricultural Organization in the second World Food Survey:

TABLE 17.5

ESTIMATED POPULATION AND DAILY FOOD INTAKE BY MAJOR WORLD REGIONS, 1958

Region	Population	Daily Food Consumption, 1958			
		Calories	All Protein	Animal Protein	Fat
	(millions)	*(no.)*	*(grams)*	*(grams)*	*(grams)*
Canada	19	3,085	91	58	137
Latin America	210	2,660	66	23	59
Western Europe	310	2,920	79	41	106
Mediterranean Europe	96	2,660	44	25	75
Eastern Europe	341	2,925	77	28	83
Western Asia	84	2,365	76	15	39
Africa	263	2,455	62	11	44
Far East	890	2,100	56	8	32
Mainland China	725	2,200	65	6	32
Oceania	16	3,210	103	67	136
United States	177	3,220	97	66	149
Russia	209	2,985	92	26	70

Source: FAO, *Second World Food Survey*, Rome and Foreign Agricultural Service; Food Balance Sheets USDA; *The World Food Deficit, a First Approximation*, Foreign Agricultura lService, USDA.

Latin America	2,500
United States	2,640
Canada	2,710
Mediterranean Europe	2,430
Other Western Europe	2,635
Soviet Union	2,710
Other Eastern European	2,635
Oceania	2,650
Western Asia	2,400
Africa	2,375
Far East	2,300
Mainland China	2,300

The above figures represent attempt to provide uniform energy supply for all countries and regions, with variations to accommodate differences in climate, body size and age and sex distributions. The average data of Table 17.5 obscure the meagerness of human rations in some of the less developed nations. For examples, daily caloric intake is estimated to be less than 2,000 for Bolivia, Dominican Republic, Ecuador, El Salvador, Haiti and Nicaragua. Thirteen Latin American countries were estimated in 1958 to have less than 2,500 calories per day and only seven with more; the latter raising the average above 2,500. In Western Asia, out of seven countries, four have less than 2,400 calories. In Africa, nine out of 21 have less than 2,375 while every country in the Far East, aside from Taiwan and Japan, or nine out of 11, has less than the 2,300 specified above. Mainland China also has less than 2,300. The daily caloric, protein, and fat intakes per day for Asian countries and China are estimated as:

Country	Calories (no.)	Protein (all) (grams)	Fat (grams)
Taiwan	2,340	60	37
Japan	2,310	66	23
Malaya	2,290	51	40
Mainland China	2,200	65	32
Thailand	2,185	45	35
Burma	2,150	51	26
Philippines	2,145	56	39
Indonesia	2,125	48	38
Ceylon	2,060	46	59
India	2,050	57	34
South Korea	2,040	60	19
Pakistan	2,030	54	20

The last 10 countries above include more than half of the world's total population. Not only is caloric intake low enough that hunger does prevail, but protein intake is generally below the daily 65 grams recommended for physiological well-being. While the averages are as high as shown, the distribution is uneven in many countries, with a great many people having even less calories and protein than the average. If the diet of persons having less than the specified minimum standard were brought up to this level, it would not be possible to reduce the average of other persons to this level; the averages thus understating the total food problem. Table 17.6 indicates estimated deficits for major regions averaging less than the minimum standards. The total estimated world food deficit for 1962 thus is provided in Table 17.7 from FAS estimates. (As mentioned above, total food required to bring consumption up to the minimum levels would be somewhat greater, unless persons with intake above these levels were reduced to them.) The protein requirements suppose a minimum of 65 grams per day, with 7 grams of this from animals, and 17 grams in total from animal and pulse sources. The remaining protein requirement is estimated in terms of wheat equivalent to bring total per daily protein intake up to 65 grams. The remaining caloric deficit is specified in terms of wheat, beyond that indicated as wheat equivalent in "other" protein (to bring total protein up to 65 grams per day). The

TABLE 17.6
DAILY FOOD DEFICIT PER CAPITA OF CALORIES AND PROTEINS, 1958.
WORLD REGIONS WITH DEFICITS

Region	Calories (*No.*)	Proteins (*grams*)		
		Animal	Pulse	Other
Latin America	117	.05	0	4.2
Western Asia	150	0	.1	.05
Africa	43	.4	.5	3.6
Far East	200	1.0	.1	8.1
Mainland China	100	1.0	0	0

Source: *The World Food Deficit, A First Approximation*, Foreign Agricultural Service, USDA, March, 1961.

figures of Table 17.7 estimate total imports needed in food deficit countries, as specified above, to bring food intake up to the minimum levels. The total estimated world deficits in terms of wheat (1000 metric tons) are 40,665 in 1958, 44,185 in 1962 and 47,100 in 1965.

These countries are in the lower reaches of economic development, as is any one where people are still hungry or suffer from malnutrition. They could use large food quantities in bringing diets up to minimum levels and without approaching the more than 3,200 calories (and over 90 grams of protein) per head daily in advanced countries such as those of North America and Western Europe. Leaving out the United States, using it as the possible exporting nation, FAS has estimated these gross shortages for the remainder of the world (thousands of metric tons):[20]

	1962	1965
Fats and oils	2,265	2,489
Coarse grains	9,080	9,850
Wheat	53,717	57,098
Pulses	837	866
Animal protein	1,449	1,599

These quantities represent a lot of food, just to bring consumption up to broad nutritional improvements of the nature mentioned above. They far exceed the annual rate of surplus production in the United States. Why, then, it might be asked, do these countries not buy up all these surpluses and feed their consumers better? The answer is about as easy as the question: the less developed countries are short on both capital and foreign exchange to buy the materials of economic development. While the United States could not, politically and in consistency with its level of affluence, have a large stratum of its population hungry, or with food intake below the recommended minimum, some countries have had to do just that. To divert their limited capital and foreign exchange to food imports would cause limited resources to be shifted into subsistence products, rather than plant to generate capital accumulation and job oppor-

[20] Foreign Agricultural Service, *Estimates of the World Food Deficit*, USDA, March, 1961 (Mimeo.).

TABLE 17.7

ESTIMATED WORLD FOOD DEFICIT FOR 1962, FREE WORLD AND COMMUNIST ASIA
(1000 metric tons)

Food Category	Free World			Communist Asia		
	1958	1962	1965	1958	1962	1965
Animal protein*	947	1,025	1,090	700	755	800
Pulse protein*	352	380	400	0	0	0
Other protein*	32,815	35,615	38,020	0	0	0
Remaining caloric deficit†	1,400	1,570	1,680	6,540	7,000	7,400

Source: *The World Food Deficit*, Foreign Agricultural Service, USDA.

* Animal proteins in terms of nonfat milk solids; pulse proteins in terms of dry beans and peas; other protein in terms of wheat to provide remaining protein requirements.

† Caloric requirement in terms of wheat, beyond that provided by wheat in "other protein."

tunity. It is a hard fact that many nations have had to decide to let large strata, or all on average, of the population go somewhat hungry and undernourished in order to use scarce capital and foreign exchange in accumulating funds to stimulate growth and to have employment and higher nutrition plane for subsequent generations. Few if any prefer to do so, but it has been a choice that many have had to make, knowing that the current generation is not unacquainted with, or unwilling to accept, the given status of diets to which it has been frozen. Some nations, with large populations and labor forces exceeding full employment opportunity for the decade ahead, even if labor cannot work up to its full physical potential because of inadequate food intake, may have even had to make this decision: Diets will be kept below minimum specifications (e.g. as above) because of labor excess and because capital accumulation is not generated by a "little more weight or a slightly better filled stomach." Countries concerned with people and welfare maximization for this generation may not do so, but those concerned with maximization of growth and welfare over succeeding generations may decide thus. In this case, and on the basis of these criteria, food imports to boost nutritional level at the current time might have marginal urgency of zero—unless food is given to them, with the gift of other than nontransitory nature for this generation. But nations more advanced in welfare goals and concern with this generation cannot use this calculus.

Not all, and perhaps few, if any, nations would prefer to have others provide food gratis, to bring the level of diet up to nutritional standards. They certainly would not prefer it if this added supply were in sight for only a couple of years. Once it was cut off, they would not be better off diet-wise, and psychologically they would be worse off. Some, or perhaps most, would not even prefer food supplied in this vein if it were guaranteed free for 15 years. They would prefer, where it is economic, to develop and extend their own food supply function, both as a reaction against pure charity and economic dependence, a "weak" colonialism, and as a basis of a firmer foundation in economic development. If capital quantities were free up to a limited restraint, as choice between food and heavy goods for industrialization, many would prefer the latter with their installation for economic development to create permanent employment, even with some continued undernourishment of present population strata which cannot be effectively engaged in the developmental process.

Much of American food surplus disposal has been offered in even shorter time framework, with high uncertainty for any nation which might latch themselves to it. More would have preferred use of U.S. surplus foods had the promise been at hand to help them develop their own agricultures rapidly, as a "take over" precaution when and should U.S. food aid cease. Early U.S. policy did, however, clearly prevent use of food and P.L. 480 funds as aid in development of the food supply functions in these same countries. Here was a point at which U.S. interest in food disposal and economic development of underdeveloped areas clearly came into conflict. If we had not let the surplus facet come to dominate our developmental interest, we would have wiped this restraint entirely away. In fact we would have tried to provide less developed countries not with food especially, but with that complement of resources which caused U.S. food supply function to move ahead rapidly. In other words, we would have helped increase the supplies of knowledge, scientists, capital and material items of production necessary in improvement of food supply functions in less developed countries. This was, and still is, the successful mix in pushing the U.S. food supply schedule to the right. But in this mix of U.S. development also was another ingredient through the private sector: the supplying of inputs to agriculture at a low and declining real price. Along with the scientists, supply of fertilizer and like improvements shipped to these countries often would be more beneficial than shipment of food. As was mentioned in Chapter 16, world development may come better if more of the scientific resources now used in the United States, where the supply function is still shifting rapidly, are loaned to underdeveloped countries where it is moving tardily.

AID, DEVELOPMENT AND SURPLUS DISPOSAL

A food and developmental program to aid in food needs and maximize progress in less-developed countries would take quite different complexion from one with emphasis on food disposal. With the latter being the overriding force of a program, the commodity mix shipped is that arising under surpluses in the United States and tied to our historic production patterns, and not that most consistent with consumer preference in recipient countries (although a more complex analysis of interrelationships among production possibilities and consumer indifference maps, in reflecting comparative advantage in increasing welfare levels, is necessary for definitive statements here). Pork surplus and price problems of the United States can hardly be solved by disposal of this food in Pakistan.

In numerous countries, food imports under these programs are aimed at consumer welfare and lower real price of food.[21] At the same time, effort is underway to provide resource prices and supplies which will encourage growth in the agricultural supply function. Where this opportunity is great over the long run and farmers are restrained mainly by knowledge and other resources in the short run, use of U.S. surpluses which prevent food price increases may have no important supply or output effects in the recipient countries.

But our Martian friend from Chapter 1 would be almost certain to ask: "Why have an international food transfer program which increases prices to producers in a country of surplus and rapid supply march but decreases prices in countries short on food and with tardy supply increase? Wouldn't we expect this price structure to encourage further the output in surplus countries and depress it in deficit countries?"

Here may be another inconsistency of the same general nature: the United States allows technical experts and other capital forms for farm improvement to be drawn from local currencies arising under foreign disposal of food surpluses. This attempt, taken by itself, is to promote development and commodity supply increase. Yet food disposal programs are of theoretical nature to suppress price and curtail response of output in the same countries. More analysis needs to be made of the negative interaction which may arise in this type of mixing in surplus disposal and foreign assistance directed towards development. In some countries, internal rate of progress in supply is too slow to prevent high rise of prices to consumers without supplementary source of food. Even with high food prices, short-run supply elasticity may be too low to prevent consumer misery without imports. Yet policy oriented truly to economic development needs better to view the extent that investment in resources such as knowledge, fertilizer, improved strains and irrigation equipment is more important than food imports in increasing food supply elasticity and augmenting consumer welfare over the long run. There are countries in Latin America and Africa where the food supply function might be greatly increased quantitatively and in elasticity, if more of the resources mentioned above were available.

In a nation such as the United States where public investment has been extremely important in extending development of agriculture, the questions posed above also need to be asked: Can the variables which have been changed in magnitude to promote rapid domestic development of farming be similarly manipulated and included in foreign assistance programs to cause a parallel change in less advanced countries? Should many more of our own stock of public scientific resources be allocated to nations with tardy food supply, rather than to domestic agriculture where we have surpluses? Is it desirable to concentrate all of the U.S. public investment in scientific resources at home, and produce more surpluses; or would efficiency be increased by financing many more

---

[21] See Kindleberger, *op. cit.*, pp. 266–76 for some added notes on agricultural development and aid.

of them abroad, helping output to catch up, or maintain pace, with population growth in underdeveloped countries? Would given U.S. assistance outlay go further in development if we shipped fertilizer for use elsewhere, rather than to convert it to domestic crops and then ship their greater weight? Or, along the same line, would given developmental funds go still further towards progress if we shipped the capital, materials and technical knowledge to produce fertilizer and improved seeds in the foreign country rather than to keep them at home for use in producing agricultural inputs and farm outputs which eventually show up as domestic surpluses to be shipped out of the country under aid programs?

These are core questions to be analyzed and answered before we can ascertain the pattern of assistance which allows maximum development from given U.S. outlays for the purpose. In numerous cases, it is most likely that the resources mentioned would be more effective than food in promoting sustained development. Given comparative advantage in immobile natural endowments, but also supply of transferable resources, the optimum mix would undoubtedly include both commodities and farm inputs from the United States to be used by less developed countries. The proportions, however, would undoubtedly deviate widely from the pattern of the last decade. So also would the relative mix of (1) development funds lacking restraint on countries from which supplies of inputs and commodities would be obtained, and (2) resources and commodities relating to food and flowing from the country. Finally, the mix would change with time as (1) the supply function of farm commodities is pushed ahead in less developed countries and (2) industrial development progresses allowing developing nations to take advantage of world markets in line with their comparative advantage in products from farm and industrial sectors.

AGRICULTURAL VERSUS INDUSTRIAL DEVELOPMENT

The extent to which population and income variables have the effects in world food markets implied in Figure 17.2 and Table 17.4 depends on the relative rate at which industry and agriculture are developed in less advanced countries. If development and rise in per capita income come largely from growth in the industrial sector, rise in food demand will be filled largely through imports from countries which currently have a large and elastic suppply of farm products. This demand condition will be allowed, of course, only if industrial growth in less developed nations leads to products and international markets wherein foreign exchange can be obtained for food imports. If, on the other hand, less developed countries concentrate on agricultural development and push food supply forward as fast as growth in population and per capita incomes, demand for food from current-surplus countries will grow relatively little.

Two periods possibly exist in respect to demand by currently less developed nations for food from nations with more abundant supply of all commodities, and present prices are not an accurate indication of relative prices in future periods when income may attain different levels, or of the total mix of commodities to which less developed nations will aspire as their goals in development are attained. First is a near-term period when supply of food might be pushed ahead quite rapidly in selected ones of the less developed nations. The potential for increasing food supply in aggregate is quite large over such nations as India, Philippines, Malaya, and much of Africa and Latin America. The potential is large in comparison with current techniques of production in use and with natural endowments. The potential can, of course, be realized only if pricing and supplying of resources for this purpose are reflected in developmental investment and policy and if particular sociological and other obstacles are overcome.[22] Food supply should be given priority in these economies in extent that developmental funds can be best used thus, considering the marginal productivities of capital in development of agriculture and industry and the comparative advantage of these two sectors in world trade. But while the potential in increase of the food supply function and its elasticity would appear to be fairly great over a near-term period of 25 years, over a longer period (as suggested in the population potential projected in Table 17.4), the burden of supplying world food may fall back more on countries now with an elastic food supply function. In contrast to the near-term period, slack in under-utilization of natural endowments of many less developed and highly populated nations would be expected to have been largely "taken up" over the long run, as against the nations with current high development and little population pressure.

It is, of course, the next 25 years which are crucial in world economic development. The extent to which less developed nations should invest in progress of agriculture relative to industry has not yet been well determined. Balance in development is desired, but not simply in diversification so that supply functions of both food and industrial sectors are increased apace. Allocation should best be in terms of marginal resource productivities (1) within the restraints of minimum supplies of food available for growing populations and maximum desired rates of growth and (2) in comparative advantage of the two industries in world markets. But the guides in marginal value productivities and prices are not so readily available as they are in developed economies. Fairly rapid rates of growth in per capita income would result in demand expansion for numerous commodities and services now well out of the reach of masses of consumers in nations at low stages of progress.

Agriculture has short-term advantage in development over durable and producer goods industries in the sense that high payoff is in prospect for the near term. Capital investment to increase supply of fertilizer, improved seeds and knowledge is small relative to the prospective growth in product of agriculture in such nations as India and the Philippines. Returns on these investments are likely to be as high as those outlined in Chapter 16 for research and education in U.S. agriculture. Often it is not

[22] For example, see B. F. Hoselitz, *Sociological Aspects of Economic Growth*, The Free Press, Glencoe, Ill., 1960.

new research knowledge which is pressingly needed, but the supplying of inputs already known to have high productivity. Still, a nation which poured all of its investment funds into agriculture would be faced with eventual imbalance in supplying others of its projected consumer demands and with declining productivity of capital if it pushed farm improvement much beyond levels needed to upgrade consumer diets. While food demand has high income elasticity when consumer income is low, the price-caloric elasticity drops sharply with improvement of food supply and satiation of physical requirements. Now, as in the future, the world market is more pressed with "farm commodities trying to find a demand," than for other commodities and services which give rise to foreign exchange. This is a prospect which might well prevail in the future if all potential food resources were fully developed.

As mentioned above, prospects in productivity of resources used for development of agriculture are high up to an extent. The "balance line" is yet to be specified, however. Some writers on development emphasize that priority should be given to agriculture.[23] Here the supposition is that industrial development cannot proceed or is highly restrained without progress in agriculture. Emphasis also has been given to the need for "balanced growth," with the criterion of balance differing among writers.[24] Finally, there are those who emphasize need for priority or industrial development, because of either national needs, opportunities in foreign exchange or to change factor prices and thus alter the structure of subsistence agriculture; or disagree with the notion that development policy needs to follow a path of "balanced growth."[25]

Investment in Farm Productivity and Surplus Disposal

There is, of course, no definite and exact specification which can be applied to growth of all less developed countries. The optimum in alloca-

[23] *Cf.* A. J. Coale and E. M. Hoover, *op. cit.* pp. 115–25. (Also see Chap. 10 on behavior of agriculture under economic development.); B. Higgins, *Economic Development*, Norton and Co., New York, 1959, pp. 385–402 and 717–30; W. W. Rostow, "The Takeoff into Self-Sustained Economic Growth," *Econ. Jour.*, 1956; A. E. Kahn, "Investment Criteria in Development," *Quar. Jour. Econ.*, Vol. 55; G. Hakim, "Technical Aid from the Viewpoint of Receiving Countries," in B. Hoselitz (ed.), *Progress of Underdeveloped Areas*, University of Chicago Press, Chicago, 1952, p. 264.

[24] For discussions of balanced growth, see: A. W. Lewis, *Theory of Economic Growth*, Allen & Unwin, London, 1955, pp. 141, 191, 274–83; W. W. Rostow, "Trends in Allocation of Resources in Secular Growth," in L. H. Dupriez, ed., *Economic Progress*, Institut de Recherches Economiques et Sociales, Louvain, Belgium, 1955; Kindleberger, *op. cit.*, Chap. 9; A. N. Agarwala and S. P. Singh, *Economics of Underdevelopment*, Oxford University Press, Oxford, 1958, pp. 179–85; H. B. Chenery, *Development Policies and Programmes*, Econ. Bul. for Latin America, March, 1958; K. Bekker, "The Point IV Program," in Hoselitz, *loc. cit.;* P. T. Bauer and B. S. Yamey, *Economics of Underdeveloped Countries*, University of Chicago Press, Chicago, 1957, pp. 247–57; and G. M. Meier and R. E. Baldwin, *Economic Development: Theory, History, Policy*, Wiley, New York, 1957, pp. 343–51, 400–403.

[25] *Cf.* Harvey Leibenstein, *Economic Backwardness and Economic Growth*, Wiley, New York, 1957, pp. 261–63; A. O. Hirschman, *Strategy of Economic Development*, Yale University Press, New Haven, 1958, Chaps. 3 and 4.

tion of investment among sectors within any one country depends on natural endowments of resources adapted to various products, the current stage in level of supply and consumer expenditures for particular products, the amount of investment funds available (and whether these must come from internal capital formation or can be imported, with or without "strings" attached), the extent of scale economies in specific industries, availability of entrepreneurial resources in particular industries and possibilities in international demand. Japan is a nation which attained "balance" by adding industry for exports to an agriculture which grew efficient. Obviously, however, the short-term productivity of, or need for, investment in particular sectors of less developed nations will depend on the status of consumption and the extent to which primary wants are satiated. Certainly, balance has quite different meaning, for example, in Puerto Rico and the Philippines where nature's endowment towards agriculture differs greatly.

Development of agriculture, drawing it to a capital intensive structure, is meaningless and uneconomic as long as great underemployment of labor exists and price of this resource is low relative to capital. This type of transformation of agriculture promises to have low payoff under the conditions cited. Regardless of the country, the supply of labor to agriculture tends to be great and of low elasticity relative to other industries. Supply is larger and elasticity is lower inversely to degree of economic development, level of literacy and other communication characteristics. The causes, detailed elsewhere in this volume, extend the supply of labor to agriculture, forcing its marginal cost to be low, and to approach zero or subsistence with low industrialization rates. Accordingly it can be used in quantities causing its marginal productivity to be low. Agricultural technology in less developed countries rests on labor accordingly and its structure is not necessarily obsolete and uneconomic, but consistent with the conditions of factor supply and prices. For example, aside from biological gains from deep plowing which might be proven, it is not necessarily inefficient for the cultivator of India to plow his field a half dozen times with a stick. While a moldboard plow would do it in one operation and save labor, he would have no alternative use for his labor. Similarly, Japanese rice culture with tedious hand planting, has much more to offer India than American mechanized sowing methods.

The need, then, is largely to (1) expand supply of capital and knowledge, allowing current labor and land of agriculture (especially the latter) to become more productive and (2) invest in industrial growth which provides employment opportunity and which can lead to eventual change in factor prices which favors greater mechanization of agriculture. Until that time, "balance" of food shipments from the United States against development of "backward agriculture," or of the latter against industry in the same nations, needs to be made in terms of a large unemployed supply of labor which has few near-at-hand opportunities.[26]

[26] Also see Meier and Baldwin, *op. cit.*, pp. 376–83.

The objective in many less developed countries is necessarily that of both output and employment. To replace labor in agriculture would only increase unemployment in most countries at the low end of development. Hence, high mechanization of agriculture best must await industrialization which creates large demand for labor in industrial sectors.

But there are investments, particularly those representing biological capital forms, in agricultural productivity which do not serve largely as substitute for labor, but increase the productivity of labor and land. The use of improved seeds and fertilizer and similar practices are examples. It appears quite obvious, at current levels of economic development, and in total cost of resources with alternative opportunity, that productivity of specified funds would be greater if used to thus promote agricultural progress in selected underdeveloped economies than to ship food from the United States. The specified funds to which we refer are those public outlays which go into paying for production of surplus commodities (i.e. the fertilizer, seed, fuel, etc. embodied in them), storing the commodities and transporting them. The labor used in producing them has alternative uses in the United States, as in steel plants used at less than capacity and which can fabricate producers' goods for development of other countries. The labor on cultivators' farms, which is otherwise replaced by U.S. food exports, does not always have similar employment opportunity in industry fabricating capital for development. In this sense, and supposing optimization of given resources in international economic development, capital resources for agriculture rather than food would be the preferable import for some less developed countries. Many have opportunities as great as those in Japan where development was encouraged and took place in both agriculture and industry. Here was a country where investment in agricultural advance gave high productivity, but industrialization also was rapid, with the two having positive interaction with each other.[27]

Surplus Food and Surplus Labor With Zero Opportunity Costs

Still, given institutions and market restraints as they prevailed over the world, unemployed food and unemployed labor have existed during the same time period, with neither caused by the other and both having low opportunity costs at times. To have used unemployed food to put unemployed labor to work in producing selected items of social overhead capital would not have drawn resources away from industrialization in countries such as India. Too, U.S. costs of surpluses would not have grown so great in treasury outlays and resources for storage. Opportunities in this direction led to a 1956 proposal, by Millikan and Rostow for example, that food be used to compensate unemployed labor in underdeveloped countries to build roads, schools and plants.[28] Given the fact of

[27] For further discussion of rates of progress in Japanese agriculture, see S. Kuznets, *et al.* (eds.), *Economic Growth in Brazil, India and Japan*, Duke University Press, Durham, N.C., 1955, pp. 136–38.

[28] Millikan and Rostow, *op. cit.*, Chap 9.

absolute existence of these two sets of unemployed resources, food and labor, resources are not thus drawn away from any other employment in mixing them into a useful world social product. To be emphasized too is the fact that development comes largely from change and improvement of people—a process possible only through education and communication. More development of this nature, use of unemployed food with unemployed labor to develop social overhead capital, could have been attained in the decade of the 1950's had specific program along this line been utilized. However, it is not necessary that U.S. farmers must forever be compensated, for income and welfare losses growing out of rapid technical progress, in a manner to build up surpluses which become unemployed and immobilized in costly storage. To the extent that procedures of Chapters 11 through 16 can be used as alternative compensation mechanisms, greater flexibilities in use of capital for "eventual development" exist as outlined above.

An amendment to P.L. 480 in 1959 allowed use of surplus foods as grants to foreign countries which would use them in the manner of "wage goods" or direct payment in kind to labor used for working on dams, roads, ports and similar public projects. Since much labor is underemployed in less developed countries, entirely beyond that which can be absorbed by economic growth rates of the next decade, and since food is the main "wage good" preferred by these persons, such public projects need not divert major resources from other national development activity. But provision made by the U.S. was too short: It was to expire in 1961. Obviously nothing but meagre projects can be planned, initiated and completed in a year and a half. Who wants an inventory of half-completed ports and roads?

Investment for Development

Mixed optimally, many less developed economies would find investment in both agriculture and industry to be optimum, with some food coming from developed countries such as the U.S., especially under programs such as P.L. 480 where immediate growth in food needs could be met with discounted purchases from the U.S., a portion of the payment in local currency then being used for internal development. In extending productivity of internal agriculture to eventually replace food imports, many less developed countries will need to extend capital and knowledge resources to agriculture. However, capital supply is more the immediate restraint, than supply of technical knowledge, in bringing forth greater productivity in many regions of underdeveloped agriculture; or, at the minimum, the two resources are technical complements. Cultural orientation, values and customs also sometimes serve as stronger restraints than labor-knowledge in technological change.[29] Supply of technical knowledge is limited to wide strata of cultivators, but in many of these same regions it also is true that many farmers already have enough knowledge to

[29] For an interesting explanation of these aspects, see L. W. Shannon (ed.), *Underdeveloped Areas,* Harper and Brothers, New York, 1957, pp. 399–433.

increase productivity if capital limitations did not prevent investment and assuming of added risk. Cultivators exist in every village of Asia who stand above fellow villagers in per acre yields and in effective use of labor and capital. Frequently, entire villages excel neighboring villages. This empirical evidence is near at hand and exists for cultivators who are illiterate and must act in terms of "facts."

The cultivator who needs added technical knowledge also requires added capital to put it to use. There are few important practices or innovations in agriculture which do not require purchase of a material. The isoquant relating capital and knowledge as resources has some range of negative slope for literate farmers experienced in management. However, it more nearly approaches a 90 degree angle for cultivators who cannot read and are deeply imbedded in methods by custom and immobility. As two technical complements, one is not less or more important than the other and, extended alone, one has zero productivity. While the extreme is not quite this great, this condition is somewhat characteristic of agriculture over fairly broad regions of the world. In this framework, a decrease in the supply price of capital or knowledge alone can do little to productively increase the demand or use for the factor. Added knowledge of improved seeds, fertilization, irrigation lifts and other resource-using technologies is meaningless unless capital supply is increased in the sense of greater credit availability with favorable interest rates. But equally, magnification of credit facilities may only inflate the prices of resources representing existing techniques if knowledge and supplies of material factors are not extended also.

The supply of farm practice knowledge is partly a function of stages of economic growth. Under paucity of the national stock of capital, private firms invest relatively little in scientific investigation and concentrate more on products for markets representative of wealthier consumer strata. Farm inputs flowing through commercial markets have small demand because of the income and capital position of farmers. The production of scientific knowledge is represented by a decreasing cost industry. As development, education and research are increased, knowledge can be produced and communicated at a declining real cost. Public investment thus cannot only produce and communicate new knowledge but it also aids private firms in producing it at declining cost. The knowledge retailed by commercial firms, producing inputs and knowledge to be used in U.S. agriculture, is eased and its cost is reduced because of the large scale research units of the land-grant colleges and the USDA. Private research for agriculture in the U.S. is now far beyond the "takeoff" stage. Per our earlier discussion, diversion of scientific and educational resources for U.S. agriculture would now have quite ready substitutes. Those public resources shifted elsewhere would soon be replaced by those of the private sector. This substitution and shift, for the reasons mentioned above, are easily possible at high stages of economic development. It is much less so, however, at low stages of growth and it is for this reason that the highly-roundabout substitution might best take place: scientific resources from the United States substituting for those in underdeveloped countries with private research substituting more for public research in maintaining advance of the food supply function in the United States. The productivity of resources used to produce and increase the supply of technical knowledge for farming stands to be greatest in less developed countries when invested in applied rather than in pure or fundamental research. Up to some point in magnitude of knowledge this is likely to be true because a less developed country can import knowledge of fundamental or pure research produced in other countries at a low, and sometimes zero, cost. While fundamental research has the same application in all regions, applied research does not have equal international applicability.[30]

The hypothesis is often forwarded, and some scattered data are available to support it at a few locations, that the supply function in agriculture sometimes is "backward sloping" over the masses in such countries as India, Africa and Southeast Asia. Prices which increase earnings supposedly cause people to work fewer hours and to allocate more of their time to leisure.[31] Under the demand regime portrayed in Table 17.4 and Figure 17.2, pure existence of this supply condition in less developed countries would, as they progress, cause extreme draw on food supply from more developed countries where farmers quickly respond to upward price incentives. But the aggregate data of less developed nations with vigor in growth plans do not support a backward sloping supply function forever. The rigor in price responsiveness in these countries may be low partly for reasons of consumer orientations in production and because of other customs and institutional restraints attached to low growth stage. A better hypothesis, as applied to the masses and in terms of potential in growth is, however, that restricted supply and real prices of capital and knowledge resources are the stronger restraints on food supply and its elasticity in these less developed countries. Ceiling to economic development would not appear to exist in inflexibility of consumption habits and extreme attachment to leisure, particularly after development of social overhead capital for human investment and betterment through improved education, government, transportation and communication facilities.

To be certain, the patterns of consumer preference do differ, at various levels of per capita income. Even if all individuals had identical indifference maps, the mix of commodities and services consumed would change with level of income, unless the algebraic nature of the utility surface were characterized by a function such as the Cobb-Douglas.[32]

---

[30] Also see E. Staley, *The Future of Underdeveloped Countries*, Harper and Brothers, New York, 1954, pp. 246–50.

[31] *Cf.* P. T. Bauer and B. S. Yamey, *op. cit.*, pp. 84–86.

[32] The isoclines of this function are straight lines through the origin. Hence, for a given set of commodity prices, the same mix of consumption is specified for a given set of consumer prices regardless of the level of the budget line or utility level to be attained.

Experience and data indicate that this is not the form of the indifference map and that preferences of people change at different levels of income because both (1) indifference curves change in slope, for a given indifference map or set of values, along a scale line in the utility plane and (2) the indifference map itself changes as income of people grows and investment is made in them with consequent alteration of customs and values. The relative role of agriculture in the total food complex also changes for this reason. In this sense, a difference in food demand between less developed and developed economies is illustrated in Figure 17.4 where D_1 is the demand function and p_1 is food price at farm level

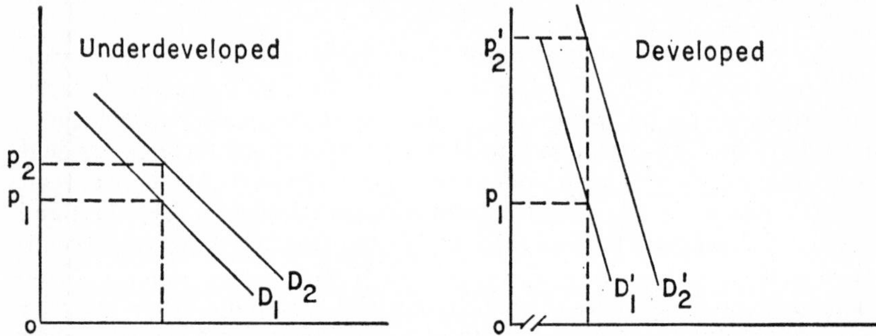

Fig. 17.4. Relative Demand for Food and Related Services.

while D_2 and p_2 are corresponding quantities at retail level. The cultivator's "share of the consumer's dollar" is thus expected to be greater in the less developed economy and less in the highly developed economy. The food processing sector makes up a smaller proportion of the demand price for food and the total mix of services used by the consumer. Given time, education, growth in income and presence of consumer goods, it is expected that cultivators and other consumers in currently underdeveloped economies will have preferences which turn more to nonfood and nonleisure goods and that motivation of farmers in production will be similar. Tardiness in food output, because of backward sloping functions, certainly is not expected then and farmers of advanced nations cannot count on premium export demand centering around economic growth and "inverted" supply functions in less developed countries.

As we stated above, consumer preference is highly a function of income, although it also is affected by cultural and related variables. Yet as Figures 17.5 and 17.6 show, direct consumption of calories in cereals and starchy food declines over nations with level of per capita income exceeding about 250 U.S. dollars (at 1948 prices). Starchy foods are replaced by fats and oils, proteins and fruits and vegetables. Still, over the cross-sectional data included for the comparisons, per capita total consumption of cereals and starches increases continuously, almost linearly, with income because they are required to produce the fats, oils and meat from livestock associated with diets at higher income levels.

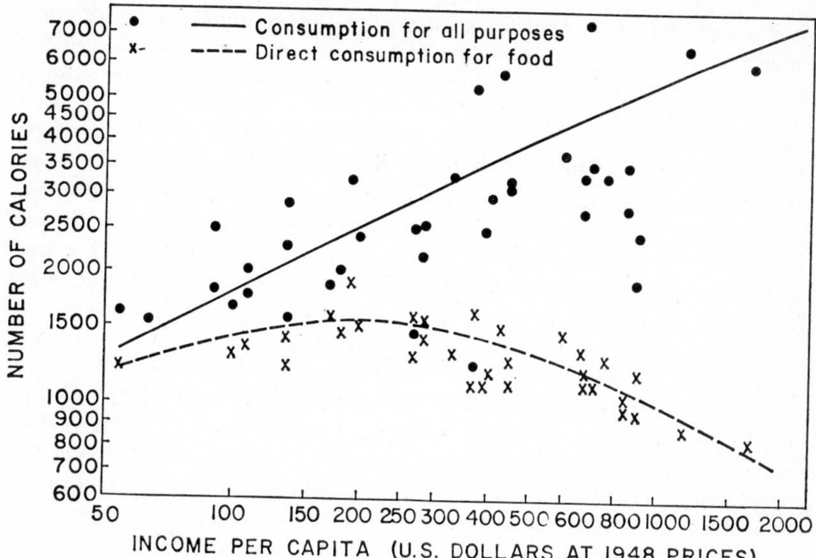

Fig. 17.5. Per Capita Consumption of Cereals and Starches in Relation to Per Capita Income. Cross-Sectional Comparison Among Countries. (Source: FAO, *ibid.*)

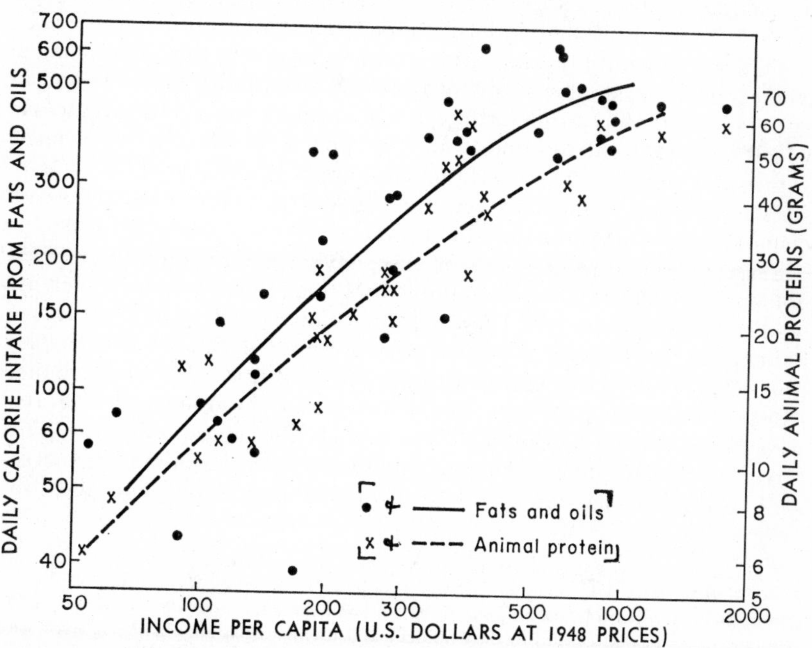

Fig. 17.6. Per Capita Daily Intake of Fats and Oils and Animal Protein in Relation to Per Capita Income. Cross-Sectional Comparison Among Nations. (Source: FAO. The State of Food and Agriculture, Rome, 1957, pp. 90, 92.)

Time will prove these consistencies, rather than unique backward sloping supply functions and complete turn to leisure and similar consumer patterns, as national incomes increase and people acquire more education and communication.

RECAPITULATION: SURPLUSES IN DEVELOPMENT

If U.S. surpluses must be taken as a fact and if they have no alternative use, they can make positive contribution in the Pareto-better sense outlined later for "unemployed labor and unemployed food." They are best looked upon in this Pareto-better sense, and not in terms of optimizing economic development from the total U.S. capital or funds represented by summation of investments in surpluses and foreign development programs. Where surpluses do exist as fact and in storage, they can increase welfare and growth in recipient nations as aid in upgrading diets and strength of labor; in serving as developmental funds in the sense that they act as lower-priced substitutes for imports which would be necessary anyway; in providing buffer stocks to lessen price gyrations, uncertainty of producers and frustration of consumers;[33] in providing funds for assistance which Congress and the public would not otherwise appropriate, to the extent that disposal outlay is above other forms of assistance; in suppressing inflation where governments might initiate developmental programs in absence of sufficient wage goods; in providing wage goods for projects of intensive-labor nature which otherwise require a long time to initiate and implement; in acquiring foreign exchange where surplus food allows shift of resources to export industries; and in allowing capital formation in the sense that they replace national income which formerly went to imports and can now be diverted to investment within the country. These attainments are predicated on the basis of surpluses which would exist even if they were not routed to foreign disposal and/or developmental assistance.

Surplus disposal promises to, or may, have negative outcome in developmental effect if: normal imports and food increments to increase worker health are exceeded in recipient countries, depressing returns of agriculture below levels consistent with optimum development;[34] surplus imports become charged against total developmental capital or exchange assistance provided to the recipient country by the United States (especially where development requires large capital obtained with foreign exchange); food is not accompanied by other capital items necessary to initiate and implement developmental projects;[35] and, aid pro-

---

[33] For several discussions of policy to stabilize prices of primary products, see "The Quest for a Stabilization Policy in Primary Producing Countries," *Kyklos*, Vol. 11.

[34] Millikan and Rostow, *op. cit.*, pp. 91–92; and Sen, *loc. cit.*

[35] For discussions of capital in development and its allocation among alternatives, see: R. Nurkse, *Problems of Capital Formation in Underdeveloped Countries*, Blackwell Press, Oxford, 1953; J. Tinbergen, *The Design of Development*, Johns Hopkins University Press, Baltimore, 1958; and V. A. Aziz, "The Interdependent Development of Agriculture and Other Industries," *Malayan Econ. Rev.*, Vol. 4.

vides great uncertainty in use, because of the limited time for which it will be available, or causes political unrest in countries which do not use it when it is available for these purposes.

Analysis of U.S. surplus disposal under P.L. 480 and Food for Peace programs suggests that it has had both these positive and negative elements and its sum value is not easily evaluated if the criterion is extent of economic growth of less developed countries. It has likely had positive-sum outcome in the sense of developmental attainment, but with return on developmental capital much lower than would have been possible under U.S. policy emphasizing economic development rather than surplus disposal.

Index

Index

C

F

W

Y

D

376